GW00995069

THE ICE CONDITIONS OF CONTRACT

FIFTH EDITION

A COMMENTARY

AUSTRALIA
The Law Book Company Ltd.
Sydney : Melbourne : Brisbane

CANADA AND U.S.A.
The Carswell Company Ltd.
Agincourt, Ontario

INDIA
N. M. Tripathi Private Ltd.
Bombay
and
Eastern Law House Private Ltd.
Calcutta
and
M.P.P. House
Bangalore

ISRAEL
Steimatzky's Agency Ltd.
Jerusalem : Tel Aviv : Haifa

MALAYSIA : SINGAPORE : BRUNEI
Malayan Law Journal (Pte.) Ltd.
Singapore

NEW ZEALAND
Sweet & Maxwell (N.Z.) Ltd.
Wellington

PAKISTAN
Pakistan Law House
Karachi

THE ICE CONDITIONS OF CONTRACT FIFTH EDITION

A COMMENTARY

BY

I. N. DUNCAN WALLACE, Q.C., M.A.(OXON.)

of the Middle Temple, Barrister-at-Law

LONDON

SWEET & MAXWELL

1978

Published in 1978 *by*
Sweet & Maxwell Limited of
11 *New Fetter Lane, London*
and printed in Great Britain
by The Eastern Press, Ltd.
of London and Reading

ISBN 421 21240 3

PREFACE

I am aware of, and apologise to readers for, the delay in publishing this book. This commentary has unfortunately taken longer to complete than any other for which I have been responsible. While this was partly due to other commitments, it was also the result of my intention to write a commentary in rather greater depth than my previous books on civil engineering forms. Having formed this intention, I discovered in the course of writing that the contract, which I knew to be " difficult " from an initial appraisal and article which I was asked to write for the *New Civil Engineer*, was in important parts so complicated and the language so obscure, that I was virtually halted in my tracks for considerable periods analysing and re-analysing it in the effort to arrive at its meaning or intention. I can truthfully say that it is the most difficult standard form which I have ever reviewed. One of the reasons for my desire to comment in depth was that I believed that the contract might form the basis of the new FIDIC International Contract (on the last edition of which, itself largely based on the ICE Fourth Edition, I have, of course, a commentary in print) and that a Supplement to this present volume could relatively easily and cheaply provide in due course an adequate commentary for the new FIDIC. At page 5 of my FIDIC commentary I expressed the hope that, in fact, the Fifth Edition would not be used as the basis for the new FIDIC, and whether or not this influenced the draftsmen and those responsible it is apparent that they evidently considered and studiously avoided, all the principal difficulties (and indeed innovations) in the Fifth Edition, as well as a number of the anomalies in the Fourth Edition (with the singleexception of the difficult Maintenance Certificate provisions in Clause 62, which have been swept away, quite rightly, in the Fifth Edition, but which are retained unchanged in the 1977 FIDIC contract).

In the present book, I have adopted the same pattern as in my previous commentaries on standard forms—namely an introductory chapter which is, in effect, a fairly detailed summary and critique of the contract as a whole, followed by a principal chapter with the text of individual clauses set out in convenient stages followed by commentary, and with separate shorter chapters on the associated documents. I have also included for the first time a number of Appendices containing various articles in legal periodicals and the *New Civil Engineer* which I believe will be of interest to readers concerned with various subjects closely allied to any civil engineering contract; such as the use of Bills of Quantities, the rapidly expanding area in the Anglo-Saxon jurisdictions of tortious liability for economic loss of all parties connected with building and civil engineering projects; the rise and fall of the *Dawnays*' " bill of exchange " theory of interim certificates; and policy criticisms and justifications of the present contract. In the commentary, I have adopted a historical approach and referred back to earlier versions of the clauses in previous editions wherever this seemed helpful, at least in seeking to understand the subjective intentions of the draftsmen, or to explain the significance of any new departures.

It may help readers if I indicate what other works by myself are available in this field, since they are all still in print. *Hudson on Building and Civil Engineering Contracts,* 10th edition, is the principal general work. It was published in 1970, but a very full Supplement covering England and the Commonwealth jurisdictions, including South Africa, together with some U.S. material, has been completed and will soon be available. I hope, other commitments permitting, to rewrite Hudson completely with a substantial increase in its U.S. content, by 1981 to 1982, but the Supplement will contain all the necessary material (except for further U.S. material) on which this rewriting will be based (apart, of course, from cases occurring during the intervening period), and will be, in effect, a preview of the next edition.

Building and Civil Engineering Standard Forms (1969, with Supplements in 1970 and 1973) covers the RIBA main contract forms, the FASS/NFBTE nominated sub-contract form, the RIBA " Fixed Fee " contract, and the ICE Fourth Edition. A further Supplement to " BCF " is now being researched by my colleague Mr. Anthony Thornton.

Further Building and Engineering Standard Forms (" FBEF ") was published in 1973, and covers CCC/Wks/1 (in fact very close to the later GC/Wks/1), the Electrical and Mechanical " Model A " Contract, the FCEC " ICE " Sub-Contract, the FASS/NFBTE non-nominated sub-contract, and the NFBTE " Design and Build " Contract.

The International Civil Engineering Contract (" ICEC ") was published in 1974 and is a commentary on the 1973 reprint of the FIDIC International Contracts. I hope, probably by the end of 1979, to produce a second volume dealing with the new FIDIC conditions which were published in March 1977. Meanwhile, readers with problems on this contract, which contains few major departures from earlier contracts but is much clearer and more simplified in its language, may derive help from both " BCF " Part IV, and " ICEC."

CONTENTS

TABLE OF CASES

Table of Cases

Table of Cases

TABLE OF STATUTES

CHAPTER 1

INTRODUCTORY

THIS new " Fifth Edition " of what is commonly known as " the I.C.E. Conditions of Contract " was published in June 1973. Its sponsoring bodies were the Institution of Civil Engineers, the Association of Consulting Engineers, and the Federation of Civil Engineering Contractors. It therefore, in practical terms, represents a negotiated, or at least approved, document by the bodies representing both the professional engineering institutions on the one hand, and the contracting side of the industry on the other. It has been described as a " modest revision " of the Fourth Edition, in the light of the abandonment some few years previously of a completed draft of what had been intended to be an entirely new contract. In reality the Fifth Edition *is* a new contract, and is profoundly different from the Fourth Edition in its commercial and financial consequences and in its allocation of risks and legal responsibilities as between employers and contractors, though this tends to be concealed by the adoption of virtually identical numbering and titles to the clauses, and by a draftsmanship technique involving the maximum possible use of the old traditional wording (itself derived from contracts used at the beginning of the century) as the stock on which to graft the new modifications or changes. As a result some of the changes or their significance can easily escape even a practised eye. Inevitably, given the obscurity and complication of much of the language of the Fourth Edition, and the special drafting difficulties of any piecemeal task of modification and amendment of a lengthy document, there are many areas of difficulty and obscurity in the new contract, as well as inconsistencies or overlapping. Moreover, in some places where wholly new or independent provisions have been introduced, those responsible appear to have been quite undaunted by any consideration of the complication and extraordinary detail of their new requirements, or of the intellectual strain these might be likely to impose on those who will have to administer the contract in everyday life, or their legal advisers in cases of difficulty or, I am afraid, upon this commentator, who at times has felt in need of the (sadly lacking) qualities of a Senior Wrangler rather than of a legal commentator.

The main new features of the contract are (in no particular order of importance):-

1. *Nominated Sub-Contractors*

A whole new code for the nomination of sub-contractors has been created (clauses 58, 59A, 59B, 59C, and 60 (7), provisos (a) and (b)). An excellent and clear series of definitions and powers (the first in any U.K.

standard form) in clauses 58 and 59A (5) is followed by a much more sophisticated and flexible series of powers, with suitable modifications of rights and obligations in appropriate cases, should objection be successfully taken to a nomination—see clause 59A (1) to (3) inclusive. (Incidentally, the thorny question of design services performed by Nominated Sub-contractors is also skilfully dealt with—see clause 58 (3).) Then, however, there follow major and extraordinarily complicated invasions of the " no privity " principle. Briefly, in the case of breaches of contract by nominated sub-contractors, the Employer undertakes not (in the last resort) to recover damages from the main Contractor unless the latter is able in turn to obtain satisfaction from the Nominated Sub-contractor, or if he does, to reimburse the main contractor. There are, however, serious flaws, extremely damaging to the Employer, in the machinery for this, even accepting the policy (equivalent, in addition to the main Contractor's usual wide rights of objection to a nomination, to at least a partial guarantee of the Sub-Contractor's solvency). First, no thought has been given to a case where the Contractor recovers sufficient sums from the Nominated Sub-contractor to meet his own losses, though not those of the Employer. Secondly, an ill-considered proviso to clause 60 (7) prevents the Employer from deducting payment on interim certificate in respect of a defaulting Sub-contractor's work, even in a situation where this cannot possibly harm the main Contractor, and would act as a useful sanction against a persistently defaulting sub-contractor. In the more serious case of a possible termination of a sub-contract, a massive set of provisions of the most extraordinary complexity carries the position even further—here the Employer in effect guarantees, not only the Sub-contractor's financial ability, when sued by the main Contractor, to meet the Employer's damages, *but also the Contractor's own damage resulting from the termination.* Furthermore, while on its face the Employer may appear to be given the power to control the decision whether or not to terminate the sub-contract, close analysis shows that this is totally misleading, and his true option is either to consent or refuse—but refusal of consent will not affect the main Contractor's powers or rights in any way, however, unless the termination of the sub-contract by him in defiance of the employer's refusal turns out to be unjustified as against the sub-contractor. These provisions for termination of nominated sub-contracts (clause 59B) contain many other serious difficulties and anomalies and a major ambiguity—primarily concerned with the not uncommon real-life situation where an employer may be faced with a main Contractor and Nominated Sub-contractor blaming each other, and not himself sure which is in the right, or where the Employer or Contractor have differing commercial motives as to the desirability of termination (as under this contract they are increasingly likely to have). The principal anomalies and ambiguities arise if in these situations the Employer consents to a termination which is ultimately held to be unjustified as against the Nominated Sub-contractor—but there are also major ambiguities in regard to interim payment and the re-nomination position in a case where the Employer refuses consent but the Contractor nevertheless terminates the sub-contract. The total simplicity of the principal government form of contract in the U.K. (GC/Wks/1) in its adherence to the " no privity principle " on this subject—see clauses 31(2), 31 (3) and 38 (5) of that contract—finds no echo, either in policy or clarity of language, in the present contract. It so happens that, as an accident of the new draftsmanship, an amendment designed to incorporate the considerable advantages of the new clauses, while avoiding the complications and anomalies involved by their invasion of the " no privity " principle, can be very easily effected if desired—see *post* pages 199–200.

2. *New Clause* 13 *Claim*

An extraordinary new claim is now permitted (by clause 13 (1)), which applies the old clause 12 test of " reasonable foreseeability by an experienced contractor " to the cost, not of physical conditions or artificial obstructions as in clause 12, but of " delay or disruption of his arrangements or methods of construction " caused by compliance with *an ordinary instruction of the Engineer* relating to *original contract unvaried work* which (*i.e.* the delay or disruption) was not so reasonably foreseeable. The consequences of the wording cannot be accidental or unintended—see clause 71 (2) (a) which, in the field of metrication claims, specifically invokes clause 13 (1) in a particular situation where the original contract intention is confirmed to the Contractor by the Engineer.

3. *Possible Obligation to Order Variations*

Extremely subtle changes of wording in clauses 7 (1) and 51 (see also clauses 11 and 13 (1)) are clearly designed to encourage the possibility of a claim by the Contractor that the Engineer will owe *a duty to the Contractor* to vary the work in undefined circumstances which may render this " necessary." This latter expression, depending on the pressures on the Contractor or enthusiasm of his advisers, might even be said to include, apart from situations of unexpected physical difficulty or excessive expense in completing the contract work, changes, in the interest of completion of the permanent works, made as a consequence of defective work by the Contractor himself.

4. *Bills of Quantities*

Express provisions, forming part of the new clauses governing remeasurement of the work in accordance with the prices in the Bills of Quantities, expressly invite departure from those prices, either if the ultimate quantities differ from the estimated or stipulated quantities (clause 56 (2)), or if " errors or omissions " (undefined) exist in the Bills (clause 55 (2)). It is vital to appreciate that these provisions relate to *unvaried* work. Varied work is, of course, valued under clause 52 and presents no problem. The justification advanced by their protagonists in the U.K. for Bills of Quantities (these are hardly used at all elsewhere in the world, at least in the special English remeasurement sense, except where U.K. professional advisers are able to secure their introduction, notably in the case of the F.I.D.I.C. International form of Contract) and for the very considerable professional and other expenses involved in their preparation and use during the administration of the contract, is their alleged superiority as documents enabling tenders to be compared, interim payments to be calculated, and the contract work itself to be remeasured at the end of the day with far greater precision, so it is said, than by any other means, and as a consequence effecting a considerable reduction in both the cost of tendering and the level of tender prices. It does not seem to be appreciated by those responsible that the development in the U.K. of provisions in contracts regulating the use of Bills such as clauses 55, 56 and 57 of the present new contract, coupled with the almost total freedom permitted in the internal pricing allocation by the Contractor of preliminary and overhead expenditure, itself due partly to the lack of any clear Standard Method definition or guidance as to the pricing of preliminary Bills,[1] and partly to the readiness of Engineers and Engineer arbitrators to allow the principle of such claims, simply abandons all these alleged advantages (save only the last, since a low, though increasingly fictitious, price results at the tender stage). In view of the new provisions, contractors will be increasingly well-advised to employ more and more highly qualified staff, both before tender and during the construction period, to study the possibility of making claims of this kind, whether or not the quantities have in the event differed, and Engineers will be obliged, in my view, to allocate further staff to consider and attempt to refute such claims, particularly since " consultation with the Contractor " (which always took place in practice to such extent as an Engineer considered reasonable) has now for some reason become a contract obligation (see clauses 52 (1) and 56 (2)) of unspecified extent, which will no doubt be used by dissatisfied contractors to require still further meetings to discuss rejected claims.

The English system of remeasurement with Bills is such a vitally important and so easily misunderstood subject that in Appendix A, *post*, p. 305, a comprehensive article of mine in the *Journal of Maritime Law and Commerce*, Washington D.C., April 1975, on the use of Bills of Quantities in the United Kingdom and referring (*inter alia*) both to the wording of the present Fifth Edition and its predecessor, has been reprinted in full. It is perhaps sufficient to say here that in the present

---

[1] See, however, on this point the new " C.E.S.M.M." in 1976 commented on under clause 57, *infra*, pp. 193–5.

contract any principle that (barring variations, fluctuations, or other recognised claims) the work actually carried out will be revalued at the prices for it contained in the Bills of Quantities, appears to have been deliberately abandoned (unless every optimistic assumption made by the Contractor at the pricing stage can be shown to have been fulfilled in the event). It is impossible to exaggerate the weakness, in regard to the ultimate price, of the position of the Employer and his advisers under these new provisions, particularly having regard to the ingenuity of the " loophole engineer " and the pricing arguments which have become such a feature on the contracting side of the U.K. industry in recent years, and the total absence, if this type of claim is to be encouraged as a matter of policy, of any contractual machinery requiring a detailed make-up of the successful contractor's prices to be supplied at least before work commences, if not prior to final acceptance of the tender, so as to prevent alleged internal pricing arguments being advanced after the event tailored to suit the eventual outcome of the quantities of physical work, or the known conditions in which it has been in fact carried out.

5. *Final Certificate*

Provision is now made for a final certificate—clause 60 (3)—but happily neither it nor the Maintenance Certificate (see now clause 61 (2)) are accorded any permanent binding force. The freedom to recover damages for defective work for the full period of limitation will be welcomed by Employers (notwithstanding their new-found entitlement to sue in tort—see *Dutton* v. *Bognor Regis U.D.C.* [1972] 1 Q.B. 373, (1976) 3 B.L.R. 11, as now upheld and explained by the House of Lords in *Anns* v. *Merton B.C.* [1977] 2 W.L.R. 1024, (1977) 5 B.L.R. 1, (as to the very wide implications of this latter case, see the author's article in (1978) Vol. 94 L.Q.R. 60, set out in appendix D, *post* p. 374 *et seq.*).

6. *Contractors' Claims*

New procedural machinery has been provided for claims by the Contractor. All the Contractor's claims expressly permitted by the contract (there are in fact well over 30 of these, listed in the commentary to clause 60 (1)) are payable on Interim Certificate (clause 60 (1) (d) and 60 (2) (a)). Moreover the notice requirements for all clauses (including clause 12 claims) have been standardised and considerably relaxed, so that in very few cases will the Contractor suffer any serious disadvantage (other than on interim payment) by failing to give notice (see clause 52 (4) and the commentary thereto). Incidentally, the word " Cost ", frequently used by the Contract when expressly permitting claims, is now defined as including overhead costs off the site—see clause 1 (5)—and clause 12 claims for unfavourable physical conditions, etc., are now to include *profit* on additional work or plant. Furthermore, in some rather lax new wording, interest is now payable at $\frac{3}{4}$ per cent. over M.L.R. on

" failure by the Engineer to certify in accordance with clause 60 "—care is, however, needed to ascertain the exact meaning of this latter expression —see the commentary to clause 60 (6), *post*, p. 238.

7. *Payments*

An entirely new payments clause has been provided. On the whole (disregarding the objectionable Provisos relating to Nominated Sub-contractors in clause 60 (7)) the new clause 60 is in fact a greatly improved payments clause, resolving many of the old difficulties as to the time for release of retention moneys, the date for submission of final accounts, the final certificate, and the payment of the final balance, as well as setting out much more precisely the various sums to be included in interim certificates (there appears, however, to be a minor procedural error in regard to the treatment of previous payments by the Employer, and little interest has been shown either in clarifying or providing any standardised system for deduction by the Employer).

8. *Miscellaneous Changes*

There are a number of other changes. Under clause 47 liquidated damages (apart from those referable to the whole Works) are now recoverable for " Sections " (*i.e.* phases of the work, if expressly provided for, with separate completion dates and liquidated damages, in the Appendix to the Form of Tender); or for " parts " (where no pre-contract provision has been made but the Employer in the event goes into possession of a part with the consent of the Contractor, whereupon liquidated damages for the Section or whole are then reduced on the basis of the proportionate value of the part so occupied). There is now also a clause, optional at the discretion of the Employer if notified by him to the Contractor in the Appendix to the Form of Tender, for selected classes of materials or goods *off* the Site to be the subject of interim payment (clause 54). Clause 26 (compliance with statutes, by-laws etc.) has been completely revised so that virtually no financial liability will now fall on the Contractor. The main Contractor is entitled to retain for himself an unlimited discount for prompt payment of Nominated Sub-contractors (clause 59A (5) (a)). Labour-tax fluctuations (including National Insurance contributions) are now a permanent feature of the contract (clause 69) but the " Contract Price Fluctuations Clause " (the ingenious and elegant index-based form first published in March 1973 and republished in June 1973 and commented on *post*, p. 292) remains optional. The Engineer is now given power to obtain information as to the Contractor's structural and other design criteria for temporary works, but a complicated (and from both Engineer's and Employer's point of view disadvantageous) code of obligatory responses and actions will thereby be automatically brought into play (clause 14 (3) to 14 (6)). The Engineer is now required to make extension of time decisions, on no less than *three* different occasions in turn, for *each* matter justifying such an extension, and on the last two occasions whether an extension of time is requested or not—see clause 44 (2) (3) and (4). The contract, incidentally, now provides expressly at a number of points for an extension of time in a very large number of specific situations, and no longer relies exclusively on the old single generalised (and highly vulnerable in legal terms) ground in the old clause 44. There is a new altered metrication clause 71, which is so loosely worded as to be open to claims not in fact based on metrication difficulties at all. The improved V.A.T. clause published shortly before the contract itself is also permanently incorporated—see clause 70.

A mere catalogue such as the foregoing will show that the changes are almost without exception in favour of the Contractor—the single exception being the removal of any possible binding force from the Maintenance Certificate (itself always a difficult and controversial provision lacking any clear authority—see B.C.F.,[2] pp. 424–429 and at p. 447). It must be said that, making all allowances for a strong and influential contractor presence at the negotiating stage, the contract at many points shows itself quite obviously careless or indifferent to the Employer's interest, evidenced as much by the inadequacy of the remedies and sanctions provided in support of the Enployer's express contractual rights as by opening the floodgates to new claims by the Contractor.

Thus the new clause 54, conferring a new, albeit discretionary, entitlement to payment for goods off the site, fails adequately to protect the Employer against liens or rights less than ownership which may very well exist against goods in this particular situation. Again, in regard to clause 60, while the Contractor is expressly permitted to seek payment of *any* claim under the contract on interim certificate, and while specific mention is made of previous payments by the Employer, no mention whatever is made of any Employer's right to deduct in respect of cross-claims under the terms of the contract, or under a general power of set-off. This cannot be by accident. The contract was published in June 1973, when the doctrine of *Dawnays Ltd.* v. *Minter Ltd.* was at its zenith (see the author's article in January 1973, criticising six then recent decisions in the previous two years of the Court of Appeal, in (1973) 89 L.Q.R. 36) and at a time when the case of *Modern Engineering* v. *Gilbert-Ash* (*Northern*) *Ltd.* was still to be decided in the House of Lords (on July 25, 1973). The contract provisions about deduction, where they exist, are scattered and by no means uniform in wording; in addition a number of the Employer's cross-claims do not specifically mention deduction at all; furthermore, *Dawnay*'s

[2] *Building and Civil Engineering Standard Forms* (1969) (1st Suppt. 1970) (2nd Suppt. 1973), referred to subsequently in this book as " B.C.F."

case itself involved overriding an apparent express right to deduct (as did the *Gilbert-Ash* case in the Court of Appeal). Yet the contract was published with, presumably, knowledge of all this and in a form which can only suggest that its sponsors were perfectly happy to see the Employer deprived of any effective right to deduct by the so-called *Dawnay* principle. Happily, the *Gilbert-Ash* decision in the House of Lords restored the position, overruling all the *Dawnay* cases and the alleged principle on which they were based. In view of the very great financial importance and the legal difficulty of this topic I have included my original *Dawnay* article (" Set Back to Set-off ") together with two subsequent Notes in the L.Q.R. (" Set Fair for Set-off " and a Note on the case of *Mottram* v. *Bernard Sunley*) in Appendix B, *post*, p. 317 which I believe will be of assistance in understanding the law on a problem which, in the present economic climate, is of almost daily occurrence for the specialist practitioner.

Again, the Employer's right of re-entry, with its attendant financial remedies, under clause 63 may in certain situations provide a less satisfactory remedy than the common-law power of rescission—yet, despite this having been pointed out in previous commentaries, no provision is made to indicate that the clause 63 remedy is without prejudice to other remedies of the Employer and can be exercised contemporaneously with or as an alternative to those remedies—indeed new wording gratuitously introduced for no apparent reason might even suggest the contrary. It is again hard to believe that this is accidental—compare, for example, the care taken in the present contract to keep alive the power of the Contractor to continue to elect, notwithstanding service of no less than *two* notices by him upon the Employer under clause 40 (2), on whether to exercise his remedy on suspension of the work for three months or, in the F.I.D.I.C. form of International Contract, the express savings, made not once but *actually twice over in the same clause*, for the alternative exercise of any other remedies available in the closely analogous *Contractor's* determination clause in clause 69 of that contract (where in fact the need for alternative remedies, if it existed at all, could hardly be very serious). A further omission in clause 63, despite a new provision for compulsory assignment of sub-contracts to the Employer, is the absence of any general power to pay unpaid Sub-contractors for pre-re-entry work.

Again, particular wording used in the Proviso (a) to clause 60 (7) (already touched on *supra*) means that where a Nominated Sub-contractor is continuing to work on the Site, the earlier stages of whose work, previously paid for, have now been found to be defective, the Employer cannot make any deduction from current payments in respect of the earlier defective work—this damaging provision is totally unnecessary, even accepting in full the policies of clause 59A (6) in regard to Nominated Sub-contractors' breaches. It simply follows from the way the Proviso has been worded, itself presumably due to a failure to envisage the situations likely to arise from any point of view but that of the main Contractor. Again, in the case of a terminated nominated sub-contract, the impression is overwhelming that clause 59B has been drafted throughout with no consideration of the practicalities of the situation in which the Employer is likely to find himself, particularly in cases where the Contractor's termination of the sub-contract turns out to be unjustified.

Again, in regard to defective work, in real life the practical response of a responsible Engineer or Employer to the discovery of serious defects may often be to order a certain amount of precautionary opening-up and investigation, either to discover the cause or to confirm that the breaches are not repeated elsewhere in the work, followed very often by a change in the design or specification to obviate the need for wholesale opening-up, demolition or reinstatement. Yet no savings whatever exist (*e.g.* in regard to clause 38 (2) (opening-up), 50 (search) or 51 (variations)) to cover the situation where the instructions given are the reasonable and prudent consequence of defective work or any other breach of contract by the Contractor. (It may be argued that some or all of this expenditure would be recoverable as damages, but if so this would be in the face of apparently express provisions to the contrary—clauses 38 (2) and 50, for example. Reasonable solicitude for the Employer's interest would not permit any doubt.) Similarly, the new express power for the Engineer to require information as to the Contractor's intentions and proposals and design criteria in clause 14 (3), previously metnioned,may appear to be for the Employer's benefit, but if exercised this immediately triggers-off a series of provisions imposing *duties* on the Engineer and requiring him to make overt decisions when he may well have come to the conclusion that no sufficiently impelling reasons exist, in his client's interest, for taking any other than a neutral position and leaving the responsibility with the Contractor.

Turning to clause 40 (2), this has now been reworded so as to allow the Contractor to determine the contract after a three-month suspension of work in circumstances which really cannot, on any reasonable view, justify such a remedy—*i.e.* suspension necessary by weather conditions, or for the proper execution of the work, or for the safety of the Works.

Again, clause 71 (metrication) contains the new words " or additional expense " after " without undue delay "—thereby suggesting that if the obtaining of goods in the other measure is considerably *cheaper*, the Contractor can serve notice and recover compensation under the clause. (Fortunately the clause later appears to have made an erroneous reference to clause 13 which may undo the mischief of these ill-considered words.) Moreover, and perhaps even more importantly, clause 71 *still* does not deal with the serious objection (pointed out in B.C.F., 1st (1970) suppt. under p. 455) that it is so worded that ordinary industrial bottlenecks, or even breaches of contract by the Contractor's suppliers, and not metrication (*i.e.* the unavailability of the goods in the particular measure as such) may be the subject of a claim by the Contractor, which seems obviously unjustifiable, particularly in the latter case.

Again, in the vitally important field of remeasurement of work in accordance with the Bills, clauses 55 (2) and 56 (2) seem to indicate no experience or understanding of the kind of unmeritorious claims, so prevalent in the industry already, to which they are such a direct encouragement, or, if these claims are to be encouraged, of the position of procedural disadvantage in which the Employer's advisers will find themselves placed due to the contract's failure at least to ensure that the basis of the Contractor's internal pricing is sufficiently known before work commences.

By contrast, solicitude for the Contractor in regard to procedure and remedies appears to be omnipresent—as already indicated, "Cost" is to include Head Office overheads, profit is recoverable on additional work and materials under clause 12, the responsibility for Nominated Sub-contractors has been dramatically reduced—and in the case of termination the Contractor's own costs due to the termination are safeguarded. Moreover, in the necessary proceedings which will have to be brought against Nominated Sub-contractors the Employer must bear the costs even if the Contractor fails in those proceedings—clause 59B (6)—and it would seem that, whatever the outcome of the ultimate proceedings between the main Contractor and Sub-contractor, *all* the Contractor's expenditure and costs will be financed during the currency of the contract until at least Final Certificate—clause 59B (4). Failure to give notice of monetary claims, or of claims for extension of time, will no longer seriously prejudice the Contractor. Again, clause 66 (2) is specifically designed to afford the Contractor (as opposed to the Employer) "early arbitration" of most matters likely to affect his interest.

I should like finally to return to the question of complication. Clause 47 contemplates, as already stated, separate liquidated damages for individual Sections as opposed to the whole Works, and a reduction of liquidated damages in either case if a "part" is occupied under clause 48 (2) (b). If the resulting complications were not sufficient, the clause, however, also contemplates that a *different* sum from the liquidated damages for each Section may be inserted in respect of that Section to represent the reduction in the liquidated damages for the whole Works which is to take place on completion of that Section. Those gifted with the brain of a Grand Master may be able to trace a logical path, or even deduce an explanation, for the detailed provisions of sub-clauses 47 (1) and (2), or to give guidance to Engineers and others when preparing the contract documents as to the pricing of columns 2 and 3 for each Section of the work in the Appendix to the Form of Tender. The commentary to that clause in Chapter 2 must be regarded as dominated principally by awe and bafflement.

Equally, in regard to breaches of contract by Nominated Sub-contractors, the understanding and assessment of the exact combined effect of clauses 59A (6), 59B and the two Provisos to clause 60 (7) present a formidable intellectual challenge to the interpreter which it is hoped that, after much hesitation, the commentary to those clauses has successfully survived, in particular in regard to terminations consented to by the Employer but ultimately held to be unjustified as against the Nominated Sub-contractor, and in ascertaining the precise intention as to the interim arrangements should Employer and Contractor be in dispute about the termination. A further example of intellectual refinement, with many of the characteristics of a Chinese puzzle, lies in the relationship between paragraphs (a) (Proviso) and (b) (v) of Clause 22 (1) (Contractor's indemnity to Employer) on the one hand, and the Proviso to sub-clause (2) (Employer's counter-indemnity to Contractor) on the other. Clause 36 (3) contains another (traditional this time) somewhat convoluted provision in regard to payment for testing. Again, the new provisions for multiple reviews of extension of time decisions in clause 44 can be expected to provide intellectual stimulation for Engineers during the currency of the Work, particularly if subsequent reviews produce increases in previously granted extensions and are combined with the provisions for multiple completion dates, differing liquidated damages and " credits " for Sections of the Work, and also for parts of the Work, to be found in clause 47.

Very importantly, the arbitration clause leaves two interlinked and most difficult questions unanswered, despite their having been fully canvassed in the past in B.C.F. and elsewhere—namely, first, whether proceedings in the courts are possible without any reference to the Engineer in the first place at all, and, secondly, what precisely are the disputes under clause 66 (2) where " steps may be taken " (whatever that expression may mean) in an arbitration before the end of the work—as will be seen from the commentary, clause 66 (2) does not, when analysed in depth, appear to have any real meaning or practical effect, and it is a great pity that the opportunity was not taken either to abolish it altogether and permit " early " arbitration in all cases, or else to make its exact intended effect clear.

There are in fact problems or surprises in almost every line of the Fifth Edition, stemming partly from the traditional, archaic, diffuse wording and jargon, so much of which has been retained, and partly from the piecemeal process of addition and alteration. Unfortunately, this greatly adds to the length and burden of any commentary, much of which must amount to a discussion of possible meanings rather than a statement or explanation of the meaning. It is certain there will be many problems not covered by this commentary, and not even noticed by this commentator—it is remarkable how often when a specific problem arises in practice, and reference is accordingly made to the contractual provisions, a new difficulty or doubt is immediately seen to emerge.

I have adopted the policy of my other commentaries on the U.K. Standard Forms in assuming that the reader, be he lawyer or engineer, consultant or contractor, will be familiar with the text and probably have it available (though it is reproduced in selected stages for convenience in this book), and that he will have some knowledge of the contract and of the industry. I have not felt it necessary to explain or comment on the parts of the Conditions which are reasonably clear or seem to present no problem, except in regard to wholly new or unusually difficult sets of provisions. I have concentrated the commentary principally on matters of interpretation where there may be doubt or difficulty, and on the legal and practical consequences of the provisions where they are clear. I have frequently referred to the history of particular provisions, believing it to be of interest to readers from the point of view of analysing and detecting changing policy trends, and also of ascertaining the subjective intentions of those responsible for this contract or of their draftsmen, but readers should appreciate, however, that the history of a provision in earlier contracts will not generally be of assistance, at least as a matter of evidence, in the final interpretation of a doubtful provision in the courts—so that to that extent caution should be observed against giving undue weight to the history. It is in fact usually impossible to determine whether an anomaly or difficulty in the contract is due to the policy directives of the various bodies responsible for it, or to failures of draftsmanship, traditional or new, or to simple inadvertence. Those with experience of drafting on the instructions of parties with conflicting interests will know that it is by no means unusual for the draftsman to point out ambiguities or difficulties or anomalies but to be told nevertheless that the wording should stand either because the state of uncertainty is satisfactory to the parties, or because it is impossible to agree on what should replace the the criticised wording. In practice, doubt and obscurity in the wording appears to favour contractors in the U.K. by providing a basis for claims to be advanced, whereas doubtful wording rarely enables employers to obtain an advantage against a contractor.

It goes without saying that in my opinion contractors will be well advised to use the Fifth Edition whenever possible. Employers on the other hand should appreciate that the contract now really contains no firm prices and is in essence a contract for services, with nearly all pricing risks carried by the Employer, and with the original tender prices only likely to be applied to the work in the event of every favourable pricing assumption made at the time of tender being vindicated. Moreover, in the reassessment of the contract prices so frequently permitted or even encouraged or called for by the Contract, as already stated, the Employer's advisers are provided with no contractual guidance or machinery (above all, in the form of a detailed make-up, as between labour, plant, materials and the various overheads and other preliminary expenditure, of the tendered Bill prices) by which to distinguish between excessive and justified monetary claims. The measure for payment is, quite simply and disregarding the contractual verbiage, the Engineer's opininon of what is reasonable, whether under clauses 52 or 55 or 56 or the many permitted claims for "Costs," and on the Engineer's acumen in accepting or rejecting assertions and arguments, without the benefit of contemporary pricing documentation before the event, as to the items of expenditure which the various prices in the Bills are alleged to represent. To discharge this function efficiently while subject to such handicaps the Engineer would in reality have to have a considerable experience of contracting, and particularly of pricing. The same will apply to an arbitrator, more frequently than not likely to be appointed by the President of the Institution from a limited panel of selected arbitrators and now, apparently, likely to apply or follow, in the conduct of the reference, procedural rules to be issued from time to time by that Institution (see clause 66). It must be a matter for employers' judgment whether a contract enabling so many departures from the price of such uncertain extent, and with this machinery for determining the new price, can meet their financial needs. As already stated, quite apart from his difficulties on price, the Employer may often find that his own remedies in the event of default by the Contractor may not be well adapted for his needs, or difficult to enforce speedily and effectively, or even virtually non-existent.

It gives me no pleasure whatever to comment in this vein on a vitally important English Standard Form of Contract. Nor is there any element of pro-Employer or anti-Contractor bias involved in the views which I have expressed. In my view, contractors are entitled to and should both understand and exploit to the full any weakness or provision in their favour which, in the field of commerce, a person of full age and judgment enters into with them, particularly if the document in question is in fact a negotiated and respected standard form of contract. But in fact, as I have indicated elsewhere in print, I believe contracts of this kind to be desperately unfair to the efficient contractor who would like to achieve his commercial success by his superior proficiency in the organisation and construction of engineering projects and by achieving a reputation for doing good work and sticking to his price. The U.K. system of competitive tendering, with its strong bias in favour of the lowest tenderer, coupled with contracts like the present one envisaging or permitting every type of claim, will place this type of efficient contractor at a serious disadvantage as against contractors whose principal skills and energy lie in the discovery, presentation and successful conduct of claims, and whose tendered contract prices will reflect that skill. For that type of contractor, this type of contract, and its machinery for dealing with claims, can only be said to be ideal. For the other, as for the Engineer anxious to devote his energies principally to his professional task of securing the construction of a well-built and designed work of engineering, this contract will in my view offer little comfort. I also believe it to be in the national interest that this latter class of contractor should be encouraged, both domestically and internationally, and that professional manpower, both engineering and legal, should not be so absorbed as it is at present in the presentation and refutation of claims which would be far better eliminated by a less permissive contract and, if the contractor sees fit, to have any contingent element provided for in a higher tendered contract price. Where, of course, the amount of a claim in a given event can be ascertained with real precision, as for example in the case of a fluctuations clause (and in particular the new index-based fluctuations clause) the counter-argument is perfectly valid that the permitted claim will be balanced by a closely comparable reduction in the tendered contract price, and if the contingent event is one which may never occur at all then undoubtedly the Employer has the advantage of a lower contract price which, if the event does not materialise, will be of real benefit to him. But this counter-argument fails when no clear guide-lines exist for the ascertainment of the amount of the claim in question, or for segregating the contingent element in the contract price against the contemplated risk—as *e.g.* by the use of a Provisional Sum or Contingency Sum. These latter are in my view the legitimate ways of protecting both Employer and Contractor from a particular described eventuality, and will ensure that the Employer does indeed obtain the benefit of a lower contract price. It is the principal criticism of the present contract that the extent of the permitted claims is so unpredictable, and that the extent to which they may have been already taken into account in the tendered contract price is unknown, so that quite apart from the possibility of unmerited claims, the accurate comparison of tenders becomes impossible.

The criticisms which I have developed in the last part of this introductory chapter are for the most part the same as those advanced by me in an article in the *New Civil Engineer* in November 1973 (though I am inevitably by now more familiar with the detail of the contract provisions). That article was the subject of a considered reply on behalf of the joint contracts committee for the Fifth Edition, and I replied shortly in May 1974. Since this will give the reader an opportunity to hear the arguments in support of the Fifth Edition policies and draftsmanship, and the Committee's replies to my own criticisms, this series of articles is reprinted in full as Appendix C, *post*, pp. 345 to 373. It will be for the reader's judgment whether he considers my criticisms, either of policy or obscurity, to be well-founded.

Apart from this first introductory chapter, the form of the book involves the principal commentary on the Contract Conditions themselves in Chapter 2, and a short commentary on the Forms of Tender, Agreement and Bond in Chapter 3. The three Appendices A, B, and C have already been described. References to other books by myself are to Hudson (10th ed, 1970), " B.C.F. " (see *supra* p. 7), " F.B.E.F. " *Further Building and Engineering Standard Forms* (1973) and " I.C.E.C." *The International Civil Engineering Contract* (1974).

It may assist readers to know which forms of contract are covered by these publications. They are:—

(a)	" B.C.F."	(i) The four R.I.B.A. (or J.C.T.) Main Contracts
	(1969, Supplements 1970 and 1973)	(ii) The R.I.B.A. Fixed Fee Contract
		(iii) The F.A.S.S. Nominated Sub-Contract
		(iv) The Fourth Edition I.C.E. Contract
(b)	" F.B.E.F." (1973)	(i) " C.C.C. Wks. 1 "
		(ii) The F.A.S.S. Non-Nominated Sub-Contract
		(iii) Model " A " Electrical & Mechanical
		(iv) The N.F.B.T.E. " Design & Build " Contracts
		(v) The I.C.E. Sub-Contract
	and	
(c)	" I.C.E.C." (1974)	The F.I.D.I.C. International Contract (then based on the I.C.E. Fourth Edition).

Chapter 2

THE CONDITIONS OF CONTRACT DETAILED COMMENTARY

Conditions of Contract

DEFINITIONS AND INTERPRETATION

Definitions

1. (1) In the Contract (as hereinafter defined) the following words and expressions shall have the meanings hereby assigned to them except where the context otherwise requires:—

(a) " Employer " means ....
of ....
and includes the Employer's personal representatives or successors;

(b) " Contractor " means the person or persons firm or company whose tender has been accepted by the Employer and includes the Contractor's personal representatives successors and permitted assigns;

(c) " Engineer " means..........
or other the Engineer appointed from time to time by the Employer and notified in writing to the Contractor to act as Engineer for the purposes of the Contract in place of the said ....

(d) " Engineer's Representative " means a person being the resident engineer or assistant of the Engineer or clerk of works appointed from time to time by the Employer or the Engineer and notified in writing to the Contractor by the Engineer to perform the functions set forth in Clause 2 (1);

(e) " Contract " means the Conditions of Contract Specification Drawings Priced Bill of Quantities the Tender the written acceptance thereof and the Contract Agreement (if completed);

(f) " Specification " means the specification referred to in the Tender and any modification thereof or addition thereto as may from time to time be furnished or approved in writing by the Engineer;

(g) " Drawings " means the drawings referred to in the Specification and any modification of such drawings approved in writing by the Engineer and such other drawings as may from time to time be furnished or approved in writing by the Engineer;

(h) " Tender Total " means the total of the Priced Bill of Quantities at the date of acceptance of the Contractor's Tender for the Works;

(i) " Contract Price " means the sum to be ascertained and paid in accordance with the provisions hereinafter contained for the construction completion and maintenance of the Works in accordance with the Contract;

(j) " Permanent Works " means the permanent works to be constructed completed and maintained in accordance with the Contract;

(k) " Temporary Works " means all temporary works of every kind required in or about the construction completion and maintenance of the Works;

(l) " Works " means the Permanent Works together with the Temporary Works;

(m) " Section " means a part of the Works separately identified in the Appendix to the Form of Tender;

(n) " Site " means the lands and other places on under in or through which the Works are to be executed and any other lands or places provided by the Employer for the purposes of the Contract;

(o) " Constructional Plant " means all appliances or things of whatsoever nature required in or about the construction completion and maintenance of the Works but does not include materials or other things intended to form or forming part of the Permanent Works.

It will be seen that some of these definitions are circular or tautologous (see *e.g.* the various " Works " definitions) or lack any real precision (see *e.g.* " Site ") and the words " except where the contract otherwise requires " should be borne in mind in considering the whole of this clause. The headings and marginal notes referred to in sub-clause (3), *infra* are included in the text of the present commentary, but must be ignored in attempting to construe the contract—see also the commentary on the latter sub-clause, *infra*, p. 24.

" (*b*) *Permitted assigns* "

i.e. presumably under clauses 3 and 4 of the Conditions, *infra*, pp. 28, 29.

" (*c*) *or other the Engineer appointed from time to time* "

This makes it clear that the Engineer may be dismissed and replaced by the Employer for no or any reason at any time notwithstanding his powers of certification or approval or consent under the contract, all of which, even including the maintenance and final certificates, are in any case now subject to ultimate review by an arbitrator (following a preliminary decision by the Engineer himself under clause 66, *infra*) and perhaps also by the courts (if no decision of the Engineer is asked for by either party—see the commentary to clause 66, *infra*, p. 269). Nevertheless, it is submitted that there must be an implied term, where words like the present are used, requiring the Employer to see that there is a duly appointed Engineer in charge of the contract at all material times—see Hudson, 10th ed., pp. 320–322, and 484–489.

The wording does not give any indication of what is to happen where the Engineer is a firm or limited company—presumably if either of these is named, any partner, or duly authorised executive director acting on behalf of the firm or company, will validly exercise the powers of the Engineer. For the status of Engineers generally, see Hudson, 10th ed., pp. 89–92.

" (*d*) *Engineer's Representative* "

This definition, which is rather oddly worded, requires to be read with clause 2, *infra*. In the industry the individual referred to is usually known as the " resident engineer "—as to whom see Hudson, 10th ed., pp. 92–95, 149–155. It is not clear whether " of the Engineer " governs

" assistant " only or " the resident engineer " as well, nor is it clear whether " appointed from time to time by the Employer or the Engineer " governs only the clerk of works, or the other two categories of person as well. Resident engineers may in practice be employed either by the Employer or by the Engineer, and the division of responsibility for their conduct as between Employer and Engineer is often by no means clear, and rarely the subject of any documented arrangement or agreement.

Whatever the category, it would seem that the Engineer must notify the Contractor in writing (for service of the notice see clause 68 (1)) that the individual concerned has his authority to " watch and supervise the construction . . . of the Works." It is by no means clear, incidentally, what powers, if any, this function is supposed to confer (see the commentary on clause 2 (1)), although the Engineer may apparently confer further specific powers under the contract under sub-clause (3) *either* on the Engineer's Representative *or* on " any other person responsible to the Engineer " (whatever that latter expression may mean) following service of another notice.

" (*e*) *Contract* "

It should be noted that the contract very sensibly confers no special status or priority on any particular document for purposes of interpretation—see also clause 5, *infra*, for ambiguities and discrepancies. Incidentally, the Bills of Quantities are now sometimes referred to in the contract as the " Priced Bills of Quantities " (see *e.g.* the present provision and clause 11 (2) and the Form of Agreement) but is not consistent about this (see clauses 55, 56, and 57 and the Form of Tender).

" (*e*) *the written acceptance thereof* "

Written acceptance of the tender will create a binding contract until the formal sealed contract contemplated by clause 9 of the Conditions (*infra*, p. 38) is executed—see the fourth paragraph of the Form of Tender (*post*, Chapter 3, p. 297). The puzzling and anomalous reference to a " Schedule of Rates and Prices " found in this paragraph in the Fourth Edition has now been omitted.

" (*f*) . . . *specification . . . and any modification thereof or addition thereto* "

A specification is, of course, primarily a description of the quality of the various processes and materials required for the contract work. The Specification is in fact only rarely mentioned as such in the contract Conditions—it should apparently identify the drawings (clause 6 and paragraph (*g*), *infra*), may contain safety requirements (clause 16) and provide for tests (clause 36 (3)).

The Contractor must give adequate notice " of any further . . . specification " he may require (see clause 7 (2)), and the present words might possibly be thought to be aimed at the very important new words in clause 7 (1), *infra*, which suggest a possible *duty* on the Engineer to modify the drawings or specification (*i.e.* vary the work) in certain undefined circumstances. The words here used are, however, identical with those in regard to drawings commented on under (*g*), *infra*, and these latter were originally present in the Fourth Edition, and simply contemplated the possibility of post-contract drawings calling for variations, as opposed to working drawings implementing the original contract intention in greater detail.

" (*g*) *Drawings . . . and any modification . . . such other drawings* "

The wording is traditional but a little odd. Used in the Fourth Edition the words appeared to contemplate either variations (" modification of such drawings ") or working (*i.e.* more detailed) drawings of the original contract intention (" such other drawings "). In the present Edition the words have to be construed with the new and possibly very significant wording of clause 7 (1), *infra*, however.

" (*h*) *Tender Total* "

This new expression appears to have been coined to take account of the fact that no " original " Contract Price (with which the present expression seems synonymous) is now to be found in the Form of Tender (or Form of Agreement) and perhaps also in recognition of the fact that a very large number of financial claims now permitted by the contract renders this original tendered figure an academic one (see " Contract Price," *infra*). Its significance in the contract appears to be limited to regulating the amount of the Contractor's Bond under clause 10, *infra*, p. 38, and the upper limit of the retention reserve under clause 60 (4), *infra*, p. 236.

(*i*) " *Contract Price . . . sum to be paid . . . in accordance with the provisions* "

As indicated under " Tender Total " above, " Contract Price " now seems to mean the adjusted sum to be finally paid under the contract provisions, and not an original quoted contract price. Apart from a number of mostly new provisions which really represent claims by the Contractor for breach of contract (late information under clause 7 (2), incorrect data for setting-out under clause 17, by-law and planning compliance under clause 26 (2) (b), disturbance by other contractors under clause 31 (2), suspension of the work under clause 40 (1), late possession under clause 42 (1), and regulation of the additional payments to be made to the Main Contractor upon a termination of a nominated sub-contract under clause 59B (4) (a)), all of which will now become due on interim certificate under the new provision in clause 60 (1) (d), and various monetary claims which are not new (*e.g.* boreholes under clause 18, certain tests and examinations under clauses 36 and 38, searches under clause 50, frustration and war under clauses 64 and 65, " labour-tax " fluctuations under clause 69, and metrication difficulties under clause 70) there are a number of vitally important major claims which strike at the very root of the " inclusive price " principle in contracts for work and materials—namely that, barring variations called for in the work under express provisions, or clearly agreed variations of the price such as a fluctuations clause, the contract prices will be firm and inclusive of contingencies or any work necessary to achieve completion of the described work. These major claims or qualifications are as follows:—

(1) (Partly new) for cost beyond that " reasonably foreseeable by an experienced contractor " arising from Engineer's instructions explaining ambiguities or discrepancies in the documents (clauses 5 and 13 (3)).
(2) (New) a *possible* claim that, in certain undefined circumstances where it can be shown to be " necessary," the Engineer is *contractually obliged to vary the work* so as to assist the Contractor to complete the work (combined effect of clauses 7 (1), 13 (1), 13 (3) and 51 (1).)
(3) (Not new) cost of (but now also profit on) " reasonably unforeseeable " work due to unfavourable physical conditions or artificial obstructions (clause 12).
(4) (New) for " reasonably unforeseeable " cost of complying, it would seem, with *any contractual obligation* (clauses 13 (1) and (3)).
(5) (Not new) for cost of replacing any part of the works damaged during construction by one of the " Excepted Risks " (clause 20).
(6) (New) for cost of complying, after preliminary request of Engineer for proposals etc., with " reasonably unforeseeable " requirements of the Engineer as to the Contractor's methods of working (clause 14 (6)).
(7) (Not new) for omission or abandonment of work suspended for three months (clause 40 (2)).
(8) (New) for valuation in accordance with the rules for valuing variations under clause 52 of any " error in description in or omission from " the Bills of Quantities (clause 55 (2)).
(9) (New) for alteration of rates or prices in the Bills to take account of increases or decreases, independently of variations, in the actual quantities of work carried out (clause 56 (2)).

In addition, the startling new policy underlying clauses 59A (6) and 59B will mean that in the case of defaults by nominated sub-contractors the Employer not only guarantees the financial ability of nominated sub-contractors to reimburse the Contractor for any claims made against him by the Employer on account of their breaches, but in the event of a termination of their sub-contracts actually guarantees to the Contractor any loss caused to the Contractor thereby. In these cases the contractual machinery will mean that the extent of the Employer's financial commitment must remain speculative until a date considerably later than the final certificate itself, and that on any view the Employer must finance the Contractor against all losses during the construction period—see *ante*, Chapter 1, for a more detailed summary of these provisions and the commentary to clauses 58, 59A, 59B, and 60 (7).

(For a reasonably comprehensive summary of Contractor's claims available under the Contract, see the commentary to clause 60 (1), *infra*, p. 233.)

(*j*) " *Permanent Works* "

(*k*) " *Temporary Works* "

(*l*) " *Works* "

None of these three definitions of " Works " can be regarded as very helpful, and the separate definition for " Permanent Works " is new, no doubt resulting from the greatly improved redrafting of clause 60 with regard to interim and final payment (though the expression and concept of " Permanent Works " in this clause is not new). In the absence of any proper definition, it is submitted that the true distinction lies in the intended function of the work. Thus " Permanent Works " represent, apart from actual visible structures, all work intended to perform a continuing function after the end of the work (*e.g.* foundations and permanent drainage), and possibly work which, while it may have no permanent function, is sometimes contractually required to be left *in situ* (as *e.g.* steel-sheet piling or cofferdams or access roads, all originally built only for purposes of construction, but sometimes required to be left); whereas " Temporary Works " will not lose that character simply because for convenience they may be left permanently *in situ* without any contractual obligation to do so. Obvious Temporary Works are site huts and accommodation, possibly gantries and concrete batching-plants (though here the distinction between Temporary Works and " Plant " may become somewhat blurred) access roads and temporary fencing, cofferdams, ramps and systems for supporting the structures during construction, scaffolding and so on. As stated, the dividing line between " Temporary Works " and " Plant " may also be a fine one (see the definition of the latter *infra*, p. 23 and in clause 53 (1), which is the definitive clause regulating the Contractor's plant and which in fact includes Temporary Works in the definition of " Plant " for the purposes of that clause)—as *e.g.* in the case of a tower crane. It is also not difficult to conceive of border-line cases as between Permanent and Temporary Works, and in view of the considerable importance of the distinction (on interim payment under clause 60 (1) (d), or on damage from an Excepted Risk under clause 20, for example) the failure of the contract to attempt a more serious definition, or to make provision for the special treatment or identification of doubtful cases in the Bills, is to be regretted. Temporary Works may or may not, incidentally, be designed by the engineer—see *e.g.* clause 8 (2), *infra*, p. 37.

Other provisions in the contract which may bear on the extent of the Works are to be found in clauses 8 (1), 11, 13 (1) and 20 (2).

" (*m*) *Section* "

This refers to different physical parts of the work for which different contractual completion dates may be specified, with consequential effects on the transfer to the Employer of the risk of damage to the Works, the commencement of the maintenance period, the release of the liability to pay liquidated damages for delay, and of retention money—see clauses 20 (1), 43, 47 (2), 48 (2), 49 (2) and 60 (5). In the earlier Fourth Edition, part occupation by the Employer with the consent of the contractor was (and remains) possible with similar consequences, but no contractual scheme existed for such contractually binding differing completion dates, which are usually called " phased completion " in the industry, and are often a commercially necessary feature of civil engineering projects.

(*n*) " *Site* "

This definition is unfortunately too vague for many of the purposes of the contract. Engineering works frequently take place over wide areas, perhaps already occupied by the Employer or other persons, and of which the works may form only a small part, and with no readily recognisable limitations or boundaries, unlike the case of most building sites. Sewerage and pipe-laying work, for instance, may take place under public roads, or traverse gardens, fields or open country, or occur within an existing complex of engineering works, such as a water works, power station, or refinery. Accessibility in all such contracts is of vital practical importance, as is possession of some, but not necessarily all, of the land in the employer's occupation for the purpose of temporary works. In addition, working space outside the immediate width or area of the works or of the employer's land may be essential—*e.g.* on one or both sides of the trench in a pipe-laying contract. It is quite usual for the other contract documents to be silent about this, yet a very precise definition of what is or is not " the Site " is obviously essential for the operation of, in particular, clause 22 of the Conditions (indemnities for " surface or other damage to land being the site " and " damage to crops being on the site ") *infra*, p. 75 *et seq*; clause 32 (fossils coins etc. found on the Site); clause 37 (employer's access to the Site); clause 42 (possession of the Site) *infra*, p. 116 *et seq*; clause 53 (2) (property in plant and materials passing " when on the Site "); and clauses 60 (1) (b) and (c) and 54 (payment for goods not yet delivered to the Site)—to give a few examples.

It should be noted that the present definition requires to be separated into two different parts. First, it appears to be the area (or volume) of land in which the permanent and temporary works are to be constructed, and this part of the definition is again very generalised and might not always be appropriate—the site of a tunnel, for example, would not usually include the surface overhead. Secondly, it includes " other lands or places provided by the Employer for the purposes of the Contract," another vague expression which, in addition to working space, could arguably include access roads, storage areas or yards, batching plants, borrow-pits a considerable distance from the permanent work, and so on. The words " provided by the Employer for the purposes of the Contract " (which only appear to qualify the " other lands and places " in the second part of the definition) probably recognise the fact that many engineering contracts do define in the Bills or elsewhere the facilities of this kind which the Employer undertakes to provide, while making it plain that the Contractor is free to make his own arrangements for further facilities at his own expense should he so desire—see clause 42 (2) of the Conditions, under which the Contractor has to bear the expense of special wayleaves " in connection with access to the Site " and of any " additional accommodation outside the Site."

It is therefore in the highest degree desirable that the Specification or Bills (or drawings) should describe exactly the area over which the Contractor is entitled to have freedom of operation, and any special rights of access across adjoining land or limitations on the use of the Employer's land, and if necessary give particular definitions of the expression for the purpose of particular contractual provisions, where the policy requirements may often be quite different.

(*o*) " *Constructional Plant* "

The present definition is relevant to clauses 8 (1), 12 (2), 14 (3), 21, 30, 33 and 53 of the Conditions. Clause 53, which is the definitive provision governing the ownership of and other incidents attaching to plant has a special definition of " Plant " for the purposes of that clause which is wider than the present definition and includes Temporary Works and materials for Temporary Works (see clause 53 (1) (a)). The word " constructional " is no doubt used to avoid confusion with the parts of the permanent work, such as the machinery, pipes, valves and specials, which often form part of engineering contracts, and which are, of course, often described as " plant " quite correctly in a different context. The present sub-clause gives the only accurate and clear definition which can be attached to the word in building and civil engineering contracts—see Hudson, 10th ed., pp. 654, and 660–661. Clause 53 provides that plant, once on Site, shall be " deemed to be the property of the employer." It further contains various provisions designed to prevent the removal of plant from the site without the engineer's consent and includes a general prohibition against the use of any plant which is the subject of a hire-purchase agreement. Clause 33, on the other hand, requires the removal of all plant at the end of the contract, which is of course consistent with the present definition. It should, however, be appreciated that, as already stated in the context of Temporary Works, certain items of plant may either be designed to be or are more conveniently left *in situ*—*e.g.* certain piling or formwork—and so may constitute difficult border-line cases where it is sought to apply the present definition—see the commentary, *supra*, p. 21, on " Works " As there pointed out, the dividing-line between Plant and Temporary Works may also be a fine one in certain cases.

Singular and Plural

(2) Words importing the singular also include the plural and *vice-versa* where the context requires.

Headings and Marginal Notes

(3) The headings and marginal notes in the Conditions of Contract shall not be deemed to be part thereof or be taken into consideration in the interpretation or construction thereof or of the Contract.

Clause References

(4) All references herein to clauses are references to clauses numbered in the Conditions of Contract and not to those in any other document forming part of the Contract.

" *(3) The headings and marginal notes* "

The transposition of the wording of the Fourth Edition which is now used in this sub-clause indicates that the main headings above clauses or groups of clauses should be excluded from consideration in interpreting the contract, as well as the marginal headings. This is a pity, because the draftsmanship of the contract in general is often so obscure that assistance could well be derived from the headings—an example, for instance, is in clause 56 (2) where the marginal heading " Increase or Decrease of Rate " serves to make plain the intention of the clause, not apparent from the draftsmanship, that it is concerned with adjustments other than simple remeasurement arising from differences in the quantities. It is difficult to discern any policy reason for denying interpretative value to these headings in cases of difficulty.

" *(4) references . . . to Clauses* "

It is a little difficult to see why this new sub-clause has been inserted, since if a printed standard form is used confusion with an (obviously later) specially prepared document like the Specification or Bills would not occur. Furthermore, the Form of Tender has no numbered clauses, and the Form of Agreement has only four numbered clauses which could not be confused with their counterparts in the Conditions. It may be that the provision is inserted for the benefit of parties who employ a specially reproduced or amended version of the present Conditions in similar documentary form to the Bills or Specification.

Cost

(5) The word " cost " when used in the Conditions of Contract shall be deemed to include overhead costs whether on or off the Site except where the contrary is expressly stated.

Overhead costs " on the Site " will include, presumably, the expenses of all supervisory or clerical staff employed full-time on the site, and all direct site expenditure (often described in the Preliminary Bills) such as water, electricity, site huts, gantries and batching plants, weigh-bridges and so on. " Off-site " overheads will principally consist of a rateable proportion of Head Office expenses (rents, salaries, etc.) attributable to the particular contract. There may be some border-line cases (*e.g.* contract manager's salary, cost of specialist investigations, Contractor's yards and depots and so on).

There do not seem to be any examples of " the contrary (being) expressly stated " in the Conditions themselves. Clauses 59B (" reasonable costs and expenses of such steps and proceedings ") and 69 (2) (tax fluctuations) show the possibly unintended benefits to the Contractor of a " blanket " provision like the present (does the expression include Head Office overheads, or the time of site-staff associated with the litigation, or calculating the tax fluctuations in question, by virtue of the present sub-clause?). Of the many provisions referring to " cost," clause 7 (3) (late information); clause 12 (3) (physical conditions etc.); clause 13 (3) (" unforeseeable instruction "); clause 14 (6) (methods of working); clause 17 (setting out); clause 31 (2) (other contractors); clause 36 (3) (tests); clause 38 (2) (uncovering of work); clause 40 (suspension of work); clause 42 (1) (failure to give possession); clause 59B (4) (b) (cost caused by determination of nominated sub-contract); clause 69 (3) (tax fluctuations); and clause 71 (1) (metrication difficulties) are the principal examples.

ENGINEER'S REPRESENTATIVE

Functions and Powers of Engineer's Representative

2. (1) The functions of the Engineer's Representative are to watch and supervise the construction completion and maintenance of the Works. He shall have no authority to relieve the Contractor of any of his duties or obligations under the Contract nor except as expressly provided hereunder to order any work involving delay or any extra payment by the Employer nor to make any variation of or in the Works.

Appointment of Assistants

(2) The Engineer or the Engineer's Representative may appoint any number of persons to assist the Engineer's Representative in the exercise of his functions under

sub-clause (1) of this Clause. He shall notify to the Contractor the names and functions of such persons. The said assistants shall have no power to issue any instructions to the Contractor save in so far as such instructions may be necessary to enable them to discharge their functions and to secure their acceptance of materials or workmanship as being in accordance with the Specification and Drawings and any instructions given by any of them for those purposes shall be deemed to have been given by the Engineer's Representative.

Delegation by Engineer

(3) The Engineer may from time to time in writing authorise the Engineer's Representative or any other person responsible to the Engineer to act on behalf of the Engineer either generally in respect of the Contract or specifically in respect of particular Clauses of these Conditions of Contract and any act of any such person within the scope of his authority shall for the purposes of the contract constitute an act of the Engineer. Prior notice in writing of any such authorisation shall be given by the Engineer to the Contractor. Such authorisation shall continue in force until such time as the Engineer shall notify the Contractor in writing that the same is determined. Provided that such authorisation shall not be given in respect of any decision to be taken or certificate to be issued under Clauses 12 (3) 44 48 60 (3) 61 63 and 66.

Reference to Engineer or Engineer's Representative

(4) If the Contractor shall be dissatisfied by reason of any instruction of any assistant of the Engineer's Representative duly appointed under sub-clause (2) of this Clause he shall be entitled to refer the matter to the Engineer's Representative who shall thereupon confirm reverse or vary such instruction. Similarly if the Contractor shall be dissatisfied by reason of any act of the Engineer's Representative or other person duly authorised by the Engineer under sub-clause (3) of this Clause he shall be entitled to refer the matter to the Engineer for his decision.

This clause, which has been recast and amended to a considerable extent, needs to be read with the definition of " Engineer's Representative " in clause 1 (1) (d) and the commentary thereto, *supra*, and also with clause 13 (1), *infra*, p. 46. As will be seen, the effect of these provisions is not at all clear. For the status and authority, in the absence of express provision, of resident engineers, professional assistants and, clerks of works, see Hudson, 10th ed., pp. 92–95.

Sub-clause (1) of the present clause defines the " function " of the Engineer's Representative as to " watch and supervise " the work. " Watching " certainly does not imply any powers at all *vis-à-vis* the Contractor (other than a right of access for the purpose, specifically accorded by clause 37, *infra*, p. 106). " Supervising " equally does not, it is submitted, by itself confer any right or authority to give instructions for work to be removed or reinstated, although there is a puzzling reference in sub-clause (2) to instructions that may be given by " assistants " of the Engineer's Representative appointed under that clause. It should be noted that the power to condemn defective work in clause 39 (1) of the Conditions refers pointedly to the Engineer alone, and makes no reference to the Engineer's Representative.

The scheme of the contract, therefore, is that the Engineer must first notify the Contractor of the identity of the Engineer's Representative, and the person so notified may be a resident engineer, or an assistant of the

Engineer, or a clerk of works (clause 1 (1) (d), *supra*). As stated, this individual would appear to have no powers of any significance as a mere result of his appointment since, apart from the fact that the supply of incorrect data by the Engineer's Representative for the purposes of setting out may have contractual consequences (see clause 17, *infra*), the contract contains many references to the effect that, as in the case of the Engineer himself, approval of work by the Engineer's Representative will have no contractual consequence as between employer and contractor or bar the Engineer or Employer from subsequent action to condemn it—see particularly the new clause 39 (3) (the old paragraph (a) of clause 2 in the Fourth Edition) (prior approval during construction); clause 14 (7) (approval of methods of working); clause 39 (1) (c) (previous tests); clause 54 (3) (a) (previous payment for materials); and clause 60 (7) (work previously certified or paid for).

However, by a contractually quite separate notice to the Contractor in writing, the Engineer may under sub-clause (3) confer specific authority on the Engineer's Representative in accordance with the provisions of the sub-clause. While even a general delegation of his powers by the Engineer is apparently permitted by the opening words of sub-clause (3), in the last two lines of the sub-clause all the more important powers in the contract are excepted from its operation—*i.e.* decisions on clause 12 claims, or as to extension of time under clause 44, certification of practical completion under clause 48 (and hence the resulting maintenance, retention, liquidated damages, and insurance consequences), the issue of the maintenance certificate under clause 61, decisions on which an employer's determination under clause 63 might be based, and decisions as to disputes under clause 66. Possibly the most important power suitable for delegation under this clause is that to condemn work under clause 39 (1). Furthermore, a " right of appeal " to the Engineer from persons appointed under sub-clauses (2) or (3) exists in any event under sub-clause (4). The sub-clause (3) machinery, therefore, will not itself enable a firm of consulting engineers effectively to depute one of their partners to act as Engineer under the contract, though if the firm itself is named as the Engineer some such right must be implied—for this problem see the commentary under clause 1 (1) (c), *supra*.

It should be noted that the power of delegation in sub-clause (3) is to extend, apparently, to persons other than the Engineer's Representative who are " responsible to the Engineer " (whatever this expression is supposed to mean—perhaps the intention is that the Contractor can object to a delegation to some outside person against whom the Engineer has neither control, as in the case of an employee or partner, or recourse, as in the case of a consultant or other person either in contractual relations with, or placed contractually under the control of, the Engineer). Such a delegation, in view of the virtually non-existent powers of the Engineer's

Representative, already noted, would seem to mean that this second individual might have powers greater than the Engineer's Representative (unless the persons " responsible to the Engineer " are intended to be subordinates of the Engineer's Representative under sub-clause (2) to whom, perhaps, either equal or lesser powers than those conferred on the Engineer's Representative have been delegated by the Engineer under sub-clause (3)).

It will be seen that sub-clause (2) enables the Engineer or Engineer's Representative to appoint assistants to the latter. It is difficult to see what functions these persons could have (unless there has been a sub-clause (3) express delegation of particular powers, especially, perhaps, those in clause 39 (1)), in view of the very limited functions or powers of the Engineer's Representative himself. Certainly the " instructions . . . necessary to enable them . . . to secure their acceptance of materials or workmanship . . ." make no sense except in the context of a delegation to such assistants under sub-clause (3) of the Engineer's own powers under clauses 36 (1) (ordering of tests), 38 (covering up of work), 39 (condemning of work) or 50 (searches for causes of defect), for example. Here again, it will be seen that a " right of appeal " exists (this time to the Engineer's Representative) under sub-clause (4), and no doubt from the latter to the Engineer himself under the same sub-clause.

The whole of this clause seems unnecessarily complicated and obscure and no very clear policy is discernible.

ASSIGNMENT AND SUB-LETTING

Assignment

3. The Contractor shall not assign the Contract or any part thereof or any benefit or interest therein or thereunder without the written consent of the Employer

Sub-Letting

4. The Contractor shall not sub-let the whole of the Works. Except where otherwise provided by the Contract the Contractor shall not sub-let any part of the Works without the written consent of the Engineer and such consent if given shall not relieve the Contractor from any liability or obligation under the Contract and he shall be responsible for the acts defaults and neglects of any sub-contractor his agents servants or workmen as fully as if they were the acts defaults or neglects of the Contractor his agents servants or workmen. Provided alway that the provision of labour on a piece-work basis shall not be deemed to be a sub-letting under this Clause.

These clauses are identical with those of the Fourth Edition. English law does not permit the assignment of contractual liabilities, so that a contractor could never by a purported assignment or sub-contract escape his personal contractual and financial responsibility for the work. The law does, however, in general permit *vicarious performance* of a contractual liability, and it is this rather than assignment in the legal sense at which the prohibitions in these clauses are presumably aimed (see Hudson, 10th ed., pp. 715–720).

In the present clauses the words " assign the Contract " in clause 3 and " sub-let the whole of the Works " in clause 4 are probably synonymous, or very nearly so, as meaning vicarious performance of the whole of the works. (The expression " sub-let " is legally nonsensical in this context of a contract for work and materials, incidentally, and there is no usage in the industry which would justify its employment in the present context. It is presumably a survival from very old contracts prepared by draftsmen whose experience was limited to the field of landlord and tenant.) The sanction for assignment without consent is determination on seven days' notice under the first sentence of clause 63 (1), *infra*, p. 244. The sanction for " sub-letting " a part of the work " in defiance of the Engineer's instructions " is determination under clause 63 (1) (e), which also permits determination, whether or not there has been defiance, if the sub-letting has been " to the detriment of good workmanship," see *infra*, pp. 249, 251.

" 4. . . . *Except where otherwise provided by the Contract* "

i.e. presumably in the case of Nominated Sub-contractors under clause 58, *infra*, p. 195. These words, therefore, were quite meaningless in the Fourth Edition, but in view of the dramatic cutting down of the Contractor's ultimate liability for Nominated Sub-contractors' work now effected by clauses 59A (6) and 59B, *infra*, the present words for the first time have some significance.

" *4. . . . shall not relieve etc.*"

These words have little or no significance, since English law would not imply any such release from consent to a "sub-letting."

CONTRACT DOCUMENTS

Documents Mutually Explanatory

5. The several documents forming the Contract are to be taken as mutually explanatory of one another and in case of ambiguities or discrepancies the same shall be explained and adjusted by the Engineer who shall thereupon issue to the Contractor appropriate instructions in writing which shall be regarded as instructions issued in accordance with Clause 13.

This is a truncated version of clause 6 of the Fourth Edition (for commentary on which see B.C.F., pp. 312–314) which is now, however, expressly inter-related with the new and very difficult clause 13—see particularly sub-clause (3) of that clause, *infra*, p. 51.

The opening words of the clause, like the old clause 6, very sensibly accord equal status, from the point of view of interpretation, to all the contract documents, and enable the normal legal rules of construction to be applied (for instance, that a document specially prepared for the particular contract by the parties, such as the Specification or Bills, should be given special weight in any case of ambiguity or inconsistency, as against a printed standard document prepared by others, such as the Conditions themselves).

It is not at all easy to determine the precise scope and intention of the present clause, the more so since the Fourth Edition version, itself requiring amplification for this purpose, has instead been abridged. The old clause referred to instructions " directing in what manner the work is to be carried out," the present clause only to " appropriate " instructions. The reference to " instructions issued in accordance with clause 13 " (presumably clause 13 (1)) is on examination of no assistance, and indeed the reference to clause 13 appears to be unnecessary, since clause 13 (3), which entitles the Contractor to claim an extension of time or additional payment, is expressly applied by that sub-clause to instructions given under the present clause.

Ambiguities or discrepancies are not uncommon in lengthy and complicated contracts, and if possible these will be resolved by the usual legal rules of interpretation so as to arrive at the true contract intention—most importantly, of course, in the case of the precise work to be undertaken, upon which will depend any financial claim for a variation. It is submitted that it is clear from clause 13 (3), which requires *delay or disruption* of the Contractor's *arrangements or methods* of construction caused by the instruction as the essential basis of any financial claim, that it is only ambiguities or discrepancies affecting the *physical work* to be undertaken by the Contractor (*i.e.* in the technical documents describing the work as opposed to the Conditions themselves) that are to be " explained and adjusted " and the subject of the Engineer's instructions under the present clause. Moreover, the Engineer cannot, it is submitted, purport to resolve matters of the legal construction of the contract documents and order additional payments on the basis that the Contractor should be excused from misconstruing the contract in a different sense from its true construction. What is intended, it is submitted, is that if a genuine mistake or conflict or ambiguity exists which cannot be resolved or reconciled by the ordinary rules of construction—*e.g.* dimensional or descriptive or other discrepancies occurring between the Bills, Specification, or Drawings —the Engineer has the last word in order that he may control the permanent physical work. Such is the complication of major engineering works that discrepancies or errors of this kind can easily happen, and having regard to the exigencies of tendering it is not unreasonable that the Employer, whose agents have prepared the contract documents in detail over perhaps a long period of time, should be the one to bear the loss if an undetected mistake occurs, rather than a Contractor required to price the work at comparatively short notice. It by no means follows, however, that a Contractor has been misled to his detriment—indeed the contrary may be the case, and while clause 13 (3) does not appear to contemplate any *reduction* in the Contractor's payments (unless this could happen as the result of the very difficult reference to instructions requiring a variation under clause 51 in the last sentence of that sub-clause) the special character, which has already been referred to, of the additional payment under clause 13 should be noted—see generally the commentary under clause 13, *infra*, p. 46. It is suggested that the true relationship between the present clause and clause 13 (3) may be that where an instruction does not involve a variation (as where the discrepancy is such that no contract intention can be ascertained, or possibly where the instruction, despite an apparent contractual conflict, does reflect the true contract intention) then the additional payment in clause 13 (3) will be available if the conditions for it are satisfied. Where the instruction does involve a variation (*i.e.* in a case where the contractual intention, despite an apparent ambiguity or discrepancy, must by definition be capable of being ascertained) then the last sentence of clause 13 (3) (though strictly unnecessary and difficult to interpret in the wider context of clause 13 itself) will apply and the instruction can be valued as a variation.

" *The several documents forming the Contract* "

By virtue of clause 1 (1) (e) and (g), *supra*, these will include working drawings under clause 7, *infra.*

Supply of Documents

6. Upon acceptance of the Tender 2 copies of the drawings referred to in the Specification and of the Conditions of Contract the Specification and (unpriced) Bill of Quantities shall be furnished to the Contractor free of charge. Copyright of the Drawings and Specification and of the Bill of Quantities (except the pricing thereof) shall remain in the Engineer but the Contractor may obtain or make at his own expense any further copies required by him. At the completion of the Contract the Contractor shall return to the Engineer all Drawings and the Specification whether provided by the Engineer or obtained or made by the Contractor.

This clause appears to be intended to expand and replace the first two sentences of clause 7 (1) of the Fourth Edition. Clause 7 (2) of the Fourth Edition now reappears as clause 7 (4) in the present edition. Probably by inadvertence, the words " as aforesaid " in clause 7 (4), *infra*, would appear to refer back to the present clause and not to the earlier parts of clause 7. However this may be, there seems little doubt that the present clause requires to be read together with clause 7 (4), and that the latter would be more happily appended at the end of the present clause.

" *referred to in the Specification* "

All the contract drawings are required to be identified in this document —see clause 1 (1) (g), *supra.*

Further Drawings and Instructions

7. (1) The Engineer shall have full power and authority to supply and shall supply to the Contractor from time to time during the progress of the Works such

modified or further drawings and instructions as shall in the Engineer's opinion be necessary for the purpose of the proper and adequate construction completion and maintenance of the Works and the Contractor shall carry out and be bound by the same.

Sub-clause (1) of the present clause replaces clause 8 of the Fourth Edition but with most significant modifications of the wording. This new wording, coupled with certain significant changes of wording elsewhere in the contract, lends support to a possible claim by the Contractor which, if correct, would be largely subversive of the fundamental absolute obligation of a contractor, in a contract for work and materials, to complete the works whatever difficulties may be encountered—for this fundamental obligation see the commentary to clauses 13 and 20 (2) (both of which appear to be, if anything, consistent with the traditional view and inconsistent with the possible new claim).

The new words in the sub-clause are " and shall supply " after " have full power and authority to supply " and the words " modified or " before the words " further drawings and instructions." (Incidentally the word " instructions " is presumably wide enough to include any new specifications—see the probably unintended contrast with the wording of sub-clause (2), *infra*). The old clause 8 of the Fourth Edition simply conferred a power to issue further drawings and was the empowering " working drawings " provision in the contract. (Sub-clause (3), *infra*, it will be noted, for purposes of additional payment and extension of time refers to delay in supplying drawings or instructions " considered necessary by the Engineer in accordance with sub-clause (1).") The quoted new wording may, therefore, be used to suggest a *duty* (" *shall* supply ") to *vary* (" modified ") the work if this is " in the Engineer's opinion . . . necessary for the purpose of the proper and adequate construction (or) completion of the Works." This argument receives further support from the small but significant modifications of the wording of clause 51 (1)—" the Engineer *shall order* any variation to any part of the works that may in his opinion be *necessary for the completion of the works*." On the other hand, it should be noted that, in the specific context of difficulties encountered during construction, clause 12 (2), *infra*, p. 44, only uses permissive language—see clause 12 (2) (c) and (d) " *may if he thinks fit* . . . give written instructions as to how the physical conditions or artificial obstructions are to be dealt with . . . [or] order . . . a variation under clause 51." If the argument in favour of a duty to vary is right, it becomes, of course, essential to determine exactly what is meant in this context by the expressions " necessary for the (construction or) completion of the works "—does this mean necessary from the point of view of commercial practicability and to avoid excessive delay or expense (*i.e.* basically from the Contractor's point of view), or does it only mean if completion would otherwise be " physically impossible " within the wording of clause 13, *infra*, p. 46? (This latter should not, incidentally, be regarded as accurately depicting " the Employer's point of view." With the absolute obligation to complete which the law will generally imply the Contractor will be compelled to mitigate his breach in failing to complete exactly in accordance with the contract by varying some or all of the work free of charge in order to reach substantial completion (both under clause 48 and in the legal sense of that expression) and even " physical impossibility " will not usually avail him—see the commentary to clause 13 (1), *infra*, p. 46.) Thirdly and finally, " necessary," in the present clause at any rate, may only mean necessary from the point of view of the need to identify in sufficient time the final permanent work, whether original contract or varied, required of the Contractor, and to permit its construction without delay. The word " modify " has merely been used, on this view, to take account of the possibility that the work in question may be varied as opposed to original contract work and in the context of the *time* for giving such instructions.

It can only be said that it is remarkable that changes of wording of such potential significance as those in clauses 7 (1) and 51 (1) of the present contract can be effected in a standard form of contract without the new intention (if any) being spelt out with complete clarity. The new wording must be regarded as certain to trouble the appellate courts in the United Kingdom, and may be expected to expose engineers in charge of contracts which are running into physical difficulties, and who have their clients' interests at heart, to the most difficult dilemmas and pressures. It may well be, however, that the final view of the courts will be determined more by the wording of clause 51 (1) than by that of the present sub-clause—see the further commentary on this subject under clauses 13 and 51, *infra*, pp. 47–50 and 155–156. (See also the wording of clause 40 (1) (c), *infra*, p. 113.)

Notice by Contractor

(2) The Contractor shall give adequate notice in writing to the Engineer of any further drawing or specification that the Contractor may require for the execution of the Works or otherwise under the Contract.

Delay in Issue

(3) If by reason of any failure or inability of the Engineer to issue at a time reasonable in all the circumstances drawings or instructions requested by the Contractor and considered necessary by the Engineer in accordance with sub-clause (1) of this Clause the Contractor suffers delay or incurs cost then the Engineer shall take such delay into account in determining any extension of time to which the Contractor is entitled under Clause 44 and the Contractor shall subject to Clause 52 (4) be paid in accordance with Clause 60 the amount of such cost as may be reasonable. If such drawings or instructions require any variation to any part of the Works the same shall be deemed to have been issued pursuant to Clause 51.

Sub-clause (2) repeats unchanged the last sentence of clause 7 (1) of the Fourth Edition. The contrast between its wording " drawing or specification " with the wording " drawings and instructions " in sub-clause (1) is probably, as in the case of the Fourth Edition, inadvertent, but by virtue of the new arrangement of the sub-clauses, more noticeable. The sub-clause is important because it will qualify the time for exercise by the Engineer of his duty to supply the information prescribed in sub-clause (1) and also indicates that notice by the Contractor may be relevant to determining the time which is " reasonable in all the circumstances " before claims for additional payment or extension of time can be advanced under sub-clause (3). The provision of a programme by the Contractor (see commentary to clause 14 (1), *infra*) may also bear on this question. For the time for giving information generally, see Hudson, 10th ed., pp. 135–142, 322–326.

Sub-clause (3) is new, and for the first time in the I.C.E. Conditions adopts the R.I.B.A. policy (since 1963) of providing specifically for a certified financial claim by contractors based on late information from the professional adviser in charge of the contract. Any such claim will be payable on interim certificate by virtue of clauses 52 (4) (f) and 60 (1) (d), *infra*, pp. 166 and 233. Sub-clause (3) also indicates the new policy of the present contract to provide for extensions of time at any appropriate points of the contract rather than seek to do so compendiously in the extension of time clause, as was the case with the Fourth Edition. For a collection of these various grounds see the commentary to clause 44 (1), *infra*, pp. 118–119.

(3) " Subject to clause 52 (4) "

i.e. particularly to paragraphs (b) (notice) (d) (first interim account with full and detailed particulars) and (e) and (f) (possible reductions for non-compliance) of that sub-clause—see *infra*, pp. 166–168.

(3) " cost "

This includes overheads etc.—see the commentary to clause 1 (5), *supra*.

One Copy of Documents to be kept on Site

(4) One copy of the Drawings and Specification furnished to the Contractor as aforesaid shall be kept by the Contractor on the Site and the same shall at all reasonable times be available for inspection and use by the Engineer and the Engineer's Representative and by any other person authorised by the Engineer in writing.

As already stated in the commentary to clause 6, *supra*, this sub-clause seems more appropriate to that clause, and the words " as aforesaid " in the present provision would appear to relate back to that clause, though the present sub-clause, by virtue of the extended definitions of " Drawings " and " Specification " in clause 1 (1) (f) and (g), *supra*, will apply to drawings etc. supplied under the preceding parts of the present clause.

GENERAL OBLIGATIONS

Contractor's General Responsibilities

8. (1) The Contractor shall subject to the provisions of the Contract construct complete and maintain the Works and provide all labour materials Constructional Plant Temporary Works transport to and from and in or about the Site and everything whether of a temporary or permanent nature required in and for such construction completion and maintenance so far as the necessity for providing the same is specified in or reasonably to be inferred from the Contract.

The wording of the first part of this sub-clause overlaps substantially with the opening words of the Form of Tender and clause 3 of the Form of Agreement (*post*, Chapter 3, pp. 297 and 301). The sub-clause is the formal general statement of the physical extent of the Contractor's obligation to complete the works, and corresponds fairly closely to clause 5 of the Fourth Edition, with the addition of the now increasingly significant words " subject to the provisions of the Contract," (see the list of major claims permitted by the Contract in the commentary to clause 1 (1) (i), *supra*, p. 20 and see also the comprehensive list of financial claims in the commentary to clause 60 (1), *infra*, p. 233). An equivalent general financial statement of the inclusiveness of the Contractor's prices is in clause 11 (2), *infra*, and a further important repetition of the words of the present obligation, with perhaps somewhat more emphasis on the quality and description of the work, and with additional references to the satisfaction of the Engineer and a qualification as to legal and physical impossibility, is to be found in clause 13 (1), *infra*, p. 46.

The express obligation to complete in a contract for work and materials has very important legal consequences, since its absolute nature means that the contractor is effectively at risk until completion, subject to any express stipulation—in this context important express qualifications are to be found in clauses 13 (" physical impossibility "), clause 20 (the " Excepted Risks," including particularly " fault defect error or omission in the design of the Works ") and clause 14 (2) (suspension for more than three months), but mention should also be made of the possible arguments, based on the new wording of clauses 7 (1) and 51 (1), that the Engineer may in certain circumstances be under a *duty to the Contractor* to vary the work if this is " necessary " for its construction and completion (see *supra*, pp. 32–33 and *infra*, pp. 47–50, 155–6). In addition, the revolutionary new code imposing heavy responsibilities on the Employer in the event of repudiations of their obligations by Nominated Sub-contractors (see the summary of these provisions, *ante*, Chap. 1, pp. 1–3 and *supra*, under clause 1 (1) (i) pp. 20–21, and the closer analysis, *infra*, pp. 197–199) represents a further very substantial qualification of the Contractor's obligations under the present clause.

For further discussion on the extent of the obligation to complete see the commentary on clause 13 (1), *infra*, pp. 47–49.

" *complete* " . . . " *completion* "

The I.C.E. Conditions have not always been very precise on their use of these words—the present edition has been more careful than its predecessor to refer specifically to a certificate of completion under clause 48 (*i.e.* " substantial completion " as there defined, which may involve some outstanding works still uncompleted) where this is what is intended (see *e.g.* clause 20 (1), (works at risk of Contractor), *infra*, p. 64), so that the words used *simpliciter* (as they still are, for instance, in clause 33, clearance of site) will usually mean, as here, the completion of all the last contractual obligations of the Contractor, including the maintenance obligation, it is submitted, and not this lesser and earlier substantial completion.

A further important consequence of the express obligation to complete is that in contracts for work and materials time, for the purposes of limitation of actions, will usually begin to run against the Employer in respect of defective work as from the date of completion and not at some earlier stage when the defective work itself was carried out—see Hudson, 10th ed., pp. 368–369. In the present contract this particular breach is perhaps more explicitly covered by the, as already stated, closely analogous express wording of clause 13 (1), *infra*, where the words " in strict accordance with the contract " after the " construct complete and maintain " wording perhaps relate more closely than the present clause to the quality and description of the work.

" *maintenance* "

i.e. under clause 49 of the Conditions, *infra*, p. 143.

" *Constructional Plant, Temporary Works* "

See the commentaries to clauses 1 (1) (o) and (k), *supra*, pp. 23–24 and 21–22.

" *so far as the necessity for providing the same is . . . reasonably to be inferred from the Contract* "

The correct principle in all contracts for work and materials is that any work, whether described or not, which is ancillary to or necessary to achieve completion of the work described in the contract is *prima facie* the obligation of anyone undertaking to construct and complete the described work. Careful analysis shows that this work may be of two kinds—namely work which on the true construction of the contract will *inevitably* be required to complete the described work—" indispensably necessary work " as it is sometimes called—and, secondly, work which *contingently may* be required to complete—*e.g.* to overcome difficulties which may or may not be encountered during construction—see as to these categories of work Hudson, 10th ed., pp. 262–273. Without express provision, however, difficulties in the latter (contingent) category will usually be part of the contractor's obligation—*i.e.* " contractor's risks "—subject to the very rare impact, in building and civil engineering contracts at least, of the doctrine of frustration (as to which see the commentary to clause 13 (1), *infra*, pp. 47–48). Contractors in the past have not usually sought to dispute this obligation to complete in its physical sense (though it must be said that in the United Kingdom there is now an increasing tendency, which certainly has not been discouraged by recent developments in the standard forms, for contractors faced with difficulties, even of their own making, to refuse to proceed further without instructions from the architect or engineer, as clauses 7 (1) and 51 (1) of the present contract will undoubtedly encourage them to do) but whether or not these ancillary or contingent expenditures are included in their contract prices is, of course, a different, though closely related, matter, and the present contract, in one direction at least, appears to have opened the way to financial claims for both indispensably necessary and contingent work, based on the incorporation of the Standard Method of Measurement effected by clause 57—see the commentaries to clause 11 (2) *infra*, p. 40 and to the new clause 55 (2) *infra*, p. 182, which appears to be a positive invitation to such claims based in this way.

Contractor Responsible for Safety of Site Operations

(2) The Contractor shall take full responsibility for the adequacy stability and safety of all site operations and methods of construction provided that the Contractor shall not be responsible for the design or specification of the Permanent Works (except as may be expressly provided in the Contract) or of any Temporary Works designed by the Engineer.

This sub-clause is new. In so far as it relates to the safety and integrity of the Works themselves, it should be read with the more definitive clause 20, *infra*, p. 64. In so far as it may be concerned with the safety of persons on the site, the Fifth Edition for some reason appears to have considered it desirable, in a number of clauses in the Conditions, to emphasise the responsibility of the Contractor for the safety of his operations—see, in addition to the present sub-clause, the new parts of clauses 15 (1), 15 (2), 16 and 19, all of which contain new and additional wording on this subject. This concern seems largely unnecessary, since the old (and new) clauses 20 (1), 22 and 24 make it abundantly clear that these matters are the responsibility of the Contractor unless caused by the intervention or fault of the Engineer or the Employer, and because English law in any event has recognised clearly the independence and attendant responsibilities of the Contractor in regard to his methods of working—see Hudson, 10th ed., pp. 68–71, 139–141, 153–155, 324–325, 387, and 529–530, and the very important case of *Clayton* v. *Woodman & Sons* (*Builders*) *Limited* [1962] 1 W.L.R. 585, (1977) 4 B.L.R. 65, there referred to, and see also the commentary under clause 13, *infra*, pp. 49–51. The practical sting of the present sub-clause really lies in its proviso (which of course is closely analogous to the " Excepted Risk " of " fault error or omission in the design of the Works " in clause 20 (3), *infra*, p. 66, and is also closely connected with the exceptions to the Contractor's indemnity in clause 22 (1) (b) (ii) and (iv) and the Employer's counter-indemnity therefor under clause 22 (2), *infra*, p. 75).

The present sub-clause should also be read in conjunction with the new and important code for the supply of calculations and information by the Contractor to the Engineer on the latter's request which is contained in clauses 14 (3) to clause 14 (6), *infra*, pp. 56–58, and with the new and difficult sub-clauses of clause 13, which may mean that certain instructions of the Engineer in the field of methods of working will enable the Contractor to claim extra payment.

Contract Agreement

9. The Contractor shall when called upon so to do enter into and execute a Contract Agreement (to be prepared at the cost of the Employer) in the form annexed.

By the fourth paragraph of the Form of Tender (*post*, Chapter 3, p. 297) the written acceptance of the Tender by the Employer will constitute a binding contract between the parties. The Form of Agreement is, however, a document under seal, which will have the effect of extending the period of limitation from 6 to 12 years under section 2 of the Limitation Act 1939. This is of very considerable value to employers in the context of defective work (particularly since the contract now has no certifying provisions which can terminate this liability of the Contractor prematurely) and there seems no reason to suppose that an action for specific performance to enforce the present clause would not lie. Naturally, however, all necessary terms of the contract must have been agreed at the time of any purported acceptance.

Sureties

10. If the Tender shall contain an undertaking by the Contractor to provide when required 2 good and sufficient sureties or to obtain the guarantee of an Insurance Company or Bank to be jointly and severally bound with the Contractor in a sum not exceeding 10 per cent of the Tender Total for the due performance of the Contract under the terms of a Bond the said sureties Insurance Company or Bank and the terms of the said Bond shall be such as shall be approved by the Employer and the provision of such sureties or the obtaining of such guarantee and the cost of the Bond to be so entered into shall be at the expense in all respects of the Contractor unless the Contract otherwise provides.

This clause repeats that in the Fourth Edition. Paragraph 3 of the Form of Tender, if undeleted, does indeed undertake to provide when required sureties or a guarantee in the terms of the present clause, with the additional requirement that the terms of the Bond shall be in the form annexed to the contract. The provision of the Bond or guarantee is therefore a post-contract obligation of the Contractor, and not a condition of the contract coming into being (though doubtless it will often have been arranged prior to the formal contract agreement referred to in clause 9, *supra*). In the absence of any express sanction, therefore, an employer will have to decide whether to treat the contract as repudiated if no bond or guarantee is forthcoming, as it is submitted that he will be entitled to do, since this is clearly a fundamental obligation of the contract—see the South African case of *Swartz and Son (Pty) Ltd.* v. *Wolmaransstadt Town Council* [1960] 2 S.A.L.R. 1. The amount of 10 per cent. of the " Tender Total," traditional in the U.K., is in fact very much less than the bond usually demanded in other countries—notably the U.S. and Canada. For the definition of " Tender Total," see clause 1 (1) (h), *supra*, p. 19, and the commentary thereto.

" *the terms of the said Bond* "

The annexed bond in the contract documents is in the traditional English form (see *post*, Chapter 3, Part III, p. 302) with a wide-ranging clause designed to prevent invalidation of the bond due to post-contract variations of the work, or of the agreement itself, or concessions made by the Employer, all of which might otherwise have that effect. For bonds and sureties generally, see Hudson, 10th ed., Chapter 17.

" *such as shall be approved by the Employer* "

As a matter of business efficacy and necessary implication, any such disapproval must be on reasonable grounds, it is submitted, since it would be oppressive and potentially disruptive for the Employer to be given an unfettered discretion to reject a bond or bondsmen and rescind the contract. Disapproval based on the terms of the bond will not usually pose a problem, however, since the form of bond will usually be annexed to the contract documents in the terms of the tender (and is of course bound into the standard form of the Fifth Edition at p. 37)—see *post*, Chapter 3, p. 302. These difficulties highlight the practical need, from the Employer's point of view, for the entire Bond or guarantee arrangement to be finalised, in the form of an offer to the Employer from the bondsman or guarantor, before a contract is entered into, or at the very least by making any acceptance of the tender expressly conditional upon the Bond being provided by a named surety within a limited period of time, if the provision of a bond is regarded as commercially essential by the Employer.

Inspection of Site

11. (1) The Contractor shall be deemed to have inspected and examined the Site and its surroundings and to have satisfied himself before submitting his tender as to the nature of the ground and sub-soil (so far as is practicable and having taken into account any information in connection therewith which may have been provided by or on behalf of the Employer) the form and nature of the Site the extent and nature of the work and materials necessary for the completion of the Works the means of communication with and access to the Site the accommodation he may require and in general to have obtained for himself all necessary information (subject as above-mentioned) as to risks contingencies and all other circumstances influencing or affecting his tender.

This sub-clause, which is concerned primarily with the inclusiveness of the Contractor's prices, and is in effect a narrative leading up to the major invasion of that inclusiveness effected by the next succeeding clause 12, corresponds fairly closely to clause 11 in the Fourth Edition (though the Contractor is now only " deemed " to have inspected, and not positively enjoined to inspect), except for the addition of the new words " and having taken into account any information in connection therewith which may have been provided by the Employer." The precise significance and practical effect (if any) of this addition is difficult to determine, though it may possibly be intended to suggest that the Contractor is entitled to rely on any information provided by the Employer, and so somewhat to strengthen any claim he may make for damages based on misrepresentation (where reliance or inducement as a fact is a necessary ingredient). It may also be of relevance in interpreting the expression " physically impossible " in clause 13 (1)—see the commentary about this *infra*, pp. 47–48. It may even be an attempt to up-grade to contractual status any ex-contractual information provided by the Employer before tender, but does not seem nearly precise enough for that purpose. In the absence of the present wording (whatever its precise contractual consequences) English law would not imply any warranty on the part of an employer in relation to the physical condition or suitability of the site, notwithstanding that the design of the project emanated from his own engineer, nor would there seem to be any duty of disclosure on an employer, whose only liability would arise if there had been any positive warranty or representation given or made on his behalf to the contractor (although a considerable weight of authority in the U.S. indicates that in suitable cases an employer may impliedly warrant that completion in accordance with his Engineer's design is possible). In this context, the provisions of the Misrepresentation Act 1967, which imposes a liability in damages for innocent misrepresentations made without reasonable grounds for belief in their truth, and which subjects any attempt by way of express terms to exclude responsibility for such representations to a test of reasonableness, should be borne in mind—see Hudson, 10th ed., pp. 38–46. In fairness to contractors, it should be said that their position when tendering in this particular context may often not be satisfactory, since they themselves will only be given a relatively short period of time in which to make investigations before being required to tender, while on the other hand the employer's advisers may have been considering the geological and other implications of the site over a period of months if not years. This has undoubtedly been the basis of the more liberal attitude in the U.S. and may justify a re-examination of the English law on the subject in the future. For this subject, see Hudson, 10th ed., pp. 134, 226 and 231–232, and also the cases collected at pp. 48–49 (where, however, the U.S. cases are not examined).

Unexpected difficulties are, therefore, in principle a matter for the contractor to surmount at his own expense in order to discharge his express obligation physically to complete the described work, but the present contract not only contains a number of express and important qualifications of the physical obligation to complete—see the commentaries to clause 8 (1), *supra*, pp. 36–37, and to clause 13 (1), *infra*, pp. 47–48 —but also permits a number of financial qualifications which are referred to in the commentary under the next following sub-clause.

Sufficiency of Tender

(2) The Contractor shall be deemed to have satisfied himself before submitting his tender as to the correctness and sufficiency of the rates and prices stated by him in the Priced Bill of Quantities which shall (except in so far as it is otherwise provided in the Contract) cover all his obligations under the Contract.

This clause, corresponding to the old clause 12 (1), pays lip service to the " inclusive price principle " which, as stated *supra*, is really the financial facet of the absolute obligation to complete, and which the law in the great majority of cases will imply, whereby a price quoted for work and materials will include for all the ancillary expenditures, whether indispensably necessary in any event or contingently necessary to overcome difficulties involved in the completion of the described work—see the commentary to clause 8 (1), *supra*, p. 35. The positive legal consequences of the present sub-clause are not, therefore, of any real significance, and such interest as it may provoke will lie in the words " (except insofar as is otherwise provided)." This sub-clause was, as already pointed out, in fact the old clause 12 (1), and served as an introduction to clause 12 (2), which of course effected one of the principal invasions of the " inclusive price principle " to be found in the Fourth Edition. For a list of the principal claims provided for in the contract which override the principle, see the commentary to clause 1 (1) (i) " Contract Price," *supra*, pp. 19–20. In the particular context of the present clause, with its reference to the Bills of Quantities, new and most fundamental departures from the Bill prices are permitted under clause 55 (2) (errors in description and omissions etc. in the Bills) and 56 (2) (increases or decreases in actual quantities), quite apart from those traditionally (and rightly) permitted under clause 52 (variations). In addition there is a remarkable and, it would seem, quite generalised new entitlement to additional payment under clause 13 (3) of the Conditions, wherever the cost of compliance with Engineer's instructions is not reasonably foreseeable, notwithstanding that the instructions in question do not involve any variation but merely relate to the implementation of the original contract intention.

Adverse Physical Conditions and Artificial Obstructions

12. (1) If during the execution of the Works the Contractor shall encounter physical conditions other than weather conditions or conditions due to weather conditions) or artificial obstructions which conditions or obstructions he considers could not reasonably have been foreseen by an experienced contractor and the Contractor is of opinion that additional cost will be incurred which would not have been incurred if the physical conditions or artificial obstructions had not been encountered he shall if he intends to make any claim for additional payment give notice to the Engineer pursuant to Clause 52 (4) and shall specify in such notice the physical conditions and/or artificial obstructions encountered and with the notice if practicable or as soon as possible thereafter give details of the anticipated effects thereof the measures he is taking or is proposing to take and the extent of the anticipated delay in or interference with the execution of the Works.

This clause has not as yet any equivalent in building contracts in the U.K., or indeed in the C.C.C./Wks/1 or G.C./Wks/1 contracts, though it has of course been traditional in the I.C.E. Conditions (and indeed is common, in the form of " changed conditions " clauses, in Federal contracts in the U.S.). Its policy and probably unintentional practical consequences in the field of competitive tendering are discussed in Hudson, 10th ed., pp. 569–570.

There are a number of new points about the clause which are highly favourable to contractors, namely:—

(a) Failure to serve a notice before the expenditure is incurred will not, as it did before, bar a claim by the Contractor, so that a late notice in respect of past events and expenditure will be sufficient, unless the Engineer has been thereby " prevented from or substantially prejudiced . . . in investigating the claim " within clause 52 (4) (e), *infra*, p. 166. While it is not impossible to imagine situations where this requirement might be successfully invoked by a determined engineer arbitrator (*e.g.* an allegedly demolished or diverted underground culvert not reported until long after trenches had been filled in) in the great majority of instances giving rise to claims under this clause in practice it will be difficult to show that investigation has been substantially prejudiced. Much will depend on the determination with which engineering arbitrators, by appropriate findings of fact, are prepared to enforce the notice provision, and since it is obvious that the words " substantially prejudice " leave room for considerable argument and difference of opinion, and since on the whole engineering arbitrators in the U.K. are not unsympathetic to clause 12 claims even in the case of well-known hazards like high-water tables and running sand or rock, it would seem that the severity of the older notice requirement has been very materially reduced if not almost extinguished. In fairness to contractors, it was not always easy to comply with the very strict requirements, backed by the sanction of non-payment, as to the *contents* of the notice specifying additional work and constructional plant which were required under the Fourth Edition, but these requirements have now been materially reduced and need not be given at once if this is not practicable, and having regard to the great advantages conferred by the clause, the uncertainty it can introduce into the contract price from the Employer's point of view, and the chance sometimes to reduce cost by ordering a variation, the decision effectively to dispense with mandatory prior notice in the Fifth Edition is both surprising and significant.

(b) As stated, the requirements as to the contents of the notice have been modified and are more reasonable and may be complied with later if it is not practicable to do so at once.

(c) Any sums due under the clause are, subject to compliance with clause 52 (4), payable on interim certificate under clause 60 (see clause 52 (4) (f)).

(d) Arbitration of a dispute under this clause can take place before the end of the work (see clause 66 (2)).

(e) A percentage for *profit* on the additional work and plant can now be claimed (see clause 12 (3)).

(f) " cost " in sub-clause (3) includes off-site overheads (see clause 1 (5)).

(g) Any variation ordered by the Engineer on receipt of a notice from the Contractor will stand as a variation order justifying additional payment notwithstanding that subsequent investigation by the Engineer (or indeed an arbitrator) reveals that no claim under the clause is justified (but query how such a variation should be valued—see the commentary to sub-clause (4), *infra*, pp. 45–46). The policy behind this provision is again both surprising and significant.

" *physical conditions* "

Since obviously nothing which is superficially visible on inspection will qualify, by reason of the " reasonably foreseeable " part of the clause, since weather conditions are also excluded, and since the word " condition " may possibly mean some continuing state rather than some event like a landslide or flood, the subject-matter of a successful claim will in practice usually be some physical condition of the ground below the surface.

" *weather conditions or conditions due to weather conditions* "

Difficulties of interpretation can arise under these words, particularly the latter part. While floods which may inundate the works due, for instance, to coastal winds or a rising river, or a landslip following heavy rain, would seem to come within the description, the common experience of an unusually high water-table, due perhaps to excessive rainfall in previous years, may be more difficult to assess.

" *artificial obstructions* "

These words are undoubtedly aimed primarily at unexpected underground culverts, foundations or brickwork. Uncharted culverts, sewers or services are, of course, a commonplace of excavations in streets or highways (particularly in old towns) and the bills or specification in pipe-laying or sewerage contracts frequently require all such services to be diverted or supported at contractor's expense whenever they cross the line of the trench. A conflict can arise between such provisions and the present clause, and in general it is submitted that in cases of doubt the bills or specification, being specifically prepared by the parties for the contract in question, should prevail; no doubt it can also be argued that the presence of such clauses in the bills etc. shows the " reasonable foreseeability " of these obstructions.

" *could not reasonably have been foreseen by an experienced contractor* "

These words probably give rise to the most frequent disputes of fact which come before engineering arbitrators. The word " reasonably " introduces an element of degree but, even apart from this, the application of the words to a given set of circumstances can be extraordinarily difficult. Engineering arbitrators tend to construe the expression very generously in favour of contractors, particularly in regard to the commonest hazards arising in engineering works, namely wet ground and running sand. This attitude can be very unfair to more prudent contractors who price for such risks and in consequence lose the contract to less prudent or more litigious competitors, see Hudson, 10th ed., pp. 569–570.

Measures to be Taken

(2) Following receipt of a notice under sub-clause (1) of this Clause the Engineer may if he thinks fit *inter alia:*—

(a) require the Contractor to provide an estimate of the cost of the measures he is taking or is proposing to take;
(b) approve in writing such measures with or without modification;
(c) given written instructions as to how the physical conditions or artificial obstructions are to be dealt with;
(d) order a suspension under Clause 40 or a variation under Clause 51.

It should be noted that these actions are permissive and not mandatory, and that the Contractor's entitlement to additional payment under sub-clause (3) is independent of any action taken under this sub-clause. Under paragraph (d), a suspension under clause 40, if reasonable in the circumstances, would presumably be at the Contractor's expense under clause 40 (1) (c). Also under paragraph (d), it should be noted that, remarkably, a variation instruction under clause 51 will take effect by justifying, for example, additional payments even if it is subsequently decided by the Engineer or an arbitrator that there is no entitlement to a claim under the present clause (see sub-clause (4), *infra*). Under paragraph (c), written instructions would presumably entitle the Contractor to claim by virtue of the difficult clause 13 (3), *infra*, even though it was subsequently decided that there was no clause 12 entitlement. In both cases, however, query how such a variation, possibly *avoiding* great delay and expense to the Contractor, should be valued. See also the commentaries to clauses 7 (1) and 51 (1) in the context of a possible duty to vary the work.

Delay and Extra Cost

(3) To the extent that the Engineer shall decide that the whole or some part of the said physical conditions or artificial obstructions could not reasonably have been foreseen by an experienced contractor the Engineer shall take any delay suffered by the Contractor as a result of such conditions or obstructions into account in determining any extension of time to which the Contractor is entitled under Clause 44 and the Contractor shall subject to Clause 52 (4) (notwithstanding that the Engineer may not have given any instructions or orders pursuant to sub-clause (2) of this Clause) be paid in accordance with Clause 60 such sum as represents the reasonable cost of carrying out any additional work done and additional Constructional Plant used which would not have been done or used had such conditions or obstructions or such part thereof as the case may be not been encountered together with a reasonable percentage addition thereto in respect of profit and the reasonable costs incurred by the Contractor by reason of any unavoidable delay or disruption of working suffered as a consequence of encountering the said conditions or obstructions or such part thereof.

The financial effects of this sub-clause have already been summarised, *supra*, p. 43. The word " costs " in the context of delay and disruption may well invoke the definition of " cost " as including off-site overheads in clause 1 (5), *supra*, p. 25 (if not already recoverable under the " cost " of additional work and Constructional Plant), wherever overall delay to the project results. For comments on the definition of " Constructional Plant " see clause 1 (1) (o), *supra*, p. 23. The Engineer's decisions are, of course, subject to review by an arbitrator at the instance of either party under clause 66, and the arbitration can be an " early " one under clause 66 (2).

Conditions Reasonably Foreseeable

(4) If the Engineer shall decide that the physical conditions or artificial obstructions could in whole or in part have been reasonably foreseen by an experienced contractor he shall so inform the Contractor in writing as soon as he shall have reached that decision but the value of any variation previously ordered by him pursuant to sub-clause (2) (d) of this Clause shall be ascertained in accordance with Clause 52 and included in the Contract Price.

The first part of this sub-clause is a little over-simplified, since there might be other reasons (*e.g.* weather conditions, or a reason not qualifying as a physical condition or artificial obstruction) for disallowing the Contractor's claim.

The policy of allowing Engineer's orders given in response to a Contractor's notice under the clause to stand as variations has already been commented on, but it is submitted that in many cases a variation ordered in these circumstances may well involve a *reduction* in the contract price under clause 52 (2), *infra*, p. 158, if the facts show that the unvaried work would have been more expensive and costly for the Contractor to complete than the varied work.

Work to be to Satisfaction of Engineer

13. (1) Save in so far as it is legally or physically impossible the Contractor shall construct complete and maintain the Works in strict accordance with the Contract to the satisfaction of the Engineer and shall comply with and adhere strictly to the Engineer's instructions and directions on any matter connected therewith (whether mentioned in the Contract or not.) The Contractor shall take instructions and directions only from the Engineer or (subject to the limitations referred to in Clause 2) from the Engineer's Representative.

Mode and Manner of Construction

(2) The whole of the materials plant and labour to be provided by the Contractor under Clause 8 and the mode manner and speed of construction and maintenance of the Works are to be of a kind and conducted in a manner approved of by the Engineer.

Apart from the understandable precautionary addition of the words " connected therewith " after " any matter," sub-clause (1) is identical with the whole of clause 13 in the Fourth Edition. Under the Fourth Edition, the principal interest of the clause lay

(a) in determining the exact effect of the " legally or physically impossible " exception

(b) in determining how wide was the power to give instructions conferred by the clause, and in particular whether it entitled the Engineer to give instructions (apart from enforcing any express or implied provisions of the Specification) as to the precise methods of working adopted by the Contractor, as opposed to stipulating the final permanent work required. Ultimately it was submitted in B.C.F. (see B.C.F., p. 327) that, apart from any express or implied power in the Bills or Specification, the words of sub-clause (1) did not confer this power.

(c) in determining the effect of the reference to the Engineer's satisfaction (this now gives rise to little difficulty, since neither the final certificate under clause 60 (3) nor the maintenance certificate under clause 61 have any ultimate finality conferred upon them).

The Fifth Edition has now, however, added the new sub-clause (2), *supra*, which has been excised and transposed from clause 46 of the Fourth Edition (a clause which in that edition was primarily concerned with progress and speed of construction), and in sub-clauses 14 (3) to (6), *infra*, p. 56 has also introduced a special new code entitling the Engineer in certain circumstances to intervene and alter the Contractor's methods of construction. Furthermore, sub-clause (3) of the present clause has introduced a new financial claim, obviously with the most wide-ranging possibilities although subject to an " unforeseeability " requirement, should any Engineer's instruction given under sub-clause (1) delay or disrupt the Contractor's " arrangements or methods of construction." It is of overwhelming practical importance, and unfortunately a matter of the very greatest difficulty, to determine precisely the ambit of this last new sub-clause, which itself must turn on the precise nature of the instructions under sub-clause (1), *supra*, and which clearer draftsmanship could easily have avoided. An attempt to analyse this problem will be made in the commentary to sub-clause (3), *infra*, p. 51.

(*1*) " *Save insofar as it is legally . . . impossible* "

Presumably this means either that the works, whether in whole or in part, are or become prohibited by law (*e.g.* under licensing regulations), or infringe private or other person's legal rights which can be protected by injunction or otherwise (as to which see further the financial indemnities against claims by third persons given by the Employer by virtue of the combined effect of clauses 22 (1) (b) (iii) and 22 (2), *infra*, p. 75. This type of impossibility is one of the facets of the English law of frustration of contracts—see Hudson, 10th ed., pp. 348–358.

(*1*) " *Save insofar as it is . . . physically impossible* "

The exact meaning of these words is extremely difficult to assess. The legal consequences of this express obligation to complete, also found in the Form of Tender, Form of Agreement, and clause 8 of the Conditions, is discussed in the commentary under clauses 8 (1) and 11 (1), *supra*, pp. 36–37. See also Hudson, 10th ed., pp. 267–272. Broadly the effect is that, in the absence of express stipulation, the Contractor, while not warranting the suitability of adequacy of the design of the work for its ultimate purpose after completion, by expressly undertaking to complete the work binds himself to do any additional or even varied work which may be necessary to bring it to the point of completion, including any work necessitated by defects in the design from this limited point of view—see *e.g.* the cases collected in Hudson, 10th ed., pp. 269–272. (As stated in the commentary to clause 11 (1), *supra*, p. 40, there is, however, considerable authority to the contrary in many jurisdictions, including the Federal jurisdiction, in the U.S.) The problem is to determine the exact extent of the qualification of this state of affairs intended by the words " physically impossible." The words could be intended to apply to the works as a whole, and mean some *supervening* impossibility—such as a landslide, flood or earthquake destroying the site of the works or rendering their continuation by any means quite impossible. If so, the words probably do no more than restate the law of frustration of contracts—as to which see Hudson, 10th ed., pp. 348–358. On the other hand, the words might mean that if it could be shown that by reason of some factor already existing at the time of the contract (*e.g.* unsuspected sub-soil conditions) construction of the works as a whole was impossible by any means available (in support of this view the new wording and the words " so far as is practicable " in clause 11 commented upon, *supra*, pp. 40–41 may be of relevance) the contractor is not to be liable for failure to complete in that event. Finally, and wider still, the words might mean that the Contractor is to be excused if, notwithstanding that substantial completion of the project by some other means is possible, completion is not possible according to the exact contract design or designated method of working in regard to all or part of the works. (This would, in fact, be a restatement of the *implied* position which has been reached in many U.S. jurisdictions). On this view, the Contractor will be entitled to cease work in such a situation unless a variation order is given enabling the work to be completed, and it is for this meaning at the very least that contractors will be bound to contend when asserting that a duty to vary the work in the face of difficulties arises under clause 51 (1) and possibly clause 7 (1) (see the commentaries to those two clauses, *supra*, pp. 32–33 and *infra*, pp. 155–156). The policies underlying the permissive language of clause 12 (2) (specifically concerned with difficulties during construction), the use of the word " approval " and the absence of any reference to " instructions " in clause 13 (2), and the power of suspension on " proper execution " or safety grounds at the Contractor's expense under clause 40 (1) (c), *infra*, p. 110, would all appear to be inconsistent with this view; while the policy of clause 12 (2) (d) and 12 (4), and the " fault error or omission in the design of the Works " " Excepted Risk " under clause 20 might be regarded as consistent with it; but in the last resort the question must depend (as stated in the commentary under clause 7 (1), *supra*, p. 33) on the meaning to be attached to the word " necessary " in clauses 51 (1) and, to a lesser extent 7 (1). It is tentatively suggested that the close juxtaposition of the words " legally or physically " before " impossible" is an indication that what is aimed at is a state of affairs affecting the works as a whole, whether due to a supervening or subsisting factor; and not the wider meaning, disruptive of the usual incidence of the basic contractor's obligation to complete, that if a part of the design is impractical from the point of view of completion the contractor is excused from further performance. The present words may, however, require to be reinterpreted in the light of the new wording of clause 51 (1), but if so there can be little doubt, it is submitted, that the word " impossible " should be given its literal meaning and not be used for cases where completion may be possible though only by incurring great expense or delay (incidentally this would appear to be the better U.S. view in the case of implied terms, *i.e.* where the contract is silent).

Given, however, the uncertain state of the contract documentation on this subject, those responsible for drafting Special Conditions, Bills or Specifications should, in the Employer's interest, deal with these questions expressly on the basis that the conditions themselves do not give adequate guidance in an area where major disputes are likely to occur. In particular, it is advisable in the Employer's interests to avoid, where possible, prescribing too exactly the method of working to be adopted by the Contractor, and to make it plain that the Contractor's prices are inclusive of *any* method of working found to be necessary in order to produce the finished works, and in the event of methods of working or Temporary Works being described in the contract, that no warranties are given as to their efficacy and that the Contractor is free to adopt other methods subject to the Engineer's approval under clause 13 (2).

(*1*) " *to the satisfaction of the Engineer* "

In older contracts these words might have had the effect of making the Engineer's satisfaction.

(a) a condition precedent to payment of the Contractor on the one hand

and on the other

(b) if expressed in final form, binding on the Employer when seeking to allege defective work

—see Hudson, 10th ed., pp. 401–435. The arbitration clause 66 has the effect of nullifying (a) however (see Hudson, 10th ed., pp. 435–449) and the old difficulties about the maintenance certificate under the Fourth Edition have fortunately now been swept away—see clause 61 (2), *infra*, p. 243. Neither is the new Final Certificate binding—see *infra*, clause 60 (3).

(*1*) " *the Engineer's instructions and directions on any matter connected therewith* (*whether mentioned in the contract or not*) "

The better view of this traditional and obscure wording was that it contemplated day-to-day instructions from the Engineer either implementing or enforcing the expressed contract intention (" mentioned in the contract ") or explaining and identifying it where the contract was silent and the necessary standard would be obtained from an implied term of good workmanship or materials or from the need to obtain the Engineer's satisfaction (" not mentioned in the contract "). Usually there would be matters either covered by express description in the Specification, or else left for interpretation by the Engineer on a day-to-day basis where the Specification was either silent or of too generalised a character and needing applied interpretation when dealing with a particular matter of workmanship or quality. What is now clause 13 (1) stood alone with no attendant mention of financial claims, and additional payment would depend upon whether the Engineer's instruction could be shown to be a variation of the express or implied obligations of the Contractor. On this view the Engineer's powers were principally powers of interpretation of the final standard of permanent work required, or of implementation of those parts of the Specification which might go further and describe or specify or control actual work processes (adequate pumping, support of trench sides, number of passes of roller, placing or curing times of concrete, and so on). Whether the Engineer could go further on the basis of the present wording and actually dictate methods of working, in the sense of Temporary Works or policy choices between different methods of construction, in the absence of express power to do so in the Specification or elsewhere, seemed doubtful, particularly in the light of the general view that it is the right of the Contractor and the Contractor alone to decide how he will conduct his operations—as to this see Hudson, 10th ed., pp. 68–71, 139–141, 153–155, 324–325, 387 and 530 and the important dicta in the cases of *Clayton* v. *Woodman & Sons* (*Builders*) *Ltd.* [1962] 1 W.L.R. 585, (1977) 4 B.L.R. 65, and *A.M.F. International Limited* v. *Magnet Bowling* [1968] 1 W.L.R. 1028 there referred to. This view seems to secure support in the present contract from the wording of the new clause 8 (2) (which makes no reference to instructions of the Engineer but only to Temporary Works designed by him and which means, it is submitted, designed as a part of the original contract) and from clause 13 (2) (which it will be noted refers only to approval, as to the effect of which see the new clause 14 (7), *infra*, p. 59), but above all from the new procedure under clause 14 (3) to 14 (6), *infra*, p. 56, which suggests very strongly that the Engineer's power to intervene and dictate methods of working (apart of course from express provisions in the Bills or Specification) is limited to the situation and circumstances envisaged in clause 14 (3) to (6).

Express provisions in the Bills or Specification conferring these kinds of powers in particular parts of the work are not, of course, uncommon—for instance a specification may expressly empower the Engineer to decide whether particular methods should be used in different parts of the works (*e.g.* steel-sheet piling or close timbering as opposed to ordinary timbering, or the use of compressed air in tunnelling work). Unless separate prices are given for the different processes the contract may be construed as binding the contractor, provided the decision is an honest one, to carry out the work without extra payment—see the unreported decision of Diplock J. (as he then was) in *Neodox Limited* v. *Swindon and Pendlebury B.C.* [1958] Hudson, 10th ed., pp. 529–530, (1977) 5 B.L.R. 34, where it was held that provisions similar to the present clause, coupled with an express provision as to the choice of method of working in the specification, had this effect. There is no doubt, however, that particular instructions as to methods of working can amount to a variation not contemplated by the contract—see *e.g.* the arbitrator's findings in the House of Lords case of *Brodie* v. *Cardiff Corporation* [1919] A.C. 337 at p. 347. Furthermore, in the present Edition new words in clause 51 (1) expressly state that the Engineer's variations may include " changes in the *specified* sequence *method* or timing of construction (if any) " (this wording does not seem to cover an instruction in a matter where the specification is silent as to the method or timing, however).

It follows from the above discussion that there may be limits to the power of the Engineer to give instructions in regard to methods of working which need to be borne in mind when considering the effect of clause 13 (3), *infra*.

Delay and Extra Cost

(3) If in pursuance of Clause 5 or sub-clause (1) of this Clause the Engineer shall issue instructions or directions which involve the Contractor in delay or disrupt his arrangements or methods of construction so as to cause him to incur cost beyond that reasonably to have been foreseen by an experienced contractor at the time of tender then the Engineer shall take such delay into account in determining any extension of time to which the Contractor is entitled under Clause 44 and the Contractor shall subject to Clauses 52 (4) be paid in accordance with Clause 60 the amount of such cost as may be reasonable. If such instructions or directions require any variation to any part of the Works the same shall be deemed to have been given pursuant to Clause 51.

The effect of this sub-clause, in conjunction with clause 5 of the Conditions, has already been considered—see *supra*, pp. 30–31. The following points can be immediately noted about the present sub-clause:—

(1) It seems clear that an instruction or direction which is not a variation —*i.e.* which is enforcing or implementing the contract intention—is covered by the sub-clause—see the " If " at the beginning of the rather puzzling last sentence of the clause, and the fact that all instructions under sub-clause (1) (which will include instructions about matters " mentioned in the contract," which hardly suggests a variation) apparently qualify. If this were not the intention, the use of the word " direction " seems singularly unwise, since this word may be wider in scope than " instruction," which latter, as a matter of usage in the industry, does have at least some connection with the variation provisions in contracts, which are almost invariably expressly conditioned on an " instruction " or " order."

(2) It would seem that there is no need for the instruction to be in writing.

(3) It is only the *cost* of the delay or disruption which has to be " reasonably unforeseeable "—not the instruction or direction, or its subject-matter, which apparently may be fully foreseeable and perhaps not even a contingent obligation.

(4) Apart from the " reasonable foreseeability " test, the instruction must " involve the Contractor in delay or disrupt his arrangements or methods of construction "—thus an instruction which involved unforeseen cost but neither delay nor disruption (a perfectly possible eventuality) would not seem to qualify. " Arrangements or methods of construction "

is, incidentally, the same phrase as that used in clause 14 (1), *infra*, to indicate the matters about which the Engineer is entitled to require information within 21 days of acceptance of tender, and therefore suggests that the delay or disruption must be connected with the overall programme and progress of the works and not a more localised disturbance capable of being absorbed into the overall programme of the project. One direction at least in which a fully justified claim might be made under the present sub-clause would be in cases where the Engineer, under clauses 14 (2) or 46, gave instructions for *accelerated* progress where the Contractor was subsequently held, contrary to the Engineer's opinion, to have been entitled to an extension of time. This would " disrupt his arrangements " within the present wording. (Such action would not qualify as a variation, even under the new extended definition in clause 51,—see *infra*, p. 156.)

While it is easy to understand the policy and logic of a provision surrounded with safeguards (such as that in clauses 7 and 9 (2) of C.C.C./Wks/1 or G.C./Wks/1) entitling a contractor to additional payment if, in obedience to an instruction given under a list of express powers which in many cases are both contingent and for the employer's benefit, expenditure is incurred " beyond that provided for in or reasonably contemplated by the Contract " (which expression itself indicates that the instruction has involved at the very least a variation of the Contractor's obligations) it is difficult to appreciate the policy of a blanket provision like the present clause, which on its wording applies even if the cost of performing a known contractual obligation turns out to be " reasonably unforeseeable." Thus the wording would appear to apply, for example, to the unexpected cost of pumping out trenches in a period of " unforeseeably " unseasonal rainfall, notwithstanding the usual contractual requirement that the Contractor's prices are to include for all necessary pumping, provided only that an instruction of the Engineer (or of the Engineer's Representative within the terms of a clause 2 (3) written delegation) can be found to support the claim. Such instructions could easily be given in such a case—particularly if the Contractor, for example, appeared to be making inadequate pumping arrangements. Even a reprimand pointing out a failure to carry out an operation might be put forward as the necessary instruction, for example.

The potential scope of the clause is thus probably far wider than was intended and is obviously open to abuse, subject to such limitation as can be derived on particular facts from the " delay or disruption of arrangements " qualification. The " reasonable foreseeability " qualification on cost is also obviously of some value, but in the face of an unmerited claim nothing like so effective as that of the G.C./Wks/1 wording quoted above. An indication that the consequences of the present wording may be unintended is to be found in the new " reasonable foreseeability " claim in clause 31 (2) (facilities for other contractors—see *infra*, p. 99).

The reference to payment under clause 60 is, of course, to payment on interim certificate (see clause 52 (4) (b) and clause 60 (1) (d)) subject to compliance with clause 52 (4) (b) and (d) (*i.e.* service of notice and the subsequent provision of interim accounts with supporting particulars of the amount claimed).

It is only possible to speculate on the reasons for inserting the last sentence of this sub-clause, which seems on its face unnecessary, particularly in the light of the new express right in clause 51 (1) to issue variation orders changing the Contractor's *specified* sequence or method of working. (One case, however, has been mentioned *supra*, where *accelerated* progress is, albeit unintentionally, called for by the Engineer under clauses 14 (2) or 46, and where clause 51 would probably not apply.) As already stated, there is nothing in the present clause requiring an order in writing. Is the sentence a recognition of this and intended to dispense with the writing requirement in the case of varied work? Or is the sub-clause primarily concerned with instructions which will not themselves alter the final permanent work and is the sentence inserted (unnecessarily) to make it clear that nothing in the present clause is to prejudice the rights of the Contractor under clause 51 if such an alteration is called for?

The discussion about this clause can be summarised by saying that its scope and intention are unclear, in particular in regard to the kind of instruction or direction contemplated, and that to prevent abuse it will be necessary for engineering arbitrators to adopt a more robust attitude to the " reasonable foreseeability " test than has been the case hitherto in the U.K. in regard to clause 12 claims. (It should perhaps be pointed out that the test " reasonably to have been foreseen by an experienced contractor " is itself highly ambiguous. Does it mean foreseeable in the sense of *probability* (" not more than x inches of rainfall is likely in May on the 50 year averages ") or in the sense of *possibility* (" weather in the U.K. is notoriously unpredictable and the maximum figure for May over 50 years should be allowed for ").) It is perhaps even more ambiguous when applied, as in the present clause, to the concept of *cost*, and not to an event.

The effect of the clause, incidentally, may often entitle a contractor unable to recover under another clause in the contract (*e.g.* in a case of weather conditions under clause 12) to recover under the present clause (if he can show the necessary instruction). The moral for Engineers must be a need for the greatest circumspection in giving instructions, even in regard to what they believe to be the express contract intention, if it is wished to avoid affording the Contractor a pretext for advancing a financial claim.

It should perhaps be pointed out that there are undoubtedly liabilities of a contingent nature in engineering contracts where additional payment on a " reasonable foreseeability " basis is entirely justifiable on policy grounds, but the appropriate remedy, it is submitted, is so to provide in a clause dealing with the specific situation (as has been done, for example, in the new clause 31 (2), *infra*, p. 98, which also suggests that the wide ambit of the present provision may have been brought about *per incuriam*) or by way of Provisional or Contingency items against a described risk, or against the work processes required if the risk eventuates.

Programme to be Furnished

14. (1) Within 21 days after the acceptance of his Tender the Contractor shall submit to the Engineer for his approval a programme showing the order of procedure in which he proposes to carry out the Works and thereafter shall furnish such further details and information as the Engineer may reasonably require in regard thereto. The Contractor shall at the same time also provide in writing for the information of the Engineer a general description of the arrangements and methods of construction which the Contractor proposes to adopt for the carrying out of the Works.

This sub-clause corresponds to the old clause 14, though with changes. It should be read with clause 13 (2), *supra*, p. 46. The provision of the information is now mandatory and not " if required," and must now take place within a fixed period of time, though, as in the case of the Fourth Edition, no effective sanction is provided for non-compliance (as *e.g.* cessation of all further work without extension of time) or provision made for the event of the Engineer's disapproval. The only available (and severe) sanction for continued failure might be a determination under clause 63 (1) (d), *infra*, p. 244. Approval of the programme will, expressly, not in any way diminish the Contractor's responsibilities—see sub-clause (7), *infra*. For these reasons this sub-clause is of limited legal significance, since in nearly all cases it will be impossible for an Employer to show damage on non-compliance, and consequently neither an action for damages nor the withholding of money otherwise due will be available to enforce compliance.

The information required is (a) the *order of procedure* (b) the *arrangements* and (c) the *methods of construction* which the Contractor proposes to adopt for carrying out the work. The *order of procedure* (not necessarily dates, be it noted) will be required to enable the Engineer to plan his supply of working drawings under clause 7 (3), and also to make arrangements for access or possession of the Site in accordance with clause 42 (1), and the information provided by the Contractor under this clause may have important legal consequences in determining whether there has been any breach of contract by the Employer under either of those two clauses (though in the case of working drawings a specific notice in writing from the Contractor is also necessary under clause 7 (2)).

The reference to *arrangements* and *methods of construction* should be read together with clause 13 (2), *supra*. As explained in the commentary to clause 13 (1), *supra*, the extent of the Engineer's power to intervene and dictate the Contractor's methods of working, in the absence of express provision in the Specification or elsewhere, is, it is submitted, limited to the provisions in sub-clauses (3) to (6), *infra*, notwithstanding the very wide words used in clause 13 (1), though the Engineer is, of course, given specific authority to *vary* the "*specified* sequence method or timing of construction"—see clause 51 (1), *infra*, p. 150—but that course would be a variation, with financial consequences. Incidentally, it should be noted that, significantly, the description of the arrangements and method of construction is, in spite of clause 13 (2), provided under this sub-clause for information only and not, unlike the order of procedure, for approval—see sub-clause (7), *infra*, which also appears to confirm this.

Some contractors in the U.K. have sought to take advantage of the clause by submitting highly optimistic programmes, often showing completion considerably in advance of the contract date. If approved by the Engineer (who in general will not, of course, wish to discourage the Contractor from completing early) the approved programme date is then used by the Contractor to justify a complaint of late information (for instance in regard to Nominated Sub-contractors or suppliers whose quoted delivery or completion dates had been arranged earlier with the contract completion date in view) or to allege failure to give access or possession in time (similarly arranged beforehand), and in addition to increase the alleged period of delay upon which the monetary part of such claims (or indeed of any other claim involving delay) is calculated. Indeed, it is not unusual to find claims for delay based on programme dates when the contract period has not been exceeded. Without much more explicit agreement than the usual submission and approval of a programme, this seems quite wrong in principle. Sub-clause (7), while it makes it clear that the Engineer's approval will not enable the Contractor to escape his existing contractual obligations, does not, it is true, say in terms that the approval will not bind the Employer either—in the sense that he might be assuming a changed series of obligations, in regard to information and access, for example. But it is submitted that if this were the case, *both* parties would be bound by the new dates, so that the Contractor would be in breach of contract if he failed to meet, not the original contract completion date, but the new programme date. Neither party, it is suggested, in reality intends such consequences from the submission and approval of an optimistic programme, which is in essence a statement of order of working rather than a statement of dates having contractual force; furthermore the clause nowhere so provides, and business efficacy does not require the implication of any such term. On the other hand, there is nothing in principle to prevent a Contractor alleging that *as a fact* he could have completed early but for some breach of contract or other event entitling him to payment, and an approved programme will lend some evidentiary support for this, so Engineers in the Employer's interest should not hesitate to document any doubts they may feel as to the feasibility of an approved programme.

Revision of Programme

(2) Should it appear to the Engineer at any time that the actual progress of the Works does not conform with the approved programme referred to in sub-clause (1) of this Clause the Engineer shall be entitled to require the Contractor to produce a revised programme showing the modifications to the original programme necessary to ensure completion of the Works or any Section within the time for completion as defined in Clause 43 or extended time granted pursuant to Clause 44 (2).

This sub-clause is new, and appears to overlap from the practical point of view with the procedure referred to in clause 46, *infra*, p. 126. Here again, there appears to be little practical sanction available to the Employer or Engineer in the event of non-compliance, as in the case of the original programme referred to in sub-clause (1) (see the commentary, *supra*). Moreover, in real life the Contractor at this stage may be expected in the vast majority of cases to be contending strongly for an extension of time on one ground or another, and reluctant to put forward any revised programme at all, since by doing so he may in effect be conceding that he is in culpable delay. The sub-clause does not in fact make clear whether it is intended to be operated only in cases of culpable delay (as certainly is the case with clause 46) or whether it can also be used when there has been no culpable delay but factors justifying an extension of time have occurred so that the original programme dates (if any) are no longer applicable. Like sub-clause (1), this provision seems to be of a precatory character and it is difficult to see how it can give rise to any practical legal consequences or confer any practical benefit on the Employer in what will by now be (in cases of culpable delay at least) a controversial and arm's-length situation.

The present provision is also silent as to what is to happen if the present power is purportedly exercised by the Engineer and the Contractor complies, but is subsequently held to have been entitled to an extension of time. There may have been an instruction for which the Employer will be financially liable as a variation—but see the new extended definition of variations in clause 51 referred to *infra*, p. 156, where it is, however, submitted that the wording is not sufficiently wide to include an order to accelerate progress. Undoubtedly, however, a financial claim would appear to be justified in such a case under clause 13 (3). See also the commentary to clause 46, *infra*, pp. 126–127, for possible claims where action is taken under that clause.

Methods of Construction

(3) If requested by the Engineer the Contractor shall submit at such times and in such detail as the Engineer may reasonably require such information pertaining to the methods of construction (including Temporary Works and the use of Constructional Plant) which the Contractor proposes to adopt or use and such calculations of stresses strains and deflections that will arise in the Permanent Works or any parts thereof during construction from the use of such methods as will enable the Engineer to decide whether if these methods are adhered to the Works can be executed in accordance with the Drawings and Specification and without detriment to the Permanent Works when completed.

The last two lines of this new sub-clause suggest that the purpose of the Engineer's inquiry is limited to ensuring that the work will comply with the Drawings and Specification and not suffer damage when completed—in other words that questions of safety (from the point of view of accidents involving personal injuries) are not involved (unless the Specification contains express provisions about safety in the personal injuries sense—see *e.g.* clause 16, *infra*, p. 61—in which case the words " executed in accordance with . . . the Specification " will presumably permit inquiries directed to this). The contract *Conditions*, of course, now contain a number of new provisions about the Contractor's responsibility for safety, which in view of the lack of any practical sanction and the legal position which would obtain in any event seem largely cosmetic—see the commentary to clause 8 (2), *supra*, p. 37, and clauses 15 (1), 15 (2), 16 and 19, *infra*. The sub-clause needs to be read with clauses 8 (2), *supra*, p. 37, 13 (2), *supra*, p. 46, and the commentary under clause 13 (1), *supra*, pp. 49–51, as to the limited extent of the Engineer's powers in regard to the Contractor's methods of working, certainly in the absence of express provision and probably also under that clause.

There can be little doubt of the practical desirability of this new " power " to call for information, but it should be noted (a) that no sanction whatever is provided for its enforcement (as *e.g.* a power to suspend work at the Contractor's expense until the information is forthcoming, though if *as a fact* suspension is required on safety grounds clause 40 (1) (c) will apply) and (b) that once a request for information is made under the clause the Engineer becomes caught up in machinery which comes automatically into operation under clauses 14 (4) to (6), *infra*, under which he will be compelled either finally to approve the Contractor's methods of working or else to give positive and detailed instructions as to the method of working which will satisfy him. In the latter event a financial claim is permitted based on the " reasonable foreseeability " test now increasingly introduced into the contract (see also clause 13 (3), *supra*), as also if the Engineer unreasonably delays giving a decision or approval. It should be noted that there is no provision enabling the Engineer to adopt a neutral or " wait and see " attitude on behalf of his client, and that the nature of the Engineer's request is defined in rather general terms—" such information pertaining to the methods of construction "—so that an Engineer might easily find the machinery in the latter part of the clause invoked against him in response to a quite casual request for information. To avoid misunderstanding, therefore, Engineers would be well advised to exclude any powers under this clause from the terms of any written delegation to the Engineer's Representative under clause 2 (3), and also to make clear that any casual requests for information are not made under this clause.

" *Works* " " *Permanent Works* "

See the definition of " Works," which includes " Temporary Works " as well as " Permanent Works," in clause 1 (1) (j) (k) and (l), *supra*, pp. 21–22.

Engineer's Consent

(4) The Engineer shall inform the Contractor in writing within a reasonable period after receipt of the information submitted in accordance with sub-clause (3) of this Clause either:—

(a) that the Contractor's proposed methods have the consent of the Engineer; or

(b) in what respects in the opinion of the Engineer they fail to meet the requirements of the Drawings or Specification or will be detrimental to the Permanent Works.

In the latter event the Contractor shall take such steps or make such changes in the said methods as may be necessary to meet the Engineer's requirements and to obtain his consent. The Contractor shall not change the methods which have received the Engineer's consent without the further consent in writing of the Engineer which shall not be unreasonably withheld.

Design Criteria

(5) The Engineer shall provide to the Contractor such design criteria relevant to the Permanent Works or any Temporary Works designed by the Engineer as may be necessary to enable the Contractor to comply with sub-clauses (3) and (4) of this Clause.

Delay and Extra Cost

(6) If the Engineer's consent to the proposed methods of construction shall be unreasonably delayed or if the requirements of the Engineer pursuant to sub-clause (4) of this Clause or any limitations imposed by any of the design criteria supplied by the Engineer pursuant to sub-clause (5) of this Clause could not reasonably have been foreseen by an experienced contractor at the time of tender and if in consequence of any of the aforesaid the Contractor unavoidably incurs delay or cost the Engineer shall take such delay into account in determining any extension of time to which the Contractor is entitled under Clause 44 and the Contractor shall subject to Clause 52 (4) be paid in accordance with Clause 60 such sum in respect of the cost incurred as the Engineer considers fair in all the circumstances.

As explained *supra*, this machinery comes into operation automatically and the Engineer is compelled to approve or disapprove once the Contractor has supplied the necessary information. It is true that approval will not prejudice the Employer as against the Contractor (see sub-clause (7), *infra*) but the approval of the Engineer will certainly render the Employer and Engineer liable, or increase their liability as co-defendants in tort, as against injured third parties, and in the event of the Engineer disapproving and indicating his requirements (even if these, as would usually be the case, were more conservative than the Contractor's methods) it would become an open question whether the financial responsibility as between Employer and Contractor in respect of many matters would not pass from the latter to the former—see *e.g.* the wording of clause 8 (2) (the Engineer might now be said to have designed Temporary Works), clause 20 (3) (fault, defect, error or omission in the design of the Works), and clause 22 (1) (iv) (damage the unavoidable result of the construction of the Works) and 22 (1) (v) (any act or default committed by the Engineer).

The machinery itself is relatively straightforward and needs little comment, save that the " cost " entitlement in sub-clause (6) is, of course, quite properly, perfectly general in scope and not cut down by any " delay or disruption " requirement as in the case of the claim under clause 13 (3), *supra*, p. 51. " Cost " is itself widely defined to include overheads in clause 1 (5), *supra*, p. 25. The reference to clauses 52 (4) and 60 is to payment on interim certificate (see clauses 52 (4) (f) and 60 (1) (d)) subject to compliance with clause 52 (4) (b) (notice) and (c) and (d) (records and interim account with sufficient particulars).

Responsibility Unaffected by Approval

(7) Approval by the Engineer of the Contractor's programme in accordance with sub-clauses (1) and (2) of this Clause and the consent of the Engineer to the Contractor's proposed methods of construction in accordance with sub-clause (4) of this Clause shall not relieve the Contractor of any of his duties or responsibilities under the Contract.

This sub-clause should be read with clauses 8 (2) and 13 (2), and the commentary under clause 13 (1), *supra*, pp. 49–51, as to the limits on the power of the Engineer to intervene and dictate to the Contractor his methods of working, except in accordance with express provision in the Specification or Bills, or under the terms of the present clause. The policy of the contract in maintaining the Employer's right to hold the Contractor responsible for defective work notwithstanding earlier approval, certification or payment, is consistently maintained at many points—see *e.g.* clauses 39 (3), 14 (7), 38 (2), 39 (1) (c), 54 (3) (a) and 60 (7).

Contractor's Superintendence

15. (1) The Contractor shall give or provide all necessary superintendence during the execution of the Works and as long thereafter as the Engineer may consider necessary. Such superintendence shall be given by sufficient persons having adequate knowledge of the operations to be carried out (including the methods and techniques required the hazards likely to be encountered and methods of preventing accidents) as may be requisite for the satisfactory construction of the Works.

Contractor's Agent

(2) The Contractor of a competent and authorised agent or representative approved of in writing by the Engineer (which approval may at any time be withdrawn) is to be constantly on the Works and shall give his whole time to the superintendence of the same. Such authorised agent or representative shall be in full charge of the Works and shall receive on behalf of the Contractor directions and instructions from the Engineer or (subject to the limitations of Clause 2) the Engineer's Representative. The Contractor or such authorised agent or representative shall be responsible for the safety of all operations.

These two sub-clauses are a somewhat expanded and sub-divided version of the single paragraph clause in the Fourth Edition (which consisted of the first sentence of the present sub-clause (1) and the first two sentences of sub-clause (2)). The additions seem to have no contractual or practical significance—the new second sentence of sub-clause (1) for practical purposes adds nothing to the words " all necessary superintendence " in the first sentence, and the new last sentence of sub-clause (2) merely repeats a part of the much more comprehensive clause 8 (2), *supra*, p. 37 (which itself does no more than restate the position which would in any event obtain by implication of law in the absence of express wording to the contrary). As stated in the commentary to clause 8 (2), all these new references in various clauses of the contract to safety (compare also the additional wording in clauses 16 and 19, *infra*) are additionally superfluous by reason of the long-standing wording of other express contractual provisions such as clauses 20 (1), 22, and 24. See also the commentary to clause 14 (3), *supra*, p. 57.

The practical part of the present clause is to be found in the first two sentences of sub-clause (2), which make plain that whoever is in charge of the Site is the Contractor's duly authorised agent to receive " directions and instructions," which will include orders in writing under, for instance, clauses 40 and 51, requests and requirements of the Engineer under the new machinery in clauses 14 (3) and (4), the orders and directions under the greatly improved code for the nomination of sub-contractors under clauses 58 and 59A, and the very difficult and anomalous provisions for the termination of nominated sub-contracts in clause 59B, and many other contractual provisions. On the other hand, if the contract requires a *notice* to the Contractor—as *e.g.* under clauses 41 (commencement of work), 56 (3) (measurement) or 63 (1) (b) or (c) (termination on certain grounds)—it must be sent to the Contractor's principal place of business—see clause 68 (1), *infra*, p. 283.

It is not usually possible for an employer to prove damage for breach of this type of obligation, so that the only effective sanction for a breach (*e.g.* refusal of the Contractor to withdraw an unapproved agent) provided for in the present contract will be determination under clause 63 (1) (d)—not even an " early arbitration " under clause 66 (2) is available to the Employer.

(*1*) " *as long thereafter as the Engineer may consider necessary* "

Presumably this refers to the maintenance period and the work which may be required to be done under clause 49 (2) of the Conditions, or possibly to any special performance guarantees or commissioning obligations undertaken in the Specification or Bills. Despite the wide wording, however, there would be no effective sanction after completion to enforce compliance with this obligation, since a determination under clause 63 (1) (d) at that stage would have few if any financial consequences adverse to the Contractor, though no doubt it would formally permit the employer to make alternative arrangements for any necessary work.

(*2*) " *approved of in writing* "

It is an open question whether the disapproval of the Engineer under this sub-clause needs to be reasonable or only honest, as also the closely connected question of the extent of the Arbitrator's powers to review the matter and substitute his own opinion under clause 66 of the Conditions upon a determination under clause 63 (should the Employer exercise his only available sanction and determine under clause 63 (1) (d)) or upon a financial claim under clause 13 (3) of the Conditions (as to the difficulties of which provision see *supra*, pp. 51–53). See also on this the commentary to clause 16, *infra*.

(2) " (*subject to the limitations of clause* 2) *the Engineer's Representative* "

See the very considerable limitations and obscure provisions about delegation in clause 2, *supra*, pp. 26–28.

Removal of Contractor's Employees

16. The Contractor shall employ or cause to be employed in and about the execution of the Works and in the superintendence thereof only such persons as are careful skilled and experienced in their several trades and callings and the Engineer shall be at liberty to object to and require the Contractor to remove from the Works any person employed by the Contractor in or about the execution of the Works who in the opinion of the Engineer misconducts himself or is incompetent or negligent in the performance of his duties or fails to conform with any particular provisions with regard to safety which may be set out in the Specification or persists in any conduct which is prejudicial to safety or health and such persons shall not be again employed upon the Works without the permission of the Engineer.

This clause is, with very slight modifications, similar to that in the Fourth Edition. The new additional references to safety, a number of which are to be found in other provisions in the Fifth Edition, appear to be, for the reasons explained in the commentary to clause 8 (2) and 15, *supra*, of little practical or legal significance and mainly cosmetic.

As explained in the case of clause 15, *supra*, the only practical sanction for breach of the obligations in this clause would appear to be the remedy of determination under clause 63 (1) (d). Not even early arbitration in a disputed case is available under clause 66 (2). The same doubt must also exist as to whether the Engineer's disapproval under the present clause needs to be reasonable or only honest, though the reference to " the opinion of the Engineer " in one of the cases in the present clause, and the express power of the Engineer to give an instruction requiring removal, would seem to make it more likely, on the wording of the " open up revise and review " sentence in clause 66, *infra*, p. 276, that there is an implied requirement of reasonableness which could be reviewed by the Arbitrator should a determination under clause 63 have taken place, for example, or at the end of the work should a financial claim under the difficult clause 13 (3) (*supra*, p. 51) be advanced.

Setting-out

17. The Contractor shall be responsible for the true and proper setting-out of the Works and for the correctness of the position levels dimensions and alignment of all parts of the Works and for the provision of all necessary instruments appliances and labour in connection therewith. If at any time during the progress of the Works any error shall appear or arise in the position levels dimensions or alignment of any part of the Works the Contractor on being required so to do by the Engineer shall at his own cost rectify such error to the satisfaction of the Engineer unless such error is based on incorrect data supplied in writing by the Engineer or the Engineer's Representative in which case the cost of rectifying the same shall be borne by the Employer. The checking of any setting-out or of any line or level by the Engineer or the Engineer's Representative shall not in any way relieve the Contractor of his responsibility for the correctness thereof and the Contractor shall carefully protect and preserve all bench-marks sight rails pegs and other used in setting-out the Works.

This clause is identical with that in the Fourth Edition. Though it does not specifically say so, the Engineer must of course furnish the necessary levels and reference points (usually on his drawings) to enable the Contractor to achieve the " true and proper " setting out required by this clause—see the reference to " incorrect data " in the present clause.

The marginal note " Setting-out " (not to be regarded in the interpretation of the clause—see clause 1 (3), *supra*, p. 24) is in fact misleading in a very important sense, since it is noteworthy that the power to order errors to be rectified in the second sentence of the clause is *not* limited to inaccurate setting-out, but extends to *dimensional inaccuracies of any kind* occurring at *any stage of the works.* This important (and probably unnoticed and unintended) power conferred by the present clause should, therefore, be regarded as supplementary to the wider power to order the re-execution of defective work in clause 39 (1), *infra*, p. 107.

" *incorrect data supplied . . . by the Engineer's Representative* "

Perhaps by inadvertence, the absence of any " subject to the limitations of clause 2 " wording (compare clause 15 (2), *supra*) would seem to make this one of the few occasions in the contract when an action of the Engineer's Representative can bind the Employer, notwithstanding the absence of a written delegation by the Engineer under clause 2, *supra*, p. 25. This is probably quite unintentional and the result of earlier piecemeal drafting.

" *The checking . . . shall not in any way relieve . . .* "

For this consistent policy of the contract, see also clauses 39 (3) (replacing clause 2 (a) in the Fourth Edition), 14 (7), 38 (2), 39 (1) (c), 53 (11), 54 (3) (a) and 60 (7), all of which keep alive the right subsequently to condemn work notwithstanding earlier approvals, inspections, certification, tests or payment.

Boreholes and Exploratory Excavation

18. If at any time during the execution of the Works the Engineer shall require the Contractor to make boreholes or to carry out exploratory excavation such requirement shall be ordered in writing and shall be deemed to be a variation ordered under Clause 51 unless a Provisional Sum or Prime Cost Item in respect of such anticipated work shall have been included in the Bill of Quantities.

This clause in effect provides for payment of the Contractor for boreholes or exploratory excavation in any event, either under clauses 51 and 52 as a variation, or under clause 58 (7) (a) and clause 52 as Provisional Sum work by the Contractor, or under clause 59A (v) as nominated sub-contract work under either a P.C. or Provisional Sum. It is a serious omission, common to the RIBA forms as well, and as in the case of other more important powers of the Engineer (see *e.g.* clause 39 *infra*, p. 107) that no express saving is made for the very common practical situation where additional or varied work (or in the present case exploratory work) becomes necessary as a result of defective work by the Contractor being discovered, though no doubt employers will seek to argue that in such cases the expenditure is recoverable from the Contractor as damages for breach of contract.

The present clause is clearly aimed, however, at the special situation where the Engineer requires exploratory work to be done in order to assist him in discharging his own responsibilities for the detailed design of the permanent works (or of any temporary works if the contract requires them to be designed by him, as sometimes is the case—see clause 8 (2), *supra*, p. 37). No doubt the power is most likely to be exercised in regard to proposed varied work, since in the case of original contract work it would seem reasonable to assume that any necessary exploratory work had been done prior to contract, but it may also be necessary in cases where unexpected site conditions are encountered which throw doubt on the original design.

Safety and Security

19. (1) The Contractor shall throughout the progress of the Works have full regard for the safety of all persons entitled to be upon the Site and shall keep the Site (so far as the same is under his control) and the Works (so far as the same are not completed or occupied by the Employer) in an orderly state appropriate to the avoidance of danger to such persons and shall *inter alia* in connection with the Works provide and maintain at his own cost all lights guards fencing warning signs and watching when and where necessary or required by the Engineer or by any competent statutory or other authority for the protection of the Works or for the safety and convenience of the public or others.

The latter part of this sub-clause in regard to watching and lighting is identical with clause 19 of the Fourth Edition. It might be thought that these particular requirements would more appropriately be the subject of detailed express provisions in the Specification or Bills, but they were no doubt regarded as a sufficiently universal obligation to merit specific mention in the Conditions. The earlier (and new) part of the sub-clause reflects the rather odd policy of the Fifth Edition to insert wherever possible repeated references to the Contractor's responsibility for the safety of operations on the site—see the commentary to clause 8 (2), *supra*, p. 37, and clauses 15 (1), 15 (2), and 16, all of which contain additional new wording on this subject. As pointed out in the commentary to clause 8 (2), these references appear to have little practical or legal consequence and seem mainly cosmetic in view of long-standing express provisions like clauses 20 (1), 22 and 24 of the Conditions, and the implications of law which will in any event be made in building and civil engineering contracts, and it is furthermore noteworthy that no sanction or provision for enforcement appears to have been thought necessary (contrast the special power under clause 39 (2) in the case of defective work) so that the only remedy available to an employer would seem to be the possibly perilous one of a determination of the Contractor's employment under clause 63 (1) (d), *infra*, p. 244.

(2) If under Clause 31 the Employer shall carry out work on the Site with his own workmen he shall in respect of such work:—

(a) have full regard to the safety of all persons entitled to be upon the Site; and

(b) keep the Site in an orderly state appropriate to the avoidance of danger to such persons.

If under Clause 31 the Employer shall employ other contractors on the Site he shall require them to have the same regard for safety and avoidance of danger.

This sub-clause is new. Its precise purpose, since no sanction for enforcement is made available, any more than in the case of the various new provisions reiterating the Contractor's responsibility for safety (see the commentaries to clause 8 (2) and clauses 15 (1) and 16 as well as to sub-clause (1), *supra*) is not easy to understand, though it may be of some importance in interpreting clauses 22 and 24 (see particularly clause 22 (1) (b) (v), *infra*, p. 75) and the indemnities given by the Contractor under those clauses in respect of injuries to persons on the Site.

Care of the Works

20. (1) The Contractor shall take full responsibility for the care of the Works from the date of the commencement thereof until 14 days after the Engineer shall have issued a Certificate of Completion for the whole of the Works pursuant to Clause 48. Provided that if the Engineer shall issue a Certificate of Completion in respect of any Section or part of the Permanent Works before he shall issue a Certificate of Completion in respect of the whole of the Works the Contractor shall cease to be responsible for the care of that Section or part of the Permanent Works 14 days after the Engineer shall have issued the Certificate of Completion in respect of that Section or part and the responsibility for the care thereof shall thereupon pass to the Employer. Provided further that the Contractor shall take full responsibility for the care of any outstanding work which he shall have undertaken to finish during the Period of Maintenance until such outstanding work is complete.

Responsibility for Reinstatement

(2) In case any damage loss or injury from any cause whatsoever (save and except the Excepted Risks as defined in sub-clause (3) of this Clause) shall happen to the Works or any part thereof while the Contractor shall be responsible for the care thereof the Contractor shall at his own cost repair and make good the same so that at completion the Permanent Works shall be in good order and condition

and in conformity in every respect with the requirements of the Contract and the Engineer's instructions. To the extent that any such damage loss or injury arises from any of the Excepted Risks the Contractor shall if required by the Engineer repair and make good the same as aforesaid at the expense of the Employer. The Contractor shall also be liable for any damage to the Works occasioned by him in the course of any operations carried out by him for the purpose of completing any outstanding work or of complying with his obligations under Clauses 49 and 50.

These two sub-clauses correspond to clause 20 (1) in the Fourth Edition, and have effected a number of clarifying improvements, including, quite properly and logically, relating the cessation of liability under the clause expressly to the substantial completion certification procedures under clause 48, *infra*, and in fact giving detailed effect to what was submitted should be the intention of the clause in this respect in the case of the Fourth Edition (see B.C.F. at pp. 332–333). However, as will be seen, the date now chosen is the *date of issue* of a certificate of completion under clause 48, rather than the *certified date of completion*, which may be a cause of difficulty in certain circumstances.

The express obligation to complete assumed in nearly all contracts for work and materials means that, in the event of accidental or other damage, or even their total destruction, before completion, the Contractor is bound to repair and complete the works again at his own cost, the only qualification on this being the law of frustration, which in the context of engineering contracts is probably limited to some supervening event making completion of the works as a whole impossible—see Hudson, 10th ed., pp. 267–272, and pp. 349–360, and the commentary on clauses 8 (1), 8 (2) and 13 (1), *supra*, pp. 35–37 and 47–48, and see also the commentary under clause 64, *infra*, p. 244, which provides for specific remedies and consequences on frustration. Another way of describing this state of affairs is to say that the works remain at the risk of the Contractor until completion (completion for this purpose being specially defined in sub-clause (1), *supra*). Thereafter, the Contractor will under clause 49 receive additional payment for any work of repair during the maintenance period, unless it is due to some breach of contract by the Contractor, but on the other hand, as in the Fourth Edition, will remain liable by virtue of the last sentence of sub-clause (2) for any damage actually caused by him during the maintenance period when carrying out his maintenance obligations, or when completing any work outstanding after substantial completion as contemplated by clause 48.

Subject to these points of detail, therefore, the present sub-clauses merely restate the general legal position which would otherwise obtain (see particularly clause 8 (2), *supra*, p. 37, for a short express statement of this position) and their real significance lies in the series of qualifications involved in the phrase "(save and except the Excepted Risks)." These

" Excepted Risks " are set out in sub-clause (3), *infra*, and represent vitally important express qualifications upon the Contractor's obligation to complete, by virtue of the second sentence of sub-clause (2), which makes it plain that in the event of damage due to any of the " Excepted Risks " the Contractor need not make good the damaged part unless called upon to do so, and then only at the cost of the Employer. The insurance of the Works called for under clause 21, *infra*, is also expressly not required to cover the Excepted Risks.

(*1*) " *until 14 days after . . . a Certificate of completion* "

Note the reference is to the *issue* of the Certificate, *not* of the date of completion stated in the Certificate. This means that the insurance may have to continue for as much as 35 days after actual completion, since the completion certificate itself need only be issued within 21 days of completion of the whole, section or part under clause 48, *infra*, p. 140.

(*2*) " *from any cause whatsoever* "

These words, according to a somewhat artificial construction adopted by the courts in commercial (shipping and charterparty) cases, appear to be wide enough to include any act or neglect of the Employer or his agents—so that the Contractor, in a contract where such words are used, will be liable to reinstate free of charge notwithstanding that the Employer or his servants have negligently damaged the works—see the case of *Farr* v. *The Admiralty* [1953] 1 W.L.R. 965 applying *Travers* v. *Cooper* [1915] 1 K.B. 73, and see Hudson, 10th ed., p. 312.. *Use* or *occupation* by the Employer his agents servants or other contractors is, however, an " Excepted Risk," as to which see the commentary *infra*.

Excepted Risks

(3) The " Excepted Risks " are riot war invasion act of foreign enemies hostilities (whether war be declared or not) civil war rebellion revolution insurrection or military or usurped power ionising radiations or contamination by radio-activity from any nuclear fuel or from any nuclear waste from the combustion of nuclear fuel radioactive toxic explosive or other hazardous properties of any explosive nuclear assembly or nuclear component thereof pressure waves caused by aircraft or other aerial devices travelling at sonic or supersonic speeds or a cause due to use or occupation by the Employer his agents servants or other contractors (not being employed by the Contractor) of any part of the Permanent Works or to fault defect error or omission in the design of the Works (other than a design provided by the Contractor pursuant to his obligations under the Contract.)

As stated (see sub-clause (2), *supra*), these " Excepted Risks " represent express major qualifications upon the Contractor's principal obligation to complete. Furthermore, by clause 21, *infra*, the Contractor is not required to insure the Works against them. In practical terms, the first list of Excepted Risks, by reason of their esoteric character, does not represent any very serious invasion of this principal obligation of the Contractor.

The next following reference to " use or occupation " by the Employer seemed an abundance of caution under the Fourth Edition wording, since if the Employer was using or occupying the Works there would normally have, *ex hypothesi*, been substantial completion of that part within clause 48, so that the obligation under the present clause in any event would have ended. The new period of 14 days after the *issue* of the certificate of completion now stipulated under sub-clause (1) (*i.e.* possibly as much as five weeks after actual substantial completion, by virtue of the period stipulated for the completion certificate in clause 48, *infra*) does, however, mean that for that period this Excepted Risk might be needed to be relied on; furthermore, use or occupation by other contractors of the Employer, a new addition to the wording in the Fifth Edition, could well take place before substantial completion—as to these see clause 31, *infra*, p. 98.

It is the next words " a cause due . . . to fault defect error or omission in the design of the Works " followed by the new words " (other than a design provided by the Contractor pursuant to his obligations under the Contract) " which represent the most important qualification of the Contractor's principal obligation, and which require to be examined with the greatest care. The word " design " in the context of building and civil engineering contracts will include any requirement which may regulate or control the suitability of the completed work for its intended purpose—not merely, therefore, structural designs, calculations and dimensions, but also the choice of materials and control of work processes—see Hudson, 10th ed., p. 274. In all such contracts, even where the Engineer is in day-to-day control over the work, and provides both drawings and specification, the contract documents will in practice be silent as to many of the design requirements (often of course of the less important kind), which will accordingly become the implied contractual responsibility of the Contractor, via implied terms as to the suitability and quality of the Contractor's work and materials. In addition, the contract may expressly leave certain matters to the Contractor, or may require him to give an express performance or other suitability guarantee or undertaking. These implied or express obligations of the Contractor will be covered, it is submitted, by the new and sensible exception in brackets in the last line of the present sub-clause, though no doubt the wording may also contemplate the relatively rare cases (in civil engineering as opposed, for example, to electrical or mechanical contracts) where the Contractor is expressly required to submit specifications or drawings for approval by the Engineer. The precise extent of the implied design obligations of the Contractor is exhaustively examined and explained in Hudson, 10th ed., pp. 274–306.

The exact application of the " design " Excepted Risk to any given set of facts will usually, however, give rise to considerable difficulty, the reason being that while the " design " concept is almost invariably concerned with the suitability of the finally constructed work for its purpose after completion, the present clause is concerned only with a failure of or damage occurring to the works during construction, and in civil engineering many designs will not be stable or self-supporting during construction until the last part of the construction or work is in place (hence the need for temporary works, the propping of arches and other structures before concrete sets, shoring and support to existing or new structures, and so on, which will usually be the Contractor's responsibility—see clause 8 (2), *supra*, p. 37). It is submitted that this Excepted Risk will apply either to a design defect of the *permanent* works which would in any event have affected their safety or stability after completion, but which has incidentally caused damage or failure during construction in a case where temporary support or other special measures would not, in reliance on the assumed efficacy of the permanent design, be reasonably provided or required (as *e.g.* a failure of a completed and independent part of the works, such as an individual span of a multi-span bridge) or to a case where the Engineer or the contract documents have expressly prescribed or designed the Temporary Works or method of working to be adopted, which have been properly executed by the Contractor, and the use of other methods would have avoided the damage. The words "fault defect error or omission in the design" may, incidentally, be somewhat narrower than the simpler "due to the Engineer's design" wording in the Fourth Edition, in those not uncommon cases where the design, while not negligent in the current state of knowledge, was the actual cause of damage, but on the other hand the removal of the very important word "solely" from the Fourth Edition wording certainly may have been intended to widen the scope of this Excepted Risk even to cases where the Contractor's omissions may be at least partly responsible for the damage. In fact, however, as a matter of interpretation the new wording will still require the Engineer's design to be the *effective* cause of the damage, and cases of partial responsibility by the Contractor may go to the quantum of any financial claim made by him under the clause.

The new provisions of clause 14 (3) to (7) also need to be borne in mind in cases where the Engineer has acted under clause 14 (3) and inquired into the Contractor's methods of construction. It is clear from clause 14 (7) (see also clause 8 (2)) that mere approval of the Contractor's proposals and design will not produce an "Engineer's design" situation under the present clause, nor, it is submitted, will the imposition of any limitations by the Engineer under clause 14 (6) on the Contractor's methods of construction absolve the Contractor from his own obligations under clauses 8 (2) and 20 (1), unless the Engineer's limitations are directly contrary to or inconsistent with protective measures which the Contractor would or could otherwise have taken.

It does not seem likely that the difficulties of application to which this particular Excepted Risk can give rise have been fully appreciated, and its reinstatement, with the modifications of wording already noted, in the Fifth Edition, including particularly the omission of the word " solely," will certainly not reduce the likelihood of this Excepted Risk, as at present defined, being invoked by the Contractor in almost every case of serious damage to the works (in a situation where, it should be noted, at least the Contractor's and the Engineer's insurers will almost invariably be involved, if not separate insurers of the Employer as well—usually reliable ingredients for protracted disputes and litigation). Wording to give clearer effect to the clause's presumed intention would make it plain, it is suggested, that the application of this Excepted Risk should be limited to cases where the damage was *the direct consequence, without fault or omission on the part of the Contractor*, of the Engineer's design of the permanent or temporary works, or of compliance with an instruction by him, or (compare the wording of clause 40 (1) (c)) of any omission or default on the Engineer's part.

Consistently with the policy of this Excepted Risk, clause 40 (1) (c) has now been reworded so as to make plain that suspensions of work for its proper execution or safety, but which are due to Excepted Risks, will also be the Employer's financial responsibility.

Insurance of Works, etc.

21. Without limiting his obligations and responsibilities under Clause 20 the Contractor shall insure in the joint names of the Employer and the Contractor:—

(a) the Permanent Works and the Temporary Works (including for the purposes of this Clause any unfixed materials or other things delivered to the Site for incorporation therein) to their full value;

(b) the Constructional Plant to its full value;

against all loss or damage from whatever cause arising (other than the Excepted Risks) for which he is responsible under the terms of the Contract and in such manner that the Employer and Contractor are covered for the period stipulated in Clause 20 (1) and are also covered for loss or damage arising during the Period of Maintenance from such cause occurring prior to the commencement of the Period of Maintenance and for any loss or damage occasioned by the Contractor in the course of any operation carried out by him for the purpose of complying with his obligations under Clauses 49 and 50.

Provided that without limiting his obligations and responsiblities as aforesaid nothing in this Clause contained shall render the Contractor liable to insure against the necessity for the repair or reconstruction of any work constructed with materials and workmanship not in accordance with the requirements of the Contract unless the Bill of Quantities shall provide a special item for this insurance.

Such insurances shall be effected with an insurer and in terms approved by the Employer (which approval shall not be unreasonably withheld) and the Contractor shall whenever required produce to the Employer the policy or policies of insurance and the receipts for payment of the current premiums.

This clause, which with very minor amendments follows closely that in the Fourth Edition, is concerned with insurance of the works, of the Contractor's Constructional Plant, and of unfixed materials. Insurance against personal injuries and damage to third persons' property is covered by clause 23 (1), and the Employer's special (and necessary) sanction on failure by the Contractor to insure under either clause is provided in clause 25.

Contractors, of course, are free to take out insurance of any kind against any risk, whatever a contract may say. Generally, an Employer will require insurance as part of the contract obligation either in respect of matters which, as between himself and the Contractor under the terms of the contract, will ultimately be his own financial responsibility; or else in respect of matters which, while they may be the ultimate financial responsibility of the Contractor, are potentially of such magnitude as to cripple the Contractor's financial ability to complete the project, thereby indirectly causing a heavy financial loss to the Employer as well. In the former case, that is to say, where the ultimate financial responsibility as between Contractor and Employer will rest with the Employer, insurance in joint names is a practical necessity, since insurance by the Contractor alone would mean, in English law at least, that the Contractor's insurers would then be left free to pursue the Employer in order to recover the loss they had incurred on the policy. In the latter case, where the ultimate contractual financial responsibility lies with the Contractor, insurance in joint names is not necessary in English law since, in the event of the Contractor's insolvency, a direct statutory right against the insurance company by the Employer then becomes available. Furthermore, it is in the commercial interest of the Employer to keep contractual requirements for insurance by Contractors to a minimum, since a contractual requirement will inevitably have the effect of increasing the contract price, whereas matters where insurance is voluntary will not necessarily do so, since contractors with competent staff and of good financial standing may prefer, to a greater or less degree, to carry the risks themselves. Moreover, in cases where the Contractor is ultimately financially liable to the Employer under the terms of the contract, the liability in question may already have been secured to the Employer, at least to the extent of any bond in the approved form entered into by the Contractor, as is required in the present contract under clause 10 of the Conditions. In addition, where Contractors are tendering in competition, it is essential that the contract documents should spell out with the utmost precision the exact insurance required (compare the contractual arrangements for the terms of bonds), since otherwise the tenders will not be truly comparable until after examination of the details of a proferred insurance policy. Apart from defining the risks to be insured with precision, stipulated limits, and in particular " excesses " in the insurance sense, can do much to keep down the contract price and far more to stimulate contractors' and sub-contractors' interest in protective measures and work than repeated contractual provisions of a precatory character, in which the present contract abounds—see *ante*, Chapter 1, p. 2, where the pointlessness of these provisions is pointed out.

These are the basic principles which should govern advisers responsible for the preparation of insurance clauses on behalf of employers in building or civil engineering contracts, but it must be said that there is little indication of their being followed in the present (traditional) clause. In the first place, sub-clause (3) leaves the terms of the policy for (presumably) post-contract approval by the Employer. More importantly, however, the clause is careful to limit the Contractor's liability to insure (as does clause 23 (1), *infra*) only to those matters which, as between Employer and Contractor, are the latter's responsibility under the contract. Notwithstanding this, it will be noted that the insurance called for is, unnecessarily in English law at least, to be in joint names, though this may be explained by the fact that, in the case of plant and unfixed materials, these will be deemed for certain limited purposes to be the property of the Employer under clause 53 (2) of the Conditions—but see also clause 53 (9) on the very limited effect of this in the present context, so that on the whole it is probably too charitable to attribute the choice of joint insurance to this consideration.

In addition, disregarding altogether the absence of any insurance cover for the Employer's areas of responsibility, there are elements of both over- and under-insurance from the Employer's point of view under this clause, since the Employer will have little if any interest, for example, in the insurance of most plant or materials (except possibly any very expensive items the loss of which might cripple the Contractor), or against minor or partial damage to the works themselves, for which the Contractor is responsible (for this reason a very large insurance " excess," for example, would, as previously stated, be in the Employer's interest), and indeed the existence of such wide-ranging and compulsory insurance must inevitably act as at least a short-term inducement for Contractors to cut corners and minimise precautionary and protective measures during construction in order to maximise profits. On the other hand, the cost of repair or reconstruction of defective work or materials, expressly excluded from insurance by the proviso to the present clause, in some engineering contracts might easily cripple the Contractor financially—*e.g.* the failure of a dam or bridge or other major works at a late stage of construction—and in such an event, as already explained, the Employer will obviously have a strong commercial interest in the Contractor being insured for an amount much greater than the 10 per cent. cover of any bond given under clause 10 of the Conditions.

Turning to the clause itself, it will be seen that, though the principal requirement is defined as " loss or damage for which he is responsible under the terms of the Contract " the clause inevitably relates back, for the ascertainment of these responsibilities of the Contractor, to clause 20, just as the third party insurance cover required by clause 23 (1) is related back to clause 22 (1), which defines the Contractor's responsibilities in the case of third party claims. It is, of course, self-evident that since the "Excepted Risks" under clause 20 (2) (where the Employer will be ultimately financially liable under the terms of the contract) are expressly excluded from the required insurance, the Employer in the case of the Excepted Risks is in danger of a very substantial financial liability in respect of which there will be no insurance (apart from any professional negligence insurance cover of the Engineer) unless he himself has taken out separate insurance. As already pointed out in the commentary to clause 20 (3), *supra*, p. 67, by far the most important Excepted Risk in the United Kingdom will be that of "fault defect error or omission in the design of the Work," which in practice is likely to be invoked by the Contractor in a large number of instances of major loss or damage to the works during construction.

The detailed wording of the present clause contains a number of points of difficulty or detail which require to be noted. Before considering these, it may be helpful to attempt a summary of the broad categories of damage for which the Contractor *will* be "responsible under the terms of the contract," and so require to insure under the present clause. These would appear to be

(a) Damage *up to five weeks after actual completion* of the whole, Section or part of the Works in question (this is the effect of the "14 days after issue of the Certificate of Completion" wording in clause 20 (1)—see the commentary, *supra*, p. 66) arising from "any cause whatsoever" (see the commentary on these latter words, *supra*, p. 66) but excepting the following wide classes of damage caused by:

- (i) the "riot, war, invasion etc." generic group of Excepted Risks
- (ii) the "fault defect error or omission in the design of the Works," Excepted Risk
- (iii) use or occupation by the Employer or other contractors (usually this will be limited to the possible five week period terminating 14 days after *issue* of the completion certificate in the case of the Employer—see *supra*, p. 67, under clause 20 (3)—but not necessarily so, of course, in the case of other contractors, who may be on the Site during the construction period)
- (iv) an event justifying the "legally or physically impossible" qualification on the Contractor's obligation to complete under clause 13 (1), commented on *supra*, pp. 47–48.

and

(b) *During the maintenance period*

- (i) delayed damage arising from an insured cause or event occurring prior to substantial completion
- (ii) damage actually caused by the Contractor while working on the Site (*i.e.* in the discharge of his maintenance obligations under clauses 48 and 49)

but *not*

(c) The cost of repair or reinstatement of defective work or materials (as to the exact meaning of which see *infra*).

" *to their full value* " " *to its full value* "

i.e. without limit or any insurance " excess," presumably—not, for reasons already stated, a sensible requirement in all cases.

" *Constructional Plant* "

The Fourth Edition wording made it clear that this was plant brought to the Site, but the new rearranged wording leaves this in doubt. This could possibly be of considerable importance where delivery or allocation of major items of plant required for the project has taken place in the Contractor's depot or elsewhere off site, and more precision would be desirable.

" *all loss or damage from whatever cause arising* (*other than the Excepted Risks*) *for which he is responsible under the terms of the Contract* "

These words present no great difficulty in the case of *the Works* (defined as including both permanent and temporary works in clause 1 (1) (1), *supra*, p. 21) and the words " (other than the Excepted Risks) " can be regarded as mere surplusage (of which there is no shortage in the Contract's draftsmanship) adding nothing to the " for which he is responsible " wording. But in the case of the unfixed materials and Constructional Plant required to be insured under the present clause there is a real drafting difficulty, since the responsibilities and the Excepted Risks qualification of those responsibilities in clause 20 are limited to the Works *and make no mention of Constructional Plant or unfixed materials.* The question is whether the Contractor is required to insure plant and materials *even against the Excepted Risks* (because in the admitted absence of any qualification under clause 20 he is contractually responsible for them in any event); or whether on the other hand, despite his admitted contractual responsibility, he is excused by the present wording from insuring them against the Excepted Risks—in other words whether overriding force should be given to the words " (other than the Excepted Risks) " on the one hand (which certainly means that the words have a positive effect), or whether overriding force should be given to the words " for which he is responsible . . . ," in which event the reference to the Excepted Risks, as in the case of the Works themselves, is mere surplusage. The difficulty is compounded by the fact that clause 53 (9), *infra*, p. 175, which provides that the Employer shall not be liable for loss or injury to plant or materials brought onto the Site " save as mentioned in clause 20 " assumes, quite wrongly, that clause 20 does in fact qualify this immunity of the Employer in some way. It seems idle to speculate on the correct interpretation in the light of the ambiguity of the wording, and Contractors should probably attempt action under clause 5, *supra*, p. 29, in order to obtain an Engineer's instruction in the matter.

" *from whatever cause arising* "

See the commentary on similar words in clause 20, *supra*, p. 66.

" *for the period stipulated in clause 20 (1)* "

i.e. 14 days after *issue* of the certificate of completion or partial completion, which may therefore result in the cover continuing for as much as 35 days after completion—see the commentary to clause 20, *supra*, p. 66.

" *from such cause occurring prior to the commencement of the Period of Maintenance* "

The word " such " is new, and resolves an anomaly in the Fourth Edition by making it plain that an insurable cause as previously defined is intended. It should be noted that while the wording does not in terms restrict the cause to the construction period itself, (*i.e.* post-commencement of work) this would seem to follow from the wording of sub-clauses 20 (1) and (2), and the " for which he is responsible " wording in the present clause.

" *the repair or reconstruction of any work . . . not in accordance with the contract* "

It should be noted that this very important Proviso is limited in terms to the actual repair or reconstruction *of the defective work itself.* In engineering contracts defective work may lead to a structural or other failure which may well precipitate widespread damage or destruction to other completed work or temporary work not itself defective in any way. It is submitted that the repair or reconstruction of this consequential damage is *not* within the present Proviso, and will require to be insured under the terms of the present clause. A further question which will no doubt be raised by insurers seeking to avoid liability is whether the words " workmanship not in accordance with the Contract " would be apt to include failure by the Contractor to comply with any of the very commonly found express provisions in Bills or Specifications requiring the Contractor to take protective measures to safeguard the works during construction (*e.g.* pumping, draining, shoring and so on).

" (*which approval shall not be unreasonably withheld*) "

This reference to (presumably post-tender or even post-contract) approval of terms has already been commented upon as very undesirable from an Employer's point of view, and to avoid doubt or argument the principal terms of the policy (including particularly any permitted exceptions) should be set out in the Specification or Bills of Quantities. (In important contracts this justifies taking expert legal advice.) For the Employer's sanction on failure to insure or maintain insurance, see clause 25, *infra*. For insurance generally see Hudson, 10th ed., pp. 306–313.

Damage to Persons and Property

22. (1) The Contractor shall (except if and so far as the Contract otherwise provides) indemnify and keep indemnified the Employer against all losses and claims for injuries or damage to any person or property whatsoever (other than the Works for which insurance is required under Clause 21 but including surface or other damage to land being the Site suffered by any persons in beneficial occupation of such land) which may arise out of or in consequence of the construction and maintenance of the Works and against all claims demands proceedings damages costs charges and expenses whatsoever in respect thereof or in relation thereto. Provided always that:—

(a) the Contractor's liability to indemnify the Employer as aforesaid shall be reduced proportionately to the extent that the act or neglect of the Employer his servants or agents may have contributed to the said loss injury or damage;

(b) nothing herein contained shall be deemed to render the Contractor liable for or in respect of or to indemnify the Employer against any compensation or damages for or with respect to:—

  (i) damage to crops being on the Site (save in so far as possession has not been given to the Contractor);

  (ii) the use or occupation of land (which has been provided by the Employer) by the Works or any part thereof or for the purpose of constructing completing and maintaining the Works (including consequent losses of crops) or interference whether temporary or permanent with any right of way light air or water or other easement or quasi easement which are the unavoidable result of the construction of the Works in accordance with the Contract;

  (iii) the right of the Employer to construct the Works or any part thereof on over under in or through any land;

  (iv) damage which is the unavoidable result of the construction of the Works in accordance with the Contract;

  (v) injuries or damage to persons or property resulting from any act or neglect or breach of statutory duty done or committed by the Engineer or the Employer his agents servants or other contractors (not being employed by the Contractor) or for or in respect of any claims demands proceedings damages costs charges and expenses in respect thereof or in relation thereto.

Indemnity by Employer

(2) The Employer will save harmless and indemnify the Contractor from and against all claims demands proceedings damages costs charges and expenses in respect of the matters referred to in the proviso to sub-clause (1) of this Clause. Provided always that the Employer's liability to indemnify the Contractor under paragraph (v) of proviso (b) to sub-clause (1) of this Clause shall be reduced proportionately to the extent that the act or neglect of the Contractor or his sub-contractors servants or agents may have contributed to the said injury or damage.

Indemnity provisions of this kind are designed to " redistribute," as between Employer and Contractor, the ultimate liability for claims by third parties, should the latter choose to sue or succeed in recovering judgment against the " wrong " party whom it has been agreed under the contract shall not be responsible for the claim in question. This can easily happen in English law under the doctrines of joint torts and vicarious responsibility, and particularly in the case of projects like building and civil engineering contracts, with various potential and often overlapping liabilities in tort to third persons of the Engineer as designer and superviser, of the Contractor as an independent Contractor in exclusive charge of actual operations (see the commentary to clauses 8 (2) and 13 (1) *supra*, pp. 37–38 and 49–51) and of the Employer directly responsible in contract and tort for works which may contravene or affect the rights of adjoining owners, and possibly vicariously liable in tort as well for the negligent acts of both Engineer and Contractor. For indemnity provisions generally, see Hudson, 10th ed., pp. 306–313. In this context reference should be made to the difficult decision of Mocatta J. in *A.M.F. International* v. *Magnet Bowling & G. P. Trentham* [1968] 1 W.L.R. 1028, commented on in Hudson, 10th ed., at pp. 309–310, which held that any contributory tortious negligence, however slight, *vis-á-vis* a third party plaintiff by a defendant seeking to rely on an indemnity clause (as *e.g.* failure of a defendant Employer to supervise and detect bad or dangerous work by his co-defendant Contractor) would debar him from relying on a contractual indemnity against his co-tortfeasor, in the absence of sufficiently explicit wording in the indemnity provision designed to cover that eventuality. That decision, if correct, almost certainly meant that under the Fourth Edition wording *neither* party could have enforced the present indemnity clause's predecessor in the great majority of cases likely to arise in practice, where some slight element of blame might attach to the party seeking to enforce the indemnity.

Two further points should perhaps be made about indemnity clauses. In the first place, parties suing on an indemnity clause who find themselves defeated by the *A.M.F.* principle of interpretation may be able to succeed on a claim for direct breach of contract on the *Mowbray* v. *Merryweather* principle (Hudson, 10th ed., pp. 309–310 and 593), since many matters for which an indemnity is given are also a breach of contract by the party giving the indemnity. In the second place, actions on indemnity clauses have the very considerable practical advantage over actions for breach of contract that time does not run for limitation purposes under an indemnity clause *until damage is suffered* (*i.e.* when the claim is received)—see *County and District Properties* v. *Jenner* [1976] 2 Lloyd's Rep. 728 *per* Swanwick J., where the law on this subject is carefully summarised and considered.

The Fifth Edition has made considerable efforts both to improve a number of ambiguities which rendered the old clause 22 almost incomprehensible in places, and also to resolve the difficulty created by the *A.M.F.* case, but unfortunately the general form of the old clause has been retained, with the result that, as will be seen, the resolution of the *A.M.F.* difficulty, which presumably is the reason for the two new provisions in clause 22 (1) (a) and the Proviso to clause 22 (2), has resulted in an extraordinarily convoluted and complicated series of inter-acting provisions—namely sub-clauses (1) (a), (1) (b) (v) and (2)—the exact effect of which is extremely difficult to analyse, though the broad effect would appear to be that the clause has now opted for a policy of *contribution* between the two contracting parties wherever any " act or neglect " of the party relying on the indemnity can be said to " contribute " to the loss or damage in question. In the particular circumstances of engineering contracts, and in particular the relationship of the Engineer and the Contractor under those contracts, both these expressions raise more questions than they answer. The clause, notwithstanding minor improvements, remains an extremely difficult one to interpret at a number of points, and its practical policy and intentions are by no means easy to determine. Though it is the most important general indemnity clause in the contract, there are many other more specific ones, given by both parties, some of which quite obviously overlap with the present clause—see *e.g.* clauses 24 (injuries to workmen), 26 (2) (conformity with by-laws), 27 (7) (Public Street Works), 29 (1) (traffic and adjoining properties), 29 (2) (noise and disturbance), 30 (2) (damage to highways or bridges) and 49 (5) (a) (reinstatement of highways). While the present clause provides for a very important series of counter-indemnities by the Employer in favour of the Contractor (in sub-clause (2)) many (but not all) of the other clauses provide only for indemnities by the Contractor in favour of the Employer, and contractors sued on one of these later direct indemnities may well in appropriate cases now seek to defend themselves by setting up a relevant counter-indemnity under sub-clause (2) of the present clause.

It will be seen that the format of this clause is:—

(1) A generally worded Contractor's indemnity to the Employer in the first paragraph of sub-clause (1);

(2) a series of defined exceptions to that indemnity in sub-clause (1), Proviso (b) (i) to (v) inclusive, in respect of which the Employer then gives the Contractor a counter-indemnity under sub-clause (2); and

(3) two provisions designed to reduce the extent of both the Contractor's indemnity and the Employer's counter-indemnity in the event of " act or neglect of the Employer his servants or agents " or " act or neglect of the Contractor or of his sub-contractors servants or agents," respectively.

Dealing first with the Contractor's general indemnity, the syntax on examination shows that this indemnity is against (a) " all losses . . . to any person or property," (b) " all . . . claims for injuries or damage to any person or property " and (c) " all claims demands proceedings damages costs charges and expenses whatsoever in respect thereof or in relation thereto " (the " thereto " must relate, it is submitted, to the " losses " in (a) and " claims " in (b) and not to the immediately preceding " Works "). It will be seen that there is unnecessary and confusing repetition, which possibly encouraged an Employer who was a *successful* defendant in an action to argue (unsuccessfully as it turned out) in the Court of Appeal that he was entitled under (c) to be indemnified by the Contractor, under the Fourth Edition version of this clause, for costs which the Employer was unable to recover from the unsuccessful and impecunious plaintiff in an action for personal injuries—see *Richardson* v. *Buckinghamshire County Council* [1971] 1 Lloyd's Rep. 523, (1977) 6 B.L.R. 58. It will be seen that the loss or claim must " arise out of etc." the construction of the Works.

Unlike the Fourth Edition, the Fifth Edition makes it plain that loss or damage to the Works themselves is (quite logically and correctly) excluded from the operation of the present clause, but it is impossible to be sure why the words " for which insurance is required under clause 21 " have been inserted. This may be a reference to the somewhat wider definition of the Works in clause 21 (a) as including unfixed materials, but deliberately to exclude unfixed materials from the present indemnity would seem inconsistent with clause 53 (9), *infra*, p. 175, which provides that the Employer shall not be liable in any way for these. Nor can it possibly be a reference to the risks insured against under clause 21, since that would mean that a contractor's indemnity was being given under the present clause in respect of the (Employer's Risk) excepted risks under clause 20, and was being refused in respect of the Contractor's risks under that clause, both of which propositions would be absurd and directly contrary to clause 20 (2) of the Conditions. The words in question may simply have been inserted *per incuriam*.

It will be seen that damage to " land being the Site " suffered by " persons in beneficial occupation " is included in the Contractor's indemnity, though damage to crops on the Site is excluded, but only to the extent that the Contractor has been let into possession (see Proviso (b) (i)). The exact policy intention of these provisions, and the situation at which they are aimed, is obscure, and is compounded by the unsatisfactory nature of the contract definition of " Site "—see clause 1 (1) (n) and the commentary, *supra*, pp. 22–23, where this is further discussed. It is clear, however, that the damage in question must in all cases be avoidable, and not the inevitable consequence of carrying out the work—see the two Provisos (b) (ii) and (b) (iii). The relationship of all these provisions is somewhat confusing, but would seem to contemplate, as coming within the Contractor's indemnity, avoidable damage to land on the Site at the suit of beneficial occupiers who may or may not have temporarily vacated their land while the Works are carried out, and also damage to crops, in cases where the Contractor has not yet been let into possession of the relevant part (*i.e.* he has in effect trespassed notwithstanding that at a later date he might expect to be given possession). This particular set of provisions probably contemplates the sewer/pipe-line type of engineering project which is likely to traverse many properties not belonging to the Employer, whether in open country or built-up districts, and where possession (see clause 42) is likely to be given in stages according to the Contractor's programme and progress. The words " in beneficial occupation " indicate that damage to the reversionary interests of adjoining owners not in possession (*e.g.* landlords) may not be within the Contractor's indemnity. The word " crops " is too simple and may cause difficulty, incidentally; will damage to trees being grown for timber, or to fruit trees themselves (as opposed to their crops of fruit) be covered by the wording? On any view, it is obvious that the definition of " Site " in clause 1 (1) (n) should be given greater precision, particularly for the purposes of the present clause, at some point in the contract documents, preferably in the Bills or Specification, and indeed the opening words of the present clause " (except if and so far as the Contract otherwise provides) " should be borne in mind in considering whether to simplify or alter the very complicated requirements of the present clause as a whole.

(*1*) " *against all losses and claims for injuries or damage to any person or property* "

The not very elegant sub-division is into " losses . . . to any person or property " and " claims for injuries or damage to any person or property." The first will therefore enable the Employer himself to recover his own losses (apart from the exception as to the Works already commented on *supra*, p. 78), whereas the latter is the third party element in the indemnity. The wording will mean that for purposes of limitation the cause of action on the indemnity will not arise until the Employer suffers damage on receiving, and quite possibly not till meeting, a claim—see the recent decision of Swanwick J. reviewing the authorities on this subject in *County and District Properties* v. *Jenner* [1976] 2 Lloyd's Rep. 728.

(*1*) " *Provided always that:—* (*b*) *nothing herein contained shall be deemed to render the Contractor liable . . .*"

Proviso (b) (which by virtue of sub-clause (2) sets out the opposite cases where the Employer indemnifies the Contractor) has been clarified in the Fifth Edition. Proviso (b) (iv) is a new general exception, consistent with the general policy of the proviso to clause 8 (2), *supra*, p. 37, and the " design " Excepted Risk in clause 20 (3), and requires to be read together with Proviso (b) (ii), to which it does not in fact add a great deal. The first (new) half of (b) (ii) relates to use or occupation of land *provided by the Employer* either for the Works themselves or as a working space or for access (*i.e.* " the Site " as defined in clause 1 (1) (n), *supra*, p. 17), while the second (Fourth Edition) half deals with interference with a number of rights less than full ownership; but the wording makes it clear that *both* halves of (b) (ii), like (b) (iv), must also be the *unavoidable* result of constructing the works in accordance with the Contract. Proviso (b) (iv), therefore, may possibly add to the first half of (b) (ii) by applying to damage to property other than the Employer's, and to the second half by applying to infringements of rights of ownership or possession as opposed to the lesser rights there mentioned. To this extent proviso (b) (iv) also probably overlaps with the traditional (b) (iii), though the latter no doubt is aimed at claims where title is in issue and which might not necessarily be concerned with physical damage as in (b) (iv). There is obviously, however, a considerable element of overlapping in these various provisions, which are a mixture of the early wording and later piecemeal additions and alterations.

In Proviso (b) (ii), " other easement " would include the (in practice) rather important rights of support to buildings and to have fences maintained. " Quasi-easement " is not a very precise legal term, but would seem to include restrictive covenants, local customary rights held by special classes of persons *e.g.* commoners, and certain rights in the nature of true recognised easements but existing as between different parts of land held in one ownership. The word " unavoidable " in both (ii) and (iv) is, it should be noted, unqualified by any provision of reasonableness. The burden of proof on the Contractor will, therefore, be a heavy one, it is submitted. Proviso (b) (i) in regard to crops has already been commented on *supra*, pp. 78–79.

Proviso (b) (v) is traditional, but an earlier doubt has been resolved in that there is now an explicit reference to the Engineer as well as the Employer. The new addition of the words " statutory duty " is, however, puzzling, as at first sight the Contractor, via the safety regulations, would be more likely to be in breach of such a duty, and in any event one would expect to find the words in Proviso (a) and also in the Contractor's indemnity in the sub-clause (2) proviso.

The broad intention of Proviso (a), Proviso (b) (v) and sub-clause (2) (as presumably seeking to avoid the invalidating effect on contractual indemnities of the *A.M.F.* case by providing for contribution between the Employer and Contractor in appropriate cases) has already been commented on *supra*, p. 77. There does, however, appear to be an almost certainly unintended and quite serious drafting anomaly, probably due to the desire to retain as much as possible of the old wording. There are also possible policy anomalies which may not have been appreciated.

The drafting difficulty arises because while the (new) Proviso (a) provides for a proportionate *reduction* in the Contractor's indemnity for " act or neglect of the Employer his servants or agents " which may have *contributed* to the loss injury or damage, the " traditional " Proviso (b) (v) provides for *no* Contractor's indemnity where injuries or damage *result from* " any act or neglect or breach of statutory duty by the Engineer or Employer his agents servants or other contractors." At first sight these two provisions can be fairly easily reconciled on the basis that (b) (v) refers to a case where the Employer's or Engineer's act or neglect is the *sole* cause of the injuries or damage (contrast " contributed to " with " resulting from "). Sub-clause (2), however, makes plain beyond doubt that the wording of (b) (v) *does* cover cases where the Contractor and Employer may have jointly contributed to the damage. There is thus a logical inconsistency between Proviso (a) (reduction of Contractor's indemnity where Employer contributes) and Proviso (b) (v) (*no* Contractor's indemnity in a case where Employer may be a contributing party and not wholly responsible). It must be presumed that the courts will disregard this anomaly, and will have principal regard to Proviso (a) on the one hand and to the Proviso to sub-clause (2) on the other. Thus if, in a case where, for example, the parties are held to be equally responsible for an unsafe system of working (say a mixture of imprudent temporary works designed by the Engineer but carelessly carried out by the Contractor) the plaintiff chooses to sue the Employer only, the latter will be able to claim a contribution under sub-clause (1) and Proviso (a), and the difficulty created by Proviso (b) (v) will be ignored.

The policy difficulty arises because it will be seen that no criteria are supplied by the clause for assessing the relative responsibility between Employer and Contractor, and if it is intended that the matter is to be approached in the same way as judges in practice fix contributions between defendants under the Law Reform (Joint Tortfeasors) legislation (*i.e.* with the relationship of each defendant to the plaintiff in mind rather than the relationship *inter se* between the defendants) undesirable results, particularly from an Employer's point of view, might well emerge which would be quite inconsistent with many provisions of the contract. Thus while the contract makes it clear at many points (see *e.g.* clauses 39 (3), 14 (7), 17, 38 (2), 39 (1) (c), 54 (3) (a) and 60 (7)), that the Engineer's duty to supervise is owed to the Employer and not to the Contractor, so that although work may have been tested or checked or approved or certified or paid for, the Contractor will nevertheless remain fully responsible for it, and that (see clauses 8 (2), 14 (7), 15 (1), 16, and 19) the conduct and safety of operations on the site is the Contractor's responsibility (see also the general law on this in Hudson, 10th ed., pp. 68–71, 139–141, 153–155, 324–325, 387, 529–530), the presence of the Engineer in a supervisory capacity in a case where he ought reasonably to have detected poor workmanship, or failed to take adequate precautions or, for example, gave approval to working methods etc. under clause 14 (3) to 14 (7), may in practice produce a very substantial allocation of responsibility to the Employer—see Hudson, 10th ed., pp. 78–80, and in particular the findings in the case of *A.M.F. International* v. *Magnet Bowling* [1968] 1 W.L.R. 1028 there illustrated. While the intention of the present clause to keep the contractual indemnities alive in the face of the difficulty created by the A.M.F. case is praiseworthy, to do so by means of a proportionate reduction in the indemnity according to some unspecified method of allocating responsibility is likely in practice to produce anomalies. The more sensible approach would have been to provide that where one party is the *effective* cause of damage or injury which will give rise to an indemnity in favour of the other, the indemnity shall not be defeated by reason of any liability to the plaintiff of the party entitled to rely on the indemnity. Alternatively, if the principle of a reduced indemnity is to be adopted, it might have been wiser to provide that the reduction should only be made in the light of the absence of any duty owed by the Engineer to the Contractor under the general law, and of the provisions of the contract in regard to the responsibility of the Contractor for Site operations safety, methods of working and defective work.

Discussion of this aspect of the clause can perhaps conclude with some regret that provisions of such extraordinary complexity and difficulty should be found in a standard form. The presence of conflicting insurance interests and the ready availability on most engineering projects of at least some facts which might arguably satisfy the vague criteria of " act or neglect " of the other party, must mean that few major third-party claims will be resolved without dispute over the exact incidence of the indemnities in the present clause.

In addition, the piecemeal drafting approach adopted by the Fifth Edition reveals itself first by the lack of any properly regulated relationship between the indemnities in the present clause and the very many other express indemnities in the contract, and secondly in many slight differences of wording in different provisions which in a document drafted *ab initio* might lead the interpreter to assume that some difference of meaning was intended,—compare, for example, " act or neglect of the Employer his servants or agents " in clause 22 (1) (a) " act or neglect or breach of statutory duty . . . by the Engineer or the Employer his agents servants or other contractors . . ." in clause 22 (1) (b) (v) and " act or default of the Employer his agents or servants " in clause 24.

Insurance against Damage to Persons and Property

23. (1) Throughout the execution of the Works the Contractor (but without limiting his obligations and responsibilities under Clause 22) shall insure against any damage loss or injury which may occur to any property or to any person by or arising out of the execution of the Works or in the carrying out of the Contract otherwise than due to the matters referred to in proviso (b) to Clause 22 (1).

Amount and Terms of Insurance

(2) Such insurance shall be effected with an insurer and in terms approved by the Employer (which approval shall not be unreasonably withheld) and for at least the amount stated in the Appendix to the Form of Tender. The terms shall include a provision whereby in the event of any claim in respect of which the Contractor

would be entitled to receive indemnity under the policy being brought or made against the Employer the insurer will indemnify the Employer against such claims and any costs charges and expenses in respect thereof. The Contractor shall whenever required produce to the Employer the policy or policies of insurance and the receipts for payment of the current premiums.

No doubt the intended effect of the rather odd negative way of describing the required insurance, inherited from the Fourth Edition, involved in the words " otherwise than due to the matters referred to in proviso (b) to clause 22 (1) " was that the insurance should be exactly co-terminous with the Contractor's indemnities given under clause 22. However, in the light of the new reduction in the Contractor's indemnity created by Proviso (1) (a) of clause 22, the present negative wording may have a different effect, since, in the absence of reference to Proviso (a) as well as to Proviso (b), the insurance called for here would appear to be *unreduced* in cases of act or neglect of the Employer " contributing to " the damage, though of course the insurer would not be on risk at all if the claim " resulted from " act or neglect of the Employer etc. under (1) (b) (v)—see the commentary on this difficult wording *supra*, pp. 80–81.

Sub-clause (2) contains a new provision in lieu of the old provision for joint insurance in the Fourth Edition (which was in fact strictly unnecessary in the light of the Third Party (Rights against Insurers) legislation) providing for a direct indemnity to the Employer by the insurers (again strictly unnecessary for the same reasons) should the Employer receive a third party claim " in respect of which the Contractor would be entitled to receive indemnity under the policy." Assuming that the Contractor's insurance conformed exactly with the sub-clause (1) requirement, this might, for the reasons already stated, give the Employer the benefit of an unreduced indemnity, though no doubt in practice many contractors' insurance will be described in positive terms of the Contractor's liability under clause 22 and not necessarily in the particular negative wording used in sub-clause (1) of the present clause.

Apart from this difficulty, the provision in sub-clause (2) may also be defective in that it contemplates only claims against the Employer—as pointed out above, claims *by* the Employer, notwithstanding the removal of damage to the Works from the ambit of clause 22, are still perfectly possible under clause 22 in the case of damage to other property owned by him on or in the vicinity of the Site.

A further difficulty would seem to arise from the words " throughout the execution of the Works " in sub-clause (1). Do these words only require the Contractor to be covered during this period, and would a policy be satisfactory if the Contractor's insurance cover ceased if no claim arose during the construction period? (Many insurance policies in the past have been of this character, which is quite unsuited to the time intervals between construction and damage which often occur in building and civil engineering contracts). The wording leaves this in doubt and the

Employer's advisers, if longer-term cover is required, as it invariably will be, should make this plain in the contract documents—as by requiring insurance in respect of any liability or claim arising out of the construction and maintenance of the works during the full period of limitation.

The Employer's sanction for non-insurance, as in the case of insurance of the Works under clause 20, is provided for in clause 25, *infra*.

Accident or Injury to Workmen

24. The Employer shall not be liable for or in respect of any damages or compensation payable at law in respect or in consequence of any accident or injury to any workman or other person in the employment of the Contractor or any sub-contractor save and except to the extent that such accident or injury results from or is contributed to by any act or default of the Employer his agents or servants and the Contractor shall indemnify and keep indemnified the Employer against all such damages and compensation (save and except as aforesaid) and against all claims demands proceedings costs charges and expenses whatsoever in respect thereof or in relation thereto.

It would seem that this slightly modified clause, as in the case of the Fourth Edition, does little more than restate, in somewhat narrower and more precise form, a particular category of claim for personal injuries already included in the Contractor's more widely expressed obligation covered by the words " claims for injuries . . . to any person whatsoever . . . which may arise out of or in consequence of the construction and maintenance of the Works " in clause 22 (1) and the exception in Proviso (b) (v) to that clause. The implication of the first part of the clause is that the Employer *will* be liable (to the Contractor, incidentally) for " act or default " (though the language of indemnity is not used in this instance, as it is in clause 22 (2) and there is no express reference to the Engineer or other Contractors as in the clause 22 (1) (b) (v) counter-indemnity given by the Employer). The expression " act or default " may be somewhat narrower, too, than " act or neglect " and connote some positive act rather than an act or error of omission. The new policy in clause 22 of reducing the indemnities in cases of contribution to the damage by the party relying on the indemnity (some of the difficulties of which have been explained under clause 22, *supra*) is reflected in the new words " or is contributed to by . . . the Employer " in the first part of the present clause and the " (save and except as aforesaid) " limitation on the contractual indemnity to the Employer in the latter part. The separate insurance cover for this particular class of personal injury claim, rather oddly called for under this clause in the Fourth Edition in addition to that in clause 23 (1), has now been dispensed with.

On the basis of the legal principle that special provisions will normally prevail over more general ones, the present clause may arguably be intended to supplant clause 22 altogether in the case of personal injury claims where the claimant is a workman of the Contractor or his Sub-contractors. If so, the language of simple contractual liability and the absence of any language of indemnity by the Employer in favour of the Contractor in the present clause may mean that time will start to run against the Contractor for purposes of limitation on the date of the Employer's act or default, and not when the workman's claim is presented to or met by the Contractor—see the case of *County and City Property Ltd.* v. *Jenner Ltd.*, referred to under clause 22, *supra*, p.76—whereas in the reverse situation, where the Employer is pursuing the Contractor upon the indemnity in the present clause, time will not run against the Employer until the loss in meeting the claim is incurred.

Remedy on Contractor's Failure to Insure

25. If the Contractor shall fail upon request to produce to the Employer satisfactory evidence that there is in force the insurance referred to in Clauses 21 and 23 or any other insurance which he may be required to effect under the terms of the Contract then and in any such case the Employer may effect and keep in force any such insurance and pay such premium or premiums as may be necessary for that purpose and from time to time deduct the amount so paid by the Employer as aforesaid from any monies due or which may become due to the Contractor or recover the same as a debt due from the Contractor.

For the general policy of the contract in only requiring insurance by the Contractor of his own contractual responsibilities to the Employer, see the discussion under clause 21, *supra*, p. 71. A remedy of the present kind is essential in the case of all obligations to insure, since until a risk has eventuated which there are neither contractor's nor insurance funds available to meet, the Employer is not in a position to show that any damage has resulted from the Contractor's failure to insure; and by then, of course, it is too late for him to have any effective remedy for the breach, since he will merely have an additional claim for breach of contract against an insolvent Contractor.

" *any other insurance which he may be required to effect under the terms of the Contract* "

i.e. in the Bills or Specification, which often call for special insurance of one kind or another, or modify that called for by the Conditions. As pointed out in the commentary to clause 20, *supra*, in the area of insurance of the Works and materials and Constructional Plant there are, from the Employer's commercial point of view, important elements of both over- and under-insurance in the insurance called for by the Conditions. See also the warning in regard to the inadequacy of the cover possibly called for or furnished by insurers under clause 23, *supra*.

Giving of Notices and Payment of Fees

26. (1) The Contractor shall save as provided in Clause 27 give all notices and pay all fees required to be given or paid by any Act of Parliament or any Regulation or Bye-law of any local or other statutory authority in relation to the execution of the Works and by the rules and regulations of all public bodies and companies whose property or rights are or may be affected in any way by the Works. The Employer shall repay or allow to the Contractor all such sums as the Engineer shall certify to have been properly payable and paid by the Contractor in respect of such fees and also all rates and taxes paid by the Contractor in respect of the Site or any part thereof or anything constructed or erected thereon or on any part thereof or any temporary structures situate elsewhere but used exclusively for the purposes of the Works or any structures used temporarily and exclusively for the purposes of the Works.

Contractor to Conform with Statutes etc.

(2) The Contractor shall ascertain and conform in all respects with the provisions of any general or local Act of Parliament and the Regulations and Bye-laws of any local or other statutory authority which may be applicable to the Works, and with such rules and regulations of public bodies and companies as aforesaid and shall keep the Employer indemnified against all penalties and liability of every kind for breach of any such Act Regulation or Bye-law. Provided always that:—

(a) the Contractor shall not be required to indemnify the Employer against the consequences of any such breach which is the unavoidable result of complying with the Drawings Specification or instructions of the Engineer;

(b) if the Drawings Specification or instructions of the Engineer shall at any time be found not to be in conformity with any such Act Regulation or Bye-law the Engineer shall issue such instructions including the ordering of a variation under Clause 51 as may be necessary to ensure conformity with such Act Regulation or Bye-law;

(c) the Contractor shall not be responsible for obtaining any planning permission which may be necessary in respect of the Permanent Works or any Temporary Works specified or designed by the Engineer and the Employer hereby warrants that all the said permissions have been or will in due time be obtained.

Sub-clause (1) and sub-clause (2) (until the very important new Provisos (a) and (b)) reproduce with one very minor addition the Fourth Edition version of this clause. As was pointed out in the commentary to the Fourth Edition (B.C.F., pp. 344–345) that clause departed from most standard form provisions of this kind in only permitting reimbursement in the case of the " fees " and the " rates and taxes . . . in respect of the Site etc." mentioned in the present sub-clause (1), and no compensation for the much more important compliance or non-compliance with the regulations, by-laws etc. required by sub-clause (2) was provided for, which would be very unfair to the Contractor if the non-compliance stemmed from the Engineer's area of responsibility under the contract rather than the Contractor's. This has now been rectified by the sensible and self-explanatory savings made in Provisos (a) and (b) of sub-clause (2). (Proviso (c) repeats an equally sensible exception which was also in the Fourth Edition.) The words " at any time " in Proviso (b) are important, since (unlike the RIBA forms) they will cover a situation where the Contractor has already carried out work in breach of a regulation, though no doubt if he did so after notice or warning without affording the Engineer an opportunity to issue a variation instruction, a valuation of the variation under clause 52 might not take any abortive expenditure into account.

(1) " save as provided in Clause 27 "

By clause 27 (3) the Employer and not the Contractor is liable to serve all notices required by the Public Utilities Street Works legislation. See also sub-clause (2) Proviso (c), which expressly excepts notices in regard to planning permission from its operation.

(*1*) "*fees . . . in relation to the execution of the Works*"

This expression will not include, it is submitted, special payments levied *on the industry—e.g.* under the Industrial Training legislation.

(*1*) "*rules and regulations of all public . . . companies whose property or rights are or may be affected . . .*"

The word "company" seems too wide in this context. The use of the words "rules and regulations" suggests that what is intended is not trading companies but the public bodies of one kind or another known to lawyers as "statutory undertakers" or public corporations—that is to say, charged or permitted by Parliament to carry out some public function, such as drainage or electricity authorities, or water companies or non-commercial nationalised undertakings.

(*1*) "*taxes . . . in respect of the Site*"

Again, these words suggest taxes directly linked to land or property, and not to the industry or to engineering projects as such.

(*1*) "*or any temporary structures situate elsewhere but used exclusively . . . or any structures used temporarily and exclusively*"

The latter (temporary use of a presumably permanent structure) is new. The words (not new) "situate elsewhere" (*i.e.* off "the Site" as defined in clause 1 (1) (n), *supra*, pp. 17 and 22–23) seem to depart from the policy of the contract, and indeed of nearly all civil engineering contracts, which distinguish between "the Site" (*i.e.* land and access provided by the Employer) and optional land or access off the Site for which the Contractor is required to make his own arrangements and assume full responsibility—see *e.g.* clause 42 (2), *infra*, p. 117, and clause 22 (1) (b) (ii), *supra*, p. 75.

Public Utilities Street Works Act 1950—Definitions

27. (1) For the purposes of this Clause:—

(a) the expression "the Act" shall mean and include the Public Utilities Street Works Act 1950 and any statutory modification or re-enactment thereof for the time being in force:

(b) all other expressions common to the Act and to this Clause shall have the same meaning as that assigned to them by the Act.

This clause is for practical purposes identical with its predecessor in the Fourth Edition.

The Act of 1950 creates a necessarily complicated system for the co-ordination of work in "streets," which are very widely defined by section 1 (3) of that Act, (for the definition, see the commentary to sub-clause (4), *infra*) so that the street authority or managers and the various statutory undertakers responsible for constructing or maintaining services in or under the street are given notice of and protection in regard to any works which may affect their own interest in or responsibility for the street or their own particular service.

Part I of the Act (sections 1 to 20) requires all statutory undertakers to submit plans of their proposed work to the street or other authority concerned for approval or settlement (ss. 3 and 4), to give notice before commencing work (s. 6), to carry out the work according to the approved plans and to reinstate promptly and efficiently, subject to the street authority electing to reinstate themselves (s. 7), and to fence guard and light during construction (s. 8). The Act applies not only to highways maintained by a highway authority, but to " prospectively maintainable highways " as defined by section 1 (4) (*b*) of the Act, and to privately maintained highways, and to streets which are not highways at all. The Act also applies to " controlled land " as defined by the First Schedule to the Act, that is to say land abutting on a street which belongs to the street authority, or which has been authorised for compulsory requisition by them, or which lies between the street boundary and an improvement line under the Public Health Acts, and in which the undertaker may by virtue of section 5 of and the Third Schedule to the Act be required to carry out his work rather than in the street itself. As one would expect, the restrictions as to notice and deposit of plans are mitigated in the case of " Emergency Works," which are defined in section 39 (1) of the Act.

Part II of the Act (ss. 21 to 25) gives financial protection to undertakers where road or bridge works by the road or bridge authority affect their services in streets or controlled land. Finally, Part III of the Act (s. 26) imposes restrictions, by way of notice and compliance with reasonable requirements for protection, on undertakers whose operations in streets or controlled land may affect the " apparatus " of other undertakers (known for this purpose as the " operating undertakers " and " owning undertakers," respectively), with similar mitigation in the case of " Emergency Works."

The code laid down by the Act as a whole is complicated, but the above very short summary should suffice to enable the policy of the remainder of this clause to be understood. While sub-clause (3) of the present clause requires *the Employer* to give all necessary notices under the Act, the clause as a whole is silent about the very important matter of the submission and settlement of plans. There should, it is submitted, be an implied term that the Employer will obtain the necessary settlement or approval of plans in time to permit the Contractor, after expiry of his notice to the Employer under sub-clause (4), to proceed with the work in accordance with his programme. Certainly this would be consistent with the policy of the contract—see *e.g.* clause 26 (2) (c), *supra*, p. 86, and perhaps also with the express requirements of clauses 7 (1) and 51 (1)—but see however, the commentary to sub-clause (7), *infra*.

Notifications by Employer to Contractor

(2) The Employer shall before the commencement of the Works notify the Contractor in writing:—

(a) whether the Works or any parts thereof (and if so which parts) are Emergency Works; and

(b) which (if any) parts of the Works are to be carried out in Controlled Land or in a Prospectively Maintainable Highway.

If any duly authorised variation of the Works shall involve the execution thereof in a Street or in Controlled Land or in a Prospectively Maintainable Highway or are Emergency Works the Employer shall notify the Contractor in writing accordingly at the time such variation is ordered.

At first sight, the purpose and policy of this sub-clause is obscure. It should be observed that the notification is to be *after* the contract, though before commencement of work, despite the fact that by sub-clause (7), *infra*, the Contractor has to comply with all the requirements of the Act as to the carrying out of work at his own expense. Presumably, it is thought that the fact that the work is in a maintainable highway will generally be self-evident from the drawings or description or appearance; but that it may not be clear to the Contractor that some of the work is emergency work (and hence that the restrictions of the Act as to deposit of plans and notice will be somewhat mitigated); furthermore, controlled land or a prospectively maintainable highway might not, from the drawings or other contract description or their physical appearance, be obviously subject to the Act. Certainly in the case of the latter, one might have expected that the position would be set out in the contract documents, such as the Bills or Specification, rather than communicated to the Contractor after the contract is signed. The primary reason for the requirements of the present sub-clause is that the Contractor's obligation under sub-clause (4), *infra*, to give notice to the Employer before starting the work in question (which the Employer will need so that he can, pursuant to sub-clause (3), himself serve the necessary notices in time on the various interested parties under sections 6 and 26 of the Act) is itself conditional upon the Employer having previously notified the Contractor under the present sub-clause as to which is the relevant work in respect of which he will require a sub-clause (4) notice from the Contractor—see *infra*, p. 90.

" *Prospectively Maintainable Highway* "

i.e. a street declared likely to become a maintainable highway by the appropriate local authority and registered as a local land charge (see section 1 (4) (*b*) of the Act).

" *Controlled Land* "

See the definition *supra*, p. 88 and paragraph 1 (1) of the First Schedule to the Act.

" *Emergency Works* "

i.e. (*inter alia*) works required to put an end to or prevent danger to persons or property, interruption of undertakers' supplies or services, or serious loss to undertakers or a transport authority (section 39 (1) of the Act).

Service of Notices by Employer

(3) The Employer shall (subject to the obligations of the Contract under sub-clause (4) of this Clause) serve all such notices as may from time to time whether before or during the course of or after completion of the Works be required to be served under the Act.

Notices by Contractor to Employer

(4) The Contractor shall in relation to any part of the Works (other than Emergency Works) and subject to the compliance by the Employer with sub-clause (2) of this Clause give not less than 21 days' notice in writing to the Employer before:—

(a) commencing any part of the Works in a Street (as defined by Sections 1 (3) and 38 (1) of the Act); or

(b) commencing any part of the Works in Controlled Land or in a Prospectively Maintainable Highway: or

(c) commencing in a Street or in Controlled Land or in a Prospectively Maintainable Highway any part of the Works which is likely to affect the apparatus of any Owning Undertaker (within the meaning of Section 26 of the Act).

Such notice shall state the date on which and the place at which the Contractor intends to commence the execution of the work referred to therein.

Sub-clause (3), in contradistinction to the Contractor's general obligation under clause 26, *supra*, p. 85, to serve all notices required by statute etc., places the responsibility for notices under this Act on the Employer. The " subject to sub-clause (4) " reference presumably is intended to mean that the Employer will not be in breach of contract or financially responsible for delays due to failure to serve in time a notice required by the Act if the Contractor has not previously served the appropriate notice on him under sub-clause (4). The 21 days' notice required by sub-clause (4) compares with the seven or three days' notice to the other interested persons required from the Employer under the Act.

(*3*) " *subject to the obligations of the Contract under sub-clause* (*4*) "

The word " Contract " is an obvious misprint for " Contractor " —see the Fourth Edition where " Contractor " was correctly used.

(*4*) ". . . *subject to compliance by the Employer with . . . sub-clause* (*2*) *of this Clause* "

The Fourth Edition referred in error to sub-clause (3) (see B.C.F., pp. 347 and 348) but this has now been corrected.

(*4*) " *Street* (*as defined by Section 1* (*3*)) "

i.e. " any length of highway (other than a waterway), road, land, footway, alley or passage, any square or court, and any length of land laid out as a way whether it is for the time being formed as a way or not; irrespective of whether the highway and road or other thing in question is a thoroughfare or not."

(*4*) "*apparatus of any Owning Undertaker*"

i.e. of any other undertaker affected by the works (see the commentary, *supra*, p. 88). "Apparatus" includes a structure constructed to lodge the apparatus (s. 39 (1)).

Failure to Commence Street Works

(5) If the Contractor having given any such notice as is required by sub-clause (4) of this Clause shall not commence the part of the Works to which such notice relates within 2 months after the date when such notice is given such notice shall be treated as invalid and compliance with the said sub-clause (4) shall be requisite as if such notice had not been given.

Delays Attributable to Variations

(6) In the event of such a variation of the Works as is referred to in sub-clause (2) of this Clause being ordered by or on behalf of the Employer and resulting in delay in the execution of the Works by reason of the necessity of compliance by the Contractor with sub-clause (4) of this Clause the Engineer shall take such delay into account in determining any extension of time to which the Contractor is entitled under Clause 44 and the Contractor shall subject to Clause 52 be paid in accordance with Clause 60 such additional cost as the Engineer shall consider to have been reasonably attributable to such delay.

Sub-clause (5) means that a further notice under sub-clause (4) needs to be served by the Contractor if work has not started in time.

Sub-clause (6) is strictly unnecessary, because the Contractor would, on receipt of any variation order, in any event be entitled to an extension of time under clause 44, and to additional payment under clause 52. The order would presumably only "result in delay" if it came so late in the day that the Contractor would otherwise have been in a position to carry out the work within 21 days of receiving the order.

Contractor to Comply with Other Obligations of Act

(7) Except as otherwise provided by this Clause where in relation to the carrying out of the Works the Act imposes any requirements or obligations upon the Employer the Contractor shall subject to Clause 49 (5) comply with such requirements and obligations and shall (subject as aforesaid) indemnify the Employer against any liability which the Employer may incur in consequence of any failure to comply with the said requirements and obligations.

This sub-clause seems to create an anomaly. As stated *supra*, p. 88, the clause as a whole is silent as to the very important (and lengthy) matter of submission and settlement of plans. The rest of the clause "otherwise provides" within the opening words of this sub-clause only in respect of the quite short *notices* required to be served under the Act (sub-clause (3), *supra*). On the wording of the present sub-clause, the Contractor appears to be liable to submit and settle the plans, which seems unlikely to be the intention (if it were, for instance, sub-clause (6) would surely on any reasonable view expressly provide for this). It has been suggested *supra* that there should be an implied term to the effect that this is the Employer's responsibility, but the present sub-clause certainly represents a difficulty in the way of such a term. It is odd that the opportunity has not been taken to clarify this in the Fifth Edition, since the difficulty was pointed out in B.C.F. (pp. 347 and 349) and the other error pointed out in B.C.F. (the incorrect reference in sub-clause (4)) has been corrected. It may have been thought that the new wording of clauses 7 (1) and 51 (1) in regard to the Engineer's duty to supply information covered the matter, but the present wording in a very special situation may well override those general provisions, and the absence of clarification is unfortunate.

" *subject to the provisions of Clause 49 (5) hereof* "

The reference appears to be to the indemnity given by the Employer in the last sentence of clause 49 (5) (a), which brings the Contractor's obligations to an end, *i.e.* where permanent reinstatement is, under the terms of the contract, to be carried out by a highway authority or other third person, and either the period of maintenance has expired or the authority or other person has taken over to carry out the permanent reinstatement.

Patent Rights

28. (1) The Contractor shall save harmless and indemnify the Employer from and against all claims and proceedings for or on account of infringement of any patent rights design trade-mark or name or other protected rights in respect of any Constructional Plant machine work or material used for or in connection with the Works and from and against all claims demands proceedings damages costs charges and expenses whatsoever in respect thereof or in relation thereto.

Royalties

(2) Except where otherwise specified the Contractor shall pay all tonnage and other royalties rent and other payments or compensation (if any) for getting stone sand gravel clay or other materials required for the Works.

The two sub-clauses of this clause deal with quite unrelated subject-matters, and probably owe their inclusion in the same clause (which was not even divided into sub-clauses in the Fourth Edition) to confusion between the word " royalty " in its special context of winning materials from quarries etc. (as in sub-clause (2)) and its perhaps better known usage for payments made in connection with patents and copyrights.

The Contractor's liability under sub-clause (1) appears to be quite unqualified. While it does not expressly purport to deal with the expense of any licensing or other agreement—only with " claims and proceedings for . . . infringement of any patent . . . or other protected rights "—it in effect means that, to avoid such proceedings, the Contractor will have to make, if he can, licensing arrangements for any necessary process. No doubt, however, this would be taken into account in valuing the Contractor's work under clause 52, but only if the necessity arose from a variation ordered by the Engineer. In the case of a Nominated Sub-contractor's work, the Contractor would no doubt have an implied right of indemnity against the Sub-contractor, if exposed to a claim of this kind by some third person. Only in the case of original contract work of the Contractor himself is his liability likely to be really unqualified, therefore.

The second sentence makes it clear that if a source of materials is indicated in the contract documents (as is quite frequently the case) the Contractor must make his own special arrangements for obtaining them unless there is an express term to the contrary.

(*1*) " *the Works* "

These include Temporary Works—see the definition in clause 1 (1) (l), *supra*, pp. 16 and 21.

(*1*) " *Constructional Plant* "

See the definition in clause 1 (1) (o) and the commentary thereto, *supra*, pp. 17 and 23–24.

Interference with Traffic and Adjoining Properties

29. (1) All operations necessary for the execution of the Works shall so far as compliance with the requirements of the Contract permits be carried on so as not to interfere unnecessarily or improperly with the public convenience or the access to or use or occupation of public or private roads and foot-paths or to or of properties whether in the possession of the Employer or of any other person and the Contractor shall save harmless and indemnify the Employer in respect of all claims demands proceedings damages costs charges and expenses whatsoever arising out of or in relation to any such matters.

Noise and Disturbance

(2) All work shall be carried out without unreasonable noise and disturbance. The Contractor shall indemnify the Employer from and against any liability for damages on account of noise or other disturbance created while or in carrying out the work and from and against all claims demands proceedings damages costs charges and expenses whatsoever in regard or in relation to such liability.

Sub-clause (1) corresponds exactly to clause 29 of the Fourth Edition with a minor error (noted in B.C.F. at p. 352) corrected. Sub-clause (2) has been lifted bodily out of the old clause 46 (where in fact it was not very appropriately included).

The words in sub-clause (1) " so far as compliance with the requirements of the Contract permits " and the words " unnecessarily or improperly " mean that this obligation is qualified, to the extent that it only requires the Contractor to ensure that damage is not caused *unnecessarily* to the interests referred to. Furthermore, it seems to overlap substantially in a number of respects with the Contractor's general indemnity in clause 22 (1), *supra*, and needs to be read with Proviso (b) (ii) and (iv) of sub-clause (1), and the Employer's counter-indemnity given under sub-clause (2), of that clause, on which the Contractor will need to rely in appropriate cases, since the present sub-clause is silent as to any Employer's counter-indemnity in favour of the Contractor.

While the initial requirement as to noise and disturbance in sub-clause (2) has a qualification of reasonableness, this is only in the context of defining the exact extent of the Contractor's contractual obligation to the Employer (and might, therefore, for example, justify intervention by the Engineer without exposing the Employer to financial liability). The Contractor's indemnity to the Employer appears on the other hand to be unqualified, and it seems clear that since clause 22 (1) is concerned with damage to *persons or property*, neither Proviso (b) (ii) nor (iv) of clause 22 (1) can apply, in a noise or disturbance case, so as to give the Contractor the benefit of the Employer's counter-indemnity under clause 22 (2)—in other words the Contractor will be *absolutely* liable for noise and disturbance claims brought successfully against the Employer, even if they were unavoidable. While this seems reasonably clear, it can only be speculated whether in fact it represents the policy intention, but it illustrates the consequences of the complication of clause 22 itself, together with the lack of any clear contractual scheme relating it to the many other piecemeal indemnities to be found throughout the contract.

Avoidance of Damage to Highways, etc.

30. (1) The Contractor shall use every reasonable means to prevent any of the highways or bridges communicating with or on the routes to the Site from being subjected to extraordinary traffic within the meaning of the Highways Act 1959 or in Scotland the Road Traffic Act 1930 or any statutory modification or re-enactment thereof by any traffic of the Contractor or any of his sub-contractors and in particular shall select routes and use vehicles and restrict and distribute loads so that any such extraordinary traffic as will inevitably arise from the moving of Constructional Plant and materials or manufactured or fabricated articles from and to the Site shall be limited as far as reasonably possible and so that no unnecessary damage or injury may be occasioned to such highways and bridges.

This clause as a whole appears to be drafted with the provisions of section 54 of the Road Traffic Act 1930, now section 62 of the Highways Act 1959, in mind. That section enables highway authorities to recover the cost of special repairs from persons " by or in consequence of whose order " a highway has been subjected to " excessive weight or other extraordinary traffic," or alternatively to agree a sum for compensation beforehand—see for a full discussion *Pratt & McKenzie on Highways*, 21st ed., pp. 575–595. Actions of this kind by highway authorities arising out of a " building contract or work " have to be commenced within 12 months of the damage or within six months of completion of the contract in question—section 62 (2). " Extraordinary traffic " is not in fact defined in the Acts, but the meaning has been built up by case law, under the Highways and Locomotives Acts which they replaced, as indicating an increase in the frequency of traffic or a change in its character. The old case law suggested that a single journey of excessive weight could not constitute extraordinary traffic, but the use of the word " other " in the sections quoted above now suggests the contrary. There seems little doubt that a common law remedy in nuisance (or where applicable, trespass) is also available to highway or bridge authorities, which might well be used in practice to avoid any restrictions on the statutory remedy.

The present clause makes an important new departure in distinguishing between " Constructional Plant equipment or Temporary Works " (sub-clause (2)) and " materials or manufactured or fabricated articles " (sub-clause (3)) when providing (very differently) for the financial consequences, as between the parties, should damage to highways etc. occur. In the light of the wide definition of " Constructional Plant " in clause 1 (1) (o), *supra*, p. 17, the new category of " materials or manufactured or fabricated articles " referred to must, it is submitted, be intended for incorporation into the permanent works (compare the traditional use of the expression " materials manufactured articles and machinery " in clause 37) and the draftsmanship seems (particularly since clause 1 (3) forbids reference to the marginal headings of the clause) somewhat lacking in not making this quite plain.

Sub-clause (1) imposes a general duty of care on the Contractor to take all reasonable steps to avoid extraordinary traffic on the highways or bridges " communicating with or on the routes to the Site." The duty appears to be defined relatively narrowly in " extraordinary traffic " terms, unless the later words " in particular shall select routes and use vehicles and restrict and distribute loads . . .so that no unnecessary damage or injury may be occasioned to such highways or bridges " impose a wider duty of care to avoid damage in general. This general duty applies both to Constructional Plant and " materials or manufactured or fabricated articles."

Transport of Constructional Plant

(2) Save insofar as the Contract otherwise provides the Contractor shall be responsible for and shall pay the cost of strengthening any bridges or altering or improving any highway communicating with the Site to facilitate the movement of Constructional Plant equipment or Temporary Works required in the execution of the Works and the Contractor shall indemnify and keep indemnified the Employer against all claims for damage to any highway or bridge communicating with the Site caused by such movement including such claims as may be made by any competent authority directly against the Employer pursuant to any Act of Parliament or other Statutory Instrument and shall negotiate and pay all claims arising solely out of such damage.

As already stated, this sub-clause, which is quite new and replaces the old and very puzzling " Special Loads " sub-clause (see B.C.F., pp. 353–354) deals with " Constructional Plant equipment or Temporary Works," and its exact effect and indeed intention is not easy to determine. Whereas sub-clause (1) refers to highways or bridges " communicating with or *on the routes to* the Site " the words " on the routes to " are absent in the present sub-clause. Precisely when can a highway or bridge be said to be " on the route to " but not " communicating with " the Site? The words " Save insofar as the Contract otherwise provides . . ." would not seem to be a reference to any other clause of the Conditions (*e.g.* clause 22,

Proviso (b) of which would not appear to contain any exceptions factually applicable to the subject-matter of the present sub-clause) and perhaps envisages the possibility that the parties may seek to modify the operation of the present sub-clause in the Bills or Specification to take account of the special needs of a particular project. Furthermore, as pointed out in B.C.F. at p. 353 when commenting on the old " Special Loads " sub-clause, there does not in fact appear to be, as seems to be suggested, any specific statutory right for persons to offer to carry out temporary strengthening works to bridges or highways to enable their vehicles to use them without damage, or for their authorities to call for them, though no doubt such authorities might have implied power to make the arrangements envisaged by this clause as part of their express power under the Act to agree compensation beforehand.

The policy of the sub-clause appears to be that the Contractor should assume unqualified financial responsibility for the transport of his own plant, contrary to the case of materials etc. in sub-clause (3), *infra*, the reason probably being that, knowing his own intentions in this regard, he is in a position, as the Employer is not, to estimate expense of the present kind at the tendering stage and to price accordingly. It will be noted that the sub-clause covers both the cost of any prior precautionary expenditure and any subsequent claims for damage.

" *arising solely out of such damage* "

i.e. the Contractor's power to negotiate is to arise only if no element of Employer responsibility *vis-à-vis* the Contractor is involved. In other cases, presumably, the Employer will negotiate, but it is not easy to see what situation is envisaged, except for damage arising partly from the transport of plant and partly of materials (as to the latter the Employer has negotiating powers under sub-clause (3), *infra*).

Transport of Materials

(3) If notwithstanding sub-clause (1) of the Clause any damage shall occur to any bridge or highway communicating with the Site arising from the transport of materials or manufactured or fabricated articles in the execution of the Works the Contractor shall notify the Engineer as soon as he becomes aware of such damage or as soon as he receives any claim from the authority entitled to make such claim. Where under any Act of Parliament or other Statutory Instrument the haulier of such materials or manufactured or fabricated articles is required to indemnify the highway authority against damage the Employer shall not be liable for any costs charges or expenses in respect thereof or in relation thereto. In other cases the Employer shall negotiate the settlement of and pay all sums due in respect of such claim and shall indemnify the Contractor in respect thereof and in respect of all claims demands proceedings damages costs charges and expenses in relation thereto. Provided always that if and so far as any such claim or part thereof shall in the opinion of the Engineer be due to any failure on the part of the Contractor to observe and perform his obligations under sub-clause (1) of this Clause then the amount certified by the Engineer to be due to such failure shall be paid by the Contractor to the Employer or deducted from any sum due or which may become due to the Contractor.

By contrast with the case of Plant under sub-clause (2), this sub-clause places the ultimate financial responsibility for *unavoidable* damage to bridges or highways due to the transport of " materials or manufactured or fabricated articles " on the Employer. As stated above, the latter part of the expression must be *sui generis* with " materials," *i.e.* intended for incorporation in the permanent works (the definition of " Constructional Plant " in clause 1 (1) (o), *supra*, would otherwise be wide enough to be included in " manufactured or fabricated articles ") and the words " in the execution of the Works," which seem to be inept in their particular context immediately after " from the transport of materials or manufactured or fabricated articles," suggest that there may have been some error or omission during the drafting or printing of some provision designed to make this clear—possibly the omission of the word " required."

The reference to a statutory liability on " the haulier " of such materials etc. is not entirely clear. As stated, the Act imposes liability on the person " by or in consequence of whose order " the excessive loads are imposed. In cases where an employer has used an independent contractor, there is a very considerable body of case law as to the person who will be liable —in a civil engineering contract it might be the Employer, the Contractor, a Sub-contractor, or a transport company, depending upon which party could be said to be " ordering " the excessive loads or traffic with sufficient knowledge of the likelihood of excessive traffic resulting or control over the kind of loads to be used—see Pratt & McKenzie, 21st ed., pp. 587–590. The reference may, therefore, be to the case law on the person liable under the 1959 Act in those cases where the transport company is liable by reason of its control over the loads and over what may be avoidable damage—or it may be to other quite different (*e.g.* licensing) legislation. The policy may be that in such cases the Contractor will be left to protect his own interests as against his transport contractors, and the Employer will be " out of the picture."

The machinery (particularly in the final Proviso) of the sub-clause for the resolution of the ultimate financial responsibility as between Employer and Contractor in the " other cases " (*i.e.* non-" haulier " cases) is not particularly elegant. Apparently the Employer is to negotiate and pay, and also if necessary indemnify, the Contractor against claims which should theoretically be limited, by virtue of the " notwithstanding sub-clause (1) " wording at the beginning of the sub-clause, to claims for *unavoidable* damage; but the Proviso in effect means that once the sum has been negotiated or ascertained (or, no doubt, in a case where this is not possible, decided in litigation) the Engineer is apparently required in an appropriate case to certify the amount of any Contractor's contribution to the damage on the footing that the damage is either wholly or in part avoidable by the Contractor. The only way to reconcile these provisions would seem to be to regard the Employer as bound to negotiate *all* claims for damage (other than the " haulier " cases) arising from transport of materials etc. (whether partly or even wholly caused by the Contractor's breach of sub-clause (1)), and then to pay them, following which an Engineer's certificate may be issued in an appropriate case entitling the Employer to deduct from the next interim payment or recover from the Contractor the amount so certified as representing the Contractor's contribution to the damage. This may not be a very satisfactory procedure from the Contractor's point of view, particularly in a case where the whole of the damage is due to lack of reasonable care by the Contractor (or his suppliers) who will accordingly be ultimately responsible, as against the Employer, for the whole claim, but on the other hand there may in many, if not most, cases be disputes on the facts, so that the Engineers' control over negotiations has something to commend it.

The Engineer's opinion and certificate will, of course, be open to review under clause 66.

Facilities for Other Contractors

31. (1) The Contractor shall in accordance with the requirements of the Engineer afford all reasonable facilities for any other contractors employed by the Employer and their workmen and for the workmen of the Employer and of any other properly authorised authorities or statutory bodies who may be employed in the execution on or near the Site of any work not in the Contract or of any contract which the Employer may enter into in connection with or ancillary to the Works.

Delay and Extra Cost

(2) If compliance with sub-clause (1) of this Clause shall involve the Contractor in delay or cost beyond that reasonably to be foreseen by an experienced contractor at the time of tender then the Engineer shall take such delay into account in determining any extension of time to which the Contractor is entitled under Clause 44 and the Contractor shall subject to Clause 52 (4) be paid in accordance with Clause 60 the amount of such cost as may be reasonable.

Sub-clause (1) is identical with clause 31 in the Fourth Edition. Sub-clause (2) is new.

Without some such clause as the present it is always an open question whether the Employer, by employing others on the Site, is in breach of an express or implied term that he should afford the Contractor free and uninterrupted possession of the Site. While the power to engage such " other contractors " is perfectly general in sub-clause (1), there are in addition specific options to do so conferred in other parts of the Conditions —see *e.g.* clause 59A (2) (b) (upon reasonable objection being taken by the Contractor to the appointment of a particular nominated sub-contractor) and clause 59B (3) (upon termination by the Contractor of a nominated sub-contract)—see *infra*, pp. 203 and 211.

The term for possession is expressly set out with some particularity in clause 42 (1), *infra*, which needs to be read together with the present clause. No doubt the present clause will not entitle the Employer to interfere with the degree of possession assured to the Contractor under clause 42—see also Hudson, 10th ed., pp. 317–320, 327–329. There are, however, some other contractual provisions which do so—see *e.g.* clauses 39 (2) and 49 (4) (remedying of defective work) and 62 (urgent repairs).

The old clause was silent on the question of additional payment for the affording of facilities—presumably " reasonable " facilities would not carry additional payment, but " unreasonable " would (as a variation following the " requirement of the Engineer "). Nevertheless even this might be very unfair to a contractor who might not have reason to anticipate some or all of the " other contractors " at the time of tender. This is, therefore, one of the contractual obligations where a " reasonable foreseeability " test for additional payment (see sub-clause (2)) is entirely justifiable on policy grounds, since the extent of the obligation will often be quite incapable of estimation by the Contractor. It may also be commented that the special inclusion of the new sub-clause (2) lends support to the view that the quite general entitlement to " reasonably unforeseeable " cost in clause 13 (3), commented on at length, *supra*, p. 52—may have been drafted *per incuriam* or with no very clear situation in mind, since on the view, which seems inescapable, of the wording of clause 13 (3) which has been expressed in the commentary to that provision, there would appear to be little if any need for the present new sub-clause.

For a special new provision placing responsibility for the safety of the operations of the other contractors upon the Employer, see the new clause 19 (2), *supra*, p. 64.

Fossils, etc.

32. All fossils coins articles of value or antiquity and structures or other remains or things of geological or archaeological interest discovered on the Site shall as between the Employer and the Contractor be deemed to be the absolute property of the Employer and the Contractor shall take reasonable precautions to prevent his workmen or any other persons from removing or damaging any such article or thing and shall immediately upon discovery thereof and before removal acquaint the Engineer of such discovery and carry out at the expense of the Employer the Engineer's orders as to the disposal of the same.

This clause is identical with clause 27 in the Fourth Edition. For the difficulties in defining " the Site," see the commentary to clause 1 (1) (n), *supra*, pp. 22–23. The definition there given could obviously give rise to disputes in applying the present clause, and emphasises the desirability of a clearer definition in the Specification, Drawings, or Bills.

" *as between the Employer and the Contractor* "

These words are particularly necessary in the present context, since the Employer in engineering contracts frequently does not own the land in or near or even actually on, over or under the Works, so that there may well be a claimant to objects found on the site whose title will prevail over that of the Employer. As between Employer and Contractor, however, the clause will take effect. On its wording, however, it is submitted that the clause may not operate upon the compensation or value paid for treasure trove, which is the property of the Crown.

Clearance of Site on Completion

33. On the completion of the Works the Contractor shall clear away and remove from the Site all Constructional Plant surplus material rubbish and Temporary Works of every kind and leave the whole of the Site and Permanent Works clean and in a workmanlike condition to the satisfaction of the Engineer.

This clause needs to be read, in the case of Constructional Plant, with clause 53 (8), *infra*, p. 175, which confers specific and detailed powers on the Employer in the event of non-compliance with the clause. Both Constructional Plant and materials, are, on being brought onto the Site, " deemed to be the property of the Employer "—see clause 53 (2)—but the present clause is a good example of the essentially qualified nature of such purported transfers of ownership in building and civil engineering contracts—old plant and any surplus materials will nearly always be intended to revest in the Contractor in the absence of express provision to the contrary—see the commentary to clause 53, *infra*, pp. 169–171, and **Hudson, 10th ed., Chapter 12.**

" *On the completion of the Works* "

Particularly in the light of the drastic powers of sale etc. in clause 53 (8), this phrase lacks sufficient precision and does not really meet either the practical or contractual requirements of the contract. Under clause 48 (1) it is clear that the certificate of substantial completion under that clause may be given notwithstanding that there may be outstanding work to be finished during the maintenance period, and under clause 48 (4) that, in the case of completed Sections or parts of the work, ground or surfaces may still require reinstatement after the sectional or partial completion certificates. Some plant and materials may well be needed on the Site after substantial completion, therefore, whereas the Employer will rightly wish to have unnecessary plant or materials removed after that date so that his occupation will not be unnecessarily disturbed. The present provision is also ambiguous in that it is not clear whether the word " completion " means substantial completion (as it does, for example, in clauses 43 and 47 (1) (b), for example) or whether it means the final completion of all outstanding work, or of the making good of defects (see clause 60 (5) (c)). The contract really requires a power for the Engineer to order the removal of Plant or materials when in his opinion their presence on the Site is no longer necessary, but neither the present clause nor clause 53, *infra*, confer any such power.

LABOUR

Rates of Wages/Hours and Conditions of Labour

34. (1) The Contractor shall in the execution of the Contract observe and fulfil the obligations upon contractors specified in the Fair Wages Resolution passed by the House of Commons on the 14th October 1946 of which the following is an extract:—

Extract from Fair Wages Resolution

" 1 (a) The contractor shall pay rates of wages and observe hours and conditions of labour not less favourable than those established for the trade or industry in the district where the work is carried out by machinery of negotiation or arbitration to which the parties are organisations of employers and trade unions representative respectively of substantial proportions of the employers and workers engaged in the trade or industry in the district.

" (b) In the absence of any rates of wages, hours or conditions of labour so established the contractor shall pay rates of wages and observe hours and conditions of labour which are not less favourable than the general level of wages, hours and conditions observed by other employers whose general circumstances in the trade and industry in which the contractor is engaged are similar.

" 2 The contractor shall in respect of all persons employed by him (whether in execution of the contract or otherwise) in every factory workshop or place occupied or used by him for the execution of the contract comply with the general conditions required by this Resolution.

" 3 In the event of any question arising as to whether the requirements of this Resolution are being observed, the question shall, if not otherwise disposed of, be referred by the Minister of Labour and National Service to an independent Tribunal for decision.

" 4 The contractor shall recognise the freedom of his workpeople to be members of Trade Unions.

" 5 The contractor shall at all times during the continuance of a contract display, for the information of his workpeople, in every factory, workshop or place occupied or used by him for the execution of the contract a copy of this Resolution.

" 6 The contractor shall be responsible for the observance of this Resolution by sub-contractors employed in the execution of the contract."

Civil Engineering Construction Conciliation Board

(2) The wages hours and conditions of employment above referred to shall be those prescribed for the time being by the Civil Engineering Construction Conciliation Board for Great Britain save that the rates of wages payable to any class of labour in respect of which the said Board does not prescribe a rate shall be governed by the provisions of sub-clause (1) of this Clause.

This clause is for all practical purposes identical with that in the Fourth Edition, except that a requirement that the Contractor should, if requested by the Employer, give a certificate of compliance with paragraph 2 of the Resolution during a period of three months up to the date of tender (see B.C.F., p. 357, and a discussion of the possible purposes of such a certificate) has now been dispensed with.

The purpose of " fair wages " clauses, as they are usually called, is probably to give the Employer some assurance that official union action against the Contractor will be kept to a minimum. Rather oddly, perhaps, their effect (if any) will be to enlist the Employer on the official union side in any conflict between Contractor employers and their employees' unions, though in practice these clauses rarely appear to have any practical consequences in contractual terms as between the Employer and Contractor. There is, in fact, no specific sanction in the contract for enforcement of this clause, other than the general right to determine on the ground of the

Contractor being " persistently or fundamentally in breach of his obligations under the contract " under clause 63 (1) (d), *infra*, p. 244, which itself does little more than restate a situation in which at common law an employer would in any event be entitled to treat the contract as repudiated. In addition, the power to require disclosure of information about labour in clause 35, *infra*, seems wholly inadequate—see the commentary thereto, *infra*. It is difficult to avoid the impression, therefore, that the present provision is inserted for political or public relations reasons rather than contractual reasons, and this impression is strengthened by the removal, in the Fifth Edition, of the only trace of enforcement machinery in the earlier clause.

Returns of Labour and Plant

35. The Contractor shall if required by the Engineer deliver to the Engineer or at his office a return in such form and at such intervals as the Engineer may prescribe showing in detail the numbers of the several classes of labour from time to time employed by the Contractor on the Site and such information respecting Constructional Plant as the Engineer may require. The Contractor shall require his sub-contractors to observe the provisions of this Clause.

This clause is identical with the Fourth Edition, except for the new additional last sentence in regard to sub-contractors. In the case of personnel, a power to require information would certainly be necessary to supplement the requirements as to superintendence, as also to oversee compliance with the requirements of clause 34, and certainly would be necessary for certain types of Variation of Price clause, but the present clause only in terms appears to relate to the number of employees in the different classes of labour, and does not appear to require disclosure of names, or the amount of wage payments or salaries, or conditions of employment, or to apply to supervisory staff. No doubt in appropriate cases where a financial claim was to be made (and this would include some variation of price clauses) this more detailed information would need to be provided under clause 52 (4) (b) and (c), *infra*, p. 166, subject to the sanctions in clause 52 (4) (e) and (f), *infra*, p. 166. More general wording, such as that used in the present clause in regard to the information about Constructional Plant, would therefore have been preferable. So far as Constructional Plant is concerned, the present power overlaps with clause 53 (5), which entitles the Employer to be informed as to its ownership, and in hired plant cases as to the existence of one term of the agreement, but the present wording is, of course, in wider terms.

The reference to sub-contractors in the last sentence means, for practical purposes, that the Contractor must incorporate a similar clause to the present in all his sub-contracts.

WORKMANSHIP AND MATERIALS

Quality of Materials and Workmanship and Tests

36. (1) All materials and workmanship shall be of the respective kinds described in the Contract and in accordance with the Engineer's instructions and shall be

> subjected from time to time to such tests as the Engineer may direct at the place of manufacture or fabrication or on the Site or such other place or places as may be specified in the Contract. The Contractor shall provide such assistance instruments machines labour and materials as are normally required for examining measuring and testing any work and the quality weight or quantity of any materials used and shall supply samples of materials before incorporation in the Works for testing as may be selected and required by the Engineer.

Apart from the additional reference to " such other places as may be specified in the Contract " this sub-clause is identical with that in the Fourth Edition.

The technical description of the quality of materials and workmanship is left to the other contract documents—*i.e.* " described in the Contract " (for the present purpose this will mean the Specification or Bills of Quantities—see the definition of " Contract " in clause 1 (1) (e), *supra*, p. 16). While the law will imply an obligation that, in so far as the documents are silent, the materials and workmanship shall be of reasonable quality and suitable for their purpose (see Hudson, 10th ed., pp. 273–306, where this subject is exhaustively examined) it is nevertheless desirable in the Employer's interests that, in the absence of any such provision in the Conditions themselves, the Bills or Specification should contain an express provision that, unless otherwise expressly described in the contract documents, all work and materials should be of the best quality reasonably available and suitable for their purpose.

For other powers comparable to the power to order tests, see the power to order the opening or uncovering of work in clause 38 (2), *infra*, p. 106, and the power to order a search for defects in clause 50, *infra*, p. 149. For the powers of the Engineer in regard to detected defective work, see clause 39, *infra*, pp. 107–108.

" *and in accordance with the Engineer's instructions* "

The " and " is important—see the commentary to clause 13 (1), *supra*, and the limited extent to which, where the contract is silent, the Engineer may have power to control the method of working without giving rise to a variation.

" *from time to time* "

It seems very possible, particularly since clause 50, *infra*, p. 149, appears to confer a power to test and search during the maintenance period, that the general powers of testing in the present clause may not be exercisable after a substantial completion is certified under clause 48, *infra*, p. 140, except in regard to works still incomplete at the time of certification. The other contract documents, however, might make it plain that tests after completion were intended.

" *machines . . . normally required for . . . measuring . . . any work* "

These words, and the words " quantity and weight " need to be construed, it is submitted, in the context of this clause, which is concerned with ascertaining whether, or ensuring that, work or materials to be used in the works are in accordance with the contract. It is suggested that they do not apply, as on their face they might be thought to do, to the measurement of work for purposes of payment. For instance, it is suggested that the clause would apply to hoppers or batch weighing or other machines for purposes of mixing concrete in the right proportions, but would not apply to weighing machinery used to calculate the price of work done—*e.g.* weighbridges in contracts for quarry production of stone or other materials or for winning gravel from pits, where the present Conditions of Contract are not infrequently used. Such measurement plant will usually be expressly provided for in such contracts.

" *at the place of manufacture or fabrication* "

See also for the Engineer's or other authorised persons' right of access to these, clause 37, *infra.*

Cost of Samples

(2) All samples shall be supplied by the Contractor at his own cost if the supply thereof is clearly intended by or provided for in the Contract but if not then at the cost of the Employer.

The word " Contract " has been substituted for " Specification or Bill of Quantities," but otherwise this sub-clause is identical with that in the Fourth Edition and is self-explanatory.

Cost of Tests

(3) The cost of making any test shall be borne by the Contractor if such test is clearly intended by or provided for in the Contract and (in the cases only of a test, undo load or of a test to ascertain whether the design of any finished or partiall finished work is appropriate for the purposes which it was intended to fulfil) is particularised in the Specification or Bill of Quantities in sufficient detail to enable the Contractor to have priced or allowed for the same in his Tender. If any test is ordered by the Engineer which is either:—

(a) not so intended by or provided for; or

(b) (in the cases above mentioned) is not so particularised;

then the cost of such test shall be borne by the Contractor if the test shows the workmanship or materials not to be in accordance with the provisions of the Contract or the Engineer's instructions but otherwise by the Employer.

This sub-clause is identical with sub-clauses (3) and (4) in the Fourth Edition, except that a third party category of test (c) (tests by independent persons off the site) has now been removed from the second sentence of the clause, and in the first sentence " the Contract " has been substituted for " Specification or Bills of Quantities " at one point but not (presumably *per incuriam*) at another point in the sentence where the expression is also to be found. (There seems no significance whatever in this change in any event—see the definition of " Contract " in clause 1 (1) (e), *supra*, p. 16.)

The practical effect of the sub-clause is that the Contractor is to pay in any event for:

(a) tests shown clearly as intended by the documents other than the Conditions (sub-clause (1), of course, contemplates that tests may be ordered *at will* in any part of the work, but this will not, the context indicates, be " clearly intended by or provided for " in the Conditions, it is submitted, within the present wording).

(b) tests intended as above which are either " tests under load " or tests of the finished work or any part of it made to determine its ability to fulfil its intended function (as opposed to tests of its materials or workmanship to determine their compliance with the contract) *provided that the tests in question are described with sufficient particularity for the Contractor to be able to make a proper allowance for them when pricing* (so, for instance, even carefully described tests where the total number to be carried out is left to the Engineer's discretion will not qualify).

Any test ordered which does not fall within the above definitions is paid for by the Employer or Contractor depending upon the outcome of the tests—*i.e.* unintended tests (which will include, it is submitted, any tests ordered solely under sub-clause (1) and which are not otherwise mentioned in the Contract Documents), or intended but insufficiently particularised " under load " or design tests, as defined, of the completed work.

It is a little difficult to see, however, how a test " to ascertain whether the design of any . . . work is appropriate for the purposes which it was intended to fulfil " would, if unsuccessful, necessarily " show the workmanship or materials not to be in accordance with the contract " and so deprive the Contractor of payment, unless the Contractor had given an express or implied warranty as to the performance of the finished product, and even then mere failure to meet the guaranteed performance standard might not always be within the wording. (Clause 20 (3) contemplates, it should be noted, that the Contractor may assume design obligations under the Contract—see the commentary thereto, *supra*, p. 67.)

Usually, however, mention of tests in the Bills will mean that they are the subject of a provisional sum, in which case the Contractor will be paid for them in any event.

The (traditional) draftsmanship of this clause is extremely difficult to follow, and wherever testing is contemplated the Specification or Bills should make it quite clear whether additional payment is to be made or not.

For a further criticism of the policy of the clause in not making it plain that the costs of tests should be borne by the Contractor in any event, independently of their results, in cases where the need for testing is a reasonable consequence of previously detected defective work or its symptoms, see the discussion of the general weakness of the contract in this respect under clause 39, *infra*, pp. 108–109.

Access to Site

37. The Engineer and any person authorised by him shall at all times have access to the Works and to the Site and to all workshops and places where work is being prepared or whence materials manufactured articles and machinery are being obtained for the Works and the Contractor shall afford every facility for and every assistance in or in obtaining the right to such access.

This clause, as in the case of clause 31, *supra*, establishes beyond doubt a right of access which otherwise might be regarded, on a very legalistic view, as inconsistent with a Contractor's right to possession of the site—as to which see clause 42, *infra*, p. 116. In fact, to give effect to the many powers of the Engineer, such a right would have to be implied in any event. But under this clause any person can be authorised by the Engineer for this purpose, it should be noted, so that, for instance, he could authorise visitors or others not directly concerned with the supervision of the contract to have access—compare also the very wide classes of persons to whom the Engineer or Resident Engineer can delegate powers under clauses 2 (2) and 2 (3) of the Conditions, *supra*, pp. 25–26.

In so far as some of the places described might well not be in the occupation or control of the Contractor (*e.g.* sub-contractors' or manufacturers' premises) the clause in regard to them merely requires such facilities or assistance as the Contractor is in a position to give, and does not on its wording (contrast clause 35, *supra*, p. 102) appear to require either expressly or impliedly the inclusion of a similar clause to the present in his sub-contracts, though no doubt the Contractor will remain liable for failure or refusal to give access in the same way as for any other act or omission of a sub-contractor constituting a breach of the main contract.

Examination of Work before Covering up

38. (1) No work shall be covered up or put out of view without the approval of the Engineer and the Contractor shall afford full opportunity for the Engineer to examine and measure any work which is about to be covered up or put out of view and to examine foundations before permanent work is placed thereon. The Contractor shall give due notice to the Engineer whenever any such work or foundations is or are ready or about to be ready for examination and the Engineer shall without unreasonable delay unless he considers it unnecessary and advise the Contractor accordingly attend for the purpose of examining and measuring such work or of examining such foundations.

Uncovering and Making Openings

(2) The Contractor shall uncover any part or parts of the Works or make openings in or through the same as the Engineer may from time to time direct and shall reinstate and make good such part or parts to the satisfaction of the Engineer. If any such part or parts have been covered up or put out of view after compliance with the requirements of sub-clause (1) of this Clause and are found to be executed in accordance with the Contract the cost of uncovering making openings in or through reinstating and making good the same shall be borne by the Employer but in any other case all such cost shall be borne by the Contractor.

Apart from the removal of a right of the Employer to recover or deduct the cost of uncovering and making good etc., from the last lines of sub-clause (2), which was perfectly justifiable since the right was clearly inappropriate to the facts and must have been inserted into the earlier editions of contract *per incuriam*, the present clause is identical with that in the Fourth Edition. The clause is admirably clear and logical, and needs little comment. It should be noted that the contract, at many points apart from this clause, makes it plain that no approval or passing of work or payment or certificate can bind the Employer or Engineer if the work is later found to be defective—see in particular clauses 2 and 39 (3), 14 (7), 17, 39 (1) (c), 54 (3) (a), and 60 (7))—and even old difficulties about the possible effect of the maintenance certificate have now been removed—see clause 61 (2), *infra*, p. 243. The " and " is important in the second sentence of sub-clause (2), meaning that, notwithstanding the work is found to be satisfactory on being opened or uncovered, the Contractor will have to pay the cost of doing so if he covered up the work originally without the approval of the Engineer in sub-clause (1). On the other hand, a previous covering up with approval does not protect the Contractor if a subsequent re-opening discloses defective work. For other comparable powers in the contract see the power to order tests in clause 36 (1) and (3), *supra*, pp. 102–104; to order a search for defects in clause 50, *infra*, p. 149; and to carry out urgent repairs under clause 62, *infra*, pp. 243–244. For detected defects, see the powers in clause 39, *infra*.

For a criticism of the policy of some of these clauses and of the present clause in not providing for the financial costs to be borne by the Contractor in any event, independently of the results, in cases where the opening up etc. is the reasonable consequence of previously detected defective work or its symptoms, see the discussion of the general weakness of the contract in this respect under clause 39, *infra*, pp. 108–109.

A careful comparison with clause 50 (see the commentary, *infra*, p. 149) suggests that the power in sub-clause (2) of the present clause will not be exercisable after substantial completion (except perhaps in regard to work not completed at the time of substantial completion)—see the definition of substantial completion in clause 48, *infra*, pp. 140–141.

Removal of Improper Work and Materials

39. (1) The Engineer shall during the progress of the Works have power to order in writing:—

(a) the removal from the Site within such time or times as may be specified in the order of any materials which in the opinion of the Engineer are not in accordance with the Contract;

(b) the substitution of proper and suitable materials; and

(c) the removal and proper re-execution (notwithstanding any previous test thereof or interim payment therefor) of any work which in respect of materials or workmanship is not in the opinion of the Engineer in accordance with the Contract.

Default of Contractor in Compliance

(2) In case of default on the part of the Contractor in carrying out such order the Employer shall be entitled to employ and pay other persons to carry out the same and all expenses consequent thereon or incidental thereto shall be borne by the Contractor and shall be recoverable from him by the Employer or may be deducted by the Employer from any monies due or which may become due to the Contractor.

Failure to Disapprove

(3) Failure of the Engineer or any person acting under him pursuant to Clause 2 to disapprove any work or materials shall not prejudice the power of the Engineer or any of them subsequently to disapprove such work or materials.

Sub-clauses (1) and (2) are identical with the Fourth Edition clause. Sub-clause (3) has been transposed from a rather similar provision in clause 2 (a) of the Fourth Edition which related, however, to the Engineer's Representative only. The considerable widening of the wording in the present sub-clause is significant in emphasising beyond doubt a policy which has, however, been indicated in a number of other traditional clauses in the contract for many years—see *e.g.* sub-clause (1) (c) itself, the new clause 14 (7) and clauses 17, 54 (3) (a), 60 (7) and the new clause 61 (2).

The present clause confers the principal power of the Engineer under this contract to require defective work to be re-executed during the course of construction (see also the very wide power in the case of dimensional inaccuracies in clause 17, *supra*, p. 62, which is of considerable and, by virtue of its incorporation in an otherwise inappropriate clause, probably unintended importance). For the equivalent powers after completion during the maintenance periods see clause 49 (2) and (4), *infra*. It can be enforced, in the event of non-compliance, by determination under clause 63 (1) (c) as well as by the special remedy in sub-clause (2) of the present clause, the latter a most potent weapon, though rarely used by employers in practice in the U.K. (see also the overlapping remedy available under clause 62, *infra*, pp. 243–244). Paragraphs (a) and (b) of sub-clause (1) probably refer to unfixed materials, and paragraph (c), of course, to the workmanship or materials of completed work.

Notwithstanding the elements of elaboration and duplication in the express powers conferred by the contract in regard to defective work, there is in fact a real practical weakness in the contract in this respect, as in the case of virtually all the U.K. standard forms. This arises because in practice it is very often more satisfactory, when the symptoms of defective work emerge, to vary the work in some way rather than to order whole-scale demolition, thereby avoiding considerable and perhaps unrealistic delay and expense, and the risk of damage to sound work during the demolition process. The difficulty in the present contract is compounded by new and different wording in clauses 7 (1), 13 (3) and 51 (1) which suggest a possible *duty* on the Employer/Engineer to issue instructions or to vary the work in undefined circumstances where this can be said to be " necessary "—see the commentaries to those clauses at pp. 32–33, 47–50 and 155–156. Indeed contractors in the U.K., faced with the emerging symptoms of defective work of potentially important proportions, have for some years now fastened on this weakness in the forms and not infrequently refused to continue working until instructions are received. When received, these instructions are then used as a pretext for presenting financial claims. An express power to give instructions to suspend work, carry out investigations, and, if so advised, vary the work, at no additional cost to the Employer when the instruction or permanent variation is due to defective work or other breach of contract by the Contractor (compare clause 9 (4) of GC/Wks/1), is an essential remedy for Employers in this situation, notwithstanding that it may possibly be arguable that contractual obligations to make additional payments resulting from instructions themselves the consequence of breaches of contract are recoverable as damages for the breach—a superficially attractive but logically difficult argument of a somewhat circular character, and lacking the firm legal basis of a clear express power.

Much the same objection in fact applies to the various provisions for the testing or investigation of the work in search of defects—*e.g.* clauses 36 (3) (testing), 38 (2) (uncovering), and 50 (search), all of which entitle the Contractor to additional payment if no defective work is revealed. Where, however, the investigation itself results as a reasonable precaution following the discovery of defective work or its symptoms, in most cases it is clear that the cost of reasonable investigations to ascertain the extent or cause of the trouble should be borne by the Contractor in any event, and would certainly be treated as recoverable as damages for breach of contract but for the existence of these express provisions requiring payment in the event of no further defect being found.

" *notwithstanding any previous test thereof or interim payment therefor* "

As stated *supra*, compare clauses 2 and 39 (3), 14 (7), 17, 38 (2), 54 (3) (a), 60 (7) and 61 (2), all of which make it plain that no prior approval test, payment or certificate in respect of work can avail the Contractor if it is subsequently found to be defective.

" *in respect of materials or workmanship is not . . . in accordance with the Contract* "

These words may not be wide enough to cover cases where an express design or suitability obligation is given by the Contractor (which the contract undoubtedly contemplates as a possibility—see *e.g.* clauses 8 (2), 20 (3) and 36 (3)). No doubt in such cases, however, the sanction of an action for damages for breach of the undertaking will usually be sufficient to persuade the Contractor to re-execute the work if the matter is detected during construction.

(*1*) " *the opinion of the Engineer* "

If the Contractor disputes the matter, he should insist on an order in writing, give any appropriate notices under clause 52, and *after compliance* claim additional payment for a variation (refusal to comply will expose the Contractor to a determination, with all its consequences, under clause 63 (1) (c)). An arbitrator (or the courts, it is submitted) will have power ultimately to resolve the matter—see the commentary to clause 66, *infra*, p. 276.

Suspension of Work

40. (1) The Contractor shall on the written order of the Engineer suspend the progress of the Works or any part thereof for such time or times and in such manner as the Engineer may consider necessary and shall during such suspension properly protect and secure the work so far as is necessary in the opinion of the Engineer. Subject to Clause 52 (4) the Contractor shall be paid in accordance with Clause 60 the extra cost (if any) incurred in giving effect to the Engineer's instructions under this Clause except to the extent that such suspension is:—

(a) otherwise provided for in the Contract; or

(b) necessary by reason of weather conditions or by some default on the part of the Contractor; or

(c) necessary for the proper execution of the work or for the safety of the Works or any part thereof inasmuch as such necessity does not arise from any act or default of the Engineer or the Employer or from any of the Excepted Risks defined in Clause 20.

The Engineer shall take any delay occasioned by a suspension ordered under this Clause (including that arising from any act or default of the Engineer or the Employer) into account in determining any extension of time to which the Contractor is entitled under Clause 44 except when such suspension is otherwise provided for in the Contract or is necessary by reason of some default on the part of the Contractor.

Suspension lasting more than Three Months

(2) If the progress of the Works or any part thereof is suspended on the written order of the Engineer and if permission to resume work is not given by the Engineer within a period of 3 months from the date of suspension then the Contractor may unless such suspension is otherwise provided for in the Contract or continues to be necessary by reason of some default on the part of the Contractor serve a written notice on the Engineer requiring permission within 28 days from the receipt of such notice to proceed with the Works or that part thereof in regard to which progress is suspended. If within the said 28 days the Engineer does not grant such permission the Contractor by a further written notice so served may (but is not bound to) elect to treat the suspension where it affects part only of the Works as an omission of such part under Clause 51 or where it affects the whole Works as an abandonment of the Contract by the Employer.

This clause incorporates wholly or partially two improvements suggested in B.C.F. (at pp. 363–364), in that in sub-clause (1) the Contractor is given protection where the suspension arises from matters in the Employer's or Engineer's sphere of responsibility, and in sub-clause (2) the Employer is similarly given protection where the suspension results from the Contractor's default. The Contractor's notice of claim and the extension of time provisions in sub-clause (1) also follow the new Fifth Edition schemes for these matters. Otherwise the clause follows the Fourth Edition closely, but with an outstanding anomaly in sub-clause (2) still unresolved.

The main importance of sub-clause (1) is that it defines the situations in which the Contractor must suspend work at his own expense (the grounds are identical with those in the Fourth Edition, subject to the special savings now made in sub-clause (1) (c) in regard to act or default of Employer/Engineer or the Excepted Risks). Sub-clause (2), however, enables the Contractor to bring matters to a head if the suspension lasts more than three months (not necessarily a very long period, it should be noted by employers, in some engineering projects where weather, seasonal, tidal or other physical considerations may be of dominating importance during the construction period). In considering sub-clause (2) in the light of the usually unqualified nature of the Contractor's obligation to complete (see commentaries to clauses 8 (1), 11 (1) and 13 (1), *supra*, pp. 35–37, 40–41 and 47–48) it is essential to bear in mind that the present clause only applies to suspensions *for which instructions have been given by the Engineer*. There is no obligation whatever on him to call for such a suspension, even if weather or safety considerations render such a course advisable, it is submitted, and whatever the disaster or difficulties which may have occurred it is the Contractor's duty to resume, and if necessary re-execute the work without delay (unless an Excepted Risk is involved). The power in the present clause is purely discretionary for the convenience of the Employer and the protection of the latter's interests (in particular, of course, danger to the permanent works, or to surrounding property or persons in the vicinity, or delay to the project as a whole which an accident might cause), and not a power which the Employer is bound to exercise in order to afford the Contractor an escape from his basic contractual obligations when serious difficulties arise.

On the other hand, it should be borne in mind when considering the present clause that the Fifth Edition does now contain new and difficult wording in clauses 7 (1), 13 (3) and 51 (1) which arguably may import a contractual *obligation* on the Engineer to *vary* the work in certain not easily defined circumstances—see the commentary to those clauses, *supra*, pp. 32–33, 47–50 and *infra*, pp. 155–156, and the difficulty of ascertaining the meaning of the words " necessary for the purpose of the proper and adequate construction completion and maintenance of the Works " in clause 7 (1) and " necessary for the completion of the Works " in clause 51 (1), which compare with " necessary for the proper execution of the work " in sub-clause (1) (c) of the present clause. The policy of the contract in this most fundamental matter appears to be uncertain, with the uncertainty evident even in the present clause, where a three-month suspension on " necessary for proper execution or safety grounds " is at the Contractor's expense under sub-clause (1), but thereafter an omission or determination of work under sub-clause (2) at, in effect, the Contractor's option and the Employer's expense, can be brought about after three months have elapsed. This particular policy has been noted and criticised in Chapter 1, *supra*, p. 9, as inconsistent with the reasonable interests of the Employer and anomalous in cases where he bears no moral or legal responsibility, such as weather, the interests of the permanent work, or safety.

(*1*) " *subject to clause 52* (*4*) "

The Fourth Edition requirement of notice under the present clause was without doubt a condition precedent to a claim (and was so held by the courts—see B.C.F., 1st suppt. under p. 363). For the far milder sanctions attending a failure to give notice under the present contract, however, see the commentaries under clauses 12, *supra*, pp. 42–43, and 52 (4), *infra*, p. 166.

(*1*) " *in accordance with clause 60* "

i.e. clause 60 (1) (d), as qualified by clause 52 (4) (f).

(*1*) " *Cost* "

see the extended definition in clause 1 (5), *supra*, p. 25.

(*1*) (*a*) " *otherwise provided for in the Contract* "

i.e. expressly dealt with in the Bills or Specification—there do not appear to be other provisions in the Conditions themselves. The saving in regard to extension of time for this particular category is somewhat odd—see *infra*.

(*1*) (*b*) "*weather conditions* "

This exception is, of course, consistent both with the commercial realities and the policy, for example, of clause 12, which also exempts weather conditions from the provisions of that clause.

(*1*) (*b*) " *default on the part of the Contractor* "

(*1*) (*c*) " *act or default on the part of the Engineer or the Employer* "

The first of these expressions is traditional, but the second is new. There is almost certainly no special situation envisaged by the difference of wording, which appears to be characteristic of this contract, arising no doubt from the piecemeal character of its alteration and redrafting, and possibly from the difficulty of negotiating changes in traditional wording in the present clause—compare the differences of wording " act or neglect," " act or neglect or breach of statutory duty " and " act or default " in clauses 22 and 24, for example. Nevertheless, the use in the present clause of the word " act " is regrettable, since what will constitute an " act " of the Engineer or Employer which will activate the safeguard is not at all clear, and the " acts " of an engineer in administering a contract are legion and may not involve any element either of responsibility or even direct causation. Indeed there would seem to be little purpose in this saving at all, since the later saving in regard to the Excepted Risks (recommended in B.C.F. at p. 363) will include the Engineer's design of the works in the new and wider wording of clause 20 (3)—see *infra*.

(*1*) (*c*) " *or from any Excepted Risk* "

i.e. under clause 20 (3), *supra*, p. 66. The financial saving in the present sub-clause is logically consistent with the policy of clause 20 (2), and, in regard to the very important " fault defect error or omission in the design of the Works " Excepted Risk, for all practical purposes overlaps to a very considerable extent with the " act or default " saving.

(*1*) (*c*) " *necessary for the proper execution of the work or for the safety of the Works* "

The possibly considerable significance of this provision in assisting in the interpretation of the very difficult new clauses 7 (1) and 51 (1) of the Conditions has been pointed out *supra*, p. 48. As indicated, there seems to be a certain lack of logic in the policy of the present sub-clause, which renders the Contractor financially liable for suspension due to this particular cause or for weather conditions, but, via sub-clause (2), in effect turns the financial tables on the parties once three months have passed.

(*1*) " *except when such suspension is otherwise provided for in the Contract* "

Presumably this means if the Bills or Specification make it clear that no extension of time is to be permitted for the particular suspension—presumably it does not mean that whenever specific provision is made for a particular class of suspension to be included in the Contractor's price there should automatically be no extension of time, though the wording is certainly open to this interpretation.

(*2*) " *continues to be necessary* "

This wording is not very happy, since it may suggest that, whatever the original cause of the suspension, it is only a later default by the Contractor after the suspension, leading to its continuing more than three months, which is intended by the saving. It is difficult to see why the words " continues to be " have been inserted, since the common-sense requirement is a suspension lasting more than three months due to and following the Contractor's default at any stage, whether initially or subsequently, and the simple omission of these words would have produced that result. Nevertheless, there is sufficient ambiguity for the obvious sensible interpretation to prevail, it is submitted. In fact the whole policy of this sub-clause is open to question. In the cases where the suspension is at the Employer's cost, examination of the exceptions shows that this will be either where a purely voluntary suspension for his own purposes is ordered by the

Employer, or some act or default by him or the Engineer occurs, or an Excepted Risk eventuates. Certainly in the two former cases the Contractor, notwithstanding the benefit of financial protection in sub-clause (1), should reasonably be protected, particularly in highly inflationary and uncertain times, from an excessive period of suspension. But in the case of weather and " proper execution " or safety suspensions, and quite possibly in the case of the Excepted Risks (other than the " design " risk), there seems no reason for any such protection in cases which are beyond the control of the Employer and in the category usually regarded as Contractor's risks, let alone a protection equivalent to damages for breach of contract, including loss of profit on the abandoned work, which would seem to follow from the " abandonment of the Contract by the Employer " provision, as also probably from the " omission " provision, which will involve a clause 52 valuation. This financial protection where the suspension is due to a non-design Excepted Risk (*e.g.* riot or insurrection) or a Contractor's risk (*e.g.* weather or proper execution or safety) should be compared with the lesser entitlement of the Contractor to *quantum meruit* (in effect) under either clause 64 (frustration) or 65 (war). It is perhaps advisable to reiterate that the whole of the present clause will only apply on receipt of an Engineer's *written order*, and that there is no wording in the present clause or elsewhere in the contract to suggest that the present clause confers anything other than a discretionary and permissive power on the Engineer, who will be under no obligation to give any such order, however strongly the circumstances may warrant it, or equally to withhold permission to continue working on receipt of the Contractor's notice, however impractical continuing work may in fact be. The " may (but is not bound to) elect " wording is, given the circumstances of prior despatch of the second notice, peculiar and suggests that the Contractor may continue working, in the case of a partial suspension, for example, and later decide whether or not to perform the omitted work if this subsequently becomes possible; or in the case of the suspension of the whole Works, may wait for an indeterminate length of time before deciding to, in effect, rescind the contract. The care to preserve this right to elect for the Contractor, notwithstanding the content of his two notices, before exercising his remedy under the present clause contrasts with the lack of any similar saving in the case of the Employer's right of re-entry under clause 63, *infra*, pp. 247–248, and is noted *ante*, Chapter 1, p. 8, as an example of the relatively much greater care shown by the contract in safeguarding the Contractor's interests and remedies as opposed to those of the Employer.

COMMENCEMENT TIME AND DELAYS

Commencement of Works

41. The Contractor shall commence the Works on or as soon as is reasonably possible after the Date for Commencement of the Works to be notified by the

Engineer in writing which date shall be within a reasonable time after the date of acceptance of the Tender. Thereafter the Contractor shall proceed with the Works with due expedition and without delay in accordance with the Contract.

The next eight clauses are concerned with time for commencement and completion, provisions for extensions of time, and liquidated damages for delay. Clause 42 also, however, defines the extent and degree of the Contractor's right to possession of the Site.

The present very short clause has been considerably improved, in that (a) the Contractor is now safeguarded against unreasonable delay in fixing the Date for Commencement (on which his right to possession under clause 42 and the time for completion under clause 43 will depend); (b) *notification* (not an order) in writing is now required (*i.e.* it must be served at the Contractor's principal place of business or registered office under clause 68 (1), *infra*, p. 283, thereby correcting the error pointed out in B.C.F., p. 365); and (c) the illogical and difficult saving for matters " wholly beyond the Contractor's control " has now been removed from the second sentence.

" *within a reasonable time* "

This is, of course, a question of fact. In the present economic situation in the United Kingdom, a prompt commencement order will usually be necessary, but factors to be taken into account will include any express indications given in the tender documentation or elsewhere prior to tender, the presence or absence of a variation of price clause, and seasonal considerations—see also Hudson, 10th ed., pp. 226–228, and 317–320, and see also the case of *Swanson Construction* v. *Government of Manitoba* (1963) 40 D.L.R. 162, illustrated in Hudson, 10th ed., p. 339.

" *with due expedition and without delay in accordance with the Contract* "

A term for due expedition is an essential requisite in building or civil engineering contracts (indeed such a term will be implied, it is submitted —see Hudson, 10th ed., pp. 314–315, 608–612, where it is suggested that persistent breach of such an implied term after notice would amount to repudiation). An express sanction for breach of this term is provided by the powers of determination in clause 63 (1) (b) (failure to start or suspension of progress) and 63 (1) (d) (failure to proceed with due diligence). As pointed out in the commentary to clause 47, *infra*, p. 131, damages for breach of the present term are unlikely to be an immediately effective sanction, so that the practical alternative to determination will usually be the deduction of liquidated damages for failure to complete at the later date when the extended or contract completion date has passed. There is also a rather odd provision for acceleration of progress in clause 46, not itself supported by any sanction. The words " in accordance with the Contract " in the present clause may be intended to refer to clause 46, or to the inhibition on night and Sunday work in clause 45, and also to the contractual requirements for Sectional Completion contemplated by clauses 43 and 47, as well, perhaps, as the qualification on completion in the case of the Excepted Risks in clause 20 (2), or in the case of frustration and war under clauses 64 and 65; but strictly the words, which are new, appear unnecessary and their exact purpose is unclear.

Possession of Site

42. (1) Save in so far as the Contract may prescribe the extent of portions of the Site of which the Contractor is to be given possession from time to time and the order in which such portions shall be made available to him and subject to any requirement in the Contract as to the order in which the Works shall be executed the Employer will at the Date for Commencement of the Works notified under Clause 41 give to the Contractor possession of so much of the Site as may be required to enable the Contractor to commence and proceed with the construction of the Works in accordance with the programme referred to in Clause 14 and will from time to time as the Works proceed give to the Contractor possession of such further portions of the Site as may be required to enable the Contractor to proceed with the construction of the Works with due despatch in accordance with the said programme. If the Contractor suffers delay or incurs cost from failure on the part of the Employer to give possession in accordance with the terms of this Clause then the Engineer shall take such delay into account in determining any extension of time to which the Contractor is entitled under Clause 44 and the Contractor shall subject to Clause 52 (4) be paid in accordance with Clause 60 the amount of such cost as may be reasonable.

Apart from the omission of a reference in the Fourth Edition to " reasonable proposals of the Contractor " as a possible alternative to the programme under clause 14 (which under clause 14 in that Edition had only to be furnished by the Contractor " if required ") and the reference to the new clause 52 (4) notification machinery for financial claims and interim payment (see in particular clauses 52 (4) (f) and 60 (1) (d)) the present clause is identical with its predecessor.

There is always, of course, an implied term for possession of the site to be afforded by an employer in building and civil engineering contracts, the precise extent and degree of which may vary very considerably according to the nature of the project and the work to be undertaken—see Hudson, 10th ed., at pp. 317–320.

The present clause attempts a general express description of the Employer's duty to give possession and is relatively well-drafted, in view of the reality of many engineering contracts—namely that possession will in many cases only be needed in sequence or by stages, and that " the Site " may be an indeterminate area more difficult of precise definition than in building contracts, and not necessarily all in the beneficial occupation of the Employer (see *e.g.* clause 22 in this context). Furthermore, the Conditions themselves now contemplate the possibility of phased completion of different parts of the Works with different completion dates—see the references to completion of " Sections " in clauses 43 and 47, *infra.*

Nevertheless, there are two possible sources of difficulty in the present clause. In the first place, the contractual definition of " the Site " is not as precise as it might be—see the comment on the definition in clause 1 (1) (n), *supra*, pp. 22–23, and the suggested need for greater precision to be attempted in the Bills or Specification in the commentaries under, *e.g.*, clauses 22 and 32, *supra*, pp. 78–79 and 99. Nowhere is this more desirable than in the case of the present clause. In the second place, particularly since the duty to provide possession is tied more directly than previously to the Contractor's programme, the common practice of contractors in the U.K. in supplying optimistic programmes, commented on under clause 14, *supra*, p. 55 (and see also Hudson, 10th ed., p. 603), should be borne in mind by the Employer's advisers in case a careless or uncritical approval of such a programme should expose the Employer to a possibly premature but nevertheless embarrassing claim under the present sub-clause. As stated *supra*, the effect of the references to clauses 52 (4) and 60 will be that the Contractor will, subject to adequate notice and records etc., be entitled to payment on interim certificate.

" *Cost* "

See the new extended definition in clause 1 (5), *supra*, p. 25.

Wayleaves, etc.

(2) The Contractor shall bear all expenses and charges for special or temporary wayleaves required by him in connection with access to the Site. The Contractor shall also provide at his own cost any additional accommodation outside the Site required by him for the purposes of the Works.

This sub-clause in particular calls for a precise definition of the Site, since it gives effect to the usual practice in civil engineering contracts whereby off-site rights of way and other expenditure is the responsibility of the Contractor. The first sentence of the sub-clause refers, it is submitted, to *off-site* wayleaves etc., though it is not quite as clear about this as the second sentence. Once " the Site " is reached (see the definition in clause 1 (1) (n), *supra*, pp. 22–23) then the Employer will be responsible even if the Site land is in the occupation of persons other than himself. In pipe-line contracts, for example, it is commonplace for " the Site " to be defined as a strip of given width on each side of the centre-line of the pipes, with a consequential division of financial responsibilities as between Contractor and Employer *vis-à-vis* adjoining occupiers, if a greater width is sought to be used by the Contractor. Most Bills and Specifications in well-drawn contracts should, however, where possible make clear in some detail the access and working space to be provided by the Employer (these then qualifying as " the Site " by virue of the definition in clause 1 (1) (n)) but a mere right of way obtained by the Employer would presumably not be " lands or places provided by the Employer " and therefore should merit particularly careful express treatment in the documents.

Time for Completion

43. The whole of the Works and any Section required to be completed within a particular time as stated in the Appendix to the Form of Tender shall be completed within the time so stated (or such extended time as may be allowed under Clause 44) calculated from the Date for Commencement of the Works notified under Clause 41.

Extension of Time for Completion

44. (1) Should any variation ordered under Clause 51 (1) or increased quantities referred to in Clause 51 (3) or any other cause of delay referred to in these Conditions or exceptional adverse weather conditions or other special circumstances of any kind whatsoever which may occur be such as fairly to entitle the Contractor to an extension of time for the completion of the Works or (where different periods for completion of different Sections are provided for in the Appendix to the Form of Tender) of the relevant Section the Contractor shall within 28 days after the cause of the delay has arisen or as soon thereafter as is reasonable in all the circumstances deliver to the Engineer full and detailed particulars of any claim to extension of time to which he may consider himself entitled in order that such claim may be investigated at the time.

Clause 43 imposes the obligation to complete by a particular time (as opposed to the " due expedition " obligation in clause 41), the special sanction for which is the liquidated damages machinery in clause 47, which now also specifically provides for the possibility of separate agreed completion dates and separate liquidated damages for separate " Sections " of the work. These separate dates and damages will need to be stipulated in the Appendix to the Form of Tender—see clause 47 (2).

The scheme for extension of time in clause 44 has now been radically revised. In the first place, the Fourth Edition merely provided that extra work or "other special circumstances " should be a ground for extension, but apart from failure to give access under clause 42, and refusal of night work under clause 46, made little specific provision elsewhere in the contract for extensions of time, relying on the compendious and generalised " other special circumstances " ground. This made the whole clause legally highly vulnerable, in the sense that the entire liquidated damages machinery could be legally invalidated if even a small part of the Contractor's overall delay could be shown to be due to a breach of contract or act of prevention by the Employer, unless a sufficiently clear express power to grant an extension of time for that particular breach or act was conferred by the contract (for this purpose generalised wording such as the " other special circumstances " expression would not, on the authority of many cases, be effective)—see for the law on this rather difficult subject (followed in Canada and several but not all U.S. jurisdictions) the commentary in B.C.F. at pp. 367–368 and Hudson, 10th ed., pp. 625–635. The present contract has taken this very much to heart, and explicit extensions of time are now given for a large number of matters, including all likely breaches or acts of the Employer, as

(a) in the present clause,

(i) variation instructions under clause 51

(ii) increased quantities not due to variations (*i.e.* simple remeasurement)
(iii) exceptional adverse weather conditions

and

(b) elsewhere
(iv) failure to give information (clause 7 (3))
(v) adverse physical conditions etc. (clause 12 (3))
(vi) instructions under clause 13 (1) (clause 13 (3))
(vii) delay in approving contractors' calculations etc. (clause 14 (6))
(viii) Street Works delays due to Employer (clause 27 (6))
(ix) Other contractors of Employer (clause 31 (2))
(x) Suspension of work (clause 40 (1))
(xi) Failure to give possession (clause 42 (1))
(xii) Repudiation by Nominated Sub-contractors (clause 59B (4) (b))
(xiii) Metrication delays under clause 71 (via clauses 13 or 51)

It should perhaps be noted that no express powers are conferred in respect of the Excepted Risks under clause 20 causing damage to the Works, or in respect of strikes and industrial action, or in respect of an outbreak of war under clause 65—presumably for these it will still be necessary to rely on the " other special circumstances " ground, which has been retained in the present clause. Very importantly, no express ground exists for ordinary delays caused by Nominated Sub-Contractors not due to a repudiation or termination of the sub-contract, and it would seem clear that, in view of the special protection now afforded to the main Contractor in respect of Nominated Sub-Contractors' breaches in clause 59A (6), the " special circumstances " provision could not possibly be successfully invoked now, if it ever could have been, in such a case. A further important matter about which the contract is silent is the extent to which the ordering of Provisional Sum work under clause 58 will entitle the Contractor to an extension of time—see the commentary under clause 58 *infra*, pp. 200-201—or of work under the " General Contingency Allowance " now specifically provided for in Sections 5.17 and 5.25 of the 1976 Standard Method (C.E.S.M.M.), commented on under clause 57, *infra*, p. 194.

Secondly, while the Fourth Edition contemplated that the power to extend time would be exercised only once (*i.e.* at or after the arrival of the completion or extended completion date) and laid down no particular time limit for exercising the power, which could accordingly be exercised at any time prior to the last Engineer's certificate (see B.C.F., p. 368) an extraordinarily complicated procedure is now set out in sub-clauses (2), (3) and (4) of the present clause *infra*, which appears to contemplate at least *three* occasions on which the Engineer is required to reach decisions on an extension of time on any particular matter, and which seems likely to create many doubts and difficulties and expose Engineers to constant pressures from the Contractor on this subject.

In the third place, there is now a requirement under sub-clause (3) for notification of refusal of any further extension of time once the completion or extended completion date is past, which may be regarded as the equivalent of a certificate under clause 22 of the RIBA Conditions, so as to enable liquidated damages to be deducted—see clause 47 (4), *infra*, p. 121.

" *increased quantities referred to in clause 51 (3)* "

i.e. increases not due to a variation called for under clause 51, but to simple errors on the one hand, or under-estimates of quantities not capable of precise estimation at the time of tendering, so involving re-measurement under clauses 55 and 56. It might have been more logical and in accordance with the general drafting scheme of the present contract to have provided for this particular ground for extension of time in the new clause 56, which now expressly entitles either party (though in practice this will usually be the Contractor) to claim a financial re-calculation of the contract price, not necessarily at the same prices as those in the priced Bills, in the event of substantial differences in the ultimate quantities.

" *the Contractor shall within 28 days . . . or as soon thereafter as is reasonable* "

Not only is no sanction provided for this requirement, which is clearly not worded as a condition precedent, but sub-clause (2) invites and sub-clause (3) actually compels the Engineer (on his later second consideration of the matter) to award extensions not only where no detailed particulars have been supplied, but *even where no claim for an extension has been made at all.* This not only carries solicitude for the Contractor to excessive lengths, and requires a remarkable if not psychic knowledge of the Contractor's planning arrangements, but renders the present provision nugatory. Apart from this, the wording is not clear as to whether the particulars need only be supplied once it is possible to assess the full amount of an extension or whether (*e.g.* in the case of a still-continuing cause) the particulars need only indicate the claim in principle, or alternatively need only be supplied within 28 days of the cause commencing to operate. The words " or as soon thereafter as is reasonable " and " in order that such claim may be investigated at the time " may tend to support the one view, but the requirement of an assessment of the amount of the extension by the Engineer in sub-clause (2), *infra*, suggests the other. The lack of precision is regrettable but, in view of the absence of any sanction already referred to and the subsequent compulsion to consider an extension even without application, can only be academic.

Interim Assessment of Extension

(2) The Engineer shall upon receipt of such particulars or if he thinks fit in the absence of any such claim consider all the circumstances known to him at that time and make an assessment of the extension of time (if any) to which he considers the Contractor entitled for the completion of the Works or relevant Section and shall by notice in writing to the Contractor grant such extension of time for completion. In the event that the Contractor shall have made a claim for an extension of time but the Engineer considers the Contractor not entitled thereto the Engineer shall so inform the Contractor.

Assessment at Due Date for Completion

(3) The Engineer shall at or as soon as possible after the due date or extended date for completion (and whether or not the Contractor shall have made any claim for an extension of time) consider all the circumstances known to him at that time and take action similar to that provided for in sub-clause (2) of this Clause. Should the Engineer consider that the Contractor is not entitled to an extension of time he shall notify the Employer and the Contractor.

Final Determination of Extension

(4) The Engineer shall upon the issue of the Certificate of Completion of the Works or of the relevant Section review all the circumstances of the kind referred to in sub-clause (1) of this Clause and shall finally determine and certify to the Contractor the overall extension of time (if any) to which he considers the Contractor entitled in respect of the Works or any relevant Section. No such final review of the circumstances shall result in a decrease in any extension of time already granted by the Engineer pursuant to sub-clauses (2) or (3) of this Clause.

For the practical consequences in terms of liquidated damages, these sub-clauses need to be read with sub-clauses 47 (1) (b), (2) (b), (4) and (5).

It will be seen that these sub-clauses contemplate no less than *three* separate decisions by the Engineer at different times *on each matter* possibly justifying an extension, the first at the beginning or the end (which is not clear, see the commentary, *supra*) of each separate cause or event as it occurs during the contract. The words " at that time " in sub-clause (2) are not very apt to cover the contemplated case that there may have been no claim received from the Contractor—perhaps the intention is to refer to the time when the Contractor *ought* to have furnished the detailed particulars of his claim under the last part of sub-clause (1), which certainly would seem to attribute remarkable qualities of foresight to the Engineer. Under sub-clause (2), action by the Engineer is mandatory where particulars are received, and permissive where not, but again, no sanction is provided for the Contractor (*e.g.* that if no decision be given within a certain period any claimed extension shall be deemed to have been granted) and the decision under sub-clause (2) will in any event self-evidently not produce any immediate concrete financial results, since liquidated damages obviously cannot start to become due or be deducted under clause 47 (1) (b) and 47 (2) (b), *infra*, until the completion (or extended completion) date has passed, when a further decision of the

Engineer under sub-clause (3) is in any case required—see clause 47 (4) which confers the right to deduct the damages from sums otherwise payable at this (clause 44 (3)) stage. No account seems to have been taken in sub-clause (2), incidentally, of the fact that it is frequently not possible to reach separate extension of time decisions on individual delaying factors, which may often overlap with other matters justifying an extension or with delays for which the Contractor is responsible.

In spite of the lack of any immediate financial consequences under sub-clause (2), one serious danger for the Employer nevertheless arises under that sub-clause (as also sub-clause (3)), since contractors will undoubtedly argue that any decision which rejects the Contractor's application (which it will be seen the Engineer is bound to communicate in writing to the Contractor) can be held to be, by implication if not expressly, a statement of his opinion that the rate of progress is too slow to ensure completion by the completion or extended completion date. Taking advantage of the unfortunate mandatory language of clause 46, *infra*, the Contractor may then assert as a fact that, subsequently to the Engineer's decision, he has acted to accelerate progress, and make a financial claim on that ground, if in arbitration or litigation (or on a subsequent review by the Engineer under sub-clause (4)) he can successfully challenge the Engineer's earlier extension of time decision. See the commentary under clause 46, *infra*, p. 127, where, however, the correctness of this argument is doubted. See also the commentary to clause 14 (2), *supra*, p. 56, and to clause 51, *infra*, p. 156.

Under sub-clause (3) the Engineer's decision is now mandatory, whether or not the Contractor has applied for an extension of time. It seems a strange procedure that, with no special knowledge of the Contractor's methods or intentions other than that supplied in the clause 14 programme, and with probably even less knowledge of how the many matters justifying an extension of time under the contract may have affected the Contractor, either in simple quantitative terms or in terms of their absorption into the project without affecting the critical path of overall progress, the Engineer should nevertheless be forced into making an initial analysis, which for all practical purposes is likely to become a minimum period of extension (if granted) for negotiating purposes, in a case where the Contractor has not even claimed an extension of time, let alone supplied detailed supporting information. Indeed it will be noted that the final and later review in sub-clause (4) is expressly not permitted to reduce any extension granted under sub-clause (3). Furthermore, any increase in the extension of time on this final review may produce a financial claim for interest if any deductions of liquidated damages have taken place on the faith of the earlier decision—see clause 47 (5), *infra*.

A further ambiguity, of considerable practical importance, which in fact is present in nearly all U.K. standard forms of contract, may be expected to arise under sub-clause (4)—is the Engineer, in the course of the final review on actual completion, bound to grant still further extensions in respect of matters which did not take place until after the date of contract, or extended contract, completion, and so could not have been taken into account by him at the time of his sub-clause (3) assessment? In this context clauses 43 and 47 (1) (b) and 47 (5) need to be considered. The problem, in so far as it affects the certifier, does not usually arise in most U.K. contracts in such an acute form as it is likely to do in the present case, partly for the procedural reason that they usually contemplate only one decision on extension of time, which is designed to fix the extended contract completion date, and provide no machinery for a subsequent decision altering that date and possibly, therefore, retrospectively affecting the validity of deductions already made, other than ultimate review by an arbitrator or the courts. In these contracts the certifier will have been *functus officio* once the extended contract completion date has been fixed by him; so that the problem is more likely to concern the court or an arbitrator. Another reason why such claims for an extension of time will be defeated is that the liquidated damages clause merely quantifies what is in essence a breach of contract. Once a date is reached on which the contract ought to have been completed, the Contractor is in breach. If any supervening event occurs which might otherwise have justified an extension of time (*e.g.* bad weather or strikes), it can be argued with force that, but for the Contractor's earlier breach, the event would have had no effect—it is simply as a consequence of the earlier breach that further delay has been incurred, albeit that the delay might have been excusable at an earlier date when the Contractor was not in breach. This argument is obviously not valid, however, where the supervening event after the extended completion date is within the Employer's control or one for which he is responsible—*e.g.* the ordering of extra work, or failure to supply information on time, or the actions of other contractors of the Employer. The problem is accentuated by the fact that no machinery is to be found in any U.K. standard form regulating the adjustment of liquidated damages in such an event (where the Employer would, during the construction period, usually still be incurring damage as the result of the Contractor's original failure to complete to time). There are in fact three alternatives in such a situation—namely immediate repayment, or immediate suspension, or later suspension of liquidated damages. A little consideration will show that only later suspension is appropriate—assuming the policy, as *e.g.* in the case of clause 26 of the " Model A " standard form, commented on in F.B.E.F., p. 113, is indeed to permit extensions in respect of matters occurring after the extended contract completion date has passed (" Model A " in fact fails to grapple at all with the problem which it has created. The later suspension solution means that there must be machinery for subsequent certification of a notional completion date when, but for the supervening event, the works would in the Engineer's opinion as a fact have been completed, and for this to bring the further accumulation and deduction of liquidated damages to an end notwithstanding that all the works are not yet complete; and then to reinstate the running of liquidated damages if unjustifiable delay occurs in the completion of the outstanding balance of work.

In the present contract sub-clause (3) requires the Engineer at the extended date for completion (*i.e.* the date he judges to be the final extended date) to " consider all the circumstances known to him *at that time* " and make his assessment, notifying the Contractor of any extension, as in the case of sub-clause (2). Sub-clause (4) then requires the Engineer on *actual* completion to " *review* all the circumstances *of the kind referred to in sub-clause* (*1*) " and further provides that " *No such final review* of the circumstances " shall result in a reduced extension of time. Furthermore, clause 47 (5) refers in its opening line to sub-clause (4) as a *final review* of the circumstances causing delay, and its machinery for immediate repayment can only apply to a final decision on extension of time made after construction is completed when immediate repayment will obviously be appropriate. It is submitted that the language of sub-clause (4), therefore, contemplates a review of an earlier decision made in a pre-existing situation rather than a later decision made in the light of new facts which had not occurred and would not have been taken into account at the date of the earlier decision. The difficulty of course remains as to the position if the Engineer wishes to order extra work or some other event for which the Employer is contractually responsible (*e.g.* the encountering of unfavourable conditions under clause 12) occurs after the contract or extended contract completion date which would otherwise have entitled the Contractor to an extension of time. In some cases Contractors have even sought to argue for tactical reasons that variations cannot be ordered at this stage, but there seems no reason either of law or practical necessity why the Contractor's being in more than usually serious culpable delay should have the effect of depriving the Employer of a right to which he would otherwise be entitled. It can only be said that this contract, like the majority of the U.K. standard forms, neither appears to have contemplated the possibility of such an event, nor to provide any appropriate machinery for adjustment of liquidated damages. It would seem wrong in principle to invalidate the liquidated damages clause altogether in such a situation (as stated, it should be noted that the greater the original culpable delay on the part of the Contractor, leading for example to very little progress with the project by the contract or extended contract completion date, the greater the practical likelihood of such a subsequent event). It is very tentatively suggested that the solution may lie in some implied term bringing the liability to pay liquidated damages to an end at the time when, but for the supervening event, the work would have been completed, at least in those cases where the Employer is not in breach of contract but is financially responsible for the supervening event, and where the event cannot be shown to be a consequence of the Contractor's original breach in being late (as *e.g.* bad weather or a national strike would be, but an unfavourable physical condition under clause 12 or a variation usually would not). In cases where the Employer is in breach (as *e.g.* late instructions) the choice lies between invalidating the liquidated damages clause altogether (on the principle of the old " prevention " cases, already referred to *supra*, p. 118, and see Hudson, 10th ed., pp. 625–635) or quite simply reducing the liquidated damages appropriately as part of the damage arising from the Employer's breach—it is suggested that the latter is a both simple and sufficient escape from a problem arising essentially from the inadequacy of the contract and (usually) the gravity of the Contractor's original breach of contract. Where the supervening event would not have affected the work but for the Contractor's original breach, no difficulty, of course, arises.

No doubt the intention of the clause as a whole is to give the Contractor the earliest possible advance warning of the Engineer's attitude to the Contractor's claims for extension, so that if necessary he can balance the advantage of altering his arrangements to increase progress so as to avoid liquidated damages against the cost of doing so, and the reason for the prohibition on any reduction of earlier extensions in the final review is to prevent any such programming decisions taken by the Contractor on the faith of the earlier extensions being subsequently falsified. In addition, it may be conceded that in practice Engineers frequently do seek to avoid or postpone giving a decision on extensions of time while simultaneously calling for increased progress by the Contractor. Nevertheless, it is difficult to understand why any further review is provided for after the contract or extended contract completion date (the obviously important date, because it is then that in the Engineer's opinion the Contractor will be in breach and the Employer will become entitled under the contract to start deducting liquidated damages) and the requirement for this " final review " to take place on actual completion seems calculated only to perpetuate what in practice will often have become a voluminous and inconclusive correspondence between the Contractor and the Engineer, once the Contractor has become aware that his arguments on extension of time have not been accepted. The policy of the new sub-clause seems to be basically contractor-orientated, and to place the Engineer under the obligation, even in the absence of claims or details, to commit himself to an excessive number of successive decisions on extension of time.

It should, incidentally, be noted that the certification or notification of his decisions provided for in sub-clauses (3) and (4) differs in detail from the certification etc. assumed or required if liquidated damages are to be deducted—see clause 47 (4), which appears to assume that both sub-clauses

(3) and (4) require *certification*, and the commentary thereto, *infra*, p. 136. This appears to be *per incuriam*, but it may have the almost certainly unintended effect of preventing the Contractor from " early arbitration " of liquidated damages deductions by the Employer, since on one view at least of the wording there will be no " withholding " of a *certificate* within clause 66 (2), *infra*, until the clause 44 (4) stage. On the other hand, clause 47 (4) appears to require a certificate even at the 44 (3) stage (or rather to assume, incorrectly, that clause 44 (3) so provides).

Night and Sunday Work

45. Subject to any provision to the contrary contained in the Contract none of the Works shall be executed during the night or on Sundays without the permission in writing of the Engineer save when the work is unavoidable or absolutely necessary for the saving of life or property or for the safety of the Works in which case the Contractor shall immediately advise the Engineer or the Engineer's Representative. Provided always that this Clause shall not be applicable in the case of any work which it is customary to carry out outside normal working hours or by rotary or double shifts.

Rate of Progress

46. If for any reason which does not entitle the Contractor to an extension of time the rate of progress of the Works or any Section is at any time in the opinion of the Engineer too slow to ensure completion by the prescribed time or extended time for completion the Engineer shall so notify the Contractor in writing and the Contractor shall thereupon take such steps as are necessary and the Engineer may approve to expediate progress so as to complete the Works or such Section by the prescribed time or extended time. The Contractor shall not be entitled to any additional payment for taking such steps. If as a result of any notice given by the Engineer under this Clause the Contractor shall seek the Engineer's permission to do any work at night or on Sundays such permission shall not be unreasonably refused.

These two clauses require to be read together. No doubt the policy reasons for clause 45 arise from a combination of statutory or trades union requirements, or possibly objections by adjoining owners or occupiers. A basic ambiguity in these clauses in the 1954 edition (see B.C.F., p. 369) has now been removed, in that the new opening words of clause 46, and the reference to the Engineer's notice at the beginning of its last sentence, make it clear that the right to request night or Sunday working will only arise (a) if the Contractor is in *culpable* default on progress *and* (b) if he is in receipt of the Engineer's notice requiring accelerated progress. The specific right to an extension of time on refusal of permission has been removed, no doubt because of the wide right to an extension of time for all Engineer's instructions now conferred by clause 13 (1)—to which latter clause, in the shape of the new clause 13 (2), *supra*, p. 56, incidentally, the 1954 opening sentence of clause 46 (requiring the approval of the Engineer in regard to a wide range of matters including method and sequence of working) has now been transplanted. In addition, the provisions in regard to noise in the old clause 46 have also been moved to the new clause 29 (2), *supra*, p. 93.

It has already been pointed out in the commentary to clause 44 (*supra*, p. 122) that notification of refusal of an extension of time under sub-clauses (2) and (3) of that clause, now mandatory, might well be construed, particularly if accompanied by the adverse comments on progress likely to be used by Engineers in correspondence with defaulting Contractors, as an instruction under clause 46, with the consequence that, if the Engineer's decision was altered in favour of the Contractor on a subsequent review by the Engineer under sub-clauses (3) or (4), or by an arbitrator or the courts, a financial claim might be advanced under either clause 13 (1), or even under clause 51 (see the new and significantly wider wording of the definition of variations in clause 51 (1)—" changes in the specified sequence . . . or timing of construction." It might even be argued that the (traditional) use of the word " shall " in clause 46 now imposes a mandatory obligation on the Engineer arising during construction, particularly since the contract (see clauses 44 (2) and (3)) now specifically requires extension of time decisions to be made and refusals notified during the construction period.

It is submitted that, although the wording is not precise, this could hardly represent the policy intention, and that the clause 46 power is in the nature of an option which the Employer may or may not exercise; but in the Employer's interests the choice of wording, including the use of the word " shall," is lamentable, since it is self-evident that no sanction has been provided for the enforcement against the Contractor of clause 46, which therefore is mere verbiage from this point of view and adds nothing in practical terms to the " due expedition " obligation of the Contractor in clause 41, *supra*, and his liquidated damages liability under clause 47, *infra*, whereas the Employer becomes exposed both to a demand to be permitted to do night or Sunday working, which might be prejudicial to the Employer and give rise to third party claims, but which if refused might give rise to a claim under clause 13 (3), as well as, in the case of disallowed extensions of time, to the more general financial liability for all other costs of accelerating progress already referred to, which in view of the new requirements of clause 44 (2) and (3) cannot be regarded as entirely fanciful, but which is nevertheless plainly incorrect.

" *work . . . outside normal working hours or by rotary or double shifts* "

The commonest example of this in the civil engineering industry in the U.K. is tunnelling work.

LIQUIDATED DAMAGES AND LIMITATION OF DAMAGES FOR DELAYED COMPLETION

Liquidated Damages for Whole of Works

47. (1) (a) In the Appendix to the Form of Tender under the heading " Liquidated Damages for Delay " there is stated in column 1 the sum which represents the Employer's genuine pre-estimate (expressed as a rate per week or per day as the case may be) of the damages likely to be suffered by him in the event that the whole of the Works shall not be completed within the time prescribed by Clause 43.

Provided that in lieu of such sum there may be stated such lesser sum as represents the limit of the Contractor's liability for damages for failure to complete the whole of the Works within the time for completion therefor or any extension thereof granted under Clause 44.

(b) If the Contractor should fail to complete the whole of the Works within the prescribed time or any extension thereof granted under Clause 44 the Contractor shall pay to the Employer for such default the sum stated in column 1 aforesaid for every week or day as the case may be which shall elapse between the date on which the prescribed time or any extension thereof expired and the date of completion of the whole of the Works. Provided that if any part of the Works not being a Section or part of a Section shall be certified as complete pursuant to Clause 48 before completion of the whole of the Works the sum stated in column 1 shall be reduced by the proportion which the value of the part completed bears to the value of the whole of the Works.

Liquidated Damages for Sections

(2) (a) In cases where any Section shall be required to be completed within a particular time as stated in the Appendix to the Form of Tender there shall also be stated in the said Appendix under the heading " Liquidated Damages for Delay " in column 2 the sum by which the damages stated in column 1 or the limit of the Contractor's said liability as the case may be shall be reduced upon completion of each such Section and in column 3 the sum which represents the Employer's genuine pre-estimate (expressed as aforesaid) of any specific damage likely to be suffered by him in the event that such Section shall not be completed within that time.

Provided that there may be stated in column 3 in lieu of such sum such lesser sum as represents the limit of the Contractor's liability for failure to complete the relevant Section within the relevant time.

(b) If the Contractor should fail to complete any Section within the relevant time for completion or any extension thereof granted under Clause 44 the Contractor shall pay to the Employer for such default the sum stated in column 3 aforesaid for every week or day as the case may be which shall elapse between the date on which the relevant time or any extension thereof expired and the date of completion of the relevant Section. Provided that:—

(i) if completion of a Section shall be delayed beyond the due date for completion of the whole of the Works the damages payable under sub-clauses (1) and (2) of this Clause until completion of that Section shall be the sum stated in column 1 plus in respect of that Section the sum stated in column 3 less the sum stated in column 2;

(ii) if any part of a Section shall be certified as complete pursuant to Clause 48 before completion of the whole thereof the sums stated in columns 2 and 3 in respect of that Section shall be reduced by the proportion which the value of the part bears to the value of the Section and the sum stated in column 1 shall be reduced by the same amount as the sum in column 2 is reduced; and

(iii) upon completion of any such Section the sum stated in column 1 shall be reduced by the sum stated in column 2 in respect of that Section at the date of such completion.

Damages not a Penalty

(3) All sums payable by the Contractor to the Employer pursuant to this Clause shall be paid as liquidated damages for delay and not as a penalty.

Clause 47 needs to be read with clause 1 (1) (m), with the extension of time provisions in clause 44 (2) (3) and (4), and with the certification of completion provisions in clause 48. This new clause is far more complicated than its predecessor in the Fourth Edition, and contains major problems of interpretation. Before considering it in detail a general summary may be desirable.

By sub-clause (2), the clause now contemplates that in some contracts the Appendix will prescribe different completion dates for separate identified phases or parts of the Works (in the contract called " Sections " —see the definition of " Section " in clause 1 (1) (m)) and will state separate liquidated damages for the individual identified Sections. It might seem to follow, though the contract is not specific about this, that any part or parts of the Works which are only required to be completed on the same final overall completion date as the whole of the Works (see Column 1 of the Appendix and sub-clause (1) (a)) should not be designated or identified as a separate Section described in the Appendix in accordance with sub-clause (2) (a)—*i.e.* that Sections should usually be parts of the works with completion dates *earlier* than the overall completion date, and all other work will be covered by the overall liquidated damages sum and contract period for the whole works set out in Column 1 of the Appendix —see the wording of sub-clause (1) (b) proviso and the commentary on it *infra*, p. 132. However, machinery for *reduction* of the overall liquidated damages by fixed sums, also set out in the Appendix, to take account of previously completed individual Sections is contained in sub-clause (2)—see Proviso (iii), *infra*, to that sub-clause—and depending on the intention underlying this machinery, it may be that Sections should sometimes be so designated notwithstanding that their completion dates are the same as that for the whole Works.

Clause 48 contains the consequential machinery required for certification of completion of the separate contractual Sections so as to bring the sectional liquidated damages to an end—see clause 48 (2) (a)—but in addition it also contains the two previous powers in the Fourth Edition, one discretionary (clause 48 (3)) and the other mandatory in cases where the Employer has in fact resumed possession (clause 48 (2) (b)), for certification of completion of a part of the Works before the whole, quite independently of the provisions for completion of contractual Sections. These latter " partial completion " certificates will reduce, not by fixed sums stated in the Appendix as in the case of completed Sections, but by a proportion of the stipulated liquidated damages based on the proportionate value of the completed part, either the liquidated damages for any relevant Section of which a part has been so certified as complete (see sub-clause (2) (b) Proviso (ii)), or the liquidated damages for the whole Works (see the Proviso at the end of sub-clause (1) (b)) in cases where no Section is involved.

If this complication were not enough, it will be seen from sub-clause (2) (a) that the contract not only contemplates, perfectly understandably, that a separate sum shall be stipulated as liquidated damages for each Section (Column 3 in the Appendix) but also, as already indicated, that another quite separate *and possibly different* sum is to be stipulated for that same Section, representing the reduction in the overall liquidated damages for the whole Works if that Section is completed before the whole. No explanation for the differentiation so contemplated between these " damages " and " credit " sums for a Section is given, and an analysis of the intention, and hence of the interpretation and application of sub-clause (2) (b), which deals with the reductions in liquidated damages as various Sections or parts are completed, is in consequence a matter of the greatest difficulty, if not a near impossibility, and will also pose extraordinary problems for the professional advisers responsible for the initial preparation of a scheme for sectional completion and liquidated damages in the contract documentation.

Sub-clause (4) of the present clause seeks to confer and regulate the vitally important power to deduct liquidated damages from sums otherwise payable under the contract. Sub-clause (5) attempts to deal with the situation should the successive reviews of extension of time decisions now required by sub-clauses (3) and (4) of clause 44, *supra*, result in a later increased extension of time being awarded, after deductions have commenced based on an earlier stricter decision. As pointed out in the commentary to clause 44 (*supra*, pp. 122–125), however, the contract does not appear to contemplate or deal with the very real problem of events occurring after the contract or extended contract completion dates which would, had they occurred before those dates, have entitled the Contractor to an extension of time. As previously explained in the commentary to clause 44, *supra*, pp. 122–125, this is a matter of great difficulty even in a straightforward case of liquidated damages for the Works as a whole, let alone in cases complicated by Sectional completion dates and Sectional liquidated damages, and the requirements for repeated extension of time decisions in clause 44.

Turning to the clauses in more detail, the reference in sub-clause (1) (a), repeated in the case of sub-clause (2) (a) in the case of the individual sections, to a " genuine pre-estimate " by the Employer, together with the provisos in the two sub-clauses in regard to the alternative basis being a limit of the Contractor's liability for damages due to delay, are formal assertions that the relevant sums in the Appendix come within one or other of the two legally respectable and enforceable categories of fixed monetary damages, as opposed to the legally unenforceable category, called by lawyers a penalty—see also sub-clause (3), which, in addition, formally denies in terms that the sums are penalties. (It may be noted, incidentally, that the present wording, coupled with the wording of the Appendix gives no indication as to which one of the two permitted categories the stipulated sums in any particular contract in fact belong.)

In law, however, no statements or descriptions or assertions of this kind in a contract, particularly in standard printed conditions, will have the slightest effect, the question of penalty or no being decided as a matter of law on the particular facts—it even being irrelevant, for example, that a sum is expressly described as a penalty if in truth it is a genuine pre-estimate of damage—for the law on this subject, see Hudson, 10th ed., pp. 618–624.

At the present day, and in the context of building and civil engineering contracts, it can be said fairly safely that the nineteenth century antipathy of the English courts, in what was fundamentally a customer-dominated society, against liquidated damages imposed on contractors has, with the considerable changes in the balance of economic power in favour of producers, greatly diminished, and the convenience and practical advantages of such clauses in appropriate situations have been recognised. It is, in fact, extremely difficult for an employer in a great number of civil engineering projects to show that he has suffered clear-cut financial damage as a consequence of delay by the contractor since, for example, many public works involve no element of commercial profit, and indeed the rental or other receipts from the completed project may require to be subsidised and not even balance current expenditure, while any increased cost of capital financing due to delay is often balanced by the reduction in the interest consequent upon the postponed capital expenditure on interim payment under the contract. Indeed in projects of this kind it is often a fiction that the Employer himself will suffer any strictly financial damage at all as the result of delay, though the damage to others (*e.g.* inhabitants or ratepayers deprived of an amenity like an improved water supply or drainage or transport system) may be very substantial if intangible, while the Employer himself (as *e.g.* a local authority) may suffer intangible but substantial administrative or political damage as the result of public planning and projects being disrupted or delayed. It is, paradoxically, precisely in this sort of situation that liquidated damages for delay in meeting a completion date are such an important and useful remedy as a sanction against culpable delay by a contractor, in substitution for ordinary damages for late completion, or for breach of the " due expedition " obligation in clause 41, *supra.*

(1) (a) " . . . a rate per week or per day . . ."

Unlike the Fourth Edition, this wording will mean that if weekly damages are stipulated a complete week must elapse before the stipulated sum is recovered. Apportionment will not, it is submitted, be permitted. (See also the same wording in the case of Sections in sub-clause (2) (b), *infra.*)

(1) (b) " should fail to complete "

i.e. the " substantial " completion referred to in clause 48, which is not precisely defined—see *infra*, p. 141.

(1) (b) Proviso " not being a Section or part of a Section "

If *part* of a Section is involved, sub-clause (2) (b) Proviso (ii) will apply with the same result (*i.e.* proportionate reduction based on value) so as to reduce both the liquidated damages for the whole of the Works in Column 1, and the liquidated damages and " credit " sums for the Section (if any) in question in Columns 3 and 2 respectively. If an entire Section is involved, sub-clause (2) (b) Proviso (iii) will apply, and the reduction will be the fixed sum (if any) in Column 2 for that Section—see *infra*, p. 134. The present Proviso, therefore, applies either to cases where there are no sections at all stipulated in the Appendix, or to cases where there are some parts of the Works not comprehended in any of the stipulated Sections (it has already been suggested, *supra*, p. 129, that usually there will be no reason to designate as Sections those parts of the Works with the same completion date as the final completion date) and the present wording lends some support for this—see, however, the commentary to sub-clause (2) (b) Proviso (i), *infra.* It should be noted that the Column 2 figure, in addition to being a credit figure to be used following completion of a Section, will also have an effect under sub-clause (2) (b) Proviso (i) on the computation of Sectional liquidated damages during any period when a Section is delayed beyond the overall (extended) contract completion date for the whole Works.

(2) (a) " in Column 2 the sum by which the damages . . . in Column 1 . . . shall be reduced "

It is extremely difficult to deduce from the contract what the intention is in permitting or inviting possibly different sums to be inserted in Column 2 from the Column 3 liquidated damages for a Section, for the purpose of reducing the Column 1 liquidated damages for the whole works upon completion of the Section in question; the lack of guidance is doubly unfortunate because it might well be argued that if the Column 2 " credit " for a completed section was smaller than the Column 3 " liquidated damages " for the same Section, then the latter could not be a genuine pre-estimate, and so might be excessive and a penalty, or alternatively, if the reverse was the case and the sum in Column 2 the greater, that the Column 1 liquidated damages for the whole Works (being presumably inclusive of the Column 2 sums) might, prior to completion of the Section, be excessive and in the nature of a penalty.

One explanation given in response to inquiries has been that delay in completing a part of a project may expose the Employer to a special loss, in the shape of liability to compensate third persons such as other contractors, installers of machinery etc. or adjoining occupiers, in addition to his own loss arising solely from loss of use of the completed project or Section of the project. On this view it would follow that the damages in Column 3, representing both these elements, should exceed the " credit " in Column 2 for any relevant Section, the latter being concerned with the loss of use element only. If this is the intention, the Column 1 figure might be expected to be the total of the various Sectional Column 2 figures (plus the " use " value of any non-Sectional work) but not of the Column 3 Sectional figures. However, there seems no reason why such special " disturbance " or " third party " losses on delay of the various Sections should not be equally reflected in the stipulated overall Column 1 damages for delay for the whole Works, until such time as they were eliminated by completion of the relevant Section—if so a credit identical to, and not differing from, the Column 3 damages stipulated for the relevant Section would be appropriate.

Another related explanation might be that the damages suffered by late delivery of Sections before the overall completion date differ in kind from the damages suffered after that date, the former being primarily concerned with consequential liabilities of the Employer to third persons etc., whereas the latter would be primarily concerned with the " commercial " or other damage of delayed entry by the Employer. On this view the earlier liquidated damages for individual Sections might be smaller or greater than, but quite different in kind from, a proportionate share of the later overall damages. A third explanation might be connected with considerations of a possible limitation of liability rather than a liquidated damages basis applying either to the Sections or to the whole Works, or in varying degrees to both. Again, a particular Section might not be critical to the use of the remainder of the Works, justifying a " Nil " figure in Column 2, and no part of the Column 1 figure being attributable to it.

But whatever explanation is offered, consideration of sub-clause (2) (b) and its very difficult Provisos (i) and (iii) for reducing liquidated damages on completion of a Section may give a clue to what is intended. At first sight it would seem that, while sub-clause (2) (b) Proviso (iii) will, if a relatively large sum is stipulated in Column 2 for a particular Section, bring about an equivalent reduction in overall liquidated damages on completion of the

Section, and so will act as a relatively substantial incentive to progress should other Sections of the work be incomplete, its effect on the liquidated damages for that particular Section while it remains incomplete will, as a consequence of the " Column 1 minus Column 2 plus Column 3 " formula in Proviso (i), be substantially to reduce those liquidated damages, and hence act as a disincentive. On further consideration, however, a relationship between the three columns which will avoid such an analysis is one where, if a particular Section has a " loss of use " value x, plus a " disturbance " or " third party " value of y, then Column 2 will be x, Column 3 will be $x+y$, and Column 1 will include a sum equal to x in respect of that particular Section. After the overall completion date, the damages under Proviso (i) while the Section remains incomplete will therefore be Column 1 (includes x) less Column 2 (x) plus Column 3 ($x+y$)—*i.e.*, in total, the overall liquidated damages for the other Sections plus x plus y. If there was no " disturbance " or " third party " element of damage in regard to a Section, then Column 3 would be the same as Column 2. If this is the correct view, Column 3 should never, whatever the circumstances, be less than Column 2 (in the absence of complications such as limitation of liability being the basis for the stipulated sums).

This is, however, only speculation as to what is intended, and the only safe course, in the absence of guidance and to avoid possible arguments as to penalties, should be for Employers to see that some explanation of the relationships between the three columns should be afforded in the contract documents, particularly if dissimilar sums are stated in Columns 2 and 3 bearing no clear relationship in total to the sum in Column 1.

(*2*) (*b*) " *Provided that:—*

(*i*) *if completion of a Section shall be delayed beyond the due date for completion of the whole Works . . .*

(*iii*) *upon completion of any such Section the sum stated in Column 1 shall be reduced by the sum stated in Column 2 . . .*"

The substantive part of sub-clause (2) (b) deals with the period between the Sectional completion date and the overall completion date. During this period the Column 3 Sectional damages will apply. After the overall completion date, Proviso (i) introduces the " Column 1 less Column 2 plus Column 3 " formula which, in effect, will mean that the Column 3 damages will continue, plus the proportion of the Column 1 overall liquidated damages attributable to the other parts of the Works—provided that the three columns have been priced in accordance with the principles and explanations suggested in the commentary to sub-clause (2) (a), *supra*.

The words " any such Section " in Proviso (iii) must be intended to refer, it is submitted, to Proviso (i) (*i.e.* to any Section delayed beyond the due date for completion of the whole of the Works) as well as Proviso (ii), though the draftsmanship is not perfect and the word " such " could well have been omitted to avoid ambiguity. The words in Proviso (i) " the sum stated in Column 1 plus *in respect of that Section* " coupled with the reference to sub-clause (1) make it plain that, in the event of there being more than one Section which is incomplete, the principal sum in Column 1 for the whole works will not be duplicated in the calculation of the damages for each delayed section—*i.e.* the words are equivalent to " plus in respect of each delayed Section."

Proviso (ii) is purely consequential upon a possible exercise of the Engineer's power to certify completion of some but not all of the works in a Section either on the discretionary basis in clause 48 (3), *infra*, or on the mandatory basis in clause 48 (2) (b), *infra*. In such cases (as in the similar case of partial certifications where no Sections are involved covered by the Proviso to clause 47 (1) (b), *supra*) the concept of a proportion based on value is used to effect the necessary modifications of the Sectional liquidated damages. Final completion of the Section after its partial completion will then bring into play the machinery under Proviso (iii).

Deduction of Liquidated Damages

(4) If the Engineer shall under Clause 44 (3) or (4) have determined and certified any extension of time to which he considers the Contractor entitled and shall have notified the Employer and the Contractor that he is of the opinion that the Contractor is not entitled to any or any further extension of time the Employer may deduct and retain from any sum otherwise payable by the Employer to the Contractor hereunder the amount which in the event that the Engineer's said opinion should not be subsequently revised would be the amount of the liquidated damages payable by the Contractor under this Clause.

The preceding sub-clauses (1), (2) and (3) make provision for the payment of liquidated damages (see sub-clauses (1) (b) and (2) (b)) by the Contractor to the Employer. This has the effect in law of entitling the Employer to sue the Contractor for the sums in question. The present two sub-clauses are concerned with the alternative remedy of *deduction* of liquidated damages from sums currently due to the Contractor during the contract, the commercial preferability and importance of which, particularly in times of stringent or expensive credit, and the possible length of proceedings required finally to establish the Employer's claim, need no emphasising.

Sub-clauses (4) and (5), like most U.K. standard forms, lay down a machinery for deduction which is dependent, in broad terms, upon the opinion or decision of the Engineer as to whether the Contractor's progress has been satisfactory. It will be remembered that clause 44 provides for separate decisions by the Engineer on extension of time at three stages. It is clear that deduction could not depend upon the first stage decisions made on the occurrence of delaying events under clause 44 (2), but on the second-stage decision under clause 44 (3) (expiry of the extended contract period) a negative decision against further extensions will, if justified, signify the start of the period for liquidated damages to run. On the other hand, a positive decision giving a further extension at the clause 44 (3) stage will in effect involve a further postponement or repetition of the clause 44 (3) decision itself—this eventuality does not, however, explain the use of the words " subsequent or " in the opening words of sub-clause (5) of the present clause, which seem to be inappropriate.

It will be seen that clause 44 requires the Engineer, if he thinks fit, to " make an *assessment* of the extension of time " and, if not, so to " inform " the Contractor under clause 44 (2), but at the more important clause 44 (3) stage, so to " notify " both Employer and Contractor of his refusal. The word " certificate " as such is not used in clause 44 (2) or 44 (3). The more detailed documentation at *either* the clause 44 (3) or 44 (4) stage required by sub-clause (4) of the present clause, however, on which deduction of damages depends, is (a) *certification* and determination (which clause 44 (4) does require at that stage) of any extension of time which the Engineer has granted and (b) *notification* to both Employer and Contractor that the Engineer " is of opinion that the Contractor is not entitled to any or any further extension of time." (Whether the later requirement is the same as " a notice under this contract " so as to bring the formal delivery and posting requirements of clause 68 into play is unclear, but in view of the importance of this notification it will be prudent for Engineers to assume that this is so and act accordingly). The opening words of clause 47 (4) are in fact, therefore, not correct, since clause 44 (3), unlike clause 44 (4), does *not* make provision in terms for " determination *and certification* " of an extension. Again, Engineers will be wise formally to *certify* their clause 44 (3) extension of time decisions at that stage, as required by the present clause, and since the requirements of clause 60 (8) with regard to certificates do not apply to a certificate under the present clause, would be best advised to issue identical certificates to each party together with the necessary notification, in the absence of any indication to the contrary and in view of the dual notification requirement (the clause 44 (4) certificate is by that clause required to be issued to the Contractor only, it should be noted, but again the procedure in the present clause should be followed).

It will be seen that a number of minor inconsistencies exist between the machinery in clauses 44 (3) and 44 (4) and the present sub-clause. This may be *per incuriam*, or it may be the deliberate intention that the power to deduct in the present clause should be procedurally somewhat more circumscribed than the simple power to recover in sub-clauses (1) (b), (2) (b) and (3); but in any event it is important for Engineers to adopt the most meticulous approach to their decisions and documentation in regard to extension of time and liquidated damages, since any error, however trivial or technical, will naturally be seized upon by advisers to Contractors anxious to avoid the liquidated damages liability, in view of the strict attitude which the Courts, at least in the past, have adopted towards such clauses.

It will be seen that, as in nearly all U.K. standard forms, the scheme of the present contract is for the liquidated damages themselves not to be dealt with in any monetary certificate of the Engineer, but simply for calculation by the Employer and then deduction at his discretion from any sums certified in subsequent monetary certificates under clause 60—see the words " any sum otherwise payable by the Contractor to the Employer hereunder " in the present sub-clause, and the absence of any provision for reduction of the amount to be certified under clause 60, to which these words of course refer. Nearly all the standard forms of building and civil engineering contract in the U.K. also contain similar machinery for the determination of extensions of time, and hence the liability to pay liquidated damages, which in one way or another is dependent upon the opinion of the Architect or Engineer. Two questions of major practical importance arise in this context. These are

(a) If the Engineer has duly certified culpable delay, is the Contractor bound by the Engineer's decision?

(b) If the Engineer has refused or failed to certify delay, or has granted extensions, is the Employer bound?

(It should be made clear that, in the light of the wide powers to review the Engineer's or Architect's decisions in the arbitration clauses of most U.K. contracts, what is at issue is a question of *temporary*, not *permanent* finality—*i.e.* will the Engineer's decision be given effect to until such time as an arbitrator, or if no arbitrator the courts, have finally determined the matter? Present financial stringencies lend an importance to such questions which they have never previously had.)

The first problem is not usually a serious one, since what is involved is deduction by the Employer from sums claimed by the Contractor. Even without an express provision like the present one specifically permitting deduction of damages, a defendant setting up a bona fide claim for damages due to delay will normally be permitted to set this off against the Contractor's claim on an interim certificate—see *Young* v. *Kitchin* (1878) L.R. 3 Ex. 127 and *Hanak* v. *Green* [1958] 2 Q.B. 9. It is true that the Court of Appeal, in a number of recent decisions starting with the case of *Dawnays Ltd.* v. *Minter* [1971] 1 W.L.R. 1205, did accord such a " temporary finality " to interim certificates for payment—see the author's article in (1973) 89 L.Q.R. 36 criticising this—but the classical view was reasserted by the House of Lords in *Gilbert-Ash Ltd.* v. *Modern Engineering Ltd.* [1974] A.C. 689 (for this case and the above article see Appendix B, *post*, p. 317). There can be no doubt whatever about the position under the present contract by virtue of the express provisions permitting deduction from monies due. A case of deduction following a validly certified Engineer's decision in the Employer's favour therefore presents no problem, but the legal question would be highlighted in a case where the liquidated damages happened to outweigh any sums owing to the Contractor, thus compelling the Employer to sue the Contractor. Could the Contractor avoid judgment and obtain leave to defend on raising a prima facie case on the facts? Sub-clause (5), *infra*, makes it clear beyond any doubt (if clause 66 did not also do so) that in such an event an arbitrator would *ultimately* have power to override the Engineer's decision and award an extension, but the " sums recovered pursuant to " sub-clause (3) (which does not necessarily involve deduction) in sub-clause (5) might suggest that until adjudication in an arbitration (which incidentally can, it would seem, start before the end of the work under clause 66 (2), since the dispute will involve " the withholding of a certificate to which the Contractor claims to be entitled ") or else in the courts, effect should be given to the Engineer's decision and the Employer should be entitled to deduct *or recover* the liquidated damages, subject to later repayment as envisaged in sub-clause (5), *infra*. (Here again, however, there may very well be a drafting error, and the reference in sub-clause (5) to sub-clause (3) may be *per incuriam* and sub-clause (4) may really be intended.)

There is no authority in the U.K. on this point; it may be said that while on the one hand the English courts appear to find some difficulty in giving practical effect to the concept of " temporary finality," disputes as to extensions of time are always inherently matters of opinion on the facts, so that the court is faced with the alternative of either giving temporary effect to the Engineer's extension of time decisions made in accordance with the contractual machinery, until overruled by an arbitrator or the courts, or else holding, in effect, that the elaborate machinery provided is otiose and to be of no practical effect should the Contractor dispute the decision on the merits (as of course almost invariably happens in real life). There is also the important consideration that in the opposite situation (where the Engineer in effect takes the side of the Contractor) there is now authority which appears to recognise the concept of " temporary finality " (see immediately *infra*).

This poses the second question set out above—namely the opposite situation where the Engineer grants an extension or refuses the necessary certificate (in this case that no further extension is justified) enabling damages to be recovered. Can the Employer still deduct or sue without the necessary certificate or notification, or is he bound to await the establishment of his claim in arbitration or litigation and meanwhile pay the Contractor in full? In the present contract the relevant wording is that in the present sub-clause (4), and in the RIBA main contract forms clause 22 is the relevant provision. In the case of the FASS form of nominated sub-contract, the Court of Appeal have decided in *Brightside, Kilpatrick Ltd.* v. *Mitchell Construction* [1975] 2 Lloyd's Rep. 493, (1976) 1 B.L.R. 62, that compliance with the proviso to clause 8 (a) of that sub-contract was a condition precedent, and without the required architect's certificate (that the work should reasonably have been completed) there could be no deduction of damages by the main contractor, so that the sub-contractor was entitled to judgment in full for monies due under the sub-contract. The decision does not make it plain whether the dispute could be subsequently arbitrated or litigated, but there seems no doubt this must be so. However, the wording in that form of contract was somewhat stronger and referred expressly to the certificate in question as a " condition precedent " to the recovery of liquidated damages. In principle, it is submitted, despite the different view rightly taken by the courts as to the lack of binding force in the case of interim certificates for payment, that since a right to deduct liquidated damages for delay can have most serious adverse commercial results for both parties to the contract, they can reasonably be presumed to intend, if providing for those matters to be decided during the currency of the project by the opinion and certification of the Engineer in what is essentially a dispute situation (unlike interim certification of the value of work done) that his opinion or certificate should be binding for the time being on both parties, and that the provisions in most U.K. contracts enabling the Engineer's decision on questions of extension of time to be reviewed by an arbitrator are not to be interpreted as preventing the Engineer's decision from taking effect during the currency of the project until such time as an arbitrator or the courts have finally determined the matter. If this is so, it will usually apply, as a matter of presumed intention, whether the Engineer grants an extension of time (so preventing deduction or recovery of the damages) or refuses it (so permitting deduction or recovery). In each case, it is submitted, the decision will be " temporarily final," but the matter must await final resolution by the Courts.

Reimbursement of Liquidated Damages

(5) If upon a subsequent or final review of the circumstances causing delay the Engineer shall grant an extension or further extension of time or if an arbitrator appointed under Clause 66 shall decide that the Engineer should have granted such an extension or further extension of time the Employer shall no longer be entitled to liquidated damages in respect of the period of such extension of time. Any sums in respect of such period which may have been recovered pursuant to sub-clause (3) of this Clause shall be reimbursable forthwith to the Contractor together with interest at the rate provided for in Clause 60 (6) from the date on which such liquidated damages were recovered from the Contractor.

This clause deals with the possibility that a later decision under clause 44 may grant or increase a previously refused or inadequate extension of time. The words " subsequent or " appear to be *per incuriam*, since under clause 44 there is only one decision which can start liquidated damages running—that under clause 44 (3) after the (extended) contract date for completion and before the " final review " under clause 44 (4) (after actual completion). The present sub-clause can only apply, therefore, to the clause 44 final review. For a discussion of the very difficult problem, not covered by the contract, of an event which would otherwise justify an extension of time but which occurs in a period of culpable delay between the two decisions, see the discussion under clause 54 (4), *supra*, pp. 122–125.

There is no provision, as in the case of the liquidated damages themselves, for certification of the amount of the reimbursement, which is simply left for computation by the Employer.

COMPLETION CERTIFICATE

Certificate of Completion of Works

48. (1) When the Contractor shall consider that the whole of the Works has been substantially completed and has satisfactorily passed any final test that may be prescribed by the Contract he may give a notice to that effect to the Engineer or to the Engineer's Representative accompanied by an undertaking to finish any outstanding work during the Period of Maintenance. Such notice and undertaking shall be in writing and shall be deemed to be a request by the Contractor for the Engineer to issue a Certificate of Completion in respect of the Works and the Engineer shall within 21 days of the date of delivery of such notice either issue to the Contractor (with a copy of the Employer) a Certificate of Completion stating the date on which in his opinion the Works were substantially completed in accordance with the Contract or else give instructions in writing to the Contractor specifying all the work which in the Engineer's opinion requires to be done by the Contractor before the issue of such certificate. If the Engineer shall give such instructions the Contractor shall be entitled to receive such Certificate of Completion within 21 days of completion to the satisfaction of the Engineer of the work specified by the said instructions.

This clause now makes provision for the certification of completion of (a) the whole Works (sub-clause (1)); (b) " Sections " of the Works, if any, identified in the Appendix (sub-clause (2) (a)); and (c) *parts* of the Works or of a Section (sub-clause (2) (b) and (3)).

The certification of completion under this clause has a number of important effects. The certified completion date brings to an end the liability to pay liquidated damages for delay in completing the whole Works or individual Sections of the Works (see clause 47 (1) (b) and (2) (b), *supra*); completion of a Section will usually also automatically reduce, from the certified date, the liquidated damages for the whole (clause 47 (2) (b) Proviso (iii)). Completion of *parts* (whether of a Section or of the whole) will also similarly reduce, but on a proportionate value basis, the overall or Sectional liquidated damages (clause 47 (1) (b) and (2) (b) Proviso (ii)). The certified completion date under this clause will also start the maintenance period running, during which the Contractor's obligations will be to complete outstanding work, if any, (see this clause), and repair and make good defects under clause 49, *infra*. Certified completion will also transfer the risk of damage to the Works to the Employer, not on the completion date certified, but 14 days after the *issue* of the completion certificate of the whole, the Section or the part, as the case may be, except for outstanding work (clause 20 (1) Proviso) or damage done by the Contractor while maintaining the Works (clause 20 (2)). The present requirement of issue of the completion certificate within 21 days of the completion itself may, therefore, mean that the risk of damage to the Works will not pass until five weeks after completion (probably so as to give the Employer a reasonable time in which to resume possession and to take over operational control of the project). The Contractor's obligation to insure the works similarly terminates after the same period, except in regard to two special categories of damage occurring during the maintenance period (clause 21), but not, it would seem, the third party insurance (" throughout the execution of the works ") in clause 23, nor, of course, the many indemnities given by the Contractor to the Employer under the contract (*e.g.* clause 22). Finally, the first instalment of the retention monies becomes due to the Contractor 14 days after the *issue* of the completion certificate of the whole, Section or part, as the case may be—see clause 60 (5) (a) and (b).

" *substantially completed* "

Surprisingly, there is no attempt at definition of this. The clause contemplates that " outstanding work " may remain to be done (compare clause 20 (1) Proviso and clause 49 (2)) while on the other hand sub-clause (4) implies that a completion certificate for the whole (as opposed to a Section or part) should not be given if there are " ground or surfaces requiring reinstatement." Otherwise the contract gives no clues. No doubt in many engineering contracts readiness for what might be called " operational or functional occupation " will lead to an employer wishing to enter, and the reference to the passing of a " final test " lends some support to this. The obscurity will not embarrass the Employer in such a situation, since in a doubtful case the Engineer can act under sub-clause (3) and certify a partial completion. The obscurity may, however, embarrass Employers and Engineers and benefit Contractors who, notwithstanding defective or incomplete work, demand certification of the whole in order to obtain earlier release of retention monies. Obviously the degree of completion required may vary according to the nature of the project, and it is desirable that the Specification or Bills should, where there is likely to be any doubt about this, deal with the matter expressly and in some detail. Thus the reference to the " final test " is to one " prescribed by the Contract," which suggests that the contract will specifically indicate the tests to be carried out before substantial completion can be certified. The need for more precision is emphasised by the new machinery in the present clause, similar in policy to that in clause 14 (3), whereby it is the Contractor who now takes the initiative by serving notice on the Engineer " accompanied by an undertaking to finish any outstanding work," whereupon the

Engineer is contractually obliged to take action either by approving the request, or else by preparing, in effect, a Schedule of outstanding work to be done before completion will be certified. Should he mention items which an arbitrator considered could have been left for the post-completion period, a claim for interest on withheld retention monies may (depending on its proper interpretation) be due under the new wording of clause 60 (6) —see the commentary, *infra*, p. 238. On the other hand, should he omit an item from his list (perhaps because it was not visible as defective work, or was overlooked) which on his later inspection before finally certifying he considered indicated a serious omission or defect, the wording would, at least on its face, appear to preclude him from refusing the completion certificate. For some recent useful definitions of " completion " in England and Australia, see Hudson, 10th ed., pp. 258–259, 637 *et seq.*).

" *during the Period of Maintenance* "

the obligation to complete any outstanding work is " as soon as may be practicable after [the date of completion] "—see clause 49 (2), *infra*.

Completion of Sections and Occupied Parts

(2) Similarly in accordance with the procedure set in sub-clause (1) of this Clause the Contractor may request and the Engineer shall issue a Certificate of Completion in respect of:—

(a) any Section in respect of which a separate time for completion is provided in the Appendix to the Form of Tender; and

(b) any substantial part of the Works which has been both completed to the satisfaction of the Engineer and occupied or used by the Employer.

Completion of Other Parts of Works

(3) If the Engineer shall be of the opinion that any part of the Works shall have been substantially completed and shall have satisfactorily passed any final test that may be prescribed by the Contract he may issue a Certificate of Completion in respect of that part of the Works before completion of the whole of the Works and upon the issue of such certificate the Contractor shall be deemed to have undertaken to complete any outstanding work on that part of the Works during the Period of Maintenance.

The completion certificate for Sections under sub-clause (2) (a) is mandatory, to the same extent as a certificate for the whole Works under sub-clause (1), upon the Contractor giving notice and undertakings as to outstanding work as in that sub-clause—see the words " Similarly in accordance with the procedure set out in sub-clause (1) " in sub-clause (2). It is submitted that these words also import the substantive requirements of substantial completion and passing of prescribed final tests in sub-clause (1) into sub-clause (2). The completion date certified will terminate liquidated damages for the Section (clause 47 (2) (b), *supra*); reduce the liquidated damages for the whole (clause 47 (2) (b) Proviso (iii), *supra*); and start the maintenance period running. As already indicated, completion of Sections will also, within a stipulated period of *issue* of the certificate, transfer the risk of damage to the Section, terminate the Contractor's liability to insure the Section, and release the first instalment of retention for the Section—see *infra*, p. 237.

The completion certificate of an occupied part under sub-clause (2) (b) is similarly mandatory, subject to the new procedure for notice, undertakings etc. and with similar effects. Note, however, three separate requirements: the part must be *substantial* (probably *per incuriam* this may have been intended to mean a substantial part of a Section, where applicable—see clause 47 (2) (b) Proviso (ii), *supra*—but does not in fact say so); the part must be occupied or used; and it must be *to the Engineer's satisfaction*—again, perhaps *per incuriam*, no such wording exists in regard to the whole Works under sub-clause (1), or a Section under (2) (a), or a permissive partial completion under sub-clause (3). The effect of this partial certification (as of that under (3)) on liquidated damages where no Sections are involved is dealt with under clause 47 (1) (b) Proviso, and where Sections are involved under clause 47 (2) (b) Proviso (ii).

Certification of a part under sub-clause (3) is discretionary, not mandatory, the machinery of notices etc. does not apply, and occupation or use by the Employer and the Engineer's satisfaction are unnecessary; but the passing of any prescribed final tests, as in all the other cases, is a requirement.

Reinstatement of Ground

(4) Provided always that a Certificate of Completion given in respect of any Section or part of the Works before completion of the whole shall not be deemed to certify completion of any ground or surfaces requiring reinstatement unless such certificate shall expressly so state.

The exact intention of this wording is not very clear, but it would seem to suggest that, whereas reinstatement of ground or surfaces is not a necessary ingredient of substantial completion of Sections or parts, it is necessary before completion of the whole Works can be certified. The wording is traditional, however, and in the absence of any definition of substantial completion it seems doubtful if there is any coherent policy intention behind the wording.

MAINTENANCE AND DEFECTS

Definition of " Period of Maintenance "

49. (1) In these Conditions the expression " Period of Maintenance " shall mean the period of maintenance named in the Appendix to the Form of Tender calculated from the date of completion of the Works or any Section or part thereof certified by the Engineer in accordance with Clause 48 as the case may be.

Execution of Work of Repair etc.

(2) To the intent that the Works and each Section and part thereof shall at or as soon as practicable after the expiration of the relevant Period of Maintenance be delivered up to the Employer in the condition required by the Contract (fair wear and tear excepted) to the satisfaction of the Engineer the Contractor shall finish the work (if any) outstanding at the date of completion as certified under Clause 48 as soon as may be practicable after such date and shall execute all such work of repair amendment reconstruction rectification and making good of defects imperfections shrinkages or other faults as may during the Period of Maintenance or

within 14 days after its expiration be required of the Contractor in writing by the Engineer as a result of an inspection made by or on behalf of the Engineer prior to its expiration.

Cost of Execution of Work of Repair, etc.

(3) All such work shall be carried out by the Contractor at his own expense if the necessity thereof shall in the opinion of the Engineer be due to the use of materials or workmanship not in accordance with the Contract or to neglect or failure on the part of the Contractor to comply with any obligation expressed or implied on the Contractor's part under the Contract. If in the opinion of the Engineer such necessity shall be due to any other cause the value of such work shall be ascertained and paid for as if it were additional work.

Sub-clause (1) of this clause makes the commencement and duration of the maintenance period dependent upon the certification of " substantial completion "—see the commentary on clause 48, *supra*, for the lack of precise definition of this term, which apparently contemplates that there may be some outstanding work to be completed during the maintenance period, and in the case of Sections or parts at least, that ground or surfaces may not be fully reinstated at the commencement of the period. It will be noted that for the purpose of the present clause (unlike for example the release of the second half of the retention monies under clause 60 (5) (c), *infra*) no special significance attaches to the last part of the works to be completed—separate maintenance periods become applicable and expire separately in regard to all Sections or parts which may have been certified as complete in advance of the remainder. The present clause operates (usually retrospectively to a small extent, as a result of the time allowed for *issue* of the clause 48 certificate or certificates) as from *the certified date or dates*—see further the commentary under sub-clause (3), *infra*, for the different dates applicable under certain other provisions in the contract depending on " completion."

The words " in the condition required by the Contract (fair wear and tear excepted) " in sub-clause (2) refer, presumably, to clause 13 (1) in particular (" the Contractor shall construct complete and maintain . . . in strict accordance with the Contract to the satisfaction of the Engineer ") *i.e.* to meticulous completion in accordance with the contract descriptions of the permanent work to be found in the contract documents as a whole, subject only to fair wear and tear due to time and weather, or to the Employer's occupation and use of the Works, after they have been brought to this state, either on substantial completion or, in the case of any outstanding work, subsequently during the maintenance period. While not saying so expressly, the sense would seem to suggest that the Engineer's requirement in writing under the terms of the clause is a condition precedent to the Contractor's obligation.

However, the maintenance obligation is in reality a valuable right to the Contractor (as well as to the Employer) in that it permits the Contractor physically to return to the Site and make good defects at less cost than another contractor engaged by the Employer would be likely to incur or charge. On the other hand, since there is nothing in the wording to suggest that the Employer's rights under the clause are intended to supplant his ordinary right to sue for damages or defective work, the Employer will be able to sue for damages for the full period of limitation from substantial completion, regardless of the date of appearance or discovery of the defects or of any previous notification or non-notification —see Hudson, 10th ed., pp. 394–399. (In the case of defects notified at the end of the maintenance period but not put right by the Contractor, limitation might start to run still later, shortly after the end of the period when he should have performed his obligations under sub-clause (2).) Consistently with this, the contract now provides in the clearest terms, as it previously did not, that even the issue of the Maintenance Certificate under clause 61 on the making good of defects is not to reduce the incidence of any liability by one party to the other under the contract—see clause 61 (2), *infra*, p. 243—and there are a large number of other indications in the contract of the intention to keep alive and undiminished the Employer's rights in regard to defective work—see clauses 14 (7), 17, 38 (2), 39 (1) (c), 39 (3), 54 (3) (a) and 60 (7) and the commentaries thereto.

(*2*) " *during the period of Maintenance or within 14 days after its expiration* "

These words indicate that the Contractor will be liable if he is not available to do remedial work at any time during the maintenance period —see the remedy under sub-clause (4), *infra*, and the complementary special power of the Employer to do urgent repairs during the maintenance period at the Contractor's expense under clause 62, *infra*, pp. 243–244.

(*3*) " *due to materials or workmanship not in accordance with the Contract or to neglect or failure . . . to comply with any obligation express or implied* "

The policy of the clause, as in most U.K. standard forms, is to render the Contractor financially liable for reinstating defective work which is either due to work which does not comply with the contract requirements, or which is in some other way the Contractor's responsibility under the contract. In this latter context particular regard should be had to clause 20 of the Conditions, *supra*, p. 64. Thus, while defects in the inherent design (an " Excepted Risk " under clause 20 (3)) will be the Employer's financial responsibility whenever they occur, as also defects due to use or occupation by the Employer, defects due to some external accident or agency which is not an Excepted Risk will be the Contractor's responsibility under clause 20 (1) if the cause occurred before the expiry of 14 days from the *issue* of the relevant clause 48 substantial completion certificate (*not* the *certified date* of completion), other than any work outstanding at this later date, when the liability will, of course, continue still longer. The time lag (which affects insurance of the Works under clause 21 as well) can be as much as five weeks—see the commentary to clause 20, *supra*, p. 66.

Remedy on Contractor's Failure to Carry out Work Required

(4) If the Contractor shall fail to do any such work as aforesaid required by the Engineer the Employer shall be entitled to carry out such work by his own workmen or by other contractors and if such work is work which the Contractor should have carried out at the Contractors' own cost shall be entitled to recover from the Contractor the cost thereof or may deduct the same from any monies due or that become due to the Contractor.

The words " as aforesaid " refer to work during as well as at the end of the period—see sub-clause (2) *supra*. As not infrequently happens in this contract, this is a provision which (at least in the case of work after the period ends) in effect only confirms what the legal position would in any event be independently of the provision (in this case under the ordinary principles governing damages for breach of contract). However, in the case of work called for during the period, an argument might be advanced by the Contractor that his own right to do maintenance work at a time convenient to himself during the period was infringed by another Contractor being employed on the contract works, so that a provision like the present has some value. Compare the very similar remedy in clause 62, *infra*, pp. 243–244, and under clause 39 (2) for remedial work during the construction period, *supra*, p. 107.

Temporary Reinstatement

(5) Provided always that if in the course or for the purposes of the execution of the Works or any part thereof any highway or other road or way shall have been broken into then notwithstanding anything herein contained:—

(a) If the permanent reinstatement of such highway or other road or way is to be carried out by the appropriate Highway Authority or by some person other than the Contractor (or any sub-contractor to him) the Contractor shall at his own cost and independently of any requirement of or notice from the Engineer be responsible for the making good of any subsidence or shrinkage or other defect imperfection or fault in the temporary reinstatement of such highway or other road or way and for the execution of any necessary repair or amendment thereof from whatever cause the necessity arises until the end of the Period of Maintenance in respect of the works beneath such highway or other road or way or until the Highway Authority or other person as aforesaid shall have taken possession of the Site for the purpose of carrying out permanent reinstatement (whichever is the earlier) and shall indemnify and save harmless the Employer against and from any damage or injury to the Employer or to third parties arising out or in consequence of any neglect or failure of the Contractor to comply with the foregoing obligations or any of them and against and from all claims demands proceedings damages costs charges and expenses whatsoever in respect thereof or in relation thereto. As from the end of such Period of Maintenance or the taking of possession as aforesaid (whichever shall first happen) the Employer shall indemnify and save harmless the Contractor against and from any damage or injury as aforesaid arising out or in consequence of or in connection with the said permanent reinstatement or any defect imperfection or failure of or in such work of permanent reinstatement and against and from all claims demands proceedings damages costs charges and expenses whatsoever in respect thereof or in relation thereto.

(b) Where the Highway Authority or other person as aforesaid shall take possession of the Site as aforesaid in sections or lengths the responsibility of the Contractor under paragraph (a) of this sub-clause shall cease in regard to any such section or length of the time possession thereof is so taken but shall during the continuance of the said Period of Maintenance continue in regard to any length of which possession has not been so taken and the indemnities given by the Contractor and the Employer respectively under the said paragraph shall be construed and have effect accordingly.

This sub-clause, which repeats unchanged that in the Fourth Edition, is concerned with the subject-matter of and should be read with clause 27, *supra*, p. 87, in regard to Street Works. See in particular sub-clause (7) of that clause, which is expressed to be subject to the provisions of the present sub-clause. The financial implications of the present sub-clause, as will be seen, do not appear to follow the policy of the remainder of the contract in regard to defective work, nor that of clause 20 in regard to the Excepted Risks and the care of the Works, during either the construction or the maintenance periods. In considering this, full effect should be given to the words " shall have been broken into " at the beginning of the clause, which mean, it is submitted, that the sub-clause only applies to cases of interference by the Works with *existing* highways or roads, and not to newly constructed highways or roads forming part of the Works themselves.

Highway authorities have statutory power to require, and more frequently than not do so require in practice, that the permanent reinstatement of roads shall be carried out by themselves. For technical engineering reasons it may be desirable to postpone such reinstatement for a fairly long period, which is an additional reason for their doing the work. Less frequently, due to shortage of staff and labour or the comparative unimportance or simple construction of the road in question, they may agree that the employer may carry out the permanent reinstatement. Most engineering contracts, therefore, require the contractor only to carry out the temporary reinstatement of trenches or other works in highways; and in addition they may or may not contain a P.C. or provisional sum expressly stipulated to be for permanent reinstatement by the highway authority as a nominated sub-contractor of the Contractor (if they do not, of course, the highway authority will presumably contract directly with the Employer, though in either case the " contract " or " sub-contract " is more in the nature of an arrangement for the financial reimbursement of the highway authority, in view of its effective statutory control over both the site and specification and price of the reinstatement work). In the less common case where the authority is not to do the work, it may be billed in the ordinary way (see clause 40 of the pre-1966 Standard Method of Measurement) or more rarely, perhaps, billed as a P.C. or provisional sum so as to enable the work to be sub-contracted to a nominated sub-contractor, if thought desirable. In a case where the highway authority has not indicated its intentions as to the permanent reinstatement at the time of tender of the main contract, the work may be billed as a P.C. or provisional sum so as to keep the Employer's options open. This is the background of fact against which this sub-clause should be considered.

It will be seen from the wording of paragraph (a) that, where the paragraph applies, subsidence etc. in temporary reinstatement is the responsibility of the contractor "*from whatever cause the necessity arises*"—there is no requirement of a breach of contract by the Contractor (contrast sub-clause (3), *supra*), or any saving should the cause be the Engineer's design, or instructions given by him, or one of the other Excepted Risks under clause 20. Thus if, for example, the Engineer requires the Contractor to backfill using selected material from excavations which the Contractor objects to on suitability grounds, or to a specification which the Contractor objects to as inadequate, then notwithstanding that the Contractor is subsequently vindicated by the subsidence of the reinstatement, it would seem that the Contractor must remedy it at his own expense. The reason for the rule may be the difficulty of proving the cause of a subsidence etc. and a special incentive to the Contractor to do this particular work with special care, or it may be that as there is no control over or certainty when the permanent reinstatement will be done by the highway authority, and as defective temporary reinstatement will expose the Employer to possible claims for the indefinite period until the permanent reinstatement is done, a special strict liability is imposed on the Contractor, in a matter where poor workmanship (*i.e.* inadequate compaction or rolling or day-to-day selection of material) is much the most probable cause of any subsidence etc. On the other hand the clause clearly terminates the Contractor's liability at the end of the maintenance period, whether or not permanent reinstatement has taken place. The apparent strictness of the policy, when it is remembered that the words quoted above in italics are wide enough to include even negligent damage by the Employer or his servants—see *Travers* v. *Cooper* [1915] 1 K.B. 73, and the commentary to clause 20 (1), *supra*, p. 66, where similar words are considered—is now, however, likely to be substantially removed by virtue of the wide class of financial claims permitted under clause 13 (1)—see the commentary thereto, *supra*, pp. 51–54—at least if an Engineer's instruction has been given, as almost invariably will be the case.

(*a*) "*or by some person other than the Contractor* (*or any sub-contractor to him*)"

This means that the paragraph applies if the permanent reinstatement is carried out by

(a) the highway authority, or

(b) some person other than the Contractor and who is not a sub-contractor of the Contractor.

—in other words, the highway authority or some other person or contractor having no connection with the Contractor. As already noted, it is not unusual for an Employer to bill this work as a provisional P.C. sum pending the decision of the highway authority as to whether or not they intend to do the permanent reinstatement. In such a case, if a subsidence occurs through no fault of the Contractor, his liability to remedy it free of charge (and the unqualified indemnity given by him under this sub-clause) will depend on whether or not the highway authority has decided to do the work, but subject now in the Fifth Edition to a financial claim under clause 13 (1) if an Engineer's instruction or direction can be found, as will usually be the case.

Paragraph (b)

This paragraph appropriately terminates the Contractor's responsibility and indemnities where and to the extent that part but not all of the permanent reinstatement is commenced by the highway authority.

Contractor to Search

50. The Contractor shall if required by the Engineer in writing carry out such searches tests or trials as may be necessary to determine the cause of any defect imperfection or fault under the directions of the Engineer. Unless such defect imperfection or fault shall be one for which the Contractor is liable under the Contract the cost of the work carried out by the Contractor as aforesaid shall be borne by the Employer. But if such defect imperfection or fault shall be one for which the Contractor is liable the cost of the work carried out as aforesaid shall be borne by the Contractor and he shall in such case repair rectify and make good such defect imperfection or fault at his own expense in accordance with Clause 49.

There is no clear statement in this clause limiting its operation to the maintenance period, other than the strong implication from the reference in the last line to the provisions of clause 49. It is also the second of two clauses in a section of the contract entitled " Maintenance and defects " (the title, being neither a " marginal heading " or " note," it is submitted, *can* be considered in construing the clause notwithstanding clause 1 (3), *supra*, p. 24, though this can hardly be the intention—see the commentary, *infra*, p. 145. Other very similar powers in the contract are the ordering of tests under clause 36 (1) and (3), and the opening or uncovering of work in clause 38 (2), but these are undoubtedly powers for use during the construction period.

The power is to order a search for the *cause* of a defect, and the financial consequences are limited to the cost of searching only, and not the subsequent cost of repair (the Fourth Edition was more specific about this, but the words " as aforesaid " in the present clause have the same effect, it is submitted). It follows that the clause is aimed at cases where the *symptoms* of a defect are visible, or its existence known, but the precise cause is not known (the power to order a search where no defect is suspected or visible is implicit, it is suggested, in the wider power to open up work during construction in clause 38). On its face, the wording of the present clause is not wide enough to cover a very real exigency—namely a case where defect and cause are known, but its *full extent* (on which the nature of remedial work may depend) is not. The cause, once ascertained, should enable the cost of repair to be allocated in accordance with clause 49 (3), *supra*, if the search etc. occurs during the maintenance period. During the construction period the Contractor's responsibility for repairing defects would arise under the more strict provisions of clause 20 (2), as well as the fairly obvious obligation, if bad work is established, under clause 39 (1). But probably before, and certainly after, substantial completion under clause 48, the Contractor would be liable in damages for breach of contract in the case of bad work (see the commentary under clause 49, *supra*, p. 145) and unless they were wholly unreasonable, representing a failure to mitigate damage, the entire cost of any investigations to determine extent, cause or remedy would be recoverable as part of the Employer's damages on ordinary common law principles. Having regard to all these considerations, it seems likely that the present clause is intended to apply specifically during the maintenance period as part of the special maintenance obligations and rights of the parties (see about this the commentary to clause 49, *supra*, pp. 144–146), and this view is reinforced not only by the reference to clause 49 in the present clause but also, perhaps, by the reference to the present clause in 61 (1), *infra*, p. 243.

ALTERATIONS ADDITIONS AND OMISSIONS

Ordered Variations

51. (1) The Engineer shall order any variation to any part of the Works that may in his opinion be necessary for the completion of the Works and shall have power to order any variation that for any other reason shall in his opinion be desirable for the satisfactory completion and functioning of the Works. Such variations may include additions omissions substitutions alterations changes in quality from character kind position dimension level or line and changes in the specified sequence method or timing of construction (if any).

Ordered Variations to be in Writing

(2) No such variation shall be made by the Contractor without an order by the Engineer. All such orders shall be given in writing provided that if for any reason the Engineer shall find it necessary to give any such order orally in the first instance the Contractor shall comply with such oral order. Such oral order shall be confirmed in writing by the Engineer as soon as is possible in the circumstances. If the Contractor shall confirm in writing to the Engineer any oral order by the Engineer and such confirmation shall not be contradicted in writing by the Engineer forthwith it shall be deemed to be an order in writing by the Engineer. No variation ordered or deemed to be ordered in writing in accordance with sub-clauses (1) and (2) of this Clause shall in any way vitiate or invalidate the Contract but the value (if any) of all such variations shall be taken into account in ascertaining the amount of the Contract Price.

Changes in Quantities

(3) No order in writing shall be required for increase or decrease in the quantity of any work where such increase or decrease is not the result of an order given under this Clause but is the result of the quantities exceeding or being less than those stated in the Bill of Quantities.

This clause is concerned to confer the necessary power upon and define the authority of the Engineer to order variations, while their valuation is governed by clause 52. Despite a superficial resemblance to the Fourth Edition, both clauses have been amended, whether intentionally or not, in vitally important respects, and for this reason merit the most careful re-examination by those familiar with the old clauses, as well as close analysis by newcomers to the forms.

It may be desirable first to state some general propositions. The purpose of variation clauses is twofold. In the first place, they are designed to give the employer the *right* to order variations should he wish to do so. Without a variation clause, he could only order the work to be varied with the consent of the contractor. In the second place, since in English law at least an engineer in private practice has no *ostensible* (or implied) authority to contract on behalf of his client (see, for the contrary position in the case of full-time salaried employees of local authorities, the decision of Ungoed-Thomas J. in *Carlton Contractors* v. *Bexley Corporation* (1962) 60 L.G.R. 331 and see generally Hudson, 10th ed., pp. 108–111), which a variation of an existing contract clearly involves, variation clauses usually confer a *specific general authority* (provided the contractual requirements of form are observed) upon the engineer to vary the *work* (*not* the contract terms), so that a contractor will be protected, provided he has a properly documented variation instruction, from any assertion by an employer that the engineer ordered the variation in question without the knowledge or authority of the employer. In law, failure to observe the formal documentary requirements of the variation clause in one way or another may not seriously prejudice a contractor, since in the case of a large number of variations it may be possible to show that the employer himself authorised the engineer to order, or knew or was aware of and stood by and approved of the varying of the work, even if he did not himself actually approach and request the contractor to make the variation in question. In all these cases, unless on the true construction of the language of the contract compliance with the formal requirements of the variation clause is made *an exclusive condition precedent* to recovery, or is otherwise held to exclude the possibility of separate contracts with the employer varying the work, a contractor will be able to obtain the necessary modification of the price, not under the terms of the variation clause in his main contract, but under an express or implied separate contract made with the employer, or with the engineer if acting on the latter's behalf. See for this subject,

Hudson, 10th. ed., Chapter 8, and in particular pages 506–507, 523–524, and 536–553. Incidentally, it should perhaps be pointed out that the mere fact that the engineer may be of the opinion that a matter is a variation, and gives instructions or other documentary approval accordingly, will not usually bind the employer if, on a true construction of the contract, the work is included in the original contract price—see Hudson, 10th ed., pp. 106–108 and 523–524. In considering the present provision, however, it should not be forgotten that the new Fifth Edition now expressly appears to permit claims based on the Engineer's written instructions *even where the work has not been varied*—see clause 13 (1) and (3), *supra*, pp. 46–51.

The present clause in the Fourth Edition raised four principal problems, *viz.*:—

(1) Did the provisions as to valuation in clause 52 (which enable the contract prices to be departed from in suitable cases) apply to increases or decreases in the quantities shown in the Bills, and in particular provisional quantity items, where there had been no variation ordered (*i.e.* simple remeasurement cases under clauses 55 and 56)? (This difficulty arose principally because a proviso identical in its wording to sub-clause (3) of the present clause was present in the old sub-clause (2).)

(2) Was an order in writing from the Engineer a condition precedent to recovery by the Contractor?

(3) How effective was a Contractor's written confirmation of an oral order in writing—in particular did it retrospectively validate work already carried out pursuant to the oral order?

(4) What was the meaning of the wording " necessary for the completion of the Works " in the old sub-clause (1) (e)? Did this mean that, if the Engineer gave an instruction in a case where unforeseen difficulties arose, which the Contractor was otherwise contractually bound to overcome in order to fulfil his obligation to complete, any instruction involving a change in the work given in that situation, even simply to assist the Contractor, would be a variation entitling him to additional payment?

Dealing with these problems in turn, (1) is no longer a problem in the present contract, it is submitted. Clause 56 (2) (*infra*, p. 182) now specifically and separately states that changes in the actual quantities from those billed will enable the Engineer to increase or decrease *any* (*i.e.* any other, if necessary) rates or prices rendered unreasonable or inapplicable by the change in quantities. In addition, the opening words of clause 52 (1) now state expressly that the clause 52 valuation principles only apply to " variations ordered by the Engineer in accordance with clause 51." Simple differences in quantities not caused by a variation order now obviously fall to be valued under the remeasurement provisions contained in clauses 56 (1) and (2), so that sub-clause (3) of the present clause is in fact unnecessary and surplusage, and at best designed to prevent Employers from attempting to rely (quite wrongly on any possible view of both Editions) on the absence of an order in writing in a case of simple quantity differences. This in fact was the author's view of the intended meaning of this Proviso in the case of the very obscure wording of the Fourth Edition, and the quite unclear relationship in that Edition between the valuation of variations under clause 52 on the one hand and remeasurement of quantity differences under clause 55 on the other—see the commentary in B.C.F., pp. 382–384. The present contract now self-evidently contains quite separate codes permitting departure from the contract rates and prices for quantity differences arising from variations on the one hand and for quantity differences arising from errors in taking off quantities from the drawings, or in estimating quantities not capable of being calculated in that way (the two principal sources of quantity changes not caused by variations) on the other. See also the specific power to grant extensions of time for such (non-variation) quantity differences in clause 44 (1), *supra*, p. 118.

(2) " *No such variation shall be made . . . without an order by the Engineer. All such orders shall be given in writing provided that . . .*"

These words relate to the second problem (2), *supra*, p. 152. The Fifth Edition no longer contains the words " in writing " in its definitive first sentence in sub-clause (2) quoted above. On the wording this still, however, leaves open the question whether it is a condition precedent that the Contractor should have an Engineer's order in writing, or perhaps an oral order confirmed by the Contractor in writing, or whether in appropriate circumstances he will be able to recover payment for an orally ordered variation.

It is submitted that the wording does *not* amount to a prohibition having the effect of making an Engineer's order, whether in writing or oral, a condition precedent to recovery by the Contractor, so that in accordance with the principles set out *supra*, *e.g.* in a case where the Employer has knowledge of or has personally authorised a variation, the Contractor will not be prevented from recovering payment. (There must of course, be some request from either the Engineer or the Employer or his agent.) There are a number of indications supporting this view, it is submitted:—

(a) In the particular context of the subsidiary question whether an order in writing or a confirmed oral order is necessary, the first Proviso in the sub-clause positively requires the Contractor to obey oral orders " in the first instance " and does not in terms make this obedience conditional upon the confirmation by either party which is referred to later in the clause.

(b) Dealing with the principal question whether some order, either oral or in writing or confirmed, is necessary, the opening words of prohibition can be given full business effect if they are applied to variations *carried out by the Contractor on his own initiative.* It is not necessary, as a matter of business efficacy, it is submitted, to construe them as prohibiting a separate agreement outside the terms of the contract between the Contractor and the Employer. In other words, the clause is concerned to define the limits of the Engineer's general authority to bind the Employer under the contract, not to limit the Employer's ability to contract with the Contractor outside the terms of the contract itself, or expressly to authorise the Engineer or any other agent so to contract on his behalf.

The draftsmanship is, however, unnecessarily obscure and even misleading; and it should perhaps be made clear that, without an order of the Engineer under the contract, the valuation provisions of clause 52 (see the opening words of clause 52) will not apply and the liability of the Employer will in strict law be to pay a reasonable price for the variation —unless on a true construction of the terms of his ex-contractual authorisation or ratification of the work in question its valuation was to be carried out in accordance with the contractual provisions governing the valuation of variations ordered under the contract.

(*2*) " *Such oral order shall be confirmed in writing by the Engineer . . . If the Contractor shall confirm in writing . . .* "

These words relate to the third problem (3) set out *supra*, p. 152. For some reason it seems almost impossible to find an English standard form, whether in the building or civil engineering industries, which contains a simple and logical procedure for confirmation of written orders and which effectively validates retrospectively, as it clearly should do in the Contractor's reasonable interest, any work previously carried out, and the present wording appears to be even less clear about this than that in the Fourth Edition. The clause now provides that all " such " orders (*i.e.* variation orders) shall be given in writing, but continues immediately by way of proviso to permit oral orders if the Engineer " finds it necessary," without giving any indication of how this could arise (unless it contemplates the Engineer lacking pencil and paper or dealing with the matter by telephone) and requires immediate compliance with them. Compliance is not, it should be noted, made dependent upon written confirmation by either side. No clear indication is given as to the legal consequences of a subsequent confirmation by the Engineer—in particular, does it retrospectively validate (assuming written orders are indeed necessary for validity on the new wording) the oral order, or does it only operate as from the date (" forthwith ") when it is given? On the other hand, while upon a Contractor's confirmation " it " is deemed to be an order writing, is " it " the confirmation or the " oral order "? Or is the intention of the clause to validate any variation of the work if an order is given at any time, whether before or after carrying out some or all of the variation?

In practice these difficulties may not provoke serious problems, particularly in the light of the wide powers given to an arbitrator under clause 66, but the quite unnecessary lack of precision in the wording should at least be appreciated. For the whole subject of recovery without an order in writing, see Hudson, 10th ed., pp. 534–555.

(*1*) " *shall order any variation . . . necessary for the completion of the Works* "
" *shall have power to order any variation . . . desirable for the satisfactory completion and functioning of the Works* "

These words pose, in significantly altered form, the fourth problem mentioned *supra*, p. 152.

It is the fundamental characteristic of lump sum contracts in the legal sense (notwithstanding the existence of remeasurement provisions) that a contractor's price (adjusted if necessary on remeasurement or indeed under any other specific provisions of the contract) shall be inclusive in the sense that extra payment will not be due for expenditure incurred, for example, in meeting unexpected difficulties, or in reinstating accidental damage—see the commentary to clauses 8, 11, and 13 (1) and (2), and 20 (1) of the Conditions, *supra*, pp. 36–37, 40–41, 47–48, and 65. The words " necessary for the completion " and " desirable for the satisfactory completion and functioning " of the Works are new in the present Conditions, as is the possibly vital distinction between " shall order " and " shall have power to order " in the two different cases quoted above. They are of the greatest importance in potentially permitting a new category of claim (in addition to the claims under clause 12 for unfavourable physical conditions, clause 13 for written instructions causing unforeseeable disruption, etc., and clause 20 for damage to the Works) based upon a contractual *duty* of the Employer by his Engineer *owed to the Contractor* to order a variation if a variation can be shown to be " necessary for the completion in the Works." Coupled with the new wording " modified " in clause 7 (1) (see the commentary to that clause *supra*, p. 32) contractors will undoubtedly argue, when faced with difficulties, that a variation order calling for a new and more expensive method of working (*e.g.* sheet-piling in the face of bad ground conditions) or even a change of design of the permanent works, *must* be given, and that failure to do so will be a breach of contract.

The wording gives no guidance as to its precise meaning, and is very obscure. It is, however, submitted that changes which merely render completion more economical or speedy will not be " necessary," though they may well be " desirable " within the above wording, at least from the Contractor's point of view. Only, it is submitted, if completion in accordance with the Engineer's design or a *specified* method of working becomes *impossible* (not expensive or lengthy) can the contractual obligation arise—this will be consistent with, for example, the words " legally or physically impossible " in clause 13 (1) and with the permissive words " may if he thinks fit " in clause 12 (2) (c). It will also be consistent with the words " changes in the *specified* . . . method of construction " in the latter part of the present sub-clause. Moreover, even if there was an obligation to vary the work in circumstances of difficulty, it would be a very open question how such a variation was to be valued under clause 52 if, without it, the Contractor would have been condemned to long and costly work to achieve completion of the unvaried work.

(*1*) " *additions substitutions alterations changes in quality form character kind position dimension or line and changes in the specified sequence or method or timing of construction* (*if any*) "

These words are obviously intended to be as wide-ranging as possible, but apart from the probably not significant addition of the word " form " the noteworthy difference from the Fourth Edition lies in the words " *specified* sequence or method or timing of construction (if any)." Variation clauses do not usually permit more than a power to change the permanent work, but these latter words appear to refer either to the order of working (" sequence . . . or timing of construction . . .") or to temporary works or methods (" method . . . of construction "). As to the former, it is submitted that, as in most U.K. standard forms, the wording does *not* confer power to order an *acceleration* of work, in the sense of advancing either the contract or extended contract completion dates for the Works as a whole, though the problem is more difficult if individual Sections of the Works under clause 47 are considered. Here again, however, it seems unlikely that any such power is intended, since the application of such a power to the different stipulated sums for liquidated damages for the individual Sections, already complicated by clause 47 to the point of near incomprehensibility (see the commentary to that clause) would appear to be unworkable, particularly within an unalterable overall completion date, although the wording here used may at first sight superficially seem wide enough to permit this. So far as the word " specified " is concerned, this must mean, in regard to sequence or timing, it is submitted, specified in the contract documents, and not specified in any programme or information supplied under clause 14 of the Conditions. Similarly, in the case of " method . . . of construction," the use of the word " specified " shows that the reference is, it is submitted, to those cases where the Engineer has seen fit (as more usually he will not) to specify (*i.e.* instruct) the working methods to be used in the contract documents themselves—if so an instruction altering the method will be a variation. Usually Engineers will at best describe *possible* choices or varieties of method in the Specification, or minimum standards or working requirements, though occasionally in more important cases, where the final integrity of the permanent works is of sufficient importance to justify the financial risk to the Employer of specifying the method, this is done more precisely, usually in regard to what are called " Temporary Works " —see *e.g.* clause 8 (2), *supra*, p. 37, and the reference there to " Temporary Works designed by the Engineer " as opposed to Temporary Works left to the Contractor to select or design (as contemplated *e.g.* by the last line of clause 20 (3), *supra*, p. 66). Moreover, what may appear to be changes in working methods may, on close analysis, be seen to be changes in the permanent work—*e.g.* in specified bearing capacities of formation following a specified number of passes of an identified roller—while others may not be—*e.g.* the number of hours to be allowed for curing concrete after placing or before striking—while it always was the case, it is submitted, that a change ordered in a method of working from that which the Contractor wished to do and could show would have produced satisfactory permanent work, would in the absence of express provision amount to a variation, or even breach of contract, entitling the Contractor to additional payment or damages. Engineers should be careful, therefore, both in the light of the present wording and in view of a closely analogous possible claim under clause 13 (3) even where no variation has been called for (see the commentary, *supra*, p. 53, to that Condition), only to use the language of instruction, as opposed to permissive language, in cases where the quality of the final permanent work is threatened or other compelling commercial reasons or interests of their clients require it.

(*1*) " *omissions* "

This will not usually permit work to be omitted without the Contractor's consent if the purpose is to enable it to be carried out by another Contractor or a Nominated Sub-contractor—see Hudson, 10th ed., pp. 532–533, and the Australian case of *Carr* v. *J. A. Berriman Property Ltd.* (1955) 27 A.L.J. 273 there referred to—but see the special power in the case of certain nominated sub-contract work in clause 59A (2) (b), *infra*, p. 203.

(*2*) " *No variation . . . shall in any way vitiate or invalidate the Contract* "

In spite of the generality of the definition of the variation power in sub-clause (1), it is clear that in principle changes in the work can be ordered which, by reason of their extent or nature, cannot be regarded as " variations " at all, but as, in effect, a new contract work—see for this Hudson, 10th ed., pp. 548–553—and the present words must be read subject to this. In reality the words are otiose, it is submitted.

Valuation of Ordered Variations

52. (1) The value of all variations ordered by the Engineer in accordance with Clause 51 shall be ascertained by the Engineer after consultation with the Contractor in accordance with the following principles. Where work is of similar character and executed under similar conditions to work priced in the Bill of Quantities it shall be valued at such rates and prices contained therein as may be applicable. Where work is not of a similar character or is not executed under similar conditions the rates and prices in the Bill of Quantities shall be used as the basis for valuation so far as may be reasonable failing which a fair valuation shall be made. Failing agreement between the Engineer and the Contractor as to any rate or price to be applied in the valuation of any variation the Engineer shall determine the rate or price in accordance with the foregoing principles and he shall notify the Contractor accordingly.

Engineer to fix Rates

(2) Provided that if the nature or amount of any variation relative to the nature or amount of the whole of the contract work or to any part thereof shall be such that in the opinion of the Engineer or the Contractor any rate or price contained in the Contract for any item of work is by reason of such variation rendered unreasonable or inapplicable either the Engineer shall give to the Contractor or the Contractor shall give to the Engineer notice before the varied work is commenced or as soon thereafter as is reasonable in all the circumstances that such rate or price should be varied and the Engineer shall fix such rate or price as in the circumstances he shall think reasonable and proper.

Any sensible provision for valuation of variations must recognise that by virtue of the location, timing or simple extent of a variation it may be inequitable to price it at the rates or prices for similar or identical work to be found in the Bills. (In any event, by virtue of the lack of precision shown by the Standard Method of Measurement as to what elements of expenditure should be priced in the Preliminary Bills as Preliminary Items and what elements in the later items for the construction processes themselves, coupled with the readiness of Engineers and arbitrators to permit Contractors to " take a view " or depart from the Standard Method itself, particularly in their internal pricing of the overheads, profit and " preliminary " element in the items, considerable argument can be expected to develop even if the principle is adopted that " the rates and prices in the Bills " should be used to value a particular variation (see Appendix A, *post*, and the author's article on Bills of Quantities there reprinted and see also *infra*, pp. 159–161.

The Fourth Edition contained, in sub-clause (1), a traditional and rather vague formula for valuation of " extra or additional work " at " reasonable " prices if, in the Engineer's opinion, the contract rates were " not applicable " (no criteria for this being given). Sub-clause (2) was virtually identical with that in the present Edition, and the precise interrelationship and intention of these two sub-clauses in the Fourth Edition was a matter of the greatest difficulty—see the commentary in B.C.F. at pp. 385–387, or the expanded treatment of the subject in I.C.E.C. at pp. 101–104.

The present Edition, while retaining the old sub-clause (2) virtually intact, now introduces in sub-clause (1) a totally different formula for valuing all variations (*i.e.* omissions and substitutions as well as simply extra or additional work) which appears to be closely modelled on clause 11 (4) of the RIBA Conditions of Contract. It will be quite wrong to suppose, therefore, that any logical or closely reasoned relationship exists between the two sub-clauses in the present Edition, even if there ever had been such a relationship in the earlier Edition. Moreover, no consideration appears to have been given to the major overlap which now exists between sub-clause (2) and the new clause 56 (2), *infra*, p. 187. In particular, the old question under the Fourth Edition " What, if anything, does sub-clause (2) add which cannot be recovered under sub-clause (1)? " now becomes virtually impossible to answer affirmatively, since the earlier sub-clause, as stated, now applies to all variations and not merely to extra or additional work, unlike the old version. As will be seen, however, (probably unintended) differences between the sub-clauses on the new wording, and of the provisions about notices in the clause as a whole, are

(a) that under sub-clause (2) the Engineer is undoubtedly able to *reduce* the contract prices in appropriate cases, which perhaps may arguably not be possible under the " basis for valuation " wording in sub-clause (1); and
(b) that the notice requirement on the Contractor under sub-clause (2) is more onerous than that under sub-clause (1).

Despite refinements of meaning based on the obscurity of their related wording, there is little doubt that the combination of the present two sub-clauses, and now of clause 56 (2) in cases of simple remeasurement, make it extremely easy for the Contractor to justify a departure from the contract prices when disputing the valuation of variations. Though, as stated, sub-clause (2) clearly implies a possible *reduction* in prices (the old second proviso as to notices in this sub-clause, now dropped, was in fact explicit about the possibility of reductions and the new clause 56 (2) is also quite explicit about this) it is virtually unheard of in the U.K. for Engineers to reduce a rate for extra work on the ground that the overheads have been recovered on the contract quantities, and that very substantial increases in quantities resulting from a variation ordered in good time will mean that the Contractor's rates will be " unreasonable " or " inapplicable " as being (now) unduly favourable. This argument, which in the majority of cases must in reality be correct, depends, of course, on the extent to which preliminary items have been weighted by the Contractor so as to carry his overheads, which could only be proved with certainty if the Contractor's internal pricing methods as between the preliminary and later construction items in the Bills were known—it is a criticism of all the U.K. contracts using Bills that, at latest at an early post-contract stage, the Contractor is not required to divulge the make-up of his rates and prices, at least as regards all items of cost, or at the very least to furnish a sufficiently detailed breakdown of prices for the purpose of valuing variations. This means that in negotiations for reasonable prices of varied work Employers' advisers often feel heavily handicapped in resisting Contractors' arguments based on the alleged make-up of the original contract prices. Moreover, it is becoming increasingly common to find very large and frequently vaguely worded preliminary items " written in " or inserted in the Bills of Quantities by Contractors when pricing at the tender stage. The effect of this device is that the Contractor's rates for the work-processes which are to be found described and priced in the later part of the Bills will be correspondingly reduced, but this will not, of course, affect the Contractor's remuneration unless substantial net additions to the contract work are ordered by way of variation, and then only if the later Bill rates or prices are used extensively to value the work. The advantage to the Contractor is that he can often secure far larger interim payments at the beginning of the work based on his artificially inflated " preliminary " items; that if net omissions are subsequently ordered and valued only at the later construction rates for the actual work-processes the profitability of the contract will be increased; and that the sums in question, provided their exact constituent expenditure and purpose is not made clear and is obscured by generalised wording, can always be used to support arguments for substantial additional payment beyond the construction rates if net additions are ordered, or if for any reason the contract period is extended in circumstances where the Employer is liable to reimburse the Contractor for additional costs due to delay. In the Employer's interests such preliminary items should be scrutinised with the greatest care, and if necessary the exact expenditure represented by them, and their internal pricing and method of calculation, should be clearly stated and defined before the contract is signed so as to avoid their subsequent manipulation in this way.

It cannot be said, in this context, that even the use of the U.K. Standard Methods of Measurement is of much assistance in restraining abuses of preliminary items in this way, since in both the building and civil engineering industries the U.K. Standard Methods were extremely vague in regard to the contents of preliminary Bills, and in particular laid down no precise criteria for determining what items of expenditure should be dealt with by way of preliminary items, or whether and to what extent such expenditure could also be carried in whole or in part on the later rates and prices in the Bills, nor any rules or guidance in regard to their adjustment, in the event of variations on the one hand, or simple differences between original and ultimate billed quantities on the other, subsequently taking place on any substantial scale. In 1976, however, a new Civil Engineering Standard Method (" C.E.S.M.M.") was published, Section 7 of which has made an attempt, via the new concept of " Method Related Charges " which are to be either " Fixed " or " Time Related," to improve the precision of what is now called the " General Items " Bill—see the commentary under clause 57, *infra*, pp. 193–195.

There is no doubt that the arguments so frequently advanced in favour of Bills of Quantities by their advocates in the U.K.—namely that they enable work to be identified and valued with a far higher degree of precision for variation or interim valuation purposes, are entirely invalidated if, as is so often the case, a substantial portion of the contract price is to be found in the preliminary Bills without any prior disclosure as to its true make-up.

Bearing these general observations in mind, sub-clause (1) presupposes that a variation may involve an addition or omission which, if it is *both* of a " similar character " *and* executed under " similar conditions," will be priced at unadjusted contract rates and prices. This gives some clue as to the meaning of the key words " character " and " conditions "—the express wording of sub-clause (2) (" if the . . . *amount* of any variation ") and of clause 56 (2) (" actual quantities . . . be greater or less ") suggests that neither " character " nor " conditions " in the present sub-clause are intended to cover, for example, the major changes in the quantities for which claims can be made under sub-clause (2) or clause 56 (2). It is submitted, therefore, that " similar character " means, in effect, *the same work process* as one already described and priced, whereas " similar conditions " describes the same surrounding conditions in which the work-process is to be carried out as those contemplated when contracting. Thus a more congested working area, or more difficult access, or a different part of the Site with more difficult ground conditions than the work priced by the Contractor, or work needing to be carried out in winter, and so on, will not be carried out under " similar conditions." The expression " similar conditions " might also, perhaps, refer to a situation where the timing of the variation instruction permitted properly pre-planned working or the ready absorption of the work into the Contractor's work programme and overheads (but see the word " nature " in sub-clause (2), however, which may be more apt to fit such a claim). It is also suggested that when the sub-clause presupposes that the contract prices can be " the basis of " a new rate or price for " dissimilar " work or work executed in " dissimilar conditions " it has in mind the breakdown of the contract rates into their constituent parts of labour, plant materials and overheads and their recalculation to enable a price for a comparable but not identical work-process to be determined—*e.g.* an excavation rate for a certain depth being used as the basis of a rate for a greater depth, a rate for straight concrete as the basis for a rate for curved concrete, a composite pile-driving rate per foot driven being the basis for driving with a different type of pile from that specified, a percentage or other weighting being added to a price for greater congestion or more difficult ground, and so on. The intention throughout, including the last " fair valuation " basis, is, it is submitted, to value at prices as closely analogous as possible to the original contract prices, so that any under-pricing or over-pricing element in the original contract prices would be perpetuated or reflected in the variation valuation under the sub-clause. However, the clause lacks precision in this respect. What is a " fair valuation " if very substantial quantities of additional work are ordered in a case where it is clear that the Contractor had inadvertently greatly under-estimated, for example, the physical difficulties, or purely financial considerations such as the cost of labour in the area, which were no worse in the area or at the time of the varied work than in the area or time of the original contract work? It is submitted that a " fair valuation " should in these circumstances have regard to a valuation *as it would have been reached at the time of contracting*, unless the variation itself *was directly responsible* for the additional expense incurred by the Contractor (*e.g.* if a change of line on a trench resulted in more difficult ground being encountered from that in fact existing on the original line. However wrong a view the Contractor originally took of ground conditions, he would be entitled to the actual difference in the two costs under the " fair valuation " wording, it is submitted, but not under the " basis " wording.

As already pointed out, however, a valuation at contract or " analogous " rates and prices under the present sub-clause will mean *all* the contract rates and prices, including any relevant preliminary items which may be affected by the variation, the selection and adjustment of which may, as already explained, be a most difficult matter. This means that, if the sub-clause stood alone, major differences in quantities might automatically result in appropriate adjustment without recourse to the " work not of similar character " formula, and notwithstanding the restricted definitions suggested above for " character " and " conditions ", though of course quantity differences are expressly dealt with under sub-clause (2) as well as, in the case of simple remeasurement without variations, in clause 56 (2).

The words " after consultation with the Contractor " are new and their purpose in a contractual document is obscure (see the further commentary, *infra*). The sub-clause also contemplates an attempt at agreement, which is also new, and failing agreement notification of his " determination " by the Engineer to the Contractor, which may have consequences if the Contractor fails to serve a counter-notice within 28 days under sub-clause (4) (a) and (e), *infra*. As will be seen, however, sub-clause (4) (a) does not appear to deal with the case where the Contractor remains totally silent and neither consults with nor indicates any claim to the Engineer, who accordingly himself takes no special action (see the commentary to sub-clause (4) (a), *infra*). Furthermore, there appears to have been no consideration given as to whether a determination of the Engineer notified under the present clause will constitute an Engineer's decision under clause 66, bringing the much more severe time limit under that clause into play, should the Contractor not give notice of arbitration within the stipulated three months. On the wording of the present clause, and also of clause 66 (" including any dispute as to any . . . valuation of the Engineer ") it seems very arguable that this is so—but see the discussion under clause 66, *infra*, pp. 267, 272. There are other indications that the new notice provisions in this sub-clause have not been fully considered in their relationship to other provisions of the contract—see the commentary to sub-clause (4) (a), *infra*.

" *after consultation with the Contractor* "
" *failing agreement* "

These references are new, and seem unwise as contractual provisions—consultation or discussion usually takes place in any event, and sometimes agreement, but the suggestion that these may be contractual requirements can only assist Contractors who, when meeting resistance to their claims, refuse to accept the Engineer's decision and seek to assert that there has been insufficient consultation and demand still more meetings—an exhausting tactic by no means unknown in the industry. Various theories and recommendations for holding meetings and agreeing or fixing rates as the work progresses have been advocated in the industry from time to time, and it may be some such influence which has led to the new wording. In practice, however, such " agreements " rarely if ever dispose of matters finally, leaving the litigious contractor free to claim still more, and often enabling the contractor to take advantage in later negotiation or litigation of concessions already made previously, on what has become a " horse trade " basis in which the Employer never receives any firm *quid pro quo*. There is no advantage and much risk for the Employer in this process. There is, incidentally, no authority whatever conferred by the Contract on the Engineer, even on the present wording, to make agreements or concessions as to price which will bind the Employer.

Turning to sub-clause (2), if the views expressed about sub-clause (1), *supra*, are correct, it is probably right that sub-clause (2) adds nothing to what is already recoverable (by either side) under sub-clause (1). The principal effect of the sub-clause, on this view, is that it removes any doubts that significant changes in quantities may result in adjustment of *other* items in the contract, or that a valuation under this clause may result in a *reduction* as well as an increase in the contract prices.

It is difficult to give any precise meaning to the word " nature " in this sub-clause, in contradistinction to the expression " character " in sub-clause (1)—see the commentary *supra*, p. 161. Furthermore, the reference to " *any* rate or price " suggests, it is submitted, preliminary items as being the obvious rates or prices which might be affected by a variation other than the directly involved prices of the construction-processes themselves.

So far as the provision for notice is concerned, the very odd requirement that either the Engineer or the Contractor should give the other notice of a varied rate or price (with certain added restrictions on the timing of the Contractor's notice) leaves the observer to speculate (particularly if he has knowledge of the old sub-clause) that the intention may be that the Engineer should be obliged (without, however, there being any stipulated sanction) to notify proposed *reductions* promptly, and for the Contractor to notify any claim for an *increase* (see the language of sub-clause (4) (a), *infra*) with at least an attempted, but perhaps deliberately not very severe, sanction (see sub-clause (4) (e), *infra*) for not doing so promptly. However, the wording about this, which is new, certainly lacks clarity, and presumably a rate or price which the Engineer proposes to increase of his own volition should be notified (though, as stated, without any express sanction for failure to do so).

(*2*) " *or as soon thereafter as is reasonable in all the circumstances* "

As pointed out, the sanction for failure to give notice under the present new sub-clause (4) (e), *infra*, is not very severe. But apart from this, the Court of Appeal in England have held, in relation to words identical to those quoted above in the present sub-clause in the Fourth Edition, that a notice need only indicate the intention to make a claim and identify in general terms the additional work to which the claim will relate. In adition, the court gave generous practical effect to the words " as soon . . . as is practicable " in a case where variation instructions were given in July and August and notices were given at the end of December and February respectively—see *Tersons Limited* v. *Stevenage Corporation* [1965] 1 Q.B. 37. Hudson, 10th ed., pp. 535–536. The wording of the present contract (in sub-clause (4) (d) and (e), *infra*) suggests that the purpose of the notice in the present sub-clause is merely to enable a proper check to be kept on the Contractor's additional costs as and when they arise and not, as in the Fourth Edition, to enable the Engineer to review a decision or instruction, which he might have taken in the belief that the work would not involve the Contractor in extra expense or that it did not involve a variation of the contract work, before it is finally implemented by the Contractor.

Daywork

(3) The Engineer may if in his opinion it is necessary or desirable order in writing that any additional or substituted work shall be executed on a daywork basis. The Contractor shall then be paid for such work under the conditions set out in the Daywork Schedule included in the Bill of Quantities and at the rates and prices affixed thereto by him in his Tender and failing the provision of a Daywork Schedule he shall be paid at the rates and prices and under the conditions contained

in the " Schedules of Dayworks carried out incidental to Contract Work " issued by The Federation of Civil Engineering Contractors current at the date of the execution of the Daywork.

The Contractor shall furnish to the Engineer such receipts or other vouchers as may be necessary to prove the amounts paid and before ordering materials shall submit to the Engineer quotations for the same for his approval.

In respect of all work executed on a daywork basis the Contractor shall during the continuance of such work deliver each day to the Engineer's Representative an exact list in duplicate of the names occupation and time of all workmen employed on such work and a statement also in duplicate showing the description and quantity of all materials and plant used thereon or therefor (other than plant which is included in the percentage addition in accordance with the Schedule under which payment for daywork is made). One copy of each list and statement will if correct or when agreed be signed by the Engineer's Representative and returned to the Contractor. At the end of each month the Contractor shall deliver to the Engineer's Representative a priced statement of the labour material and plant (except as aforesaid) used and the Contractor shall not be entitled to any payment unless such lists and statements have been fully and punctually rendered. Provided always that if the Engineer shall consider that for any reason the sending of such list or statement by the Contractor in accordance with the foregoing provision was impracticable he shall nevertheless be entitled to authorise payment for such work either as daywork (on being satisfied as to the time employed and plant and materials used on such work) or at such value therefor as he shall consider fair and reasonable.

This sub-clause contemplates that the Engineer will indicate in writing, when giving an instruction, that payment is to be on a daywork basis, whereupon the Contractor must furnish daily lists identifying the labour and daily statements (save for a specific exception) identifying the plant involved, followed by monthly price statements of the expenditure on both.

" *if in his opinion it is necessary or desirable* "

Since dayworks are usually recognised as highly profitable (and may even, on the expressed basis in the present sub-clause, enable the Contractor to escape from an underpriced contract if there is no priced Daywork Schedule) there may be a dispute with the Contractor as to the necessity of a dayworks basis for the valuation of varied work—if so this can be the subject of a decision and arbitration under clause 66. The sub-clause gives no guidance about this, but dayworks are usually only used when the subject-matter of an instruction is not capable of measurement or valuation in any other way—*e.g.* work of cleaning up, watching or guarding or lighting, or work of a random character.

" *if . . . the sending of such list or statement . . . was impracticable* "

The wording makes it plain that the necessary documentation by the Contractor is indeed a condition precedent, without which no payment whatever will be due. Moreover, on its choice of wording the " impracticability " exception appears to be a very limited one, and far narrower, it is submitted, than an exception based on unreasonableness. Here, too, the Engineer's view will be open to arbitration under clause 66, however.

(4) (a) If the Contractor intends to claim a higher rate or price than one notified to him by the Engineer pursuant to sub-clauses (1) and (2) of this Clause or Clause 56 (2) the Contractor shall within 28 days after such notification give notice in writing of his intention to the Engineer.

(b) If the Contractor intends to claim any additional payment pursuant to any Clause of these Conditions other than sub-clauses (1) and (2) of this Clause he shall give notice in writing of his intention to the Engineer as soon as reasonably possible after the happening of the events giving rise to the claim. Upon the happening of such events the Contractor shall keep such contemporary records as may reasonably be necessary to support any claim he may subsequently wish to make.

(c) Without necessarily admitting the Employer's liability the Engineer may upon receipt of a notice under this Clause instruct the Contractor to keep such contemporary records or further contemporary records as the case may be as are reasonable and may be material to the claim of which notice has been given and the Contractor shall keep such records. The Contractor shall permit the Engineer to inspect all records kept pursuant to this Clause and shall supply him with copies thereof as and when the Engineer shall so instruct.

(d) After the giving of a notice to the Engineer under this Clause the Contractor shall as soon as is reasonable in all the circumstances send to the Engineer a first interim account giving full and detailed particulars of the amount claimed to that date and of the grounds upon which the claim is based. Thereafter at such intervals as the Engineer may reasonably require the Contractor shall send to the Engineer further up to date accounts giving the accumulated total of the claim and any further grounds upon which it is based.

Notice of Claims

(e) If the Contractor fails to comply with any of the provisions of this Clause in respect of any claim which he shall seek to make then the Contractor shall be entitled to payment in respect thereof only to the extent that the Engineer has not been prevented from or substantially prejudiced by such failure in investigating the said claim.

(f) The Contractor shall be entitled to have included in any interim payment certified by the Engineer pursuant to Clause 60 such amount in respect of any claim as the Engineer may consider due to the Contractor provided that the Contractor shall have supplied sufficient particulars to enable the Engineer to determine the amount due. If such particulars are insufficient to substantiate the whole of the claim the Contractor shall be entitled to payment in respect of such part of the claim as the particulars may substantiate to the satisfaction of the Engineer.

This sub-clause is clearly intended to be a comprehensive code for notification of all claims made by the Contractor under any provision of the contract, and not merely under the present clause—see paragraph (b), but see, however, the overlapping notice requirements, almost certainly due to the piecemeal historical evolution of the provision, in clause 69 (6), *infra*, pp. 285–286—and for subsequent periodical particularisation of the amount of any claim so notified—see paragraph (d). The sanction in paragraph (e) for failure to give notice or adequate subsequent particularisation is in practice unlikely either to prevent recovery by or seriously embarrass contractors, who have failed to comply with the notice requirements, in the subsequent presentation of their claims—one category at least of claims which might be embarrassed (allegations about the extent or nature of covered-up work) is protected by a considerably more powerful sanction if the Contractor is not present at measurement meetings—see clause 56 (3), *infra*, pp. 189–190—but it is difficult to conceive of any other practical situations where absence of early notification will " substantially prejudice " the investigation of most contractors' claims as usually formulated and investigated in the U.K., though there are perhaps a very few claims in the clause 12 category which might occasionally suffer some inhibition due to late presentation—*e.g.* if samples or records were no longer available. But even this is not usually likely to occur. See for a further possible category, *infra*, p. 190.

Apart from its lack of any likely practical effect in inhibiting or reducing claims without adequate early notification, there appears to be some lack of co-ordination in the draftsmanship of this sub-clause. In the first place, the wording " any additional payment pursuant to any clause of these Conditions . . ." in paragraph (b) seems extraordinarily wide—for example, does it apply to simple remeasurement of quantities under clause 56 (1)? And what precisely does " *additional* payment " mean (*i.e.* additional to what?) in the context of a contractual obligation (see the Form of Agreement) to pay " the Contract Price," which is itself defined (see clause 1 (1) (i)) as " the sum to be ascertained in accordance with the provisions of the contract "? If the intention is to inhibit claims additional to the prices and quantities totalled in the Bills of Quantities without due notice under the present clause, this hardly seems consistent with the language of, for example, the measurement clauses 55 (1) and (2) and 56 (1) and (3). Moreover, the wording " pursuant to any clause of these Conditions other than sub-clauses (1) and (2) of this Clause " in paragraph (b) do not appear, on close analysis, to cover exactly all the possible contractual claims not covered by paragraph (a). That paragraph deals only with determinations of the Engineer notified to the Contractor under the three identified contractual provisions. It has already been pointed out that clause 52 (1) contemplates consultation, disagreement, determination by the Engineer, and finally notification of the decision to the Contractor—but that it is silent as to the position if none of these events takes place, and the Contractor simply claims his higher rate or price at the end of the work. In the case of clause 52 (2) that sub-clause as a fact contains no provision for notification to the Contractor of the Engineer's determination of the rate or price, (or if it does, probably only in regard to reductions in rates and prices) whereas in the case (presumably) of increases it requires the Contractor to notify the Engineer that a rate or price should be varied, which does not fit the wording of paragraph (a) of the present sub-clause. Paragraph (b) of the present sub-clause should, therefore, have used a formula such as " In all other cases where the Contractor wishes to claim. . . ." There seems no reason, too, why clause 56 (2) is not included in the exceptions made in paragraph (b). The matter may perhaps be summarised by saying that the attempt made in paragraphs (a) and (b) to distinguish between the particular Engineer's determinations referred to in paragraph (a) and the other matters referred to in paragraph (b) appears to be inelegant and confused, as indeed do the differing provisions about the need for contemporary records in paragraphs (a) (b) and (c). On the other hand, none of these provisions overall are on any view likely to have any important practical consequences, since Contractors who do not keep records or substantiate claims are not likely to expect to be paid on an interim basis even where a contract is silent on the matter, so that paragraph (f) does little more than state the usual practice; and since, as already stated, at the end of the day there are as a fact very few claims likely to be seriously prejudiced within the wording of the sub-clause, as these are usually formulated and quantified and dealt with by Engineers, simply because they have been made for the first time at a late stage, so that paragraph (e) will rarely have any practical effect either.

PROPERTY IN MATERIALS AND PLANT

Plant, etc.—Definitions

53. (1) For the purpose of this Clause:—

(a) the expression "Plant" shall mean any Constructional Plant Temporary Works and materials for Temporary Works but shall exclude any vehicles engaged in transporting any labour plant or materials to or from the Site;

(b) the expression "agreement for hire" shall be deemed not to include an agreement for hire purchase.

This sub-clause should be read with the definitions of "Constructional Plant" and "Temporary Works," *supra*, clause 1 (1) (k) and 1 (1) (o), and the commentaries thereto. It should be noted that the present clause deals with three principal kinds of subject-matter, namely Constructional Plant (defined in clause 1 (1) (o), *supra*, as appliances or things required in the construction of the Works but not intended to form part of the Permanent Works); Temporary Works (the subject of a tautologous and unhelpful definition in clause 1 (1) (k), *supra*) including their own special unfixed materials; and finally unfixed materials or articles intended for fixing in the permanent work itself. This follows from the wide definition of "Plant" in paragraph (a) above, and from the fact that many of the more important substantive sub-clauses of the present clause are expressly applied not simply to "Plant," but to "Plant goods and materials"—see *e.g.* sub-clauses (2) and (7), concerned with vesting and revesting of property; sub-clause (6), concerned with irremovability from the Site; sub-clause (8), concerned with failure to remove at the end of the work; sub-clause (9), with accidental or other damage; and sub-clause (10), with sub-contractors. By virtue of paragraph (b) above, it would seem that the clause, rather startlingly, *actually prohibits* the use if plant which is the subject of a hire-purchase agreement—one would have thought a somewhat unrealistic ambition in U.K. conditions. It is not clear whether this is intentional, or whether the intention was merely to abandon any attempt to control hire-purchase plant if brought onto the Site, but actual prohibition of such plant would seen clearly to follow from the wording—see the commentary on sub-clause (3), *infra*.

These three kinds of subject-matter of the clause—namely Plant, Temporary Works, and materials—raise quite different legal considerations, and the practical requirements of the parties in relation to them will also be totally different. Plant (in accordance with the definition of Constructional Plant in clause 1 (1) (o)) will never become the property of the Employer in any permanent sense. Materials or goods are in an entirely different category. They are almost invariably required for incorporation into the permanent work and will become the property of the Employer irrevocably the moment they are fixed to or incorporated into the land owned by the Employer, whether or not they have been paid for, and cannot subsequently be removed by the Contractor (and would be protected by injunction if this was attempted). On the other hand, even if express provisions are found in the contract passing the property in the materials to the Employer at an early stage, as in the present case, these will almost invariably be subject to an implied term permitting their removal by the Contractor at the end of the work, to the extent that they may be surplus to the requirements of the project (or indeed permitting their removal and substitution in order to meet maintenance or repairing obligations). "Temporary Works," of which, as stated, no precise definition is attempted in clause 1 (1) (k), *supra*, are, as the expression is usually understood, in a difficult grey area between plant and materials. They may be works of construction not actually required by the Employer to be part of the final permanent result of the project, but which may be necessary in order to achieve the construction of that project. Thus access roads, which it may be intended subsequently to remove or abandon, ramps, coffer-dams behind which permanent works will be constructed, and so on, will come into this category. Sometimes these temporary works are in fact intended to be left *in situ* (as *e.g.* some coffer-dams or steel-sheet piling or some forms of form work or shuttering). Sometimes the resemblance to plant is very close (gantries, batching-plants, etc.), and they will need to be removed. Sometimes they are described and designed by the Engineer in the drawings and other technical documents (see *e.g.* clause 8 (2)) and sometimes they are left to the design and discretion of the Contractor. For this subject generally, and for the complicated body of case law built up in England on the effect of " vesting " and other provisions, particularly in regard to claims by third-party owners or hirers of plant, or the claims of other third parties such as judgment creditors or the trustees or liquidators of the contractor or the employer, see Hudson, 10th ed., Chapter 12.

Vesting of Plant

(2) All Plant goods and materials owned by the Contractor or by any company in which the Contractor has a controlling interest shall when on the Site be deemed to be the property of the Employer.

This sub-clause is concerned to preserve the continued availability to the Employer of plant etc. as against creditors and others claiming through the Contractor, including very importantly the trustees or liquidators of the Contractor or any sub-contractors. The sub-clause needs to be read with clause 33 of the Conditions, *supra*, p. 100, and with sub-clauses (6) (7) (8) and (9), *infra*. Like so many of the U.K. standard forms, the contract adopts one set of provisions to govern the temporary and permanent rights of property in quite different categories of subject-matter, despite their fundamentally different characteristics from this point of view. It also adopts a " deemed to become the property of the Employer " formula which cannot, as already explained, be accepted, particularly in the case of plant, entirely at face value. This is a traditional formula designed to give the Employer a better title than any *later* claimant deriving his title through the Contractor (*e.g.* a judgment creditor of the Contractor, or his assignee or trustee or liquidator) *at least for the duration of the work* while it is needed on the Site. Its temporary and qualified character is emphasised by the " deeming " and " when on the Site " wording, and is reinforced by sub-clause (6), which permits removal from the Site before completion with the consent of the Engineer (and which indeed in the case of hired plant imposes no restraint at all upon such removal), and even more by clause 33, which positively requires removal of plant from the site at the end of the construction period. Upon removal the " property " will revest—see sub-clause (7). It should perhaps be noted that no significance appears to be attached, in this context, to the factor of payment, whether for materials under clause 60 (1) (b), or for some Temporary Works or plant under clause 60 (1) (d).

For the quite different principles which apply to questions of ownership or possession of plant on the one hand and materials on the other, whatever the contract may say, see Hudson, 10th ed., pp. 661–674. Only *surplus* materials, of course, can be subject to removal and revesting in the Contractor, whereas this will usually be the intention with all plant. As stated, Temporary Works may be in a half-way category, depending on whether or not they are intended to be left in or as part of the permanent work (see also the special reference to payment for these in clause 60 (1) (d), *infra*). Some plant may also be intended for use to destruction, or to be left in the work (again there is a reference to special payments in clause 60 (1) (d)). Apart from these special cases, it may be said as a fair generalisation that the property in plant never passes permanently to the Employer, though special rights of sale (such as in sub-clause (8), *infra*, or under clause 63 (1), *infra*, p. 245 may become operative under the contract. In general, the temporary " deeming " effected by the wording of the present sub-clause will, on the authorities, effectively bind all persons claiming through the Contractor, such as assignees, creditors or his liquidator or trustee, *until the work is complete*, unless their title *precedes* that of the Contractor—see Hudson, 10th ed., pp. 663–674 where the rather complicated case law as between Employer and third parties is set out and analysed. The only exception would appear to be in bankruptcy (as opposed to liquidations) where the trustee may be able to invoke, as against the Employer, the special doctrine, not applicable to liquidations, of reputed ownership—see Hudson, 10th ed., pp. 789–791, and the most useful case of *Re Fox*, *Oundle and Thrapston R.D.C.* v. *The Trustee* [1948] Ch. 407 there illustrated, which distinguishes on the facts between various categories of unfixed materials, depending on their location on or off the Site, for the purposes of this doctrine. By reason of the fact that full unconditional ownership of plant is seldom held to be transferred under a vesting clause, it seems doubtful if the doctrine could ever apply to plant (other perhaps than plant purchased outright under the terms of the contract—see *e.g.* clause 60 (1) (d) in the present contract which, however, may not contemplate purchase but only an interim financing payment for plant). In the case of materials, *Re Fox* held that unfixed materials on a building site were outside the doctrine for other factual reasons, so that the scope for the doctrine, which in any event is limited to personal bankruptcies, seems very limited, probably, as in *Re Fox*, to materials off the Site but paid for by the Employer—see now the new clause 54, *infra*, which contemplates this very situation where, at the pre-contract stage, the Engineer decides to make provision for such off-Site interim payment.

" *or by any company in which the Contractor has a controlling interest* "

This recognises the widespread practice of contractors in the U.K. to vest plant in a subsidiary company, either for the purpose of defeating clauses of this kind, or because plant-hire is carried on as a separate business. The present clause cannot, however, bind such a company which is not a party to the present contract and in law has an independent existence as a separate legal person, unless

(a) the subsidiary can be regarded as a mere nominee of the Contractor parent without any independent management or existence of its own (see the cases footnoted at p. 791 of Hudson, 10th ed.)

or (b) the Contractor parent, in undertaking the present obligation, could be regarded as doing so for and on behalf of the subsidiary.

Both these grounds are, however, likely to be extremely difficult to establish. Moreover, the strong likelihood is that a subsidiary or associated plant company would have a formal hiring contract with the Contractor parent—if so there is no inhibition on removal from the Site at any time—see sub-clause (6), *infra*, which expressly excepts hired plant from its operation. The only really effective machinery would take the form of forbidding the Contractor to bring onto the Site plant owned by such companies without a firm contractual right being granted to the Employer *by the company in question* permitting him to retain the plant on Site or otherwise dispose of it for the purposes of the contract as if it was the Contractor's own plant.

The present wording does not deal, it should also be noted, with other companies in the same group—contracting companies are very frequently themselves subsidiaries of the group parent. See also the commentary on the next sub-clause.

Conditions of Hire of Plant

(3) With a view to securing in the event of a forfeiture under Clause 63 the continued availability for the purpose of executing the Works of any hired Plant the Contractor shall not bring on to the site any hired Plant unless there is an agreement for the hire thereof which contains a provision that the owner thereof will on request in writing made by the Employer within 7 days after the date on which any forfeiture has become effective and on the Employer undertaking to pay all hire charges in respect thereof from such date hire such Plant to the Employer on the same terms in all respects as the same was hired to the Contractor save that the Employer shall be entitled to permit the use thereof by any other contractor employed by him for the purpose of completing the Works under the terms of the said Clause 63.

Costs for Purposes of Clause 63

(4) In the event of the Employer entering into any agreement for the hire of Plant pursuant to sub-clause (3) of this Clause all sums properly paid by the Employer under the provisions of any such agreement and all expenses incurred by him (including stamp duties) in entering into such agreement shall be deemed for the purpose of Clause 63 to be part of the cost of completing the Works.

Notification of Plant Ownership

(5) The Contractor shall upon request made by the Engineer at any time in relation to any item of Plant forthwith notify to the Engineer in writing the name and address of the owner thereof and shall in the case of hired Plant certify that the agreement for the hire thereof contains a provision in accordance with the requirements of sub-clause (3) of this Clause.

In civil engineering contracts in particular, the continued availability of the principal plant items may, depending upon the project, be a matter of major commercial importance to the Employer in securing completion of the project to time, or even as a form of security for due performance of his obligations by the Contractor, as the present group of sub-clauses indicates. Sub-clause (2) above was concerned with preserving this availability as against creditors and others claiming through the Contractor, whereas the present group of clauses is concerned with preserving it against the owners of plant hired to the Contractor.

Sub-clause (3) should be read, however, in the light of the wording of sub-clause (6), *infra*, which surprisingly appears to indicate that hired plant can be removed from the Site at any time, even without the consent of the Engineer. This latter provision may well be a mistake, particularly since the equivalent clause in the Fourth Edition was very confused and its policy unclear, and also because it seems inconsistent with the apparent anxiety for the Employer's interest suggested by the present sub-clause.

The words of sub-clause (3) " unless there is an agreement for the hire thereof," coupled with the definition of " agreement for hire " in sub-clause (1) (b), must, it is submitted, amount to a prohibition against *any* hire-purchase plant being brought to the Site by the Contractor. Whether or not this is intentional must be the subject of speculation. Moreover, the machinery, even if supplemented by full compliance with sub-clause (5), is quite ineffective, since a third person cannot sue upon a contract made between others (in the absence of agency or assignment); consequently the Employer could not enforce the provisions in the hiring agreement against an unwilling hirer (unless the Contractor could be said to have contracted as the Employer's agent, which would be extremely difficult to establish). As against the Contractor or his trustee or liquidator, of course, the Employer could detain the plant in question by reason of sub-clause (6), *infra.* The most that can be said of this elaborate machinery is that it gives some indication to the Employer that the hirer is likely to be willing to leave his plant on site on the terms stated. Sub-clause (4), incidentally, does no more than restate at some length what would in any event result from sub-clauses (1) and (4) of clause 63. Here again, as in the case of subsidiary companies under sub-clause (2), the only effective documentary protection for the Employer (above all because of the unqualified removability of all hired plant permitted under sub-clause (6)) would be not a certificate given by the Contractor under sub-clause (5) but an indorsement in favour of the Employer and counter-signed by the Employer either on the hiring agreement or in a separate document—*in other words a short separate contract between the Employer and the Plant Owner.*

Irremovability of Plant, etc.

(6) No Plant (except hired Plant) goods or materials or any part thereof shall be removed from the site without the written consent of the Engineer which consent shall not be unreasonably withheld where the same are no longer immediately required for the purposes of the completion of the Works but the Employer will permit the Contractor the exclusive use of all such Plant goods and materials in and for the completion of the Works until the occurrence of any event which gives the Employer the right to exclude the Contractor from the Site and proceed with the completion of the Works.

Revesting and Removal of Plant

(7) Upon the removal of any such Plant goods or materials as have been deemed to have become the property of the Employer under sub-clause (2) of this Clause with the consent as aforesaid the property therein shall be deemed to revest in the Contractor and upon completion of the Works the property in the remainder of such Plant goods and materials as aforesaid shall subject to Clause 63 be deemed to revest in the Contractor.

These provisions are intended to create (and also bring to an end in due course) a status of " irremovability," as between the Employer and the Contractor, of plant, goods and materials once on the Site, which has already been the object of sub-clause (2) (as against creditors and others claiming through the Contractor) and sub-clauses (3) (4) and (5) (as against owners of plant hired to the Contractor). It has already been pointed out that sub-clause (3) in effect prohibits the bringing of hire-purchase plant onto the Site. The words " (except hired Plant) " in the present sub-clause (6) can only mean in their context, it is submitted, that hired plant *can* be removed from the Site without the written consent of the Engineer, and it is difficult to escape the conclusion that this is *per incuriam* and inconsistent with the policy of sub-clauses (3) (4) and (5) (and indeed with the reasonable interests of the Employer). Of course, the present sub-clauses could not have, by themselves, bound owners hiring plant to the Contractor (see the commentary to sub-clauses (3) (4) and (5), *supra*), but they would have bound the Contractor himself and anyone claiming through him (*e.g.* a receiver or liquidator or assignee).

(*6*) " *which consent shall not be unreasonably withheld* "

This is obviously a matter where immediate arbitration would be essential in the event of a dispute between Employer and Contractor, but though there is no doubt that the Engineer's decision could in principle be reviewed by an arbitrator (see the " open up review and revise " wording in clause 66) this does not seem to be a matter where an " early arbitration " is permitted before the end of the work—see clause 66 (2), *infra*, p. 277, which similarly fails to protect the Employer's interest in a number of other respects where early arbitration would be helpful. Presumably the Employer will be compelled to resort to the courts to prevent premature removal (an arbitrator has no power to issue an injunction in any event, of course).

The words " no longer immediately required," incidentally, suggest that consent to removal ought to be given in a case where plant is no longer required for the time being, even though its later return to the Site will be necessary.

Sub-clause (7) plays an essential part in supplementing and explaining the " deemed to be the property of the Employer " formula in sub-clause (2)—see the commentary *supra*, p. 170, and indicates the qualified nature of the operation of that sub-clause, particularly with its automatic " deemed to revest " provision on completion of the work. Here again, however, there is over-simplification. Thus the great bulk of the unfixed *materials* will have become fixed, and so irretrievably the property of the Employer; again it sometimes happens that some items of plant or Temporary Works are intended for incorporation or for use to destruction

—see the commentary, *supra*, and the special references to payment for these in clause 60 (1) (d).

Disposal of Plant

(8) If the Contractor shall fail to remove any Plant goods or materials as required pursuant to Clause 33 within such reasonable time after completion of the Works as may be allowed by the Engineer then the Employer may:—

(a) sell any which are the property of the Contractor; and

(b) return any not the property of the Contractor to the owner thereof at the Contractor's expense;

and after deducting from any proceeds of sale the costs charges and expenses of and in connection with such sale and of and in connection with return as aforesaid shall pay the balance (if any) to the Contractor but to the extent that the proceeds of any sale are insufficient to meet all such costs charges and expenses the excess shall be a debt due from the Contractor to the Employer and shall be deductable or recoverable by the Employer from any monies due or that may become due to the Contractor under the contract or may be recovered by the Employer from the Contractor at law.

The elaborate power of sale in this clause is seldom likely to be needed in modern conditions, of course. There is, unusually, no provision for certification of the monetary consequences of a sale, and the puzzling use of the words " may be recovered . . . *at law* " is difficult to understand—the intention may be to exclude the matter from the arbitration clause and permit quick recourse to the courts, and in support of this it might be argued that a dispute would be unlikely to arise in such a situation which could usefully be referred in the first place to the Engineer as contemplated by clause 66. On the other hand, the words " at law " occur elsewhere in the contract—see *e.g.* clause 24—where this restricted meaning does not seem appropriate, and a more likely explanation seems to be that they are meaningless and diffuse wording resulting, perhaps, from past piecemeal and possibly archaic drafting.

Liability for Loss or Injury to Plant

(9) The Employer shall not at any time be liable for the loss of or injury to any of the Plant goods or materials which have been deemed to become the property of the Employer under sub-clause (2) of this Clause save as mentioned in Clauses 20 and 65.

This sub-clause again re-emphasises the qualified nature of the " deemed to be the property of the Employer " formula in sub-clause (2), but the reference to clauses 20 and 65 may be a little misleading if it suggests that very much of the subject-matter of the present sub-clause will be affected by those clauses. Neither of those two clauses (the " Excepted Risks " and war clauses) applies to plant, or to unfixed materials. Both qualify the Contractor's responsibility for damage to " the Works," in the case of the Excepted Risks and war, but " the Works " is defined as the Permanent Works together with the Temporary Works (clause 1 (1)) so that those clauses, for the purpose of the present sub-clause, will only have any significance in relation to Temporary Works (Permanent Works, *i.e.* in the present context fixed materials, are not really the subject of the present clause once fixed) and indeed it seems doubtful if on the wording of clauses 20 and 65 they would even apply to unfixed materials for Temporary Works (as does the present clause—see sub-clause (1) (a) above).

Incorporation of Clause in Sub-contracts

(10) The Contractor shall where entering into any sub-contract for the execution of any part of the Works incorporate in such sub-contract (by reference or otherwise) the provisions of this Clause in relation to Plant goods or materials brought on to the Site by the sub-contractor.

This provision sounds simple, but it is in fact an invitation to a typical "loose incorporation" (as to which see Hudson, 10th ed., pp. 214, 767–769) of the present provisions into the sub-contract, since it does not make plain whether the rights secured to the Employer by the present clause are to be expressed in the sub-contract to be for the Employer's benefit or for the main Contractor's. If the former were the correct interpretation, it would not, for reasons already set out in the commentaries to sub-clauses (2) and (3), *supra*, confer any legally effective remedy on the Employer against the sub-contractor in question, nor is there any effective sanction or machinery for its enforcement by the Employer against the (main) Contractor. The present sub-clause in terms applies to every sub-contract, whether for supply only or for work.

No Approval by Vesting

(11) The operation of this Clause shall not be deemed to imply any approval by the Engineer of the materials or other matters referred to herein nor shall it prevent the rejection of any such materials at any time by the Engineer.

This provision is a further example of the consistent policy of the contract in refuting any possible argument by the Contractor that by some earlier approval, payment or certificate, the Employer is precluded from condemning defective work or materials at a later date—see the last sentence of clause 17 (checking of setting-out), clause 38 (2) (opening-up of work after approval), clause 39 (1) (c) (re-execution notwithstanding previous test or interim payment), clause 39 (3) (failure of Engineer or Engineer's Representative to disapprove), clause 50 (Contractor to search), clause 54 (3) (a) (approval of goods off the Site), clause 60 (7) (interim certificates) and clause 61 (2) (maintenance certificate not conclusive).

Vesting of Goods and Materials not on Site

54. (1) The Contractor may with a view to securing payment under Clause 60 (1) (c) in respect of goods and materials listed in the Appendix to the Form of Tender before the same are delivered to the Site transfer the property in the same to the Employer before delivery to the Site provided:—

(a) that such goods and materials have been manufactured or prepared and are substantially ready for incorporation in the Works; and

(b) that the said goods and materials are the property of the Contractor or the contract for the supply of the same expressly provides that the property therein shall pass unconditionally to the Contractor upon the Contractor taking the action referred to in sub-clause (2) of this Clause.

This new clause follows a recent trend in U.K. standard forms in *permitting* interim payment for materials or goods not yet on the Site, and though no doubt primarily of early financing advantage to the Contractor, it may also confer an important benefit on the Employer, in giving him an earlier title to those goods and materials than would otherwise be the case, which will bind the trustee or liquidator or assignee of the Contractor, or even in some cases sub-contractors—see the law and passages in Hudson referred to in the commentary under clause 53 (2), *supra*, pp. 170–171. The choice of any goods or materials which may qualify for this privileged treatment is intended to be left to the Engineer at the pre-tender stage (see the footnote (e) to the Appendix to the Form of Tender). Paragraph (a) above makes it plain that the goods or materials must be in an advanced stage of manufacture or preparation, which suggests " goods " (*i.e.* articles fabricated by the Contractor or a sub-contractor) rather than " materials " in their more primary sense (*e.g.* stockpiled fill material at a quarry or borrowpit off the Site). While the Engineer's selection in the Appendix may show an intention to accord advanced payment under this clause to basic or primary materials, much of sub-clause (2), *infra* (*e.g.* the provision for marking or identification), suggests that the clause is principally aimed at fabricated goods. Paragraph (b) is, of course, an essential safeguard to the Employer in the contemplated situation. Property under a contract of sale or manufacture will usually pass to the Contractor from his supplier or sub-contractor on delivery to him, but if not, or if such delivery has not taken place, the express provision required by paragraph (b) of the present sub-clause to be in the supply sub-contract (to the effect that the property must pass from the supplier to the Contractor upon the Contractor taking the action under sub-clause (2)) is in fact tautologous and unnecessary, since whether or not the supplier agrees to such a term it must follow that the property will have passed to the Contractor by the time that the Engineer, following due performance of the sub-clause (2) requirements, inspects or approves under sub-clause (3), when the property finally passes to the Employer. Moreover, the required sub-contract provision, in a dispute as to whether or not the property has passed at a particular time (*e.g.* with a trustee or liquidator of the Contractor or of his supplier) will be found to be insufficiently precise, since under sub-clause (2) a number of different acts of the Contractor or the supplier, all likely to occur in succession at somewhat different times, are specified, leaving it quite unclear precisely when the property is to pass. The words beginning " or the contract for the supply of the same expressly provides . . ." would have been better omitted altogether from paragraph (b), or else a single definitive time or event (*e.g.* upon the goods being substantially ready for incorporation into the works, or immediately prior to the Engineer's approval in writing under sub-clause (3)) should have been specified if it was desired to regulate exactly the supplier/Contractor transfer of property. The provisions also fail to safeguard the Employer properly against third parties' liens or other rights less than ownership, which may well exist where materials, etc., are stored off site—see the commentary, *infra.*

Action by Contractor

(2) The intention of the Contractor to transfer the property in any goods or materials to the Employer in accordance with this Clause shall be evidenced by the Contractor taking or causing the supplier of the said goods or materials to take the following action:—

(a) provide to the Engineer documentary evidence that the property in the said goods or materials has vested in the Contractor;

(b) suitably mark or otherwise plainly identify the said goods and materials so as to show that their destination is the Site that they are the property of the Employer and (where they are not stored at the premises of the Contractor) to whose order they are held;

(c) set aside and store the said goods and materials so marked or identified to the satisfaction of the Engineer; and

(d) send to the Engineer a schedule listing and giving the value of every item of the goods and materials so set aside and stored and inviting him to inspect the same.

The wording of this clause, coupled with that of sub-clause (3), *infra,* indicates that the property will not finally pass to the Employer until all the requirements of the present clause have been met and inspection and/or approval by the Engineer under sub-clause (3) has taken place. In a case where the property is already the Contractor's, no problem arises; but in a case where this is not yet so the documentary evidence in (a) cannot presumably be furnished until some late stage when the obscure requirement as to the passing of the property between the supplier and Contractor under sub-clause (1) (b) has been satisfied—as to the difficulties of which, see the commentary, *supra.*

The marking and identification of the goods under paragraph (b) of the present sub-clause will be needed (a) to pass the property from the supplier to the Contractor where the goods or materials in question are not specific and (b) to prevent the doctrine of reputed ownership defeating the Employer's title as against the trustee in bankruptcy of the Contractor or sub-contractor (see *Re Fox, Oundle and Thrapston R.D.C.* v. *The Trustee* [1948] Ch. 407, Hudson, 10th ed., p. 790) which does not apply, however, in the more usual case of limited company Contractors or suppliers and Companies Acts liquidations.

As to the avoidance of liens on the goods or materials (*e.g.* by suppliers or for storage charges), which should have been dealt with in the present sub-clause if the Employer's interest was to be properly safeguarded, see sub-clause (4), *infra.*

Vesting in Employer

(3) Upon the Engineer approving in writing the said goods and materials for the purposes of this Clause the same shall vest in and become the absolute property of the Employer and thereafter shall be in the possession of the Contractor for the sole purpose of delivering them to the Employer and incorporating them in the Works and shall not be within the ownership control of disposition of the Contractor.

Provided always that:—

(a) approval by the Engineer for the purposes of this Clause or any payment certified by him in respect of goods and materials pursuant to Clause 60 shall be without prejudice to the exercise of any power of the Engineer contained in this Contract to reject any goods or materials which are not in accordance with the provisions of the Contract and upon any such rejection the property in the rejected goods or materials shall immediately revest in the Contractor;

(b) the Contractor shall be responsible for any loss or damage to such goods and materials and for the cost of storing handling and transporting the same and shall effect such additional insurance as may be necessary to cover the risk of such loss or damage from any cause.

This is undoubtedly a full-scale transfer of ownership with the usual consequences (subject to continued contractual responsibility of the Contractor under Proviso (b)), unlike that effected by clause 53 (2) (as to which see the commentary, *supra*, p. 170), particularly since the ultimate purpose for this particular subject-matter is incorporation into the Works, and since the materials and goods will be specific and identified, unlike some at least of the materials and goods the subject-matter of clause 53, and since payment for them will now become due. The time when the property passes will be when the approval in writing of the Engineer is given, which will then entitle the Contractor to payment, less the " agreed percentage of value " which now takes the place of retention under sub-clauses (1) (c) and (2) (b) of clause 60, upon the next monthly payment. The one doubt is whether any surplus materials or goods under the present clause can be removed from the Site (*e.g.* in accordance with clause 53 (6) before completion or clause 33 on completion) or whether the materials and goods will become permanently the Employer's property. Since, however, the basis of payment under clause 60 (2) is no different from that for other materials (*i.e.* initially a percentage of value of the materials before fixing but later, after fixing and in substitution for the earlier payment, the contract value of the work, less retention, of which the materials now form part) it would be anomalous to treat any surplus goods or materials under the present clause any differently, it is submitted, so that the ownership (and consequently value) of these will ultimately revest in the Contractor in accordance with sub-clauses (7) and (8) of clause 53.

Proviso (a) is, of course, consistent with the general policy of the contract evidenced at many points—see *e.g.* the other contractual provisions referred to in the commentary to clause 53 (11), *supra.* Proviso (b) will, as in case of the remainder of the Works, apply until 14 days after the *issue* (not the certified date) of the Engineer's certificate of completion under clause 48—see clauses 20 (1) and 21, which means that the liability may continue for as much as five weeks after substantial completion.

Lien on Goods or Materials

(4) Neither the Contractor nor a sub-contractor nor any other person shall have a lien on any goods or materials which have vested in the Employer under sub-clause (3) of this Clause for any sum due to the Contractor sub-contractor or other person and the Contractor shall take all such steps as may reasonably be necessary to ensure that the title of the Employer and the exclusion of any such lien are brought to the notice of sub-contractors and other persons dealing with any such goods or materials.

For liens generally and analogous contractual rights of detention, see Hudson, 10th ed., p. 678.

Notwithstanding a transfer of ownership to the Contractor duly evidenced to the Engineer under sub-clause (2), it would nevertheless be possible for a lien in the proper sense to exist (*e.g.* for storage or repair charges) in favour of some person not the owner, or even a contractual right of detention (*e.g.* against payment of the price, or for carrying out some work of maintenance or assembly, for example)—rights of this latter kind are sometimes referred to, though not correctly, as " liens." The present sub-clause will be effective to negative any liens of any kind *as against the Contractor*, of course, but it cannot bind sub-sontractors or third persons in a position to claim such rights prior to the transfer of property to the Employer under the present contract, nor could the requirement that the Contractor should " take all steps . . . to ensure that the title of the Employer and the exclusion of any such lien are brought to the notice of sub-contractors and other persons," even if duly carried out by the Contractor, in any way diminish their rights if they had arisen before the Employer obtained his title, as in practice might often be the case. It is, therefore, surprising that such words as " and right to immediate possession of " have not been included in sub-clause (2) (a), *supra*, which would have afforded the Employer the necessary formal protection, coupled with an effective sanction (*e.g.* deduction of sums previously paid for the materials to the Contractor) should such rights be discovered after payment.

Delivery to the Employer of Vested Goods or Materials

(5) Upon cessation of the employment of the Contractor under this contract before the completion of the Works whether as a result of the operation of Clause 63 or otherwise the Contractor shall deliver to the Employer any goods or materials the property in which has vested in the Employer by virtue of sub-clause (3) of this Clause and if he shall fail to do so the Employer may enter any premises of the Contractor or of any sub-contractor and remove such goods and materials and recover the cost of so doing from the Contractor.

These goods will usually have already been paid for (less the " agreed percentage ") by the Employer under clause 60 (1) (d) (though there may, of course, be an interval between the approval in writing and vesting under sub-clause (3), *supra*, and the next following interim payment under clause 60). As pointed out in the commentary to sub-clause (3), *supra*, the basis of interim payment under clause 60 will change once the goods or materials have become incorporated into the work, and any surplus materials or goods on completion will, it is there submitted, revest in the Contractor and be the subject of removal and revesting provisions in clauses 33 and 53 (7) and (8).

The latter part of the present sub-clause makes the same incorrect assumption, as do so many other provisions in the Contract, that provisions in the main Contract can effectively bind sub-contractors at the suit of the Employer and for his benefit. " *Re*-entry " will not usually apply to sub-contractors, and removal from sub-contractors' premises will usually depend upon the Employer being able to show a concluded agreement to that effect made between the Employer *and the sub-contractor himself.* So far as suing for the goods or their value is concerned, the Employer will need to show better title—namely that the property has passed unconditionally from the sub-contractor to the main Contractor and/or himself—and also that there are no third party rights less than ownership, against which the present clause provides no effective safeguard or sanction, and which are quite likely to exist—see *supra*, sub-clause (4) and the commentary thereto.

Incorporation in Sub-contracts

(6) The Contractor shall incorporate provisions equivalent to those provided in this Clause in every sub-contract in which provision is to be made for payment in respect of goods or materials before the same have been delivered to the Site.

This type of provision (compare clause 53 (11) and see the commentary thereto) is a further example of attempted " loose incorporation " of main contract terms into sub-contracts, which is usually extremely difficult to spell out in detail when applied to the quite different main-contractor/sub-contractor situation and the sub-contract documentation itself. Does the sub-clause mean, for example, that sub-contractors should be entitled to have an early off-site interim payment code set up for themselves as against the main Contractor? If so, who selects the classes of goods or materials involved? Or is the intention simply to provide supporting sub-contract provisions to enable the present provision to be given full effect as between main Contractor and Employer, in cases where the designated materials or goods in the main contract happen to involve sub-contractors? Does it apply to every simple supply contract entered into by the main Contractor for main contract designated goods and materials, or only to sub-contracts for work (*e.g.* fabrication and manufacture)? The objects of the sub-clause are, it is submitted, too generalised and obscure to be given any clear contractual effect.

MEASUREMENT

Quantities

55. (1) The quantities set out in the Bill of Quantities are the estimated quantities of the work but they are not to be taken as the actual and correct quantities of the Works to be executed by the Contractor in fulfilment of his obligations under the Contract.

Correction of Errors

(2) Any error in description in the Bill of Quantities or omission therefrom shall not vitiate the Contract nor release the Contractor from the execution of the whole or part any of the Works according to the Drawings and Specification or from any of his obligations or liabilities under the Contract. Any such error or omission shall be corrected by the Engineer and the Value of the work actually carried out shall be ascertained in accordance with Clause 52. Provided that there shall be no rectification of any errors omissions or wrong estimates in the descriptions rates and prices inserted by the Contractor in the Bill of Quantities.

This and the next following clauses 56 and 57 constitute the remeasurement provisions of this contract, The three clauses taken together are a close repetition of the language used in the Fourth Edition clauses, subject, however, to two major new provisions of fundamental importance and novelty. These are the two sub-clauses (2) of clauses 55 and 56 respectively, which have been grafted (or inserted) as new additions to the earlier clauses and wording. Without a knowledge of the old provisions, this approach, as it has been carried out, can be misleading and indeed puzzling, suggesting perhaps that the principal fundamental process of remeasurement—*i.e.* recalculation of the contract price (actually in the Fifth Edition of the " Tender Total," since there is no figured " Contract Price " as such)—in accordance with the actual quantities has been provided for in one or other of these new sub-clauses (*i.e.* using the clause 52 provisions in the one case, or a " reasonable and applicable " basis in the other). In fact, as the commentary, *infra*, will indicate, this is not so, although English law raises considerable evidentiary difficulties about using the earlier history or evolution of a contract document in order to interprete a successor document, and the following commentary should be read with this in mind. There can, however, be little doubt as to the subjective intentions of the new draftsmanship, once the earlier history is appreciated, even if it may have failed to express them.

As a matter of general comment on all three clauses, the essential characteristic of the English contract " of which Quantities form part " or a " Bill [of Quantities] Form of contract " or a " remeasurement " contract, as such contracts are variously described, is that the contract price will be recalculated *quite independently of variations being called for*, should the actual quantities in the event differ from those stated in the Bills. This type of contract differs from older and simpler " Schedule " or remeasurement contracts in that in the modern " Bill " forms the quantities are estimated with fair precision beforehand, enabling a grossed-up total contract price (known in this Edition, at the two points where it has been felt necessary to refer to it, as the " Tender Total," as opposed to the " Contract Price "—see the definitions of these terms in clause 1 (1) (h) and (i), *supra*, pp. 16 and 19) to be tendered and accepted. The Bills have traditionally also been used for the valuation of variations, though almost invariably with savings clauses enabling the Bill prices (perfectly understandably in this case) to be departed from should the circumstances of the variation justify it—see the extensive commentary about these permitted departures, with particular regard to preliminary items, under clause 52, *supra*, pp. 159–162. A controversial question for many years has been the extent to which the rules permitting departure from the contract rates and prices in the case of *variations* could be applied in the case of a simple *remeasurement* not arising from variations—(this latter due principally either to errors occurring in " taking off " the quantities from the drawings, or because the quantities themselves were incapable of precise estimation—*e.g.* items or quantities, sometimes described as provisional, for contingent work such as removing unsuitable material and substituting fill, and so on, which are particularly common in engineering as opposed to building contracts).

The author's view was that, while scope for adjustment of prices might exist by way of appropriate adjustment of preliminary items even on a simple remeasurement, in the case of the Fourth Edition (unlike the RIBA standard forms) the wording of the contract distinguished between differences in quantities caused by variations and those arising on simple remeasurement, and that in the absence of any sufficiently express provision the clause 52 permitted departures from the contract rates and prices in the case of variations were not available in the latter case—see B.C.F., pp. 382–3, and 385. This distinction now appears to be accepted in the present Edition—see as examples, first, the distinction itself explicitly recognised in relation to extensions of time in the opening words of clause 44 (1) of the Conditions, and secondly, the obvious overlap between the new clause 56 (2) and clause 52 (2), and indeed the specific reference to clause 52 in clause 55 (2), both of which are explicable only on the basis that clause 52 is not to apply in a simple remeasurement case unless (as in the case of clause 55 (2)) it is specifically so provided.

As a general summary of the present three clauses, it would appear, in the light of the wording of the earlier Edition, that the subjective intention of the draftsman of the present Edition has been

(a) To provide for remeasurement in accordance with the actual quantities at Bill rates and prices by virtue of sub-clauses 55 (1) and 56 (1) (remarkably enough, these two extremely short and vague provisions were *all* that existed in the earlier Edition on the subject—see B.C.F., p. 398).

(b) To provide (in clause 55 (2)) for an exceptional valuation procedure *using the clause* 52 *rules* in the case of " errors in description in " or " omissions from " the Bills (whatever these expressions are supposed to mean exactly will be found in any particular case to be a matter of the most extreme difficulty, and has in all probability been deliberately left unclear—see *infra*, pp. 185–186).

(c) To provide (in clause 56 (2)) for a further exceptional valuation at more " reasonable and applicable " rates or prices than those in the Bills in cases where the actual increase or decrease in the quantities renders it " appropriate."

That this analysis is correct is strongly supported by the marginal headings to the various sub-clauses—but from the point of view of interpretation these must be, unfortunately, disregarded—see clause 1 (3), *supra*, p. 24. It will be seen that, on this analysis, the draftsman has selected a somewhat strange order for the old and new provisions in clauses 55 and 56. On any analysis, it can be confidently stated that the, overall intention and consequence of the new wording must be to make it extremely easy for the Contractor to escape from the Bill rates or prices. Clause 55 (2) appears both to facilitate and enshrine with explicit respectability one of the principal practices of " loophole engineering "—namely the discovery of " errors in description or omissions " in the Bills, preferably at the pre-tender stage—and clause 56 (2) to encourage claims based upon the alleged contractual make-up or weighting of the Bill rates and prices as between one part of the Bills and another (in particular, as between the preliminary expenditure items and the later items for construction processes themselves), so as to produce claims for upward valuation whenever the quantities markedly differ from the estimates. For an analysis and description of the English Bills of Quantities type of contract, and its advantages and disadvantages as it has come to be used and incorporated into the standard forms in the United Kingdom (including the Fourth and Fifth Editions) see the author's article in the *Journal of Maritime Law and Commerce*, Washington D.C., April 1975, reprinted in Appendix A, *post*, p. 305.

It is now proposed to consider the clauses in detail. Sub-clause (1) of the present clause 55 was, in the Fourth Edition, followed immediately by clause 56 (1), *infra*, and these two sentences still, it is submitted, require to be construed together, despite their present separation. Certainly no special significance seems to attach to their position relative to their two respective sub-clauses (2). Sub-clause (1) in the present clause 55 indicates that the Contractor's obligation (compare the first paragraph of the Tender, paragraph 3 of the Form of Agreement and the definition of Contract in clause 1 (1) (e) and clause 8 (1)) is to carry out whatever may be the actual quantities of work necessary to comply with (*inter alia*) the Specification and Drawings.

Sub-clause (2) of the present clause does *not* relate to *differences of quantity* between the billed and described work, which it will be seen are covered by clause 56, *infra* (see also with reservations due to clause 1 (3) of the conditions, the marginal headings to 56 (1) and (2)). This new sub-clause (2) adopts the wording of clause 12 (2) of the RIBA forms (which indeed is the general remeasurement provision in those forms) but with the vitally important removal of the word " quantity " from that provision. The sub-clause also contains a proviso rather differently worded from clause 13 of those forms, though with a similar overall intention. The Fourth Edition contained no such proviso, with the often important consequence that mistakes made by the Contractor in calculating or inserting his figures in the priced Bills would be put right upon a remeasurement (this could of course work both ways as between Employer and Contractor). On the new wording, which is not very elegant, it is submitted that a mistake, for example, in grossing-up a total from the quantities and rates, must *not* be corrected (in fact an equitable provision as against both competing Contractors who failed to obtain the contract and the Employer) and hence the proviso will override the " admeasurement " valuation under clause 56 (1), no doubt as a matter of arithmetic requiring the mistake to be artificially perpetuated in some way by those responsible for preparing the final measurement valuation—for this subject see Hudson, 10th ed., pp. 520-521.

The difficulty is to determine precisely what sub-clause (2) is contemplating when it refers to, first, " errors in description," and, secondly, " omissions " in situations where, by definition, there has been no variation of the contract work. Moreover, by what criteria is the Engineer or arbitrator to decide whether a " correction " should produce an increase *or decrease* in the value of the work? Under what may be termed the " inclusive price principle," to which lip-service at least is paid in clause 11 (2) of the Conditions, the general presumption is that a Contractor's price includes for all work, whether inevitably, or only contingently, necessary to carry out the described work. The permanent work which is the principal contract obligation is that described in the Specification and the Drawings. Is the " error in description " in the Bills a failure to give a sufficiently accurate description of the work in the Drawings or Specification? How inaccurate does the description have to be to become an " error " or " omission " in the Bills? As an example, if the drawings show 12-inch pipes, but the Bills show 18-inch pipes in the relevant section, and if the Engineer under clause 5 or otherwise confirms the drawings' requirement of 12-inch pipes, presumably there will need to be a new rate involving a reduction in value, on the assumption that the Bills have " pricing precedence." Similarly, if the Bills contain an excavation-rate for a depth not exceeding 20 feet, but the Drawings require a greater depth, there will be an increase of price on the ground of an error in description. If on the other hand varying depths are covered by a number of provisional " extra-over " rates, or provisional quantities exist for removing unsuitable material up to that depth, but no rate exists for depths exceeding 20 feet, there may alternatively simply be an " omission " of the necessary item. " Errors in description " or " omissions " of this type are a commonplace of measurement, and will usually give rise to no special problem of interpretation in practice.

It is difficult to resist the conclusion, however, that the RIBA wording has in reality been adopted in the present sub-clause not for such relatively simple aspects of remeasurement, but because in those contracts the wording has for a number of years been used to advance claims based on the contention that the Bills do not comply with the recommendations of the Standard Methods of Measurement, by failing to describe separately particular items of inevitably necessary or ancillary work, so that, however obvious the " omission " may be, to that extent there has been an " omission " of items from the Bills (this latter contention being in turn based on the wording of the contractual provision incorporating the Standard Method—in the present case clause 57, *infra*—and the " omission " or even " error " being in reality a failure to comply with the requirements of that contractual provision). These claims are, of course, in direct conflict with the general principle that, in a contract to carry out and complete described work, the price is inclusive of all ancillary work, whether indispensably or contingently necessary to complete the described work. They are based upon the single case in England (on the then RIBA forms) of *Bryant Sons Ltd.* v. *Birmingham Hospital Saturday Fund* [1938] 1 All E.R. 503, where the point was in fact conceded without argument. This subject has been fairly extensively commented upon elsewhere by the author—see B.C.F., pp. 21–23, 403–405, and see *post*, Appendix A, p. 313; and for a full discussion of the *Bryant* case and of the related House of Lords decision in *A. E. Farr Ltd.* v. *M.O.T.* (1965) see Hudson, 10th ed., pp. 515–520, now reported in (1977) 5 B.L.R. 94. See also the fuller detailed commentary to clause 57, *infra*, pp. 191–193.

A subsidiary and important question in relation to such " Standard Method " claims will turn upon the application to the particular facts of the opening words of exception in clause 57, *infra*, p. 190, obviously if the Bills " show " to the contrary, by self-evidently not following the recommendations of the Standard Method, there will have been no " omission." Only if there has been an omission not apparent to the Contractor, so that he will be misled, on the true interpretation of all the documents, as to the extent or nature of the work he is to carry out, can there be an " omission " which will activate the present clause, it is submitted. Furthermore, the language of the Standard Method in relation to the work in question, which frequently expresses its recommendations with very varying degrees of urgency, may be important. Failure to follow a permissive or mildly worded recommendation may not be an "omission." (See now, however, the radically new Civil Engineering Standard Method ("C.E.S.M.M.") published in 1976, and described under clause 57, *infra*, pp. 193–195, which is markedly more mandatory in its language and contains many innovations of considerable potential importance.)

It is difficult to avoid the conclusion that the intended scope and subject-matter of this new sub-clause, as of the RIBA forms, has not been considered with any precision, and that the main effect, if not object, of transposing the wording from the RIBA forms will be to extend, over a broad and perhaps deliberately left ill-defined area, the possibility of Contractors' claims for additional payment on remeasurement. It is certainly not possible to give any clear indication of the likely scope of this sub-clause, or as to how the courts may be expected to apply it to any particular set of facts—see the remarkable division of judicial opinion between the nine judges who considered the *Farr* case during the various stages of its progress to the House of Lords (for the facts and contractual provisions in the *Farr* case, and for a more detailed commentary on "Standard Method" claims, see clause 57, *infra*, pp. 190 *et seq.*).

Measurement and Valuation

56. (1) The Engineer shall except as otherwise stated ascertain and determine by admeasurement the value in accordance with the Contract of the work done in accordance with the Contract.

Increase or Decrease of Rate

(2) Should the actual quantities executed in respect of any item be greater or less than those stated in the Bill of Quantities and if in the opinion of the Engineer such increase or decrease of itself shall so warrant the Engineer shall after consultation with the Contractor determine an appropriate increase or decrease of any rates or prices rendered unreasonable or inapplicable in consequence thereof and shall notify the Contractor accordingly.

This clause is closely related to clause 55, and is the second in order of the three remeasurement clauses in the contract. For a general summary of these three clauses see the commentary under clause 55, *supra*. As there indicated, the expression "ascertain and determine by admeasurement" in sub-clause (1) of the present clause was the definitive remeasurement provision in the old Fourth Edition which enabled remeasurement at Bill rates and prices to take place calculated by reference to the actual quantities of work carried out. The first "in accordance with the Contract" refers, though admittedly elliptically, to the rates and prices in the Bills, it is submitted. The words "except as otherwise stated" refer, it is submitted, to the many parts of the contract which depart from the principle of measuring and calculating the value of the work at the rates and prices in the Bills, such as the special financial provisions for payment for work the subject of P.C. and Provisional Sums in clause 59A (5), *infra*, the provisions for valuation of variations under clause 52, clauses 55 (2) and 56 (2) of the present measurement provisions, and the many other special contractual provisions for additions to the Contract Price, usually based on " cost," such as clauses 7 (3), 12 (3), 13 (3), 14 (6), 20 (2), 22 (2), 26 (1), 27 (6), 30 (3), 31 (2), 36 (3), 38 (2), 40 (1), 42 (1), 49 (3), 50, 59A (3), 59B (4) (b), 65 (5) (e), 65 (6) (b) (c) and (d), 69, 70, and 71 (1), to name but a few. Many of these are based upon " cost " to the Contractor (see the definition of this in clause 1 (5)).

The history of these provisions (as stated, of perhaps doubtful evidentiary weight according to the English rules of interpretation) indicates that the purpose of sub-clause (2) of the present clause is not to provide for a general remeasurement based upon the differing actual quantities, but is to permit a further special claim, additional to the remeasurement effected under sub-clause (1), where the changes in quantities justify new grossed-up prices based not simply on the new quantities but upon different rates and prices altogether, in a case where the change in quantities is such as to justify it. This subjective view is confirmed by the marginal headings to the two sub-clauses (though their evidentiary value would seem to be nil because of the express prohibition in clause 1 (3), *supra*, denying interpretative force to these), but receives some more conventional support from the special notice requirement for claims under the present sub-clause referred to in clause 52 (4) (a), *supra*, p. 166.

It should be noted about sub-clause (2), first, that, even under sub-clause (1) and without the assistance of sub-clause (2), a measurement at contract rates and prices will, it is submitted, enable any relevant items in the *preliminary* Bills to be appropriately adjusted if the construction quantities change in such a way as to justify it—see on the details of this in the context of valuing variations the commentary to clause 52 (1) *supra*, pp. 159–162; secondly, that the present sub-clause contemplates a similar process of consultation with the Contractor, determination of disputes by the Engineer, and notification to the Contractor, as does clause 52 (1); and that there is a special notice requirement from the Contractor to the Employer under clause 52 (4) (a) if the Contractor wishes to claim more than the sum determined by the Engineer (with, however, as the commentary to that clause points out, very little if any practical sanction for non-compliance). Prices can be *reduced*, of course—see *supra*, p. 159.

" *after consultation with the Contractor* "

For the disadvantages to the Employer and the Engineer of treating this as a contractual requirement, see the commentary on this expression under clause 52 (1), *supra*, p. 163.

" *rates and prices* "

These words (*cf.* clauses 52 (1) and (2) and clause 55 (2) Proviso, *supra*), are used rather loosely throughout the Contract, without definition. " Rates " will apply to the individual rate or price which when multiplied by a quantity will produce a " price " in the right-hand column of the Bills, it is suggested. As a matter of usage, " price " can mean either this initial individual rate, or the grossed-up sum in the right-hand column, it is further suggested.

Attending for Measurement

(3) The Engineer shall when he requires any part or parts of the work to be measured give reasonable notice to the Contractor who shall attend or send a qualified agent to assist the Engineer or the Engineer's Representative in making such measurement and shall furnish all particulars required by either of them. Should the Contractor not attend or neglect or omit to send such agent then the measurement made by the Engineer or approved by him shall be taken to be the correct measurement of the work.

By reason of the methods of measurement used in most Standard Methods, the need for actual physical measurement of work *in situ* is kept to a minimum, and in the great majority of work the quantities are arrived at by calculation from the contract or later working drawings. Indeed, unless the contract work has been varied, it is quite usual to accept the billed quantities without even recalculation—though either party is entitled to demand recalculation if it is thought a mistake has been made. This follows, not so much from the wording of this sub-clause, which indeed seems to suggest that " measurements " will be taken at the Engineer's discretion, but under the arbitration clause 66, which expressly gives the arbitrator power to " open up, review and revise any decision . . . *or valuation* of the Engineer."

The reference to measurement and attendance by the Contractor in the present clause is, therefore, primarily aimed at the often limited amount of work needing physical measurement on the Site, *i.e.* nearly all work the subject of provisional quantity items, or not by its nature likely to be susceptible of calculation or shown on drawings of one kind or another. The presence of the Contractor may, however, be additionally required at the meetings off the site so that recalculations of changes in quantities caused by varied work can be agreed or any calculation disputes rapidly settled.

" *notice to the Contractor* "

It would seem that this notice must be sent to the Contractor's principal place of business, or registered office if a company—see *infra*, clause 68 (1). This could be important if the Employer was seeking to rely on a measurement made by the Engineer in the absence of the Contractor.

"*Should the Contractor not attend . . .*"

It is suggested that this provision will bind an arbitrator or the courts—the power to open up, review and revise in the arbitration clause does not in terms refer to measurement, but only to valuation. Otherwise, the present provision becomes virtually meaningless and gives no protection to the Employer where protection is in fact essential, since once work is completed or covered up, alleged quantities or dimensions put forward by a contractor, in those cases where real physical measurement is necessary, are extremely difficult to check or refute. (On any view, of course, a very heavy onus of proof would fall on the Contractor if he had absented himself from a measurement meeting.) It also may be a question whether clause 52 (4) (b) applies to the contractor's claim, and if so whether the notification and other procedures of that clause have been complied with—if so this might be one of the rare cases where the sanction in clause 52 (4) (e) is fully effective. But there are some doubts whether clause 52 (4) (b) will apply to claims under clause 56 (1)—see the commentary to clause 52 (4), *supra*, p. 167.

Method of Measurement

57. Except where any statement or general or detailed description of the work in the Bill of Quantities expressly shows to the contrary Bills of Quantities shall be deemed to have been prepared and measurements shall be made according to the procedure set forth in the "Standard Method of Measurement of Civil Engineering Quantities" issued by the Institution of Civil Engineers and reprinted in 1973 or such later or amended edition thereof as may be stated in the Appendix to the Form of Tender to have been adopted in its preparation notwithstanding any general or local custom.

This is the last of the three remeasurement clauses in the contract. For a general summary of their total effect see the commentary under clause 55, *supra*, pp. 182–184, and for a commentary particularly applicable to the present clause, see the commentary to clause 55 (2), *supra*, pp. 185–187.

Standard methods of measurement are documents designed partly to try and secure uniformity in the ways in which engineering or building work is to be sub-divided into its component parts or items for purposes of pricing in Bills, and partly to indicate the principles or formulae to be applied when actually measuring (or calculating, see the commentary, *supra*, p. 189) the quantities of work done. Thus to take a simple example in the latter category from the pre-1976 Standard Method, the quantities of excavation are, except in certain circumstances, to be the net cubic content, in cubic yards, of the voids to be formed by the removal of the materials excavated in accordance with the specification and drawings, and no allowance is to be made for bulking (see rule 40 of the pre-1976 Standard Method, but see now Section 8E Note 8 of the 1976 C.E.S.M.M.). Examples in the former category are, for instance, that in relation to concrete, it is provided that "separate items shall be provided for: Shuttering . . ." (rule 53), and again in relation to shuttering (rule 57) that

" separate items are to be provided for rough and wrought shuttering . . . and for . . . curved work." Many examples in the former category are not expressed in mandatory language—" *it may be necessary* to provide a separate item to cover the cost of any additional excavation . . . required beyond the net width of the structure " (rule 40), " *it may be necessary* to provide for the removal and reinstatement of field drains " (rule 40), " *it is advisable* to provide special items for temporary works in cases . . ." (rule 9) and so on. Again, the 8th para. of the Introduction to the Standard Method states: " While definite recommendations have been made, it is necessary to consider each . . . work on its merits, and in some cases to adopt special methods . . ., " and clause 12 of the " General Principles " in the Standard Method provides that descriptions attached to the items in the Bills are only to be in sufficient detail to ensure identification of the work with that shown on the drawings and described in the specification, the exact nature of the work to be made clear by reference to the specification. (The references are to the pre-1976 Standard Method.)

Undoubtedly the real purpose of most standard method provisions in building and engineering contracts is to incorporate by reference the various technical rules of measurement in the latter category, so that Bills can be kept as short as possible, and so that there is no doubt, for example, what a cubic yard of ordinary excavation for a structure means and how it is to be measured.

Contractors in the United Kingdom have, however, put forward arguments of great ingenuity for extra payment, based on alleged incorporation of those provisions of the Standard Methods which are in the former category and which have (often quite obviously) not been complied with in the Bills of Quantities, so as to defeat the usual presumption in all contracts for work and services that an unqualified undertaking to carry out and complete described work for a price includes an undertaking to do for that price any work indispensably necessary to achieve completion of the described work or any work contingently necessary for the purpose —see *e.g.* the commentary to clauses 8, 11, 13 and 20 in the present Edition. Thus to take some examples, if an item in the Bills reads " Form concrete plinth at base, 10″ × 2″ — cubic yards " it is obvious at once from the description (and probably also from the drawings) that shuttering or formwork is indispensably necessary to complete the described work. Again, shuttering may be billed, without any verbal description, which is quite obviously, by reference to the drawings, curved or, by reference to the specification, wrought. Again, contingently necessary work may not be mentioned in the Bills. Thus (where no expectation of meeting rock exists) the item for excavation may read " Excavate in any material — cubic yards," but according to the Standard Method, " The various classes of excavation are to be sub-divided, as necessary, so that opportunity may be given for fixing different prices in the several classes for . . . excavation in hard material or rock" (rule 39), and rock is then encountered in fact. Again clauses 18 and 19 of the pre-1976 Standard Method state that the Contractor should have the opportunity of pricing separately items for services or allowances, and also items for profit, in connection with work billed as a P.C. sum. Bills of Quantities frequently omit to provide such separate items, however.

In all these cases, ordinary rules of construction (see also clause 11 (2), *supra*, p. 40) would normally leave no doubt that the Contractor's price was inclusive, but claims are very frequently advanced in such cases based (when appropriate) on the allegation that the Contractor's price is for the cheaper of two alternatives, though there may be no overt indication of this in the Bills' description of the item in question. It is submitted that such claims are without legal validity and represent a distortion of the effect and purpose of the incorporation of, or reference made to, the Standard Method in clauses like the present clause. While it is perfectly permissible, it is suggested, to have regard to any provisions of the Standard Method to help resolve *ambiguities* in the Bills or other documents, and they can indeed prove invaluable for that purpose, it is not permissible to treat directions or recommendations in the Standard Method, whether couched in mandatory or precatory or advisory terms, as overriding what would otherwise be the clear meaning of the contract documents as a whole and the Bills in particular. The words "Except where any statement or general or detailed description of the work in the Bill of Quantities expressly *shows* to the contrary" (note the word is "shows" and not "states") are also, it is suggested, of vital importance in considering the validity of such claims, many of which are often totally devoid of merit, in the sense that the Contractor has never as a fact been misled when pricing his tender. But it should be emphasised that these provisions can be helpful, and that what is always involved is the true construction of the contract. Thus if, by reason of some ambiguity in the Bills themselves, or in the original contract drawings or specification, it is not possible to tell whether an item of shuttering in the Bills is for plain or wrought, or straight or curved work, then it may well be possible to rely on a standard method to help to show that the Contractor's rate had in fact been for the cheaper work, and the Contractor would be entitled to extra payment—but this would be by virtue of the provisions of clause 5 of the Conditions, *supra*, p. 29, as to ambiguities or discrepancies, or on the ground that the work as finally executed constituted a variation, and not by reason of any substantive cause of action based on the present clause alone.

The prevalence of these claims owes its origin to the doubtful case in England of *Bryant & Sons Ltd.* v. *Birmingham Hospital Saturday Fund* [1938] 1 All E.R. 503, but that was a decision on the RIBA forms of contract, whose quite different wording—" any . . . omission of items from the Contract Bills . . . shall be corrected and deemed to be a variation . . ." undoubtedly renders claims of this kind at least arguable under those forms of contract, although it is submitted that they are also invalid under those forms—see Hudson, 10th ed., pp. 516–520, where the authority of *Bryant* is doubted. The House of Lords' decision in *A. E. Farr Ltd.* v. *Ministry of Transport* [1965] (Hudson, 10th ed., p. 520, now reported in (1977) 5 B.L.R. 94) is not an authority to the contrary, because in that case the relevant provision from the Standard Method was actually inserted as a contractual term into the Bills of Quantities *verbatim*. Even so, two judges in the House of Lords and a unanimous Court of Appeal were in favour of the usual presumption of the inclusiveness of the contractor's price, and would not have allowed the provision, though made part of the Bills, to rebut it. (The provision read " Any additional excavation which may be required for working space etc. will be paid for under separate items . . ." and the dispute arose because there were in fact no separate items in the relevant part of the Bills, though such items did exist in parts of the Bills relating to other sections of the work).

It is in the light of the foregoing remarks that the effect of the new sub-clause 55 (2), *supra*, which introduces RIBA-style wording comparable to that in *Bryant's* case into the present contract for the first time, needs to be considered. As there stated, it is not possible to ascertain with any certainty the intention of the key words " error in description in the Bill of Quantities or omission therefrom," or of the provision for their " correction " by the Engineer followed by a clause 52 valuation of the work carried out. It is suggested that, coupled with the opening words of exception in the present clause, the new provision may be little more than a safety-net to enable new rates to be fixed where, on their true construction, the Bills have no reasonably applicable rate available for the purpose of remeasurement of the work actually carried out, of which some examples have been given in the commentary to clause 55 (2), *supra*, pp. 185–186.

The preceding views have been expressed in the light of the Standard Method current at the time of publication in 1973 of the Fifth Edition and until 1976, which will therefore continue to regulate disputes in the U.K. for some time to come. In 1976, however, the Institution of Civil Engineers published an entirely new and radically revised Standard Method (" C.E.S.M.M."). Among many new features, a number likely to give rise to problems may be mentioned, namely:—

(a) It makes a major attempt to create more satisfactory methods of pricing " Preliminaries " (now called " General Items ") by means of provisions for " Method Related Charges " in Section 7, which are to be either " Fixed " or " Time Related." The " General Items " are now to exclude items of cost which are related only to the quantities of work. There appear to be major ambiguities, however, in regard to how, if at all, Time Related Charges are to be adjusted (see Section 7.6 which merely provides that Method Related Charges are not to be subject to " admeasurement "), particularly in the context of the possible differing grounds for extension of the contract period, or in the case of any further period of culpable delay by the Contractor.

(b) Provision is made for a " General Contingencies Allowance " by way of Provisional Sum (Sections 5.17 and 5.25), the intended adjustment of which, with particular regard to the precise purposes for which this allowance is supposed to be expended, and whether the original stipulated contract period and other General Items are intended to be inclusive of expenditure under this allowance, are not explained.

(c) Similarly, provision is made for a global " Adjustment Item " which may be written in by the Contractor (Section 5.26), the application of which to an altered ultimate Contract Price, whether as a result of nominated sub-contractor's work, or variations, or permitted claims under the contract, or an extended contract period, is obscure (see Sections 6.3 and 6.4).

(d) The scope for unsuspected " separate itemisation " requirements seems to be very much enlarged—see Section 3.2, for example, which provides that every C.E.S.M.M. requirement for even an " additional description " in an item shall be deemed to require separate itemisation of any similar component of work showing a different additional feature from that described (Section 3.5).

(e) A number of " Notes " appear to be specifically designed to facilitate claims (*e.g.* Note 6 to Section 8E—" material to be excavated shall be deemed to be natural material other than rock or topsoil unless otherwise stated in item descriptions ").

In general the document is far more detailed than the previous Standard Method in its pricing breakdown, and its language less permissive. Inadvertent failure to comply with it in detail may be confidently expected to occur, particularly during the years while experience in its use builds up, and it may be predicted with some certainty that, via Clause 55 (2) *supra*, the new Standard Method may well prove a fertile source of claims of many different kinds, on which it would be premature to speculate, based on failure of the Bills to comply with the new Standard Method, or upon ambiguities within the Standard Method itself. Parts of the new document almost give the appearance of being a new or additional substantive contract within the contract contained in the Conditions themselves. It remains to be seen what the Courts will make, in such cases, of the incorporating words of the present clause 57, from which alone the Standard Method itself can derive any contractual force between the parties. It will be seen that in regard to separate itemisation the new document appears to have moved in the opposite direction from the composite rates and greater simplicity advocated in the author's article in Appendix A, *post*, p. 309 (which was published shortly before the new Standard Method in 1975) though the attempt to improve the " Preliminaries " or (as it now is) " General Items " Bill with the device of " Method Related Charges " is greatly to be welcomed, and is of the first importance in spite of the ambiguity in making really clear provision for the adjustment of " Time Related Charges " or, as already indicated, of the " General Contingency Allowance " and the " Adjustment Item."

PROVISIONAL AND PRIME COST SUMS AND NOMINATED SUB-CONTRACTS

Provisional Sum

58. (1) " Provisional Sum " means a sum included in the Contract and so designated for the execution of work or the supply of goods materials or services or for contingencies which sum may be used in whole or in part or not at all at the direction and discretion of the Engineer.

Prime Cost Item

(2) " Prime Cost (PC) Item " means an item in the Contract which contains (either wholly or in part) a sum referred to as Prime Cost (PC) which will be used for the execution of work or for the supply of goods materials or services for the Works.

Design Requirements to be Expressly Stated

(3) If in connection with any Provisional Sum or Prime Cost Item the services to be provided include any matter of design or specification of any part of the Permanent Works or of any equipment or plant to be incorporated therein such requirement shall be expressly stated in the Contract and shall be included in any Nominated Sub-contract. The obligation of the Contractor in respect thereof shall be only that which has been expressly stated in accordance with this sub-clause.

Use of Prime Cost Items

(4) In respect of every Prime Cost Item the Engineer shall have the power to order the Contractor to employ a sub-contractor nominated by the Engineer for the execution of any work or the supply of any goods materials or services included therein. The Engineer shall also have power with the consent of the Contractor to order the Contractor to execute any such work or to supply any such goods materials or services in which event the Contractor shall be paid in accordance with the terms of a quotation submitted by him and accepted by the Engineer or in the absence thereof the value shall be determined in accordance with Clause 52.

Nominated Sub-contractors—Definition

(5) All specialists merchants tradesmen and others nominated in the Contract for a Prime Cost Item or ordered by the Engineer to be employed by the Contractor in accordance with sub-clause (4) or sub-clause (7) of this Clause for the execution of any work or the supply of any good materials or services are referred to in this Contract as " Nominated Sub-contractors."

Production of Vouchers etc.

(6) The Contractor shall when required by the Engineer produce all quotations invoices vouchers sub-contract documents accounts and receipts in connection with expenditure in respect of work carried out by all Nominated Sub-contractors.

Use of Provisional Sums

(7) In respect of every Provisional Sum the Engineer shall have power to order either or both of the following:—

(a) work to be executed or goods materials or services to be supplied by the Contractor the value of such work executed or goods materials or services supplied being determined in accordance with Clause 52 and included in the Contract Price:

(b) work to be executed or goods materials or services to be supplied by a Nominated Sub-contractor in accordance with Clause 59A.

This clause, together with clauses 59A, 59B, 59C and the provisos (a) and (b) to clause 60 (7), constitute an entirely new and radically changed code for nominated sub-contracts, for a concise summary of which see Chapter 1, Introductory, *ante*, pp. 1–3. The provisions of these clauses may be said to fall into the following principal sub-divisions:—

(1) Clause 58 (1) (2) (4) (5) (6) and (7) contain precise definitions of P.C. and Provisional Sums and of the extent of the power to nominate conferred thereby.

(2) Clause 59A (1) (2) and (3) contains a new and well-considered code governing objections to a nomination and consequential powers and obligations.

(3) Clauses 58 (3) and 59A (4) and (5) spell out the legal and financial consequences of a nomination in broadly traditional terms but with greatly improved clarity.

(4) Clauses 59A (6), 59B, and 60 (7), however, taken together effect a fundamental and massive reduction in the Contractor's legal responsibility to the Employer for Nominated Sub-contractors' work whereby, in the case of ordinary breaches by the Nominated Sub-contractor, the Employer in effect guarantees the Sub-contractor's ability to reimburse the main Contractor for any claim made by the Employer against the main Contractor in respect of the Sub-contractor's breaches, and in the case of terminated sub-contracts, actually guarantees the main Contractor against losses caused to him by the termination of the sub-contract. These provisions are extremely difficult and complicated, and the language is in places superficially quite misleading when analysed in detail. There also appear to be a number of errors, anomalies and ambiguities of considerable practical importance which are likely to render the administration of this part of the code, particularly in termination cases, a constant source of difficulty to the Employer's advisers.

(5) Clause 59C confers a new and improved power for payment direct of nominated sub-contractors.

The salient features of the new provisions may be stated in somewhat more detail as follows:—

(a) *Provisional Sums* are to cover work or goods which are truly provisional (*i.e.* they may never be carried out or purchased at all) and may at the Engineer's discretion be carried out by either the main Contractor or a Nominated Sub-contractor—clause 58 (1) and (7).

(b) P.C. Items are for work or goods which affirmatively *will* be carried out or purchased, and *must* be the subject of a nomination unless the Contractor agrees to do the work himself (clause 58 (2) and (4)).

(c) In both cases any obligation to provide services by way of design or specification must be expressly stated in *both* the main contract *and* any sub-contract—if not the Contractor is to be under no design obligation (clause 58 (3)).

(d) A nomination can be refused on any reasonable ground, or because a term of the sub-contract is " incompatible " with the main contract obligations (clause 59A (1)) but, apart from a new nomination on satisfactory terms, in the latter case the Engineer may confirm the original nomination notwithstanding the offending sub-contract provisions, in which case the Contractor's own main contract obligation will be correspondingly downgraded, coupled with financial safeguards (clause 59A (3)). Alternatively, the Employer may enter into a separate direct contract with another Contractor, in respect of the originally nominated work with loss of profit on the omitted work (if a P.C. Item) paid to the Contractor—clause 59A (2) (b).

(e) A discount for " prompt payment " *of unlimited amount* is permitted to the Contractor, who will be paid gross of any such discount (clause 59A (5) (a)).

(f) In the case of *non-determination* breaches of contract by Nominated Sub-contractors, while the Employer may obtain a judgment or award against the Contractor for breach of contract (*e.g.* for defective work or delay) he undertakes not to enforce the judgment or award until such time and to the extent that the Contractor (with an indemnity for costs from the Employer) has recovered, by payment or execution of judgment or award, the sums in question from the Sub-contractor (clauses 59A (6) and 59B (6)). The contract is silent, however, as to what is to happen if the Contractor is only successful in recovering enough money to reimburse the Contractor, wholly or partially, for his own special losses caused by the Sub-contractor's breach, but not the Employer's as well. Moreover, in the very usual case of defective work where the defects are known in sufficient time and the Employer would normally wish to protect himself by deduction on a later interim certificate from sums previously certified, in most cases he will be expressly prevented from doing so, and must wait till the final certificate (clause 60 (7), Proviso (a)). (This inhibition will even apply in a case where the Sub-contractor is still on the Site doing work and earning further interim payments at the time that the earlier work is condemned and the deduction sought to be made.) In general, the Employer is here undertaking not to penalise the main Contractor financially during the contract in any way in regard to

Nominated Sub-contractors' defaults, and to make ultimate recovery of his loss conditional upon both the legal liability and financial viability of the Sub-contractor being satisfactorily established at the end of the day. Recovery by deduction can first be made on the final certificate, but any deduction will itself need to be refunded by the Employer to the Contractor, with interest, should the Contractor subsequently be unable to obtain the payments from the guilty Sub-contractor—clause 60 (7), Proviso (b).

(g) In a case where the Nominated Sub-contractor's breach is so serious as to justify termination of the sub-contract, an extraordinarily complicated code is created by clause 59B (2), whereby the Contractor may request the Employer's consent to termination of the sub-contract; but it is clear that, with or without consent, he may nevertheless terminate it. In addition (but on close analysis only if the Contractor decides to enable the Employer to do so by serving an appropriate notice on him) the Employer may " direct " the Contractor to terminate the sub-contract. (The language of this provision is particularly misleading.) In any of these events (*i.e.* with consent, without consent, or " directed ") the Employer

(i) must either nominate an alternative Sub-contractor, or enter into a direct contract, or omit the work, subject to compensating the Contractor for loss of profit (clause 59B (3));

(ii) must pay the Contractor on interim certificate the value to date of the guilty Sub-contractor's work (clause 59B (4) (a) (iii)); the additional cost of completing the work by the main Contractor (if applicable) (clause 59B (4) (a) (i)); or by any substitute Sub-contractor (clause 59B (4) (a) (ii)); *and the amount of any additional costs due to the determination suffered by the main Contractor* (for which he is also granted an extension of time)—clause 59B (4) (b), an important additional obligation for which no comparable provision exists in the case of non-termination breaches);

(iii) may on final certificate recover from the main Contractor the difference between his total payments under (ii) above, and what should have been due had the sub-contract been properly performed, together with any other damages suffered by the Employer, but subject to repaying the main Contractor with interest in the event of the latter ultimately failing to recover payment from the Sub-contractor (clauses 59B (4) (c) and 59B (5)).

The effect of these provisions in termination cases is that the Employer undertakes not only not to penalise with his own damages, but actually to finance the main Contractor until the end of the contract in respect of all the damages suffered by the main Contractor due to the termination of the nominated sub-contract, with ultimate recovery by the Employer again conditional on the Sub-contractor satisfying the main Contractor's claim. However, in spite of its complication and apparent attention to detail, it is almost impossible to judge the precise intention of the termination code in clause 59B in a case where the Employer consents to a termination of the sub-contract which is subsequently held to be unjustified as against the Sub-contractor. Moreover, no clear provision appears to be made for the perhaps very long period until the final certificate in a case where the Employer disputes the need for termination or considers the main Contractor to be at fault rather than the Sub-contractor, so that he withholds consent; or on the other hand where the main Contractor disputes the need for termination and refuses to serve the enabling notice without which no " direction " for termination can be given by the Employer (in this latter case it seems clear that in fact the Employer will be helpless). The impression persists that, policy questions apart, the code, despite its extraordinary detail, has not been sufficiently thought through in the light of the practical situations in which it will be required to operate. In particular, it does not seem to have been appreciated that the main Contractor and Employer can be expected to have very conflicting interests in a termination—particularly with the remarkable protection of the clause and the claims which it will permit, the Contractor can be expected to do all he can to persuade the Employer to consent to or " direct " a termination, while the Employer may prefer to accept some delay rather than incur the perhaps greater delay of making new arrangements as well as the substantial financial liabilities under the clause. Nor does it seem to have been appreciated that the Employer and his advisers may often find main Contractor and Sub-contractor blaming each other for delays or defective work, so that here again the Employer will not wish to become involved by consenting to or " directing " the termination. The total failure of this part of the code to indicate precisely what are to be the interim consequences of a termination without consent is its most obvious omission.

(h) The power of payment direct is now identical with that in the RIBA forms, arising whenever a Nominated Sub-contractor has not been duly paid under an earlier certificate—see clause 59C. (In the Fourth Edition further sums had to be certifiable *to the same Sub-contractor* before the power could be exercised, which was a restriction which could create serious difficulties in practice—see B.C.F., p. 417.)

If the policy and complication of these clauses does not commend itself to Employers or their advisers, it is in fact extremely easy to effect the necessary changes, as a matter of draftsmanship. This can be achieved simply by removing the words " and in Clause 59B " from clause 59A

(4), by striking out sub-clause (6) of clause 59A, and by striking out the whole of clause 59B, together with the two Provisos (a) and (b) to clause 60 (7), and relettering clause 59C. The result would be perhaps the most satisfactory Nominated Sub-contractors' code yet evolved in a U.K. standard form. The clauses will now be considered in detail.

Clause 58 may be said to lay down the first logical and clear definitions of Provisional Sums and P.C. Items and of the attendant nominating power to be found in any English standard form (compare the strictures on the long-established RIBA wording by the Court of Appeal in *Bickerton* v. *N.W. Metropolitan Board* [1969] 1 All E.R. 977, quoted in Hudson, 10th ed., Introduction, pp. xi and xii, and the commentary on the hopelessly muddled Fourth Edition in B.C.F. at pp. 405–411). This sub-clause (1), together with sub-clause (7), show that Provisional Sum Items may apply equally to sub-contracts for work or work and materials on the one hand, and supply-only sub-contracts on the other; the words " may be used " in sub-clause (1) in contrast to the words " *will* be used " in sub-clause (2), indicate that the important distinguishing feature of " Provisional Sum " as here defined is the *provisional* or *contingent* character of the work (for the quite different origin of the word " Provisional " in this expression in early English contracts as a corruption of " Provisions " see Hudson, 10th ed., at p. 758) and the Engineer has an unfettered discretion to order the work to be carried out by the main Contractor and valued in the same way as varied work, or on the other hand by a Nominated Sub-contractor, in which event it will be valued as provided in clause 59A (5). P.C. Items, on the other hand (see sub-clauses (2) and (4)) are to represent work which it is positively intended will be carried out—so that omission of the work, unlike Provisional Sum work, can only be effected by compensating the Contractor for profit and charges forgone—see clause 59A (2) (b) for an example of this. The implication is that the Contractor should price his tender on the assumption that P.C. Item work will be carried out, but a problem in regard to Provisional Sum work, as to which the contract is silent, is whether any preliminary items in the Bills should be treated as inclusive of this work, or whether and if so to what extent a valuation under clause 52 should proceed on the basis that any preliminary items that could be affected by volume of work or length of time should also be increased to take account of the value or amount of any Provisional Sum work being ordered—indeed it is a question almost impossible to answer under this contract whether an extension of time should be given if Provisional Sum work of the stipulated extent is ordered—clause 44 (1), for example, is silent about this—on the footing that the contract period cannot be expected to take account of work which may never be ordered. Neither the pre- nor post-1966 Standard Methods give any guidance about this, or the related question of extension of time, which in the case of the 1976

C.E.S.M.M. is the more surprising, since that document expressly contemplates Provisional Sums being used for both specific contingencies and a " General Contingency Allowance "—see Sections 5.17 and 5.26.

In the case of P.C. Items the words " with the consent of the Contractor " in sub-clause (4) mean in effect that the Engineer *must* nominate a Sub-contractor for this work, unless the Contractor agrees to do the work himself or the Engineer decides to omit it Sub-clause (5) appears, by the use of the words " and others nominated in the contract," to contemplate that the contract documents (*i.e.* Bills or Specification) may themselves name (*i.e.* nominate) the intended Sub-contractor, in addition to the two (post-contract) powers to nominate conferred on the Engineer by sub-clauses (2) and (7) in the case of P.C. Items and Provisional Sums respectively.

Sub-clause (3) is a novel but sensible attempt to grapple with an increasingly troublesome problem—namely the use of Nominated Sub-contractors to perform design services. Nevertheless, there is an element of over-simplification in the wording used, which taken literally could certainly go far beyond the obvious intention of the draftsman. This is because all contracts for work and materials contain an implied term of suitability (*i.e.* a design obligation) on the part of the Contractor *to the extent that the Employer relies on the Contractor's skill and judgment.* Where architects and engineers are used by an employer to design a project, there are nevertheless almost invariably small (usually, of course, very minor) parts of the permanent work to which the engineer's specification or drawings will not condescend in detail, and in respect of which the contractor's suitability or design obligation will accordingly come into play—see for a very full treatment of this subject Hudson, 10th ed., pp. 273–306. In the context of the present sub-clause (3) the words " the *services* to be provided " indicate, it is submitted, that what the sub-clause is concerned with are the major or principal design functions (including choice of specification) or the performance of the subsidiary design or other services, such as the preparation and submission of shop drawings for approval, often performed by or in association with an adviser or consultant of the employer, and not the minor design or suitability responsibilities for which contractors and sub-contractors may be liable, by way of an implied term as to workmanship or suitability, notwithstanding the presence of an architect/engineer/consultant of the employer. If this view is correct the final words of the sub-clause will not serve to exclude these normal responsibilities. The sub-clause itself and its general policy are both new in the United Kingdom and to be welcomed, not least in the Employer's interest in bringing into the open the extent to which design services may have been delegated by his own principal advisers without his knowledge, and also in indicating the necessity in such cases for obtaining appropriately drafted direct warranties in favour of the Employer from the Nominated Sub-contractor. It should, however, be appreciated that any protection afforded to the Contractor by the sub-clause is largely unnecessary in the light of clause 59A (6) (assuming that clause is allowed to remain in the contract). The clause, incidentally, will obviously make it impossible for contractors to object to a nomination under clause 59A, *infra*, on the ground that it delegates design services to the Sub-contractor, provided the requirements of the sub-clause for express provision in the main contract is met; equally, failure so to describe the work is a clear indication that objection may be successfully taken if the sub-contract work is not so described.

Another consequence of sub-clause (3), arising from the last sentence of the sub-clause, bears upon what has long been a difficult problem without authority in this field—it was always arguable that if the circumstances warranted it, a specialist Sub-contractor might in the sub-contract *impliedly* warrant the suitability of his design to the main Contractor. If so, there seemed no difficulty about implying a similar warranty by the main Contractor to the Employer in the main contract, notwithstanding the former's lack of expertise, known to all, in the particular specialist field involved—see on this Hudson, 10th ed., at pp. 761–764, and the tentative views there expressed. The present provision, however, effectively negatives any such *implied* term in the main contract, it is submitted, whatever the position may be in the sub-contract. Notwithstanding the important " and " in the expression " shall be expressly stated in the Contract *and* shall be included in any Nominated Sub-contract," the final sentence, with its pointed repetition only of the words " which has been expressly stated " suggests that, notwithstanding the absence of a term requiring design services in the sub-contract, when they are *in fact* provided (not an uncommon event in the U.K.) the necessary obligation will arise if stated in the main contract, but not, of course, the reverse situation—the latter a fair enough limitation, since the main Contractor should be made aware of the intention at the tender stage of his own contract.

Nominated Sub-contractors—Objection to Nomination

59A. (1) Subject to sub-clause (2) (c) of this Clause the Contractor shall not be under any obligation to enter into any sub-contract with any Nominated Sub-contractor against whom the Contractor may raise reasonable objection or who shall decline to enter into a sub-contract with the Contractor containing provisions:—

(a) that in respect of the work goods materials or services the subject of the sub-contract the Nominated Sub-contractor will undertake towards the Contractor such obligations and liabilities as will enable the Contractor to discharge his own obligations and liabilities towards the Employer under the terms of the Contract;

(b) that the Nominated Sub-contractor will save harmless and indemnify the Contractor against all claims demands and proceedings damages costs charges and expenses whatsoever arising out of or in connection with any failure by the Nominated Sub-contractor to perform such obligations or fulfil such liabilities;

(c) that the Nominated Sub-contractor will save harmless and indemnify the Contractor from and against any negligence by the Nominated Sub-contractor his agents workmen and servants and against any misuse by him or them of any Constructional Plant or Temporary Works provided by the Contractor for the purposes of the Contract and for all claims as aforesaid;

(d) equivalent to those contained in Clause 63.

Engineer's Action upon Objection

(2) If pursuant to sub-clause (1) of this Clause the Contractor shall not be obliged to enter into a sub-contract with a Nominated Sub-contractor and shall decline to do so the Engineer shall do one or more of the following:—

(a) nominate an alternative sub-contractor in which case sub-clause (1) of this Clause shall apply;

(b) by order under Clause 51 vary the works or the work goods materials or services the subject of the Provisional Sum or Prime Cost Item including if necessary the omission of any such work goods materials or services so that they may be provided by workmen contractors or suppliers as the case may be employed by the Employer either concurrently with the Works (in which case Clause 31 shall apply) or at some other date. Provided that in respect of the omission of any Prime Cost Item there shall be included in the Contract Price a sum in respect of the Contractor's charges and profit being a percentage of the estimated value of such work goods material or services omitted at the rate provided in the Bill of Quantities or inserted in the Appendix to the Form of Tender as the case may be;

(c) subject to the Employer's consent where the Contractor declines to enter into a contract with the Nominated Sub-contractor only on the grounds of unwillingness of the Nominated Sub-contractor to contract only on the basis of the provisions contained in paragraphs (a) (b) (c) or (d) of sub-clause (1) of this Clause direct the Contractor to enter into a contract with the Nominated Sub-contractor on such other terms as the Engineer shall specify in which case sub-clause (3) of this Clause shall apply;

(d) in accordance with Clause 58 arrange for the Contractor to execute such work or to supply such goods materials or services.

Direction by Engineer

(3) If the Engineer shall direct the Contractor pursuant to sub-clause (2) of this Clause to enter into a sub-contract which does not contain all the provisions referred to in sub-clause (1) of this Clause:—

(a) the Contractor shall not be bound to discharge his obligations and liabilities under the Contract to the extent that the sub-contract terms so specified by the Engineer are inconsistent with the discharge of the same:

(b) in the event of the Contractor incurring loss or expense or suffering damage arising out of the refusal of the Nominated Sub-contractor to accept such provisions the Contractor shall subject to Clause 52 (4) be paid in accordance with Clause 60 the amount of such loss expense or damage as the Contractor could not reasonably avoid.

See the summary of all the Nominated Sub-contractor provisions under clause 58, *supra*, pp. 196–200, for the general effect of these three sub-clauses, which form a code governing the Contractor's right to object to a nomination which is on the whole well-considered and of considerably greater sophistication than any hitherto contained in any U.K. standard form. Two matters which should be borne in mind when considering it are

(a) that in the light of the protection afforded by sub-clause (6) of the present clause in regard to the main Contractor's greatly diminished responsibility for Nominated Sub-contractors' breaches, by clause **59B** in regard to responsibility for conduct by Nominated Sub-contractors resulting in termination of their sub-contracts, and by the two clause 60 (7) Provisos (a) and (b), an objection on the "any reasonable objection" ground will probably need a strong case to be successful—though as will be seen the Contractor is given no guarantee under clause 59A (6) against his own loss or damage in non-termination cases, and a not quite unlimited one in regard to his own damage in termination cases under clause 59B (see clause 59B (4) (b) and the commentary thereto, *infra*, p. 218);

(b) that a valid objection on the mere ground that the sub-contract requires design services to be performed by the Nominated Sub-contractor will self-evidently be impossible to establish in the light of clause 58 (3) if the stipulations in that sub-clause are met—see the commentary to that sub-clause, *supra*, p. 202—but equally that design services provided by Nominated Sub-contractors in other cases may, depending on the facts, be a valid ground of objection.

Sub-clause (1) calls for little comment other than that already made in regard to "reasonable objection", *supra*. There are two broad grounds of objection—first, any reasonable objection on any reasonable ground, and, secondly, objection if the terms of the sub-contract offend against any of the requirements in paragraphs (a) to (d) inclusive. Of these, (a) (b) and (c) are eminently sensible and necessary, but (d) is seriously lacking in precision. What does "equivalent to" mean in this context? And does the reference to clause 63 mean with the main Contractor substituted for the Employer in that clause, and in consequence virtually all matters between Contractor and Sub-contractor regulated by the Engineer's certificate or notice or warning? Or should the Contractor be substituted for the Engineer under clause 63, so that notices warnings and certificates are given by the Contractor? Or will the requirement be satisfied if the *grounds* of determination are similar to those in clause 63 without any of the procedural formalities of clause 63? Examination of clause 63 (1) will show still further combinations and possibilities. See further for this the commentaries to clause 59B (1) and (2), *infra*.

The opening words of sub-clause (2) dispose of what in some contracts is a most difficult problem lacking authority—namely what is the result if the Contractor enters into a sub-contract without objection or after protesting? The words "*and* shall decline to do so," on which the important courses of action in (a) to (d) depend, suggest very strongly, it is submitted, that the Contractor will forfeit his rights if he places the order without objection. Of the four possible courses of action, that under paragraph (a) needs no comment. So far as paragraph (b) is concerned, without this express power it would be a breach of contract for the Employer to order an omission of P.C. Items (*i.e.* an affirmative part of the permanent work—see clause 58 (2) above—and not a contingent part like Provisional Sums as defined in clause 58 (1), above) if the intention was to have the work carried out by someone else (see the commentary on " omissions " under clause 51 (1), *supra*, p. 157—accordingly the clause correctly provides that the Contractor shall receive due compensation amounting to his loss of profit on the omitted work in the case of P.C. Items only. The expression " charges and profit," incidentally, appears to be a term of art for profit or financing, and " charges " does not indicate some item of physical expenditure by the Contractor—see clause 59A (5) (b) and (c) and the Appendix to the Form of Tender.

So far as the power in paragraph (c) is concerned, the reference to the Employer's consent is puzzling—obviously the Engineer may in an appropriate case owe his client a professional duty to consult and obtain approval beforehand, but the object of inserting this provision into a contract between Employer and Contractor is difficult to understand—it can hardly be designed to put the onus on the Contractor to satisfy himself that the Employer has consented, it is submitted. On the whole, however, this is a new and most desirable power, giving the Engineer a degree of flexibility in what may be a very difficult situation. It should be noted that the whole of sub-clause (3) is devoted to giving the Contractor the most comprehensive protection in the event of the power being exercised. So far as the power in (d) is concerned, the reference to clause 58 means that it can be exercised as of right in the case of Provisional Sums (see clause 58 (7) (a)) but only with the Contractor's consent in the case of P.C. Items (clause 58 (4)).

Sub-clause (3) is largely self-explanatory. The Contractor's protection, should the powers in sub-clause (2) be exercised, is (rightly) as comprehensive as legal draftsmanship can achieve, but it should perhaps be noted that the words " damage arising out of the refusal of the Nominated Sub-contractor to accept such provisions," are specifically aimed at the main contractor's own losses due to delay or disturbance, which may be irrecoverable from the Sub-contractor where a nomination is disputed on this ground but nevertheless confirmed, and cannot be applied to losses arising from the " reasonable obligation " ground—here the Contractor (assuming he can surmount any difficulty if he does not object to the nomination) will have to allege breach of contract based on an implied term requiring the nomination of a suitable Nominated Sub-contractor in sufficient time—as to which see Hudson, 10th ed., pp. 738–739, and p. 329. The references are to the not very severe requirements of notice of claims under clause 52 (4) (see particularly clause 52 (4) (b)) and to interim payment (see particularly clause 60 (1) (d) and (2) (a)). In the event of a dispute as to the validity of a nomination it would obviously be desirable to have some machinery for early resolution of the dispute, but here again early arbitration under clause 66, *infra*, does not appear to be available on the wording of that provision, so that the parties will presumably have to abide by the Engineer's decision under the early part of clause 66 until completion.

Contractor Responsible for Nominated Sub-contracts

(4) Except as otherwise provided in this Clause and in Clause 59B the Contractor shall be as responsible for the work executed or goods materials or services supplied by a Nominated Sub-contractor employed by him as if he had himself executed such work or supplied such goods materials or services or had sub-let the same in accordance with Clause 4.

Concealed within the words of exception at the beginning of this sub-clause are the complicated provisions removing a very wide area of financial responsibility for defaulting Nominated Sub-contractors from the main Contractor. The references to " this Clause " are to sub-clause (3), *supra*, as already stated a very reasonable exception, and to sub-clause (6), which effects a major reduction of responsibility for all Nominated Sub-contractor's breaches other than breaches resulting in termination or rescission (*i.e.* an accepted repudiation) of the sub-contract. Clause 59B similarly effects a massive reduction in the main contractor's responsibility for breaches resulting ultimately in termination or rescission of the sub-contract. Sub-clause (6) adopts the principle of an ultimate financial guarantee by the Employer of the Nominated Sub-contractor's ability to meet the Employer's claim for damages against the main Contractor, should the main Contractor be unable to recover full reimbursement of the Employer's damage from the Nominated Sub-contractor. Clause 59B goes further, and guarantees payment of the main contractor's costs arising out of the termination of the sub-contract. If this remarkable new policy is not acceptable to Employers or their advisers, the removal of the reference in sub-clause (3) to clause 59B, of clause 59B itself, and of sub-clause (6) (together, as a matter affecting interim payment, with the two provisos to clause 60 (7)) would bring the contract into line, for example, with the " no-privity " policy which until recent times has been the basis of all U.K. standard forms of contract, and which is most clearly expressed today in the G.C. Wks. 1 contract (see clauses 31 (2), 31 (3), and 38 (5) of that contract).

Payments

(5) For all work executed or goods materials or services supplied by Nominated Sub-contractors there shall be included in the Contract Price:—

(a) the actual price paid or due to be paid by the Contractor in accordance with the terms of the sub-contract (unless and to the extent that any such payment is the result of a default of the Contractor) net of all trade and other discounts rebates and allowances other than any discount obtainable by the Contractor for prompt payment;

(b) the sum (if any) provided in the Bill of Quantities for labours in connection therewith or if ordered pursuant to Clause 58 (7) (b) as may be determined by the Engineer;

(c) in respect of all other charges and profit a sum being a percentage of the actual price paid or due to be paid calculated (where provision has been made in the Bill of Quantities for a rate to be set against the relevant item of prime cost) at the rate inserted by the Contractor against that item or (where no such provision has been made) at the rate inserted by the Contractor in the Appendix to the Form of Tender as the percentage for adjustment of sums set against Prime Cost Items.

This is the provision regulating the amounts payable to the main Contractor in respect of all Nominated Sub-contractors' work, whether ordered under the provision in clause 58 (4) relating to P.C. Items, or by virtue of the special power in clause 58 (7) (b) relating to Provisional Sums. Paragraph (a) makes it clear that the principal figure will be the price due (not necessarily paid) to the Sub-contractor for his work, disregarding any penalties or damages due from the main Contractor to the Sub-contractor, but the wording shows that this sum will be gross of any " prompt payment " discount. No definition is given of what constitutes " prompt payment," nor is there any limit on the amount of the discount. The Fourth Edition, unlike nearly all U.K. standard forms, allowed no cash discount at all (except in a situation rarely likely to occur in practice—see B.C.F., pp. 411–412) but the present provision has gone to the other extreme and could be open to serious abuse and collusion unless (as will no doubt often be the case) the Engineer has satisfied himself, following competitive tenders or on inquiry, as to the reasonableness of the Sub-contractor's (gross) price.

Paragraphs (b) and (c) contemplate items for the main Contractor's attendance or labours being available for pricing in the Bills in the case of P.C. items, but a valuation of these being made in the case of Provisional Sum Sub-contractors. Paragraph (c) appears to contemplate that in the case of P.C. sums there may either be an item for " all other charges and profit " in the Bills in the case of P.C. items, or, if not, in the Appendix to the Form of Tender, and that even if not expressed as a percentage in the Bills, the item will nevertheless be applied on a percentage basis to the final actual price. There seems to be a lacuna in the case of Provisional Sum sub-contracts where no percentage is inserted in the Appendix to the Form of Tender, since there will obviously be no " rate set against the relevant item of prime cost " which could be used for the Provisional Sum sub-contract. The contract intention would obviously seem to be for an Engineer's valuation to be made as in paragraph (b).

Nominated sub-contract work is, of course, subject to the provisions for interim payment and retention, like any other work in clause 60—see the last sentence of clause 60 (1), read together with clause 60 (1) (a).

Breach of Sub-contract

(6) In the event that the Nominated Sub-contractor shall be in breach of the sub-contract which breach causes the Contractor to be in breach of contract the

Employer shall not enforce any award of any arbitrator or judgment which he may obtain against the Contractor in respect of such breach of contract except to the extent that the Contractor may have been able to recover the amount thereof from the Sub-contractor. Provided always that if the Contractor shall not comply with Clause 59B (6) the Employer may enforce any such award or judgment in full.

This key provision overturns, in two sentences, the fundamental characteristic of the English system of nominated sub-contracts—namely that, once a nomination is effected, the nominee becomes, from the point of view of the main contractor's legal responsibility for due-performance, no different from any other sub-contractor. Experience and logic both show that attempts to " break the chain " of responsibility (whereby the employer looks and looks only to the main contractor for due performance, while the main contractor in turn pursues his remedies against individual sub-contractors, or they only against him) will only produce unforeseen anomalies and difficulties and reduce or remove the main contractor's essential function of control over and co-ordination of the sub-contracted work. This " chain of responsibility " principle has already been recognised and applied perfectly logically twice in the present contract—see clauses 58 (3) and 59A (3) (a). As already pointed out, however, the present clause is so radical in its effect that it greatly reduces the need for those provisions, and indeed for the elaborate right of objection in clause 59A (1). Nevertheless it should be appreciated that the present clause is limited to *the Employer's* damage, and does not amount to a guarantee of due performance of the Nominated Sub-contractor's sub-contract so far as concerns the main Contractor's *own " private " damage* caused by the Nominated Sub-contractor's breaches. It should also be noted that no attempt is made to qualify or restrict the circumstances in which the Contractor fails to recover from the Sub-contractor and so qualifies for reimbursement by the Employer (unlike, in the case of terminated sub-contracts, the Proviso to clause 59B (4) (c), *infra*, which contains a vitally important exception for acts or defaults of the main Contractor) and there is no apparent reason to suppose, for example, that the present sub-clause would not operate in favour of the main Contractor in a case where the Contractor had failed to secure proper terms in the sub-contract (*e.g.* where he had allowed a clause limiting damages to pass unnoticed). Nor is it clear what the position would be if the Contractor failed to recover in whole or in part because of counterclaims by the Nominated Sub-contractor for defaults of the main Contractor.

The present sub-clause applies to breaches of contract by the Sub-contractor which may cause damage to the Employer—*e.g.* defective work, delay, *implied* warranties of quality or of suitability (*i.e.* design), and indeed express obligations, if they exist, to perform design services (see in that particular context clause 58 (3), *supra*) or express design or performance guarantees or other suitability undertakings—unless the breach leads to a determination or rescission of the sub-contract by the main Contractor, in which case the whole of the very elaborate clause 59B, *infra*, will apply (with a similar overall policy intention, but wider protection still for the main Contractor).

Leaving aside the not inconsiderable procedural difficulties in the High Court which may be anticipated when seeking to prevent enforcement of an award or judgment against the main Contractor, it will be seen that the present sub-clause places no inhibition on arbitration or High Court proceedings up to the stage of award or judgment, but only on *enforcement* of the judgment or award. Furthermore, it is clear from clause 60 (7), and in particular Proviso (b) of that clause, that on final certificate at least the Employer can at last make a deduction in respect of his loss if the state of accounts will then permit. Enforcement by the Employer against the Contractor at that stage, or recovery by way of deduction, will only escape later reimbursement of the Contractor to the extent that payment or satisfaction of the latter's claim or judgment has been obtained from the Sub-contractor. The reference to clause 59B (6) is not at all elegant, since, in spite of clause 59B (4) (c) (ii), clause 59B (6) is on its face concerned with the quite different losses of the main Contractor arising on a forfeiture or rescission of the Sub-contract, but the present sub-clause obviously envisages proceedings brought for its own purposes which are procedurally similar to those in clause 59B (6)—*i.e.* by the Contractor *as and when required by the Employer* (see for the very important effect of these words on the question of the practical onus of securing compliance, the commentary on clause 59B (6), *infra*, p. 221) with what amounts to an indemnity from the Employer to the Contractor for unrecovered costs (though limited to a reasonable proportionate contribution in those cases where the main Contractor is also seeking to recover " private " losses of his own as well as of those of the Employer). The sanction in the Proviso to the present sub-clause in order to obtain compliance and co-operation by the main Contractor is, of course, strong, but the latter in any case has little interest or risk in not complying with the requirements of clause 59B (6). The most serious practical objection to the present sub-clause, however, is that the Employer would usually, in the interests of time and to avoid the possibility of conflicting findings of fact by different tribunals (and particularly since in many cases the liability for a breach may be disputed as between main Contractor and Sub-contractor, with each blaming the other) wish to proceed against the main Contractor, with the latter encouraged or directed by the Employer to bring Third Party proceedings against the Sub-contractor; so that upon obtaining and subsequently enforcing any third party judgment against the Nominated Sub-contractor, the Employer's judgment against the main Contractor would become fully effective in practical terms under the present sub-clause. This course will not, however, be open to the Employer in most cases, by virtue of the presence of arbitration clauses, certainly in the present main contract and possibly in the sub-contracts, and the fact that no third party procedure is, of course, available in arbitrations, nor has any attempt been made in the arbitration clause 66 of the present contract to provide any machinery to assist the Employer in this situation.

Quite apart from these procedural difficulties, an Employer will more usually wish, and often be in a position, to deduct from moneys due rather than to sue in respect of sub-contractor's breaches. This right, certainly in regard to defective work (though, perhaps inadvertently, not, it would seem, in regard to damages for delay) has also been taken away until final certificate; subject to the main Contractor being reimbursed the deduction if he subsequently fails to recover it from the Sub-contractor—see the two provisos (a) and (b) to clause 60 (7) and the commentary thereto, which require to be read together with the present sub-clause.

There is also a very important omission in the present sub-clause, which fails to deal with the not unlikely event that the main Contractor may recover some payment from the Sub-contractor by way of enforcement or otherwise, but not sufficient to satisfy both the Employer's and the main Contractor's own losses (compare clause 59B (6), which does make provision for the obvious fact that the two different categories of damage will often be claimed in the same proceedings against the Sub-contractor). It is submitted, however, that there is no reason to give any other meaning than the literal one to the words " except to the extent that the Contractor may have been able to recover the amount thereof " in the present sub-clause, and the Employer's loss will, for the purpose of the present clause, take precedence over the Contractor's own losses. If the Contractor's own damages were to be given precedence, the clause would be imposing a very different limitation on the Employer's power to recover—namely the Sub-contractor's financial inability, after meeting in full the Contractor's own " private " claims against the Sub-contractor, to meet the Employer's claim. This comes close to a qualified guarantee, at least, against damage suffered by the Contractor as a result of Nominated Sub-contractor's breaches. Such a wide guarantee, it is true, is given in the case of terminated sub-contracts (limited, however, to damages caused by the determination itself and not by the breaches or other events which may have led up to it) in clause 59B, but that is done expressly (see clause 59B (4) (b)). Moreover, if the intention of the present clause had been one of apportionment of the sums recovered, it would have been easy to provide for it expressly, as has, in fact, been done in the case of costs in clause 59B (6), *infra*, p. 220.

Forfeiture of Sub-contract

59B. (1) Subject to Clause 59A (2) (c) the Contractor shall in every sub-contract with a Nominated Sub-contractor incorporate provisions equivalent to those provided in Clause 63 and such provisions are hereinafter referred to as " the Forfeiture Clause ".

For this clause see the summary of the nominated sub-contract provisions as a whole in the commentary to clause 58, *supra*, pp. 196–200, and the concise summary *ante*, Chapter 1, pp. 1–3.

The present sub-clause reflects (this time, however, as a contractual obligation) clause 59A (1) (d), *supra* (incorporation of " equivalent " forfeiture clauses in sub-contracts). No special sanction is provided for the enforcement of the obligation, however, (and indeed sub-clause (2) *infra*, contemplates that there may be no " forfeiture clause " in the sub-contract, though this may be because a clause 59A (2) (c) situation, where the Nominated Sub-contractor will not agree to a " forfeiture clause," is envisaged). In any event, it has already been pointed out (see the commentary to clause 59A (1) (d), *supra*, p. 204) that the words " equivalent to clause 63 " lack precision and are susceptible of many different meanings once clause 63 is looked at in detail (see further on this the commentary on clause 59B (2), *infra*). The " chain of liability " principle already recognised in the present clauses (see clauses 58 (3) and 59A (3) (a)) would require some such words as " entitling the Contractor to terminate the sub-contract on the same grounds *mutatis mutandis* as clause 63 of the present contract."

Termination of Sub-contract

(2) If any event arises which in the opinion of the Contractor would entitle the Contractor to exercise his right under the Forfeiture Clause (or in the event that there shall be no Forfeiture Clause in the sub-contract his right to treat the sub-contract as repudiated by the Nominated Sub-contractor) he shall at once notify the Engineer in writing and if he desires to exercise such right by such notice seek the Employer's consent to his so doing. The Engineer shall by notice in writing to the Contractor inform him whether or not the Employer does so consent and if the Engineer does not give notice witholding consent within 7 days of receipt of the Contractor's notice the Employer shall be deemed to have consented to the exercise of the said right. If notice is given by the Contractor to the Engineer under this sub-clause and has not been withdrawn then notwithstanding that the Contractor has not sought the Employer's consent as aforesaid the Engineer may with the Employer's consent direct the Contractor to give notice to the Nominated Sub-contractor expelling the Nominated Sub-contractor from the sub-contract Works pursuant to the Forfeiture Clause or rescinding the sub-contract as the case may be. Any such notice given to the Nominated Sub-contractor is hereinafter referred to as a notice enforcing forfeiture of the sub-contract.

Engineer's Action upon Termination

(3) If the Contractor shall give a notice enforcing forfeiture of the sub-contract whether under and in accordance with the Forfeiture Clause in the sub-contract or in purported exercise of his right to treat the sub-contract as repudiated the Engineer shall do any one or more of the things described in paragraphs (a) (b) and (d) of Clause 59A (2).

To understand the implications of the present sub-clause, it is important to envisage the situation upon which it is designed to operate—in particular to appreciate that in real life a Contractor and Sub-contractor may often be in strong dispute as to the cause of defective work or delays, and that the Employer's advisers may not be entirely certain as to which of the two is at fault. Even where there may be no doubt as to the Sub-contractor's responsibility, an Employer and Contractor may have opposing commercial interests when deciding on the desirability of exercising a right to determination. In the present contract this latter consideration will be all the more influential, in view of the serious liabilities of the Employer and wide protection for the Contractor afforded by the present clause should a termination take place.

Points to notice about sub-clause (2) are

(a) It does nothing to resolve the difficulty about the precise meaning of the words " equivalent to clause 63 " in sub-clause (1)—there seems no particular connection between the procedural functions of the Engineer under the present sub-clause and those in clause 63, which may perhaps suggest that the contemplated sub-contract termination clause may not be dependent upon the notices, warnings and certificates of the Engineer as is clause 63 of the main Contract.

(b) The first sentence of sub-clause (2) assumes, (wrongly, it is submitted) that the *presence* of an appropriate " Forfeiture Clause " in the sub-contract and the exercise of a common-law rescission by the Contractor will be mutually exclusive possibilities—this is not so, and there is usually no reason, in the absence of explicit wording, why a clause affording a right of re-entry should be intended to supplant or replace the the power to rescind at common-law, which may be exercised separately, or simultaneously with and as an alternative to the " forfeiture clause " power (usually in cases, of course, where the stipulated " forfeiture " grounds are difficult to establish or apply, or the stipulated remedies inappropriate, to the events which have occurred—see on the availability of both remedies B.C.F., p. 431, the commentary to clause 63, *infra*, p. 245, and Hudson, 10th ed., p. 687). On the strict wording of sub-clause (2), however, a Contractor seeking to rescind on the basis of a common-law repudiation will be outside the terms of the present clause if there is an express " forfeiture " clause in the Sub-contract, which cannot really be the intention.

(c) It is vitally important to note that the third sentence of sub-clause (2) makes a " direction " of the Engineer to terminate dependent upon the Contractor's previous notification to the Engineer under the first sentence. On the other hand, this initial notification also appears to be a prerequistie if the Contractor wishes to terminate—the wording amounts to a prohibition against terminating without first notifying the Engineer, it is submitted. It may be inferred, therefore, that the Contractor will only give the initial notice in a situation where he desires either a direction for, or the Employer's consent to, a termination by himself, so that the words

" notwithstanding that the Contractor has not sought the Employer's consent " in relation to the power of " direction " are in real life terms meaningless, and indeed positively misleading in suggesting that a " direction " by the Employer to terminate will be possible without the Contractor's consent. Accordingly, in a case where the Contractor does not wish the Employer to direct a termination, he need only refrain from giving notice under the first sentence and the Employer will be helpless. As will be seen, not only does the contract subsequently make no distinction between the legal consequences of the Engineer's *direction* or the Employer's *consent* (see sub-clause (4), *infra*) but the words " Any *such* notice " in the last sentence of sub-clause (2), in so far as they suggest that only notices given by direction of the Engineer or with the Employer's consent will qualify as " notices enforcing forfeiture " for the purpose of sub-clause (4), are again misleading—since sub-clause (4) by its terms makes it quite clear that it applies equally to sub-contracts terminated *without the Employer's consent*, provided only that in such a case the termination is valid as against the sub-contractor. To sum up, therefore, the Employer for all practical purposes will *not* be able to direct a termination without the Contractor's consent; the Contractor *will* be able to terminate without the Employer's consent, and will nevertheless obtain the full protection and financial advantages of the clause provided he gives the initial notification; and in the latter case the only situation where the legal consequences will not be the same will be where the Contractor is in the wrong and the termination held to be invalid as against the Sub-contractor—see sub-clauses (4) and (5), *infra*. (As will be seen a further major ambiguity in the later part of the clause relates to the situation where the Employer *does* consent, but the termination is ultimately held invalid.)

" *notice in writing to the Contractor* "

For the formalities see clause 68 (2), *infra*.

" *may with the Employer's consent direct* "

This reference to consent seems pointless in a contract between the Employer and Contractor—see the commentary on the same point under clause 59A (2) (c), *supra*, p. 205.

"*Any such notice is hereinafter referred to as a notice enforcing forfeiture . . .*"

As already indicated the word " such " appears at first sight to relate back to a termination directed by the Engineer. Sub-clause (4), however, indicates that *any* notice expelling the Sub-contractor, pursuant either to an express " equivalent to Clause 63 " provision on the one hand, or to a common law rescission on the other, is to have the consequences set out in that clause. Though the wording is most obscure, the word " such " probably, however, has the effect, it is submitted, of further limiting " notices enforcing forfeiture " to cases where the Contractor has first given the initial notification to the Engineer. This requirement will be of crucial importance, since not only does sub-clause (3) impose a series of alternative obligations on the Employer in the case of " notices enforcing forfeiture " as here defined, but sub-clause (4) accords to " notices enforcing forfeiture " most valuable and comprehensive rights for the main Contractor against the Employer while work proceeds, the potential loss of which will be a most effective sanction compelling compliance by the Contractor with the initial notification requirement before he proceeds to determine a sub-contract himself.

Sub-clause (3) offers the same choice of obligations to the Employer, in the event of a " notice enforcing forfeiture," as the three relevant obligations arising on a valid objection to a nomination—namely appointing alternative Sub-contractors, or arranging a direct contract between the Employer and another Contractor, or (with consent in the case of P.C. items) ordering the Contractor to do the work himself. No provision seems to be made, however, for the case where the termination is not justified and the Employer has not consented, or for early resolution of a dispute where the Employer challenges the validity of the main Contractor's termination. The key to this probably lies, however, in sub-clause (5) (b)—see the commentary *infra*, p. 219—and it seems possible that the Employer's duty to act under sub-clause (3) may arise even where he refuses consent and disputes the validity of the termination —he will renominate etc. but may possibly refuse to pay more. It is not possible to express any confident or concluded view about this, however, despite its crucial practical importance.

Delay and Extra Costs

(4) If a notice enforcing forfeiture of the sub-contract shall have been given with the consent of the Employer or by the direction of the Engineer or if it shall have been given without the Employer's consent in circumstances which entitled the Contractor to give such a notice:—

(a) there shall be included in the Contract Price:—

(i) the value determined in accordance with Clause 52 of any work the Contractor may have executed or goods or materials he may have provided subsequent to the forfeiture taking effect and pursuant to the Engineer's direction:

(ii) such amount calculated in accordance with paragraph (a) of Clause 59A (5) as may be due in respect of any work goods materials or services provided by an alternative Nominated Sub-contractor together with reasonable sums for labours and for all other charges and profit as may be determined by the Engineer;

(iii) any such amount as may be due in respect of the forfeited sub-contract in accordance with Clause 59A (5);

(b) the Engineer shall take any delay to the completion of the Works consequent upon the forfeiture into account in determining any extension of time to which the Contractor is entitled under Clause 44 and the Contractor shall subject to Clause 52 (4) be paid in accordance with Clause 60 the amount of any additional cost which he may have necessarily and properly incurred as a result of such delay;

(c) the Employer shall subject to Clause 60 (7) be entitled to recover from the Contractor upon the certificate of the Engineer issued in accordance with Clause 60 (3):—

(i) the amount by which the total sum to be included in the Contract Price pursuant to paragraphs (a) and (b) of this sub-clause exceeds the sum which would but for the forfeiture have been included in the Contract Price in respect of work materials goods and services done supplied or performed under the forfeited sub-contract;

(ii) all such other loss expense and damage as the Employer may have suffered in consequence of the breach of the sub-contract;

all of which are hereinafter collectively called " the Employer's loss ".

Provided always that if the Contractor shall show that despite his having complied with sub-clause (6) of this Clause he has been unable to recover the whole or any part of the Employer's loss from the Sub-contractor the Employer shall allow or (if he had already recovered the same from the Contractor) shall repay to the Contractor so much of the Employer's loss as was irrecoverable from the Sub-contractor except and to the extent that the same was irrecoverable by reason of some breach of the sub-contract or other default towards the Sub-contractor by the Contractor or except to the extent that any act or default of the Contractor may have caused or contributed to any of the Employer's loss. Any such repayment by the Employer shall carry interest at the rate stipulated in Clause 60 (6) from the date of the recovery by the Employer from the Contractor of the sum repaid.

See for the exact meaning of " notice enforcing forfeiture " the commentary to sub-clause (2), *supra—i.e.* it is submitted, any notice, whether justified against the Sub-contractor or not, either invoking an " equivalent to clause 63 " termination clause, or rescinding the sub-contract at common law, but following initial notification under sub-clause (2) by the Contractor to the Engineer. The rather extraordinary and complicated scheme of the sub-clause is to make a wide range of additional payments and compensation first recoverable by the Contractor from the Employer on interim certificate, then recoverable back by the Employer by deduction or otherwise on final certificate, and then recoverable back yet again by the Contractor should he fail to obtain ultimate satisfaction from the Nominated Sub-contractor.

" *with the consent of the Employer or by the direction of the Engineer or if it shall have been given without the Employer's consent in circumstances which entitle the Contractor to give such a notice* "

It seems clear from this wording that the present clause will apply in cases where the Employer's consent or Engineer's direction have been given *notwithstanding that the forfeiture turns out to be unjustified as against the Sub-contractor*. Self-evidently, of course, a valid termination without consent will also qualify (provided initial notification under sub-clause (2) has been given). This will mean that in either case the

Employer will be bound to finance the Contractor (who by definition is in the wrong in the former case) in the most comprehensive way during the currency of the contract under (a) and (b), but on final certificate may deduct or recover all these payments from the main Contractor as " the Employer's loss," under (c). However the real sting of this sub-clause is in its tail—*i.e.* in the exception contained within the Proviso to paragraph (c). That paragraph first requires a final reimbursement to the main Contractor if, after final certificate, he cannot in turn recover from the Nominated Sub-contractor. It is submitted that in the former situation (*i.e.* an unjustified termination) the Contractor will *not*, however, be able to claim this reimbursement under the Proviso, by reason of the special " except and to the extent that the same was irrecoverable . . . " exception to the Proviso. This is inescapable on the wording, it is submitted, and indeed any other result (particularly when it is remembered that no termination can take place, even by a direction of the Engineer, without the Contractor first notifying the Engineer under sub-clause (2) that the contract can in the Contractor's opinion be validly rescinded) would be unjust and absurd. On the other hand, it should be noted that sub-clause (5), *infra* (which will prevent interim payments etc. to the main Contractor) only applies in a " no consent and no justification " situation and not a " consent but no justification " situation, and equally that sub-clause (6) (which deals with the legal costs which will have been incurred in any Contractor/Sub-contractor proceedings) again only makes an exception in favour of the Employer in the " no consent and no justification " situation and not in the " consent but no justification " situation. The matter can be summarised by saying that sub-clauses (5) and (6), *infra*, of this clause would appear to require that the Employer should pay the main Contractor for certain of the consequences of a wrongful termination of the sub-contract if, following the main Contractor's notification that in his opinion the Sub-contractor's contract can be validly terminated, the Employer has either consented to or directed a termination, but the exception to the Proviso to sub-clause (4) (c) brings about an opposite result by ensuring ultimate recovery from the main Contractor of the Employer's loss, even if the main Contractor has failed to recover himself from the Sub-contractor. The two policies seem to be inconsistent, but the explanation would appear to be that sub-clauses (4) (a) and (b) and (5) are concerned with *interim* payment rather than with *final* payment; and that the two sub-clauses define the situations or grounds on which the parties may respectively claim or resist the various *interim* payments in sub-clause (4)—thus, if the Employer consents to or directs a termination he cannot resist the initial payments under sub-clause (4), but if the termination is unjustified he will ultimately recover, without any liability to reimburse, from the Contractor. Whereas if he does not consent, while be may arguably be obliged to renominate etc. under sub-clause (3), he can resist the interim financing provisions called for under sub-clause (4) and rely on sub-clause (5) as his defence to any interim claim by the main Contractor. It also seems to have been thought appropriate that in cases where the Employer consents to or directs a termination he should pay the main Contractor's legal costs in seeking to recover from the Nominated Sub-contractor even in a case where he fails to recover because the termination was unjustified—only this policy or intention can justify the failure in sub-clause (6), *infra*, to make an exception similar to that in the Proviso to sub-clause (4) (c). Given these apparent inconsistencies and difficulties in resolving the relationship of the various provisions in a situation which is obviously of the most fundamental importance, the Employer will be well advised to adopt a neutral attitude wherever possible, and withhold formal consent in any but the clearest and most urgent situations, however. Furthermore, it may perhaps be commented that the difficulties of reconciling the provisions of these sub-clauses are so great that clarification of the intention seems to be urgently needed.

(*a*) " *there shall be included in the Contract Price* "

i.e. for purposes of interim payment under clause 60 (1) and (2) as well as on final certificate under clause 60 (3). Paragraph (a) (i) appears to deal with the possibility that, pursuant to clause 59B (3), *supra*, the Engineer has acted under clause 59A (2) (d) and clauses 58 (4) or 58 (7) (a); and paragraph (a) (ii) that he has acted under clause 59A (2) (a). (There does not appear to be any provision covering possible action under clause 59A (2) (b).) Under paragraph (a) (iii) there may, of course, be no " amount . . . due in respect of the forfeited sub-contract," depending on the terms of the sub-contract and possible defences or counter claims arising out of the determination being available by way of set-off against any sum due to the Sub-contractor.

Paragraph (b) introduces a major change which distinguishes the present clause's remedies from those under clause 59A (6) in the case of ordinary non-termination breaches, namely that the Contractor's own special " private " losses due to the termination are included in the " Employer's Loss," and so are guaranteed to the main Contractor by the Employer under the terms of the Proviso to paragraph (c). As in the case of the sums in paragraph (a), the scheme is to make the sums recoverable on interim certificate; then recoverable back by the Employer under sub-clause (c) by deduction, or otherwise by action, on or after final certificate; and finally recoverable back yet again by the Contractor under the proviso to sub-clause (c), should he fail to obtain ultimate reimbursement from the Sub-contractor. One strange effect of the present sub-clause seems to be that the Employer, by virtue of the extension of time given, will forgo liquidated damages in the main contract, but under paragraph (c) (ii) will recover back on final certificate not the liquidated damages forgone, but, presumably, such loss due to delay as he can actually prove (unless the loss of liquidated damages would qualify under the latter wording, which seems unlikely). The words " consequent upon the forfeiture " are of fundamental importance, and may have a very considerable limiting effect, it is submitted, upon the damages which the main Contractor may be able to recover. It is a feature of most contracts which are rescinded that, prior to their termination, there may have been continuing breaches of contract of one kind or another which may indeed be the principal motive for, if not the ground upon which, the " forfeiture " or rescission is ultimately based Nevertheless, it is clear from the wording that it is only losses of the Contractor *consequent upon the act of termination itself*, not the pre-existing losses caused by the earlier delays, defective work or other breaches, which will qualify for reimbursement under the present sub-clause, though these earlier losses will, of course, in so far as they may affect the Employer, be the subject of the much more limited provisions of clause 59A (6), *supra*. Thus where, for example, a sub-contract is terminated on the ground of excessive delay, it will only be the cost to the Contractor of the time lost in securing the appointment of another Sub-contractor etc., and making arrangements for the completion of work by the new Sub-contractor or direct contractor, which will be recoverable under the present paragraph, and not the possibly substantial costs occasioned by any delays which took place prior to the decision to terminate.

(*c*) " *the Employer shall subject to Clause 60 (7) be entitled . . . upon the certificate of the Engineer issued in accordance with clause 60 (3) . . .*"

The reference to clause 60 (3) is to the final certificate—*i.e.* the Employer must wait for his remedy until three months after the Maintenance Certificate for the whole Works. The reference to clause 60 (7) is to Proviso (b) to that sub-clause, which in fact very largely overlaps with, and probably adds nothing to, the Proviso to the present sub-clause (see the commentary to clause 60 (7) Proviso (b) *infra*, p. 241). The present sub-clause differs very importantly from the Proviso in clause 60 (7) in that the present provision contains the special exception to the Proviso already commented upon *supra*, which on its wording will apply, it is submitted, in all cases where the sub-contract has been wrongfully terminated by the main Contractor, and so needs to be reconciled with sub-clauses (5) and (6), *infra*, which both indicate that wrongful terminations of sub-contracts by the main Contractor will nevertheless attract some protection under the present clause, provided that the Employer has consented to or " directed " the termination—see the suggested explanation of this apparent inconsistency in the commentary, *supra*, and under sub-clause (5), *infra*.

Termination Without Consent

(5) If notice enforcing forfeiture of the sub-contract shall have been given without the consent of the Employer and in circumstances which did not entitle the Contractor to give such a notice:—

(a) there shall be included in the Contract Price in respect of the whole of the work covered by the Nominated Sub-contract only the amount that would have been payable to the Nominated Sub-contractor on due completion of the sub-contract had it not been terminated;

(b) the Contractor shall not be entitled to any extension of time because of such termination nor to any additional expense incurred as a result of the work having been carried out and completed otherwise than by the said Sub-contractor;

(c) the Employer shall be entitled to recover from the Contractor any additional expense he may incur beyond that which he would have incurred had the sub-contract not been terminated.

As already pointed out, the vital words " without the consent of the Employer *and* in circumstances which did not entitle . . ." clearly show that the Employer's consent to (*a fortiori*, of course, direction of) an invalid termination is not intended to bring the present sub-clause into operation (compare the " reverse side of the medal " wording in the first sentence of sub-clause (4)).

It has been seen that the scheme of sub-clause (4) is to provide that a number of matters " shall be included in the Contract Price " under paragraph (a) and that a limited class of compensation should be payable under paragraph (b), but on final certificate the excess of the total of these two categories over what would otherwise have been due, plus any other damage or loss of the Employer, should be the subject of a certified claim by the Employer against the Contractor. Disregarding the question of ultimate reimbursement by the Employer to the Contractor, should this last claim be irrecoverable as against the Nominated Sub-contractor, the scheme of sub-clause (4) is essentially to provide an interim financing scheme for the benefit of the Contractor, followed by a claim " down the line " for recovery from the Nominated Sub-contractor at the end of the day. The present sub-clause, on the other hand, makes it plain that in the special defined situation in which it is to operate no interim financing of any kind need occur—this, it is submitted, follows from paragraphs (a) and (b) of the present sub-clause, and see also the definition of " Contract Price " (an expression used only occasionally and somewhat erratically in the contract) in clause 1 (1) (i), *supra*, p. 16, and see clause 60, *infra*, where " Contract Price " is never used either in the context of interim or final payment—beyond payment of an appropriate proportion of the original sub-contract price as and when the sub-contract work is carried out, whether by the original Sub-contractor or anyone else. The wording of paragraphs (b) and (c) suggest that the duty of the Employer to renominate a substitute Sub-contractor, or to make one of the other arrangements provided for under sub-clause (3), *supra*, may still stand, but without any obligation on the Employer to pay more (*e.g.* for a Nominated Sub-contractor or the Contractor himself to do the work) on interim payment, and a right to compensation on interim payment if more has to be paid (*e.g.* under the Employer's option to engage a direct Contractor) by the Employer—see paragraph (c). Paragraph (c), however, will not usually enable claims due to delay to be made, it would seem, since by virtue of paragraph (b) the Employer will be entitled to full liquidated damages to the extent that delay has been caused by the termination, and it is of course elementary that the liquidated damages notionally represent the full costs of delay to the Employer. Paragraph (c) does not show much concern for the Employer's interest in that no provision appears to be made for recovery on interim payment, so that the Employer may have to rely on his common law power of set-off—see the commentary to clause 60, *infra*, pp. 230 *et seq.*

Recovery of Employer's Loss

(6) The Contractor shall take all necessary steps and proceedings as may be required by the Employer to enforce the provisions of the sub-contract and/or all other rights and/or remedies available to him so as to recover the Employer's loss from the Sub-contractor. Except in the case where notice enforcing forfeiture of the sub-contract shall have been given without the consent of the Employer and in circumstances which did not entitle the Contractor to give such a notice the Employer shall pay to the Contractor so much of the reasonable costs and expenses of such steps and proceedings as are irrecoverable from the Sub-contractor provided that if the Contractor shall seek to recover by the same steps and proceedings any loss damage or expense additional to the Employer's loss the said irrecoverable costs and expenses shall be borne by the Contractor and the Employer in such proportions as may be fair in all the circumstances.

This sub-clause seeks to provide necessary machinery to protect the Employer's interest, given the policy of the present clause to ensure that the Contractor should ultimately be reimbursed if he fails to recover in turn from the Nominated Sub-contractor. The sub-clause seems to be specifically aimed at termination cases and " the Employer's Loss " (this expression is defined in sub-clause (4), *supra*, as the damage arising in termination cases to both Employer *and Contractor*—see paragraph (b) sub-clause (4)) so that the invocation of the present clause by clause 59A (6) in the case of simple non-determination breaches of contract (see *supra*, p. 209) is not at all elegant. It is clear from the wording that the Contractor must initially be responsible for the costs of the proceedings, but later can claim reimbursement if the costs are irrecoverable unless *both* (a) the termination is held to have been unjustified *and* (b) the Employer has not consented to (or *a fortiori*, of course, has directed) the termination—this is the same formula as in sub-clause (5) and the " other side of the medal " formula at the beginning of sub-clause (4), and again it is clear that even though the termination is wrongful, so that the litigation against the Sub-contractor will fail, the Employer will nevertheless have to pay the Contractor's costs if he has consented to the termination—there is no exception such as that in the Proviso in sub-clause (4) (c) " except and to the extent that the same was irrecoverable by reason of some breach of contract or other default towards the Sub-contractor or except to the extent that any act or default of the Contractor may have caused or contributed to the Employer's loss "—so that the result (and possibly intention) of the present sub-clause will be that in " consent " cases the Contractor's costs of proceeding against the Sub-contractor will be secured to him even if the termination of the sub-contract proves to be unjustified—which is certainly unjustifiable in view of the concealed control (via his notification that in his opinion the sub-contract can be validly terminated) exercised by the main Contractor over the decision to terminate, in spite of the apparent but misleading machinery of " consent " and " direction " of and by the Employer (see as to this the commentary to clause 59B (2) and (3), *supra*, pp. 212–213).

" *so much of the reasonable costs . . . as are irrecoverable* "

It should perhaps be remembered that, even with a solvent Sub-contractor and a successful main Contractor, a loss may often arise based on the difference between party and party costs allowed on taxation and " reasonable " costs under the present clause.

The words " The Contractor shall . . . as may be required by the Employer " at the beginning of the sub-clause will be of crucial importance in the context of the references in clauses 59A (6), 59B (4) (c) and 60 (7) Proviso (b) to compliance by the Contractor with the present sub-clause as a condition of ultimate reimbursement by the Employer. They indicate, it is submitted, that there will be no failure of the Contractor so to comply unless the Employer requires him to do so. In addition, it should perhaps be noted that there will be two stages of enforcement of the main Contractor's claims against Nominated Sub-contractors—(a) *establishing liability* in arbitration or other litigation and (b) *enforcement* of judgment or award failing payment. The remedies available (disregarding a small possibility of deduction on interim certificate if the obstacles in clause 60 (7) Proviso (a)) are not present, as to which see the commentary, *infra*, pp. 240–241, are as follows:—

(a) In the case of non-termination damage to the Employer due to any Nominated Sub-contractor's breach either
    (i) deduction on final certificate followed by reimbursement if, despite compliance with the present sub-clause, the main Contractor cannot recover from the Sub-contractor (clause 60 (7) Proviso (b)), or

(ii) non-enforcement of any judgment or award against the Contractor by the Employer until the latter's recovery from the Nominated Sub-contractor, unless the main Contractor fails to comply with the present sub-clause (see clause 59A (6)), or

(b) In the case of *both* Employer's *and Contractor's* losses due to termination, action upon or deduction from the sums due under the final certificate, subject to reimbursement if, in spite of compliance with the present sub-clause, the main Contractor cannot recover from the Nominated Sub-contractor (clause 59B (4) (c) and (possibly) clause 60 (7) Proviso (b)).

While in practical terms these remedies might suggest a different onus in regard to compliance with the present clause, depending upon whether the Employer had been able to deduct or is out of pocket, the words " as may be required by the Employer " will mean that the onus will always be on the Employer, if he is to protect his interest, to take control under the present clause, unless the Contractor agrees that he need not and accepts liability.

The sensible provision in the present sub-clause for the apportionment of irrecoverable costs if (as will usually be the case) the Contractor is also claiming damage of his own in the proceedings (quite apart, in all probability, from the limited category of the Contractor's damage under sub-clause (4) (b), above, since, as already explained, *supra*, p. 218, there will often be pre-termination damage suffered by the Contractor not recoverable under sub-clause (4) (b)) makes the more noticeable the omission of any provision in clause 59A (6) to deal with cases of partial recovery of the substantive claim against the Sub-contractor. The present sub-clause, which appears to have been drafted primarily for the purposes of the present clause 59B and only incidentally incorporated by reference, it may be assumed, for the purposes of clause 59A (6), has little need to provide against partial recovery of the two parties' substantive claims against the Nominated Sub-contractor, since sub-clause (4) (b), coupled with paragraph (c), has the effect of guaranteeing the Contractor's losses (at least to the extent of losses due to the delay " consequent upon the forfeiture " and so expressly included in " the Employer's loss ") for the purposes of the present clause.

" *any loss . . . additional to the Employer's loss* "

By virtue of the definition of this expression in sub-clause (4) (c), *supra*, the expression in the present sub-clause, in the context of apportionment of costs, means other additional Contractor's losses over and above the special Contractor's losses due to " delay . . . consequent upon the forfeiture " which are payable by the Employer to the Contractor and so included in the definition. Failure to recover these last losses in proceedings against the Sub-contractor will not render the Contractor liable to make a contribution to the costs, notwithstanding that to that extent the costs in question will have been incurred exclusively for his own benefit—this may be because, in a case where the Employer has consented to the determination but the Contractor has failed to recover for one reason or another, it may have been thought that the Employer would have most to gain, and hence be in charge of such proceedings, at least to the extent of " the Employer's loss," (including, under the definition, the limited damages recoverable from the Employer by the Contractor). Nevertheless, the failure to have a saving comparable in intention to that in the exception to the sub-clause 4 (c) Proviso, *supra*, at least where the Employer has not acted unreasonably in requiring the Contractor to bring proceedings or to attempt enforcement, seems impossible to justify.

Payment to Nominated Sub-contractors

59C. Before issuing any certificate under Clause 60 the Engineer shall be entitled to demand from the Contractor reasonable proof that all sums (less retentions provided for in the sub-contract) included in previous certificates in respect of the work executed or goods or materials or services supplied by Nominated Sub-contractors have been paid to the Nominated Sub-contractors or discharged by the Contractor in default whereof unless the Contractor shall:—

(a) give details to the Engineer in writing of any reasonable cause he may have for withholding or refusing to make such payment; and

(b) produce to the Engineer reasonable proof that he has so informed such Nominated Sub-contractor in writing;

the Employer shall be entitled to pay to such Nominated Sub-contractor direct upon the certification of the Engineer all payments (less retentions provided for in the sub-contract) which the Contractor has failed to make to such Nominated Sub-contractor and to deduct by way of set-off the the amount so paid by the Employer from any sums due or which become due from the Employer to the Contractor. Provided always that where the Engineer has certified and the Employer has paid direct as aforesaid the Engineer shall in issuing any further certificate in favour of the Contractor deduct from the amount thereof the amount so paid direct as aforesaid but shall not withhold or delay the issue of the certificate itself when due to be issued under the terms of the Contract.

Without such an express power to pay direct, an employer who did so might be liable to pay twice for the same work, without even a right of recourse against the Contractor's trustee or liquidator—see *Re Holt, ex p. Gray* (1888) 58 L.J.Q.B. 5 and Hudson, 10th ed., pp. 769–772. Such an express power can be validly operated after a bankruptcy or liquidation —*Re Wilkinson, ex p. Fowler* [1905] 2 K.B. 713—and, depending on the wording, can be operated at any time prior to final certificate—*Re Tout and Finch* [1954] 1 W.L.R. 178.

It should be appreciated by Employers operating this clause that it necessarily involves double payment by the Employer in the first place (first to the main Contractor, then to the Sub-contractor) with the right later to recoup one of the payments by way of deduction from any moneys subsequently due to the Contractor. As a matter of commercial prudence, therefore, it should never be operated where the overall state of accounts is likely to be in the Employer's favour. Moreover, the conditions on which the clause is based must be strictly satisfied—the Employer may only pay amounts previously certified and not yet paid by the Contractor, not the full balance of sums currently due on the Sub-contractor's account, if these have not already been certified. Furthermore, because of the words " before issuing any certificate," the Engineer can never authorise direct payment of any sum certified for the first time in the Final Certificate (this will be unusual, but can happen on final adjustment of a Sub-contractor's account, for example) since there will be no further certificate under clause 60 entitling him to make the necessary request. In addition, the clause only in terms empowers the Employer to pay and deduct, it does *not* provide that the Contractor should " allow or pay " the sum in question to the Employer. Apart, therefore, from any questions of commercial prudence, an Employer may not be able to sue for or recover money paid direct, it is submitted, if the state of accounts is in the Employer's favour and not the Contractor's, though in certain circumstances it might be possible to frame an action in quasi-contract for money paid to the defendant's use—see Hudson, 10th ed., p. 770. For the inadequacy of the present power in cases of termination of the main contract, see the commentary under clause 63 (2), *infra*, pp. 252–253.

The power in the present clause is exercisable in the case of all nominated sub-contracts, whether for work, work and materials, or supply only—see the definition of " Nominated Sub-contractors " in clause 59A (5)—in other words Sub-contractors either named in the contract or appointed by the Engineer under clause 59A (4), in the case of P.C. items or sums, or appointed by the Engineer under clause 59A (7) (b), in the case of Provisional Sums.

Again as a matter of commercial prudence, since any failure to comply *exactly* with the contractual requirements will invalidate the payment as against the Contractor's trustee or liquidator, no payment (which of course is entirely discretionary) should be made by the Employer without obtaining a properly worded indemnity from the Nominated Sub-contractor in question.

" *Before issuing any certificate under clause 60* "

These words now refer to any (monthly) certificate and not, as in the Fourth Edition, to a monthly certificate *itself containing still more moneys due in respect of a previously unpaid Sub-contractor*. This brings the power into line with other U.K. standard forms, and greatly increases its scope and flexibility (for the difficulties of the old situation see B.C.F. p. 417).

"*(a) give details to the Engineer*"

This is a further improvement on the old wording, suggested in B.C.F. at p. 418, but " satisfy the Engineer that . . ." would be better still.

"*upon the certification of the Engineer*"

This wording now makes it plain, which the Fourth Edition did not (see B.C.F., p. 418), that a special certificate of the Engineer to the effect that the Employer is entitled to make the direct payment in question is what is contemplated.

"*and to deduct . . . from any sums due or which become due*"

The Employer may deduct at once from any outstanding certificate, possibly the immediately preceding clause 60 certificate if not yet paid, but more likely the current certificate prior to which the Engineer required proof etc. and then certified the sum for direct payment. It would seem that the deduction may occasionally, therefore, be in the first place made by the Employer from a certificate which does not in itself reflect the deduction, but the Proviso appears to compel the Engineer to show the direct payment as a deduction in the next certificate issued by him. See further, for what exactly this may involve, the commentary on clause 60 (2), *infra*, p. 229.

The principal purpose of the " or which become due " wording in U.K. standard forms is usually to make it clear that the right to deduct is not lost by a failure to make a deduction at the first available opportunity after the direct payment has been made (some old Victorian cases on special wording held that the right to deduct could be lost if not exercised promptly—see Hudson, 10th ed., pp. 635–636). It may in fact often be unavoidable to spread the deductions over a number of subsequent certificates (*e.g.* in a case where very little is being certified in favour of the main Contractor but the unpaid sums in respect of the Subcontractor's work are very large), or if not unavoidable it may be commercially desirable—*e.g.* in order to keep a main Contractor of doubtful financial buoyancy afloat until the end of the Works. If so, it would seem that this must be done by postponing the direct payments wholly or partially, since the Proviso to the present clause would seem to make this latter course impossible, once a payment direct has been made, at least within the strict terms of the contract, unless the Proviso can be construed as enabling the Engineer to postpone the deduction in the subsequent certificate in accordance with his client's wishes, which seems doubtful. It is just this type of formal difficulty which makes it so important for the Employer to obtain an indemnity from the Subcontractor before making any direct payment (see *supra*, p. 224).

CERTIFICATES AND PAYMENT

Monthly Statements

60. (1) The Contractor shall submit to the Engineer after the end of each month a statement (in such form if any as may be prescribed in the Specification) showing:—

(a) the estimated contract value of the Permanent Works executed up to the end of that month;

(b) a list of any goods or materials delivered to the Site for but not yet incorporated in the Permanent Works and their value;

(c) a list of any goods or materials listed in the Appendix to the Form of Tender which have not yet been delivered to the Site but of which the property has vested in the Employer pursuant to Clause 54 and their value;

(d) the estimated amounts to which the Contractor considers himself entitled in connection with all other matters for which provision is made under the Contract including any Temporary Works or Constructional Plant for which separate amounts are included in the Bill of Quantities;

unless in the opinion of the Contractor such values and amounts together will not justify the issue of an interim certificate.

Amounts payable in respect of Nominated Sub-contractors are to be listed separately.

Monthly Payments

(2) Within 28 days of the date of delivery to the Engineer or Engineer's Representative in accordance with sub-clause (1) of this Clause of the Contractor's monthly statement the Engineer shall certify and the Employer shall pay to the Contractor (after deducting any previous payments on account):—

(a) the amount which in the opinion of the Engineer on the basis of the monthly statement is due to the Contractor on account of sub-clause (1) (a) and (d) of this Clause less a retention as provided in sub-clause (4) of this Clause;

(b) such amounts (if any) as the Engineer may consider proper (but in no case exceeding the percentage of the value stated in the Appendix to the Form of Tender) in respect of (b) and (c) of sub-clause (1) of this Clause which amounts shall not be subject to a retention under sub-clause (4) of this Clause.

The amounts certified in respect of Nominated Sub-contracts shall be shown separately in the certificate. The Engineer shall not be bound to issue an interim certificate for a sum less than that named in the Appendix to the Form of Tender.

The draftsmanship of clause 60 as a whole was, even making allowance for the reputation of the contract as a whole, astonishingly careless in the Fourth Edition. In particular, that Edition made no reference

(a) to sums previously paid by the Employer and their deduction from the sums to be certified;

(b) to payments for Nominated Sub-contractors' work;

(c) to special payments to or claims by the Contractor under the terms of the contract;

(d) to possible cross-claims by the Employer under the terms of the contract;

(e) to a final certificate, or the time for making the final measurement or adjustment of the contract price;

(f) to the persons to whom the certificates were to be issued;

(see for these criticisms of the Fourth Edition, B.C.F., pp. 419–420).

It is essential to a proper understanding of the system of interim payment on a valuation basis as it has developed in building and civil engineering contracts in the U.K., including the ICE Conditions, to appreciate that it is based upon a *retrospective* revaluation of *all* work done up to the date stated in the certificate, and not merely of the work done since the date in the previous certificate. This approach to interim payment on a valuation basis in building and civil engineering contracts is, in fact, commercially essential for two principal reasons. In the first place, if interim payment is to be afforded for unfixed materials once brought on to the Site, the valuations which will need to take place for certification of unfixed materials and goods (and indeed now possibly for some categories of unfixed materials and goods off the Site as well under the new clause 54) must subsequently be replaced in later certificates and the work in question revalued using the prices in the Bills of Quantities for permanent work, once the unfixed materials and goods have become incorporated into and therefore a part of the permanent work. In the second place, the symptoms of defective work (as *e.g.* cracking or spalling indicating a failure of concrete which has not been properly cured, or which has been placed during adverse weather conditions) may not emerge in the completed work for some weeks or months. On a cumulative retrospective valuation basis (almost invariably, in U.K. contracts, of work, whether expressly or impliedly, *properly* carried out) such matters will create no problem of readjustment once they are discovered—in other words, interim payment and certification is essentially provisional in character for a number of reasons, and liable to subsequent adjustment. This is expressly recognised in the power in sub-clause (7), *infra*, to correct, modify or delete sums previously certified, for example.

The present clause now makes provision for the deduction from the sum certified of all previous payments by the Employer (sub-clause (2)) though, as will be seen, there appears to be an ambiguity or mistake in the draftsmanship; makes plain that amounts payable to Nominated Sub-contractors are to be included in interim certificates, and that they should be listed separately (sub-clauses (1) and (2)); makes plain that *any* claim to which the Contractor may be entitled under *any* of the provisions of the contract should be represented by an estimated amount in the certificate (sub-clauses (1) (d) and (2) (a)); lays down precise dates for release of the two retention money instalments, related to the clause 48 completion certificates (sub-clause (5)); and an equally clear date and arrangements for a Final Certificate, related to the time of the Maintenance Certificate (sub-clause (3)); and finally identifies the persons to whom the certificates under the clause should be sent (sub-clause (8)). There is also now a new provision entitling the Contractor to interest, should the Engineer "fail to certify" under the clause, though, as will be seen, the exact meaning of this expression is ambiguous (sub-clause (6)). In addition, while the express power to correct previous certificates (probably unnecessary in the case of defective work, it is submitted, but certainly most desirable in cases of other disallowances, or errors or mistakes of valuation or computation in the certificates) is a slightly modified traditional provision (sub-clause (7)) there are two new Provisos to the sub-clause, which relate to Nominated Sub-contractors' breaches of contract and in reality form part of the new special scheme in clauses 59A (6) and 59B (4), whereby the Employer in effect gives certain limited guarantees in regard to performance by the Sub-contractor in certain special respects, as a result of which later adjustments or deductions in respect of Nominated Sub-contractors' work are not permitted until the Final Certificate—as will be seen, an ill-considered and anomalous policy.

Thus virtually all the matters of omission in the Fourth Edition have been effectively dealt with, with the single very important exception that sub-clauses (1) and (2) remain quite silent in regard to cross-claims by the Employer against the Contractor, though it is perhaps just arguable that these are covered, in some types of cross-claim at least, by the " estimated contract value of the Permanent Works " expression in sub-clause (1) (a). This is the principal aspect of the clause likely to give rise to serious legal (and financially most important) difficulties on interim payment (apart from the difficult Provisos, already mentioned, to sub-clause (7) in regard to Nominated Sub-contractors' work).

The Employer's cross-claims can be of various kinds. First, they may not be specifically provided for or mentioned in the contract, but may arise out of it—as *e.g.* claims of any kind for damages for any breach of the contract, which in English law are called equitable set-offs (in the context of defending a claim brought under the contract) as well as constituting a separate (counter-) claim. Secondly, they may be specifically provided for in the contract—*e.g.* clause 22 (1) (employer's general indemnity), clause 24 (personal injuries indemnity), clause 25 (insurance premiums), clause 26 (2) (conformity with statutes, etc.), clause 27 (7) (Street Works), clause 29 (2) (noise and disturbance), clause 30 (2) (damage to highways), clause 39 (2) (remedying defective work), clause 47 (3) (liquidated damages for delay), clause 49 (4) (remedying defects during Maintenance Period), clause 53 (8) (sale of surplus plant, etc.), clause 59B (5) (c) (Employer's loss on wrongful determination of sub-contract terminated without consent), clause 59C (payment direct of Nominated Sub-contractors) and clause 62 (urgent repairs). While some of these contractual cross-claims of the Employer are supported by an express right to deduct from moneys due (see *e.g.* clauses 39 (2) (remedying defective work), 47 (4) (liquidated damages), clause 53 (8) (surplus plant), clause 59C (payment direct), and clause 62 (urgent repairs)), many others make no mention of the remedy or how it is to be enforced (*e.g.* the various indemnity provisions including the important general indemnity under clause 22, or clause 59B (5) (c) (wrongful termination by main Contractor)). In addition, in some cases (but by no means all) the contractual cross-claims are associated with some action, notification, opinion or certificate of the Engineer relating to the Employer's entitlement to the cross-claim in question—*e.g.* under clause 47 (4) in regard to liquidated damages for delay or under clause 59C in regard to payment direct of Nominated Sub-contractors.

It should be noted that the scheme of the contract, where deduction is specifically provided for, is for the deduction to be made *by the Employer* from the sum certified, *not by the Engineer in the interim certificate*—the expressions used are broadly similar, though not always identical, indicating the piecemeal growth of the contract—" the Employer . . . may deduct . . . from any monies due or which become due to the Contractor " (clause 25); " may be deducted by the Employer from any monies due or which may become due to the Contractor " (clause 39 (2)); " the Employer may deduct . . . from any sum otherwise payable by the Employer to the Contractor hereunder " (clause 47 (4)); " may deduct the same from any monies due or that become due to the Contractor " (clause 49 (4)); " the Employer shall be entitled . . . to deduct by way of set-off . . . from any sums due or which may become due from the Employer to the Contractor " (clause 59C)). (See also " the Employer . . . shall not be liable to pay the Contractor any money on account of the Contract until the expiration of the Period of Maintenance and the cost of completion . . . certified " in clause 63 (4), and " shall be deemed a debt due by the Contractor to the Employer and shall be recoverable accordingly " in clause 70 (8) of the Conditions.) The only exceptions to this general rule that the matter of deductions will not be regulated by the payment certificates, are, first, under clause 59C, the Proviso to which specifically states that in *subsequent* certificates after a direct payment of a Nominated Sub-contractor the Engineer should deduct the amount from the certificate. This seems rather an ambiguous provision—see the commentary on the clause, *supra*, p. 225—and is certainly *per incuriam* if it contemplates *both* a deduction by the Employer *and* a subsequent deduction in a certificate. In fact the clause probably contemplates that if the deduction is made by the Employer without any deduction in the certificate of the Engineer, the entitlement to the deduction is to be suitably recorded in subsequent certificates, but that in many cases the deduction will be made following on a deduction made in the certificate itself, so that in these cases there will be a genuine exception to the usual rule.The second apparent exception is in the case of unremedied defective work, but here it is submitted that, quite apart from the express power in clause 60 (7), *infra*, this is not a question of cross-claim or set-off, but simply that the valuation under sub-clause (1) is, as a matter of necessary implication, a valuation only of work properly carried out—so that work once known to be defective at the time of a later interim certificate will either not be included in the later valuation or, if it is, the valuation will contain an allowance for the cost of remedying the defects. The function of the express power in clause 60 (7) is to make plain, it is submitted, that in a subsequent certificate work not previously known to be defective can be disallowed, though this in any event follows from the retrospective revaluation of all the work which, as previously stated, is the basis of interim valuations. The two important questions likely to arise under the present clause on the Employer's cross-claims are, therefore

(a) Can the Employer deduct from a sum certified for interim payment under the general law of set-off in the many cases where the contract confers no specific power to deduct?
(b) Can the Employer deduct, in those cases where there is some special certifying or other procedural machinery regulating his entitlement to deduct, if because of disagreement with the Engineer or for some other reason he is unable to show that he has obtained the Engineer's necessary procedural support?

(It should be appreciated that in both cases the question is only one of the " temporary finality " of the Engineer's decision—in the first case of his interim certificates for payment, in the other of his certificate, opinion, notification etc. relating to the deduction entitlement of the Employer. There is no dispute that none of these decisions will have " permanent finality," being ultimately liable to review under the arbitration clause or in the courts, if notice of arbitration is given within the stipulated period (see the extremely wide " open up review and revise " power in clause 66, *infra*, p. 275). This does not, of course, in any way affect the vital commercial importance of these two problems of " temporary finality.")

In regard to the general implied power of set-off, a number of decisions of the Court of Appeal in England, starting with the case of *Dawnays Ltd.* v. *Minter Ltd.* [1971] 1 W.L.R. 1305, held that, as a matter of general presumption in interpreting provisions for interim payment in building and civil engineering contracts, those provisions were intended to preclude any Employer's right of set-off, in the absence of express contractual provision, so that payment in full on the interim certificates could not be resisted. These (six) decisions were collectively and decisively overruled by the House of Lords in the case of *Gilbert-Ash Ltd.* v. *Modern Engineering* [1974] A.C. 689. The six decisions were exhaustively examined and criticised by the author in (1973) 89 L.Q.R. 36, and subsequently the effect of the speeches in the House of Lords in the *Gilbert-Ash* case was analysed and explained in a Note in (1974) 90 L.Q.R. 21, together with a further Note on the related House of Lords decision in *Mottram Consultants* v. *Bernard Sunley* in (1975) 91 L.Q.R. 471. In view of the great commercial importance of these decisions in days of financial stringency, the author's article and two notes are reprinted in Appendix B, *post*, p. 317.

There can be no doubt, it is submitted, that in the light of the reasoning in the *Gilbert-Ash* case, the Employer will be free to raise any bona fide set-off or counterclaim as a defence against an action brought against him on interim certificates under the present clause, even in the absence of an express power to deduct, subject only to some express contractual provision negating his entitlement so to do. By virtue of clause 66 (2), *infra*, p. 277, it is clear that the Contractor is free to commence early arbitration if dissatisfied with the Engineer's certification, and there is nothing in the wording of the contract, or as a matter of necessary business implication, to prevent the Employer deducting from the certificate (if his quarrel is with the certificate, *e.g.* on valuation). This view is lent strong support by the fact that, even in a case where the dispute is referred to the Engineer under clause 66 and the Engineer disagrees with the Employer's contentions, the requirement at the beginning of clause 66 (1), in regard to giving effect to the Engineer's decisions until revision by an arbitrator, applies in terms only to the Contractor and not to the Employer. In any event, the Employer will often not be disputing the certificate as such, by virtue of the scheme of the contract, already mentioned, whereby cross-claims (other than defects) are usually not dealt with in an interim certificate. See the further commentary under clause 66 (1), *infra*, pp. 273–274.

The second question (where the Employer is contractually required to produce certification or other documentary support for his cross-claim) again arises where the Employer and his Engineer are in disagreement, and the problem is whether the certification or other action of the Engineer provided for in the contract is a " condition precedent," without which the Employer will not be entitled to deduct from sums certified on interim payment until such time as he has obtained an arbitrator's award or decision of the courts—(that time, after exhausting rights of appeal on case stated or otherwise, is likely to be long after completion of most projects, even where early arbitration is permitted under clause 66 (2), *infra*, p. 277). For a matter of such importance there is remarkably little authority in England. The question must in every case turn upon the contractual intention to be deduced from the precise wording of the contractual provisions for the approval, certification or other action of the Engineer relating to the Engineer's cross-claim, and may also be affected by the wording of the arbitration clause. In the case of *Brightside, Kilpatrick* v. *Mitchell Construction* [1975] 2 Lloyd's Rep. 493, (1976) B.L.R. 62, the Court of Appeal held that, on the very strong wording of clause 8 (a) (which specifically used the words " condition precedent ") and of the arbitration clause in the FASS forms of building sub-contract, the architect's certificate under that clause (that the work should have been completed by a certain date etc.) was a condition precedent to the deduction by the main Contractor of liquidated damages for delay, though it is not entirely clear whether the court had in mind, or was intending to decide, a question of " temporary finality " until arbitration or litigation was concluded, or of permanent finality binding in *any* later proceedings. The principal provisions in the present contract where this question might arise are clauses 47 (4) and 59C, both of which contemplate action by the Engineer (determination and certification of extension of time and notification of no further extension under clause 47 (4), and certification of the direct payment under clause 59C) before the right to deduct can be exercised (see also for an analogous case clause 63 (1) where fairly considerable action by the Engineer in the form of certification, notices and warnings, is contemplated before a re-entry by the Employer under the terms of the clause). Prima facie the language of the two sets of provisions would not appear strong enough to displace the general power of set-off and the *Brightside* wording is clearly distinguishable, but the question must be regarded as open (needless to say, of course, though it is not the fundamental question, the absence of the necessary certification, *a fortiori* positive disagreement between an Employer and Engineer, would make it correspondingly harder for an Employer to obtain unconditional leave to defend or a stay of proceedings for summary judgment brought against him on the payment certificate).

Turning now to an examination of sub-clauses (1) and (2) in detail, it will be seen that the onus will be on the Contractor to deliver his statements on a calendar month basis, should he desire payment, but a minimum figure is stipulated in the Appendix. The wording in the opening lines of sub-clause (2) does not seem correct, since the intention, at least as evidenced by the " Minimum Amount of Interim Certificates " item in the Appendix (which would otherwise be largely meaningless) and the last words of sub-clause (2) " interim certificate for a sum less than that named in the Appendix " appears to be for *the Engineer* to certify a balance due after deducting the previous payments on account *in the certificate*. The wording, however, suggests that it is *the Employer* who makes this deduction. The words " (after deducting . . .) " in brackets should obviously have followed immediately after the words " shall certify " to be consistent with the item in the Appendix and the last sentence of sub-clause (2)—or alternatively the wording of these should be modified so as to refer to the balance due after deduction.

(*1*) (*a*) " *the estimated value of the Permanent Works* "

i.e., it is submitted, of the Permanent Works *properly* carried out—a valuation will either disallow defective work known to need replacement or make an allowance for the cost of remedying the defects—see also the express power in clause 60 (7), *infra*, which is strictly unnecessary in the case of defective work, but which makes plain that work previously allowed in full can be subsequently disallowed once defects are detected. The present wording also appears to be treated as including Nominated Sub-contractors' work—see the last line of sub-clause (1), and at the end of sub-clause (2), requiring separate listing both by the Contractor and Engineer of these items, which is necessary, for example, to enable the facts for direct payment under clause 59C to be established and generally to ensure prompt payment of Nominated Sub-contractors.

(*1*) (*b*) and (*c*) " *goods or materials* "

These will be valued on an invoiced basis, no doubt, but in later certificates will be revalued at contract prices for work, once incorporated as part of the Permanent Works—see the importance of this in considering the possible " temporary finality " of interim certificates referred to in the commentary *supra*, p. 227.

(*1*) (*d*) " *all other matters for which provision is made under the Contract* "

i.e. any claim under the long list of *express* provisions permitting claims in the contract—but not simple claims for damages for breach of contract, it is submitted. In fact this is no real inhibition, since nearly all the more important Employer's breaches likely to cause damage are the subject of express claims—see *e.g.* the new clause 7 (3) (late information or instructions) and clause 42 (failure to give possession). Possible claims which will qualify under the present wording will be under clauses 5, 7 (3), 12 (3), 13 (3), 14 (6), 20 (2), 22 (2), 26 (1), 27 (6), 30 (3), 31 (2), 36 (3), 38 (2), 40 (1), 42 (1), 49 (3), 50, 59A (3), 59B (4) (b), 65 (5) (e), 65 (6) (b) (c) and (d), 69, 70 and 71—see, however, the Contractor's obligation to supply sufficient *particulars* in support of claims for purposes of interim payment, and the sanction for failure to do so in clause 52 (4) (f), and also the obligations to give *notice*, and the not very effective sanction for failure to do so, in clause 52 (4) (a) (b) and (e), and the commentaries thereto.

(*1*) (*d*) " *Temporary Works or Constructional Plant for which separate items are included in the Bills* "

See the commentaries to clauses 1 (1) (k), *supra*, p. 21, and 53 (1) (a), *supra*, p. 169, and the reference in clause 8 (2), *supra*, p. 37. Items priced in the Bills will be of a relatively unusual character, and probably relate to Temporary Works designed to be left *in situ*, and possibly running or financing charges for important items of Constructional Plant, but the contract itself gives no precise indication of what exactly is envisaged.

" *Amounts payable in respect of Nominated Sub-contractors . . .*"

i.e. the " price paid or due to be paid " by the main Contractor, it is submitted—see clause 59A (5) (a)—though it may be arguable that this could be different from " estimated contract value " in (1) (a). If so, the Contractor might be able to rely on (1) (d). But the contract is not very clear about the exact basis of interim payment of Nominated Sub-contractors.

(2) " *within 28 days . . . the Engineer shall certify and the Employer shall pay . . .*"

See, however, the need for sufficient particulars and notice etc. from the Contractor under clause 52 (4) (e) and (f). See also the sanction by way of interest for late payment in the rather ambiguously reworded sub-clause (6), *infra.* Note that both events, certification and payment, must take place within the single period named.

(2) (*a*) " *less a retention* "

Note this will apply and be calculated on all claims paid under sub-clause (1) (d), as well as on the measured work itself, subject to the limit in sub-clause (4), *infra.*

(2) (*b*) " *shall not be subject to retention* "

These words may be a little misleading. Retention proper, to which materials will not be subject, is dealt with under sub-clause (2) (a) and sub-clauses (4) and (5), *infra.* Materials etc. under (2) (b) *will* be subject to retention, in practical terms, however, to the extent that only a percentage, as stated in the Appendix, will be paid of their value. Nor is there any stipulated limit, unlike the case of " retention " proper, on this particular element of " retention." Since, however, the materials will all have become incorporated into the Permanent Works by the time of release of the first instalment of retention proper, whether on completion of a part or of a Section of the Works under sub-clause (5) (a), or of the whole Works under sub-clause (5) (b), the retention proper in respect of the Permanent Works under sub-clause (2) (a) and (4) will by then have absorbed the agreed percentage hitherto unpaid in respect of unfixed materials etc. for the part, Section or whole, as the case may be.

(2) " *The amount certified in respect of Nominated Sub-contractors* "

See also the last sentence of sub-clause (1), and clause 59A (5) for the sums to be paid. There may be a doubt whether this is " estimated contract value " under sub-clause (1) (a) of the present clause, or sums due under the sub-contract by virtue, perhaps, of sub-clause (1) (d) and clause 59A (5) in combination—see the commentary, *supra.* Separate listing is essential in the Employer's interest to ensure that prompt payment of Nominated Sub-contractors is taking place, and also to lend precision to any disputes with the main Contractor over the amount of interim valuations.

Final Account

(3) Not later than 3 months after the date of the Maintenance Certificate the Contractor shall submit to the Engineer a statement of final account and supporting documentation showing in detail the value in accordance with the Contract of the work done in accordance with the Contract together with all further sums which the Contractor considers to be due to him under the Contract up to the date of the Maintenance Certificate. Within 3 months after receipt of this final account and of all information reasonably required for its verification the Engineer shall issue a final certificate stating the amount which in his opinion is finally due under the Contract up to the date of the Maintenance Certificate and after giving credit to the Employer for all amounts previously paid by the Employer and for all sums to which the Employer is entitled under the Contract up to the date of the Maintenance Certificate the balance if any due from the Employer to the Contractor or from the Contractor to the Employer as the case may be. Such balance shall subject to Clause 47 be paid to or by the Contractor as the case may require within 28 days of the date of the certificate.

The date of the Maintenance Certificate is governed by clause 61 (1), *infra*. It will be seen that the Contractor's entitlement to the Final Certificate under the present sub-clause is, therefore, dependent upon (a) the expiry of the last maintenance period, if more than one is involved on different Sections or " substantial parts " of the Works, under clause 48 (2); (b) upon the making good of the last of the defects apparent at the end of the Maintenance Period of which he has been notified by the Engineer within 14 days of the expiry of the Period (see clause 49 (2) and clause 61 (1), *infra*); and (c) the supply of all necessary information for verification under the present clause.

There is nothing in the present clause or anywhere else in the contract which confers any sort of binding force on the Final Certificate, and in addition clause 61 (2) expressly indicates that the Maintenance Certificate itself should have no binding force. The Certificate would appear to be final, therefore, only in the chronological sense, and indeed there is not even any clear indication that the Engineer will be entirely *functus officio* once the Certificate is given—there is no statement to this effect in clause 60 (7), *infra*, for example, so that it seems at least possible that he might revise the Certificate under that sub-clause, and in any case under clause 66 disputes arising on the Final Certificate can be referred for settlement to the Engineer for preliminary settlement under that clause, upon which, presumably, he might change his mind and rule differently or value differently from the basis adopted in his Final Certificate.

" *after giving credit . . . for all sums to which the Employer is entitled under the Contract up to the date of the Maintenance Certificate* "

As already pointed out, there is no contractual provision in sub-clause (1) or elsewhere for credit to be given for the Employer's cross-claims in interim certificates, with a single and rather difficult possible exception in the case of direct payments to Nominated Sub-contractors under clause 59C.

The lack of binding force of the Final Certificate, coupled with the Employer's right to set-off in regard to matters, whether dealt with or not in the certificates of the Engineer, reduces the importance of the problem, but it is not at all clear what are the sums " to which the Employer is entitled under the Contract " up to the date of the Maintenance Certificate which the Engineer, apparently, has to take account of in his Final Certificate—see the list of the Employer's claims in the commentary to sub-clauses (1) and (2), *supra*. They will certainly include claims for breaches by Nominated Sub-contractors under clauses 59A (b), 59B (4) (c) and clause 60 (7) Proviso (b) (which cannot be advanced under these clauses until Final Certificate), but will they, for example, include an indemnity claimed by the Employer under clause 22 (1) in respect of a third party claim recently received by him? Or a premium paid direct by the Employer (and perhaps previously deducted) under clause 25? And why are the words " subject to clause 47 " (*i.e.* liquidated damages for delay) in the last sentence if, as the words quoted above might appear to indicate, they will now for the first time have been taken into account in a certificate? The impression is left that the wording of the present sub-clause has not been very carefully considered although, as stated, no serious problem is likely to arise provided that the certificate makes clear what, if any, allowances in favour of the Employer have been made—if so, the parties will be aware of the extent to which any decisions have been made and can take the necessary steps to initiate arbitration or other proceedings in relation to disputed items.

Retention

(4) The retention to be made pursuant to sub-clause (2) (a) of this Clause shall be a sum equal to 5 per cent of the amount due to the Contractor until a reserve shall have accumulated in the hand of the Employer up to the following limits:—

(a) where the Tender Total does not exceed £50,000 5 per cent of the Tender Total but not exceeding £1,500; or

(b) where the Tender Total exceeds £50,000 3 per cent of the Tender Total;

except that the limit shall be reduced by the amount of any payment that shall have been made pursuant to sub-clause (5) of this Clause.

Payment of Retention Money

(5) (a) If the Engineer shall issue a Certificate of Completion in respect of any Section or part of the Works pursuant to Clause 48 (2) or (3) there shall become due on the date of issue of such certificate and shall be paid to the Contractor within 14 days thereof a sum equal to 1½ per cent of the amount due to the Contractor at that date in respect of such Section or part as certified for payment pursuant to sub-clause (2) of this Clause.

(b) One half of the retention money less any sums paid pursuant to sub-clause (5) (a) of this Clause shall be paid to the Contractor within 14 days after the date on which the Engineer shall have issued a Certificate of Completion for the whole of the Works pursuant to Clause 48 (1).

(c) The other half of the retention money shall be paid to the Contractor within 14 days after the expiration of the Period of Maintenance notwithstanding that at such time there may be outstanding claims by the Contractor against the Employer. Provided always that if at such time there shall remain to be executed by the Contractor any outstanding work referred to under Clause 48 or any works ordered during such period pursuant to Clauses 49 and 50 the Employer shall be entitled to withhold payment until the completion of such works of so much of the second half of retention money as shall in the opinion of the Engineer represent the cost of the works so remaining to be executed.

Provided further that in the event of different maintenance periods having become applicable to different Sections or parts of the Works pursuant to Clause 48 the expression " expiration of the Period of Maintenance " shall for the purposes of this sub-clause be deemed to mean the expiration of the latest of such periods.

These three sub-clauses need to be read with sub-clause (2) (a) and (b), *supra*. Sub-clause (4) is concerned merely to fix the somewhat arbitrarily changing upper limits of retention—in effect 5 per cent. for contracts up to £30,000, £1,500 for all contracts between £30,000 and £50,000, and 3 per cent. for all contracts over £50,000. For the definition of "Tender Total," see clause 1 (1) (h), *supra*, p. 19. (Sub-clause (4) of the present clause and clause 10 appear to be the only occasions when the expression is used in the contract.) The reference to reduction by the amount of any payment under sub-clause (5) is simply to the initial release of the first instalment, either for a whole or part, under paragraphs (a) and (b), or the partial release of the second instalment of retention in cases where outstanding work for the remedying of defects remains to be done.

For the merging of the materials etc. percentage with the Permanent Works retention, see the commentary to sub-clause (2), *supra*. The scheme of the clause is that the first instalments are released and/or become due automatically and in full on the date of *issue* of clause 48 completion certificates of a " substantial part " (see clause 48 (2) (b)), a Section (see clause 48 (2) (a)) or the whole (see clause 48 (1)), notwithstanding that, as permitted by clause 48, there may still be outstanding work to be finished during the maintenance period. (Note, incidentally, that in the case of Sections or parts the figure is 1½ per cent. by value without limit, whatever the full retention limit percentage may be, whereas in the case of the whole it is one-half of the full retention limit. Note also that no *certificate* for the release of the retention is formally required, the sums becoming due automatically, though in cases of Sections or parts there may not necessarily have been a sub-divided valuation of the Section or part in question in the earlier interim certificates, and quite difficult questions (*e.g.* the splitting of Preliminaries etc.) might arise on this, so some quite difficult valuation by the Engineer may in fact be necessary to enable the instalment to be calculated.)

The second instalment of the retention money will become due only upon the expiry of the Maintenance Period of the last part of the works (see the final Proviso to clause (5) (c)) and will become due automatically, but in the event of work remaining outstanding a valuation of the Engineer, (though, strictly, no formal certification) is required to determine the proportion of the second instalment still to be withheld. The last withheld portion of the second instalment will be released and/or become due (without, it seems, any formal certification requirement) on " the completion of such Works "—*i.e.* at the time of the Maintenance Certificate under clause 61 (1), *infra.*

Interest on Overdue Payments

(6) In the event of failure by the Engineer to certify or the Employer to make payment in accordance with sub-clauses (2) (3) and (5) of this Clause the Employer shall pay to the Contractor interest upon any payment overdue thereunder at a rate per annum equivalent to ¾ per cent. plus the minimum rate at which the Bank of England will lend to a discount house having access to the Discount Office of the Bank current on the date upon which such payment first becomes overdue. In the event of any variation in the said Bank Rate being announced whilst such payment remains overdue the interest payable to the Contractor for the period that such payment remains overdue shall be correspondingly varied from the date of each such variation.

Interest will, of course, be recoverable *in any proceedings* at the discretion of the court (or an arbitrator) under section 3 of the Law Reform (Miscellaneous Provisions) Act 1934, but otherwise interest is not in general recoverable in English law in the absence of contractual provision—see Hudson, 10th ed., pp. 575–577.

The present sub-clause repeats with modifications clause 60 (3) of the Fourth Edition. It will be remembered that the time for payment is expressed in the present Edition as a single period of 28 days from delivery of the Contractor's statement, during which both certification by the Engineer and payment by the Employer must take place—see sub-clause (2), *supra.* This, it is submitted, explains the new words in the present sub-clause " failure *by the Engineer to certify or* the Employer to make payment "—it is submitted that this is only a repetitious way of saying " failure by the Employer to honour the Engineer's certificate within 28 days "—in other words, interest will become payable under the clause if there is late payment due either to a failure by the Engineer to issue a certificate or failure by the Employer to honour it within the permitted period. It is submitted that the wording does *not* mean that a certificate honoured by the Employer within the period but subsequently held to be *inadequate in amount* will carry the contractual interest—which in another context the words " failure by the Engineer to certify " could possibly be held to mean (compare, for example, the meaning to be attributed to the expression " withholding . . . of any certificate . . . to which the Contractor claims to be entitled " in clause 66 (2), where the expression probably does mean or includes certificates issued but inadequate in amount). Such interest may, however, be recoverable under the Act if proceedings have commenced.

Correction and Withholding of Certificates

(7) The Engineer shall have power to omit from any certificate the value of any work done goods or materials supplied or services rendered with which he may for

the time being be dissatisfied and for that purpose or for any other reason which to him may seem proper may by any certificate delete correct or modify any sum previously certified by him.

Provided always that:—

(a) the Engineer shall not in any interim certificate delete or reduce any sum previously certified in respect of work done goods or materials supplied or services rendered by a Nominated Sub-contractor if the Contractor shall have already paid or be bound to pay that sum to the Nominated Sub-contractor;

(b) if the Engineer in the final certificate shall delete or reduce any sum previously certified in respect of work done goods or materials supplied or services rendered by a Nominated Sub-contractor which sum shall have been already paid by the Contractor to the Nominated Sub-contractor the Employer shall reimburse to the Contractor the amount of any sum overpaid by the Contractor to the Sub-contractor in accordance with the certificates issued under sub-clause (2) of this Clause which the Contractor despite compliance with Clause 59B (6) shall be unable to recover from the Nominated Sub-contractor together with interest thereon at the rate stated in Clause 60 (6) from 28 days after the date of the final certificate issued under sub-clause (3) of this Clause until the date of such reimbursement.

Dealing first with the first sentence of the sub-clause, and excluding the Proviso, this is a rather differently worded version of the old clause 60 (4). The old clause first gave a perfectly general power to correct or modify earlier certificates (in fact an essential element of the U.K. system of interim payment, with or without such an express power—see the commentary to sub-clauses (1) and (2), *supra*) and secondly a special power to " withhold any certificate " (whatever this might precisely mean) if any part of the work was being carried out unsatisfactorily. The present wording omits the use of the word " withholding," though the word is retained in the marginal heading (not a permissible source of interpretation, however—see clause 1 (3), *supra*, p. 24) and reverses the previous order, in the first part clarifying the old " withholding " expression in the context of defective work (the new power of omission of value is, it is submitted, again strictly unnecessary, since the same result would come about on an interim valuation on a proper interpretation of the expression " estimated contract value " in sub-clause (1)—see the commentary, *supra*, pp. 229–230—although it is to be welcomed as putting the matter beyond doubt). Secondly, the present clause deals with the general power to correct etc. by using the new wording " or for any other reason which to him may seem proper." The only difficulty is to ascertain the exact extent of this latter wording. It obviously cannot be accepted entirely at its face value—for example, it is submitted, the Engineer could not use it to " punish " the Contractor for past defaults, or as a lever to secure obedience to an instruction, or more satisfactory work or behaviour in the future. As a matter of business efficacy, the power should be limited, it is submitted, to cases where the Engineer wishes to correct an error, whether of computation or of judgment or of fact, or simply to change his mind, about a sum previously certified.

The two Provisos are an integral part of the new code relating to Nominated Sub-contractors' ordinary breaches in clause 59A (6) or breaches leading to termination of a nominated sub-contract in clause 59B (4), whereby in the case of damage caused by ordinary breaches the Employer undertakes not to enforce a judgment in respect of his own losses against the main Contractor until the latter has recovered them in turn from the Nominated Sub-contractor (clause 59A (6)), but in the case of damage caused by a validly terminated sub-contract the Employer undertakes not to recover both his own loss due to the determination *and the Contractor's losses due to it* (which the Contractor will have to be paid as an addition on interim payment under clause 59B (4) (b)), until the time of the Final Certificate, with a later obligation to refund any sums so recovered if the Contractor is unable to recover them from the Sub-contractor in turn (clause 59B (4) (c)). The two provisos might well have been more conveniently included in clauses 59A and 59B.

Proviso (a) is primarily concerned with the damage caused by a Nominated Sub-contractor's breaches other than those directly due to a termination of the sub-contract (*i.e.* the implementation of clause 59A (6)). As already stated (see the commentary, *supra*, p. 229) defective work should result in reduced valuations after discovery, and other breaches would afford an equitable set-off available to the main Contractor against the Nominated Sub-contractor's claim, so that the sums would no longer be " due to be paid " to the sub-contractor under clause 59A (5) (a), and so could be deducted by the Engineer in later certificates. Even in determination cases, it could also be argued that the Engineer (in spite of possible implications to the contrary in clause 59B (4) (c)) could disallow on the next interim certificate after the determination the value of any work prior to the determination on the ground that it would no longer be " due " to the Sub-contractor under clause 59B (4) (a) (iii) by virtue of the main Contractor's right of equitable set-off for damages due to the termination. If this is correct the present Proviso would also have an application in such cases to prevent such action.

It is, of course, necessary, *given the policy* of clauses 59A (6) and 59B, to prevent interim recovery by the Employer by way of deduction if this would put the Contractor " out of pocket," but with the carelessness of the Employer's interest which is so often unfortunately a characteristic of this contract, it does not appear to have been realised that, where the Sub-contractor is still working on the Site, it may often be possible, in the case of defective work by or other valid claims against him, for the Employer to deduct on interim certificate, with the main Contractor able to deduct in turn. Very often, however, knowledge of the breach or the decision to deduct in respect of it will not have occurred before the next following interim certificate—if so, the quite unnecessary italicised words in the expression " if the Contractor *shall have already paid* or be bound to pay that sum to the Nominated Sub-contractor " will prevent subsequent deduction when the breach is discovered, since the Contractor will almost invariably have already paid for the work on a previous certificate. Without the offending words the Contractor could set off the previously paid (but now disallowed) sum against the Sub-contractor's next claim for interim payment, but if for some reason he could not (*e.g.* because the Sub-contractor had finished his work, or the terms of the sub-contract prevented such a set-off) the deletion could then be restored by the Employer, consistently with the policy of the two clauses. This is a very serious failure of reasonable protection to both Employer and main Contractor in regard to Nominated Sub-contractors' possibly persistent defective work. It can, of course, easily be rectified by deleting the *underlined* words quoted above.

The question remains, however, whether, notwithstanding the prohibition on any reduction of the sums certified in a subsequent interim certificate in respect of Nominated Sub-contractors' work, the Employer might nevertheless exercise his common law right of set-off once defective work was discovered, and deduct himself before making payment against the interim certificate. The comment of the drafting Committee of the Fifth Edition, in reply to the present criticism (see *post*, Appendix C, Part II pp. 369–370) is that in their view the *Gilbert-Ash* decision in the House of Lords (not, of course, decided at the date of publication of the Fifth Edition), which resurrected the right of set-off (see *post*, Appendix D, Part II) and abolished the " Rule in Dawnays' Case," will enable the Employer to deduct from the certificate though the Engineer may not do so. As a matter of interpretation of Clause 59A (6) and the present two Provisos this seems very doubtful, but if so there is now a serious lacuna in Clause 59A (6), which is quite inconsistent with its declared policy, in the case of non-termination sub-contractors' breaches, where the Employer has been able to deduct in this way and the Contractor, in order to qualify for full payment on the Final Certificate has been forced to remedy the defects himself, for example.

Proviso (b) would appear to apply to a breach by a Nominated Sub-contractor in either of the two above categories, but it is noteworthy that it appears to be thought to be complementary to the overlapping remedy in termination cases in clause 59B (4) (c), *supra*, p. 215 (see the words " subject to Clause 60 (7) " in that clause). Clause 59B (4) (c) entitles the Employer to deduct a wide class of losses on final certificate (including some Contractor's losses previously paid on interim certificate under clause 59B (4) (b)), subject to ultimate reimbursement of the main Contractor after final certificate should the Sub-contractor not ultimately satisfy the main Contractor's claim. The present Proviso hardly seems necessary in this context, since it only adds (if at all) to the earlier provision by seeking to deal with a possible reduction in the Final Certificate of sums previously certified—but this will have happened on Final Certificate, if the facts warrant it, under clause 59B (4) (c)—see clause 59B (4) (c) (i) with its reference back to clause 59B (4) (a). Clause 59B differs in a most fundamental and important respect from the present provision, however, in the exception there provided to the general rule requiring ultimate reimbursement by the Employer to the main Contractor on the latter's failure to recover—see the " except and to the extent that the same was irrecoverable by reason of some breach . . . or other default . . . by the Contractor " wording in the Proviso to clause 59B (4) (c) and the commentary thereto, *supra*, p. 216.

Proviso (b), therefore, will apply principally to non-forfeiture breaches by the Nominated Sub-contractor, and indicates that when the embargo on deduction from interim certificates in Proviso (a) ceases to apply, there will be a deduction on final certificate should the Employer/Contractor's state of accounts permit it, so that the provision is really complementary to clause 59A (6), *supra*, pp. 207–208.

(*b*) " *despite compliance with Clause 59B* (*6*) "

i.e. in proceedings controlled, if desired, by the Employer on an indemnity for costs. See the full commentary to this difficult clause, *supra*, pp. 220–223.

Copy Certificate for Contractor

(8) Every certificate issued by the Engineer pursuant to this Clause shall be sent to the Employer and at the same time a copy thereof shall be sent to the Contractor.

This sub-clause, which is new, can hardly be accused of over-refinement. It indicates only the *physical destination* of the certificate after " issue," and does not in terms say whether there is any *person to whom* the certificate is to be issued (contrast clause 61 (1), *infra*, with regard to the Maintenance Certificate or clause 63 (1) in regard to grounds of determination, for example). There are no express requirements of form—as *e.g.* that the certificate should be in writing, though the reference to a "copy " in the present sub-clause and to separate amounts for Nominated Sub-contractors being " shown " in the certificate in sub-clause (2) suggest, however, writing or at least some other method of recording.

For the law relating to the form and sufficiency of certificates see Hudson, 10th ed., pp. 478–483. For the required contents of an interim certificate for payment under the present clause, and the ambiguity in regard to deduction of previous payments, see sub-clause (2) and the commentary thereto, *supra*, p. 232. It will be noted that there appear to be no certification requirements as such for the release of either instalment of retention money under sub-clause (5), even though in appropriate cases some valuation will be needed for continued retention of any part of the second instalment.

Maintenance Certificate

61. (1) Upon the expiration of the Period of Maintenance or where there is more than one such period upon the expiration of the latest period and when all outstanding work referred to under Clause 48 and all work of repair amendment reconstruction rectification and making good of defects imperfections shrinkages and other faults referred to under Clauses 49 and 50 shall have been completed the Engineer shall issue to the Employer (with a copy to the Contractor) a Maintenance Certificate stating the date on which the Contractor shall have completed his obligations to construct complete and maintain the Works to the Engineer's satisfaction.

Unfulfilled Obligations

(2) The issue of the Maintenance Certificate shall not be taken as relieving either the Contractor or the Employer from any liability the one towards the other arising out of or in any way connected with the performance of their respective obligations under the Contract.

This clause is largely new, replacing clauses 61 and 62 in the Fourth Edition. The length of the Period of Maintenance is regulated by the Appendix to the Form of Tender—see clause 49 (1), *supra.* The Maintenance Certificate will be issued after the final completion of (a) work outstanding at the time of substantial completion under clause 48, (b) defects notified to the Contractor up to 14 days after the end of the Maintenance Period as requiring repair under clause 49 (2) and (c) searches ordered by the Engineer under clause 50. The last requirement is difficult to interpret, since if the view expressed as to the time when an instruction to search can be given under clause 50 is correct (see the commentary, *supra*, pp. 149–150) the reference adds nothing and seems unnecessary.

The sole contractual effect of the Maintenance Certificate appears to be to govern the time for the issue of the Final Certificate under clause 60 (3), *supra*, and also to set a time-limit on the matters which the Engineer must take into account, whether in favour of the Contractor or of the Employer, when drawing up that certificate (*e.g.* the outcome of attempts by the main Contractor to recover "Employer's losses" from Nominated Sub-contractors, possible claims under third-party indemnities, and so on).

Sub-clause (2) effects a most welcome and radical reform, sweeping away a series of provisions in the Fourth Edition as to the extent of the binding effect of the certificate, which were calculated to defy all attempts at rationalisation (see B.C.F., pp. 425–427, 447–453). The most important practical consequence will be that the Contractor's liability for defective work not detected at the end of the work will continue for the normal limitation period, with time usually running from clause 48 completion.

REMEDIES AND POWERS

Urgent Repairs

62. If by reason of any accident or failure or other event occurring to in or in connection with the Works or any part thereof either during the execution of the Works or during the Period of Maintenance any remedial or other work or repair shall in the opinion of the Engineer be urgently necessary and the Contractor is unable or unwilling at once to do such work or repair the Employer may by his own or other workmen do such work or repair as the Engineer may consider necessary.

If the work or repair so done by the Employer is work which in the opinion of the Engineer the Contractor was liable to do at his own expense under the Contract all costs and charges properly incurred by the Employer in so doing shall on demand be paid by the Contractor to the Employer or may be deducted by the Employer from any monies due or which may become due to the Contractor. Provided always that the Engineer shall as soon after the occurrence of any such emergency as may be reasonably practicable notify the Contractor thereof in writing.

During the execution of the work, this remedy overlaps with the several other comparable rights and remedies of the Employer—clause 39 (1) (and the remedy closely analogous to the present remedy in clause 39 (2)), clause 40 (1) and clause 50, and, during the period of maintenance only, clause 49 (4).

" *which . . . the Contractor was liable to do at his own expense* "

It will be noted that the present sub-clause concerns itself principally with a remedy or power, and not with financial responsibility. Clauses which will assist in determining this are clauses 20 (1) and (2), 39 (1), 40 (1) (c) and 49 (3), and see also clause 13 (1). In general, the Contractor's responsibility before substantial completion is absolute, save for the " physically impossible " limitation in clause 13 (1) and the " Excepted Risks " (including Engineer's design) in clause 20 (2). After substantial completion (except presumably in regard to works still not completed at that time) liability will depend upon whether the work or materials are not in accordance with the contract, or whether the Contractor has caused damage by his own operations in the period of maintenance (see clauses 49 (3) and 20 (1)).

Forfeiture

63. (1) If the Contractor shall become bankrupt or have a receiving order made against him or shall present his petition in bankruptcy or shall make an arrangement with or assignment in favour of his creditors or shall agree to carry out the Contract under a committee of inspection of his creditors or (being a corporation) shall go into liquidation (other than a voluntary liquidation for the purposes of amalgamation or reconstruction) or if the Contractor shall assign the Contract without the consent in writing of the Employer first obtained or shall have an execution levied on his goods or if the Engineer shall certify in writing to the Employer that in his opinion the Contractor:—

(a) has abandoned the Contract; or

(b) without reasonable excuse has failed to commence the Works in accordance with Clause 41 or has suspended the progress of the Works for 14 days after receiving from the Engineer written notice to proceed; or

(c) has failed to remove goods or materials from the Site or to pull down and replace work for 14 days after receiving from the Engineer written notice that the said goods materials or work have been condemned and rejected by the Engineer; or

(d) despite previous warning by the Engineer in writing is failing to proceed with the Works with due diligence or is otherwise persistently or fundamentally in breach of his obligations under the Contract; or

(e) has to the detriment of good workmanship or in defiance of the Engineer's instruction to the contrary sub-let any part of the Contract;

then the Employer may after giving 7 days' notice in writing to the Contractor enter upon the Site and the Works and expel the Contractor therefrom without thereby avoiding the Contract or releasing the Contractor from any of his obligations or liabilities under the Contract or affecting the rights and powers conferred on the Employer or the Engineer by the Contract and may himself complete the Works or may employ any other contractor to complete the Works and the Employer or such other contractor may use for such completion so much of the Constructional Plant Temporary Works goods and materials which have been deemed to become the property of the Employer under Clauses 53 and 54 as he or they may think proper and the Employer may at any time sell any of the said Constructional Plant Temporary Works and unused goods and materials and apply the proceeds of sale in or towards the satisfaction of any sums due or which may become due to him from the Contractor under the Contract.

This clause, with some rather odd rearrangements and changes of wording in the grounds for determination in sub-clause (1), and with the addition of a new provision in sub-clause (2) requiring the assignment of sub-contracts upon a determination, otherwise follows extremely closely its predecessor in the Fourth Edition.

Sub-clause (1) sets out the necessary prerequisites of a contractual right of determination by the Employer, described in the clause as a right " to enter upon the Site and Works and expel the Contractor therefrom." The clause is incorrectly titled " Forfeiture " in the margin (not in fact permitted to be used for purposes of interpretation—see clause 1 (3), *supra*, p. 24). The expression is incorrect because, in the first place, the word " forfeiture " is appropriate to leases but not to the rescission of contracts, and secondly because the wording of the present clause appears to be at great pains to confine it to a *right of re-entry* (contrast the use of the expression " determination of the Contract " in the Employer's other right of rescission in clause 65 (3), *infra*, p. 260). Nor does the present clause at any point use the word " forfeiture," though the expression is used to describe such clauses in sub-contracts in clause 59B, *supra*. As will be seen, these distinctions are not entirely academic.

Generally speaking, a provision of this kind is regarded in English law as being in addition to, and not in substitution for, the common law right of any party to treat a contract as repudiated (*i.e.* to rescind the contract) for any breach of a fundamental obligation, or for conduct showing an intention no longer to be bound, on the part of the other party (both of which are really different facets of the same thing—see for the law on this, Hudson, 10th ed., pp. 340–347, 681–682, and 685–687). Despite the absence of any such expression as " without prejudice to any other rights or remedies," it is submitted that there is nothing in the wording of the contract to suggest that the rights conferred by the present clause on the Employer are intended as a substitute for his common law rights. This is important, because a large number of the matters on which this clause is conditioned will in English law also entitle the Employer to rescind the contract, with a much more flexible range of remedies available in that event.

The scheme of this clause is to create machinery whereby the Employer can continue the works to completion, either by himself or by using another contractor, and the Engineer can rule upon the final state of accounts between the Employer and the original defaulting Contractor by the issue of a single further certificate once the cost of completion is known. The contractual financial machinery (in sub-clause (4)) does nothing more, however, than award the Employer the precise damages which the law would in any event allow on a repudiation, assuming that the Employer had in fact chosen to complete the work, rather than to accept it in its abandoned or incomplete state. Before considering the clause as a whole in detail, mention should be made of a major dilemma which may face an Employer confronted with a defaulting Contractor, particularly if the default occurs in the early stages of the work. It seems very arguable that by virtue of sub-clause (4), *infra*, the Employer cannot, if he acts under this clause, seek to recover damages until the work is complete—perhaps three or four years later. Yet the damage, in the shape of the cost of completion, and perhaps even of the amount of delay likely to arise from the breach, may be more or less immediately ascertainable once a completion contract is let to a new Contractor. Again, in certain rather special circumstances an Employer may have commercially " missed the bus " with his project as a result of the Contractor's default, and for that reason may not wish to complete the works at all, though he may have suffered severe financial loss of a different kind in the abortive project. Sometimes, too, the Contractor's breaches may, in an extreme case, render completion of the permanent works in accordance with the original design physically impractical. In each of these cases the present remedy will not meet his requirements and the Employer will, under English law, need to consider using his common law remedy of rescission instead. In many other situations the Employer may wish to keep his options open and use both remedies, so that if his determination fails, for instance, on common law grounds, it can be supported on the contractual grounds (or vice versa). While this position will usually be open to him under most contracts, the unfortunate tendency to diffuse and often meaningless wording in the present form creates a serious doubt whether this perfectly reasonable position is possible. The words in question which immediately follow the words " expel the Contractor therefrom," already quoted, *supra*, are " without thereby avoiding the Contract or releasing the Contractor from any of his obligations or liabilities under the Contract or affecting the rights and powers conferred on the Employer or the Engineer by the Contract." In this context not one of these otiose words or phrases is of the slightest legal or practical assistance to the Employer or Engineer, or indeed has any intelligible legal meaning, except apparently that for some unspecified purpose the contract is " kept in being " and not " avoided." This wording can at once be fastened on as being inconsistent with the English legal concept of rescission (by which the contract is often said to be " avoided " or " treated as at an end "), and it will be argued that the Employer must, in fact, make an election between exercising the common law right of rescission and the contractual right to determine, which it will be said are mutually exclusive and inconsistent with each other. The wording supporting this argument is traditional and unchanged, but the new ground " persistently *or fundamentally in breach of* his obligations under the contract " in substitution for " persistently or flagrantly neglecting to carry out his obligations under the Contract " may even lead to a second argument that the present clause is intended to supplant the Employer's common right law of rescission altogether (since the right of rescission is often said by lawyers to arise upon a " breach of a fundamental obligation " by the other party). It is submitted, however, that this second argument is wrong—in the first place, there is another category of events which justifies rescission—conduct evincing an intention no longer to be bound—so that no special significance should be attached to the new wording—and in the second place, the fact that the contract chooses to regulate the more usual commercial course which Employers will wish to take following termination should not without express stipulation be interpreted as forbidding the taking of a less usual but perfectly permissible course, should the Employer prefer not to complete, for example.

It is also submitted that the earlier argument, based on the traditional wording, that election between the two remedies is necessary, is also wrong, because it does not take account of the real nature of an English common law rescission of a contract—under common law rescissions, effect is in fact given to many contractual provisions after rescission (*e.g.* liquidated damages provisions, the arbitration clause, and so on) and the use of expressions like " avoidance " or the contract having " gone," or being " at an end," are only generalised terms used by English lawyers to describe the effect of rescission and are not definitive terms at all—see *Heyman* v. *Darwins* [1942] A.C. 356, at pp. 374, 379 and 397–399, and Hudson, 10th ed., pp. 346–347. It will, therefore, it is submitted, be possible for an Employer who has re-entered under the contractual provision to justify his re-entry, in addition, as an acceptance of a repudiation by the Contractor, if the latter's breach or conduct would justify rescission at common law, *a fortiori* if the Employer, when giving notice under the clause, has expressed it to be without prejudice to his other rights and remedies; and there is also no inconsistency, it is submitted, in employing both remedies simultaneously if the circumstances require it. Nevertheless the failure to make it plain that the Employer's remedy under the present clause is without prejudice to other rights or remedies is symptomatic of the carelessness of the Employer's interest, already noted in the context of clause 60 (7) Proviso (a), *supra*, p. 239, for example, which is typical of the English I.C.E. conditions, and should be contrasted with the two very explicit and repeated savings for alternative remedies to be found in the Contractor's determination clause 69 in the FIDIC International Conditions (see I.C.E.C., pp. 174–175)—where the commercial necessity for the savings is far less serious, if it exists at all—and also with the superabundance of savings for the Contractor in the exercise of his potent remedy under clause 40 (2), commented on *supra*, p. 114.

A word should be said about the the nature of the right of the Contractor to occupy land belonging to the Employer under a contract for services like a civil engineering or building contract. Until very recently, the view of English law was that this right amounted to no more than a contractual licence to occupy the land for the purpose of the building project, which was terminable at will by the employer, whether or not the termination of that licence might be wrongful and expose the employer to an action for damages for breach of contract—see Hudson, 10th ed., pp. 681 and 712–714. The High Court has, however, in a decision by Megarry J., held in the case of *Twickenham Garden Developments* v. *Hounslow Borough Council* [1971] Ch. 233, where the Employer had given notice determining the contract after obtaining all the necessary certification from the architect, but the Contractor had refused to vacate the Site, that, at least in the case of the RIBA forms of building contract which were used in that case, the nature of the Contractor's interest in the land is that of a contractual licence which, while not " coupled with an interest in land," is nevertheless revocable only under the terms of the licence, and if necessary that it will be protected by injunction until the conclusion of proceedings to determine whether the revocation was valid. (This case was ultimately settled and did not go to appeal, as had been anticipated at the time of the 10th ed., of Hudson.) The practical effect of this decision, if it is correct, is that if an Employer operates or purports to operate a determination clause (or indeed, it would seem, a common law rescission) and requires the Contractor to leave the Site, the Contractor will nevertheless be permitted to remain on the Site against the Employer's will, should he wish to do so (thereby sabotaging, perhaps, the entire project from the commercial point of view of the Employer, and preventing other arrangements being made for completion of the project) in the absence of the most powerful and compelling evidence justifying an injunction altering the *status quo*. Such evidence (to the effect that the determination was in fact valid under the terms of the contract) is rarely immediately available, and can usually only be resolved by litigation involving difficult questions of fact and inevitably taking months if not years before a final decision by the last appellant tribunal is obtained. It is difficult to believe that the above decision can stand for long in England without reconsideration. It is certainly out of line with the law in, for example, Australia (see *Porter* v. *Hannah Builders* [1969] V.R. 673) and also more recently in New Zealand Mahon J., in an outstanding judgment (*Mayfield Holdings* v. *Moana Reef* [1973] 1 N.Z.L.R. 309) reviewed all the authorities in the United Kingdom and in Australia and refused to follow it. It is respectfully submitted that the *Twickenham* interpretation is not only inconsistent both with the practicalities of building or civil engineering projects and the presumed intention of the parties to that type of contract, but it also cannot be supported either by principle or by authority in England, based as it appears to have been on cases where occupation by the defendant was the principal, and not merely incidental, object of the transaction between the parties.

The decision appears to have been influenced by the " theatre " and " contractual licence " cases, but there, it is respectfully submitted, the primary purpose of the transaction is the occupancy during the promised period by the ticket-holder or licensee, whereas in a building or civil engineering contract the occupancy of the Site is entirely incidental to the principal object of the transaction, which is the construction and completion of permanent work for the Employer. Moreover the decision, if correct, means that while the Contractor may be entitled to remain on the Site, he will not be entitled to any further payment until the validity or otherwise of the determination is established, which is manifestly an absurd and impractical result. The decision also implicitly denies any sort of contractual force (even of the " temporary finality " kind already referred to in the context of interim payment and liquidated damages under clauses 47 (4) and 60 (1), *supra*, pp. 137–139 and 231–232) to the certification required in most termination clauses, including the present one. See further the critical Note on the *Twickenham* case in 87 L.Q.R. 309.

" *shall become bankrupt or . . . go into liquidation* "

A determination (together with the attendant powers of seizure and sale of plant conferred by this sub-clause) on any one of these various insolvency grounds (except possibly carrying out the contract under a committee of inspection or creditors), while perfectly good in English law against the Contractor himself, is probably void as against the trustee or liquidator as infringing a basic rule of policy of the English law of bankruptcy and insolvency. The law on this, however, is by no means free from doubt—see Hudson, 10th ed., pp. 783–788. A determination will be good against a trustee or liquidator, however, if exercised upon one of the other grounds in the clause, such as failure to maintain progress, which usually are also present in insolvency situations. The legal validity of this part of the sub-clause must, therefore, be regarded as potentially suspect.

" *shall assign the Contract without the consent . . .*"

For the meaning of this expression, see the commentary to clauses 3 and 4 of the contract, *supra*, pp. 28–29. Note that in cases of " sub-letting " a part of the works, there is a more qualified right under (e) dependent upon the certificate of the Engineer.

" *shall have an execution levied* "

Being an act of bankruptcy, this too may be a ground of determination which is void in English law as against the trustee or liquidator—see *supra.*

(*a*) " *has abandoned the Contract* "

This would, of course, be a repudiation of the contract and a ground for a common law rescission.

(*b*) " *has failed to commence the Works* "

i.e. after receipt of notification in writing under clause 41. What is needed here is the original clause 41 notification in writing, then a certificate of the Engineer, and then an Employer's seven days' notice (as to which, see the commentary, *infra*). It is an open question whether, in addition, there should be a written notice to proceed from the Engineer, or whether this latter is only required in the case of suspension of progress. The wording seems quite ambiguous as to this, and *ex abundante cautela* written notice to proceed should be given.

(*b*) " *has suspended the progress . . . for 14 days* "

Note that what is required for this ground is 14 days' written notice to proceed from the Engineer, followed by a certificate of the Engineer, followed by seven days' notice from the Employer (as to the latter, see the commentary, *infra*). Again the wording is ambiguous as to whether the absence of reasonable excuse applies to this ground. Assuming that absence of excuse applies in each case, the grounds in this paragraph would amount to a repudiation of the contract and justify a determination (*i.e.* rescission) at common law, it is submitted.

(*c*) " *condemned and rejected by the Engineer under these conditions* "

i.e. under clause 39 (1). There is a valuable and less drastic alternative remedy available to the Employer under clause 39 (2), *supra*, p. 109, however. On the wording, it is suggested this ground probably would not apply in a case under clause 49 (3) during the Maintenance Period (when a power of termination is of very limited value in any event) but the Employer has a special remedy under clause 62, *supra*, in that case, and the residual ground of determination in (d) would also probably be applicable.

(*d*) " *failing to proceed with the Works with due diligence or . . . otherwise persistently or fundamentally in breach of his obligations* "

Here again, it is impossible to say whether the requirement of previous warning applies to the first ground only, or to all the grounds mentioned. There are in fact three possible grounds here—(i) failing to proceed with due diligence (see clause 41, *supra*, for the express term), (ii) being persistently in breach or (iii) being fundamentally in breach. On the assumption that the requirement of previous warning applies to the first, (i) would probably justify a rescission at common law, since while time or due diligence obligations will not usually be "of the essence" (*i.e.* fundamental) in building and civil engineering contracts (see Hudson, 10th ed., pp. 608–612) failure to improve after sufficient notice will usually justify rescission, no doubt as evincing an intention not to be bound (see Hudson, 10th ed., pp. 611–612). So far as ground (ii) is concerned, persistent breaches, certainly if following on previous warning, would usually be conduct evincing an intention not to be bound (provided the breaches were not obviously trivial and probably this would be so without warning if the breaches were substantial) so that in either case a valid common law rescission would be justified. As to ground (iii), here one single breach could justify rescission, even without prior warning, though it would have to be extremely serious, probably of a kind such as to justify commercial loss of confidence in the Contractor, to be fundamental in this sense in the average building or civil engineering project (abandonment, though separately dealt with above, of course, is an obvious example of a fundamental breach). Broadly speaking, any breach by the Contractor which was reasonably remediable and not such as to justify a permanent loss of confidence would not be fundamental—but maladministration or defective work of a kind such as to show that the project was beyond the capacity of the Contractor would be fundamental, it is submitted.

(*d*) " *despite previous warning by the Engineer* "

This warning should, it is submitted, be of a kind that would give the Contractor an opportunity to mend his ways—the word " previous " suggests, it is submitted, previous to a repetition or continuance of the breach. However, previous warning of this kind does not seem to be appropriate to a " fundamental " breach (see the suggested definition of this, *supra*) which lends some support to the view that the " previous warning " requirement is limited to the due diligence ground.

(*e*) " *has . . . sublet any part of the Contract* "

See the commentary to clauses 3 and 4, *supra*, pp. 28–29, and also under " shall assign the Contract without consent," *supra*. The two grounds are traditional. The " to the detriment of good workmanship " ground seems unduly harsh, bearing in mind that all Sub-contractors will have to be appointed with consent. The intention probably was sub-letting *without consent* to the detriment of good workmanship.

" *7 days' notice in writing* "

For service of notice on the Contractor, see clause 68 (1), *infra*, p. 283. As pointed out, *supra*, there is an omission (presumably inadvertent) to specify a prior notice calling for proper performance of the contract in relation to some of the above grounds which might, if they stood alone, lend support to the view that the present notice might be of a warning character and could only be validly acted on if no improvement occurred during the period of the notice. It appears impossible, however, so to construe the wording, since warning notices are expressly provided for in some of the above cases, and the present notice would appear to validate the Employer's entry, simply amounting to notice to the Contractor that the Employer has finally decided to exercise his right, so placing the Contractor under the obligation immediately to make arrangements to leave the Site; so that the notice will, it is submitted, operate automatically whatever steps the Contractor might try to take to remedy the situation after receipt of it.

" *enter upon the Site and expel the Contractor therefrom without thereby involving the Contract or releasing the Contractor from any of his obligations or liabilities under the Contract or affecting the right and powers conferred on the Engineer or the Employer* "

This diffuse and unhelpful wording and the possible misleading implications of it have already been commented upon—contrast with these words the simple " shall be entitled to determine the Contract " in clause 65 (3), *infra*. It is very doubtful what (if any) significance or intention can be attached to the language used, which is probably still more evidence of the piecemeal and historical way in which the wording of the contract has grown.

" *himself complete . . . or may employ any other contractor to complete* "

In either case, of course, the Employer will often wish to take over sub-contracts, whether nominated or not. If, as is usually the case, the Contractor's solvency is also in question, sub-contractors will usually be only too pleased to carry on working for a solvent Employer. Sub-contractors frequently, however, urge that their accounts for work done prior to the re-entry should be met; in general they have no sanction to re-enforce these pleas, but sometimes (*e.g.* if pipes and specials from a nominated supplier are on very long delivery dates) there is a real sanction, since recovery of their goods from the Site (which under English law the employer could usually not prevent if the goods were not fixed—see *e.g. Edward L. Bateman Ltd.* v. *Eric Reid Ltd.* [1964] 4 S.A.L.R. 151, Hudson, 10th ed., p. 658), or refusal to deliver goods fabricated and ready for delivery without assurance of payment, could severely jeopardise completion. The absence of any power to pay direct for any pre-determination work and deduct or recover from the Contractor was, therefore, a serious omission in the Fourth Edition, because the Employer in such circumstances would not be able to comply with the only express power in the contract to pay direct—in clause 59C, *supra*, p. 223 (which in any event only applies to *nominated* Sub-contractors)—because that clause only applies when a further payment under clause 60 of the conditions is about to be certified. The present clause, of course, prohibits any further certification of payment until completion by the new contractor. As already explained, an Employer who pays a Sub-contractor direct in respect of sums owing by the main Contractor without an applicable express power may be unable even to prove in a main Contractor's liquidation or bankruptcy for such sums—see Hudson, pp. 769–772, and 791–792—nor could he generally expect to recover payments for pre-determination work as part of the cost of completing the work under the present clause or as damages for breach of contract. The new right to assignment of sub-contracts under sub-clause (2), *if it can be successfully invoked*, will in such cases render an express power to pay direct unnecessary, however, it is submitted—see *infra*, p. 254. Nevertheless a separate power to pay direct on termination, as in the RIBA forms, would have been a most desirable protection of the Employer's interest, to cover cases where difficulty in effecting the assignment is met —see the further commentary, *infra*.

" *may use . . . the Constructional Plant Temporary Works and materials* "

There is no reason to suppose that exercise of the two present powers over Constructional Plant etc. will not be valid against the Contractor's trustee or liquidator, or indeed any other later claimant whose title is derived from the Contractor, unless the determination is held to have been invalid as being based on one of the bankruptcy grounds (possibly invalid in such a case for reasons of public policy, see the commentary, *supra*, p. 249) or unless (in the case of goods and materials only and not plant) the statutory doctrine of reputed ownership (which applies in a personal bankruptcy only and not in the case of a company liquidation) enables the trustee in bankruptcy to defeat the Employer's claim (for this subject, see Hudson, 10th ed., pp. 783–791, and see the commentary to clause 53, *supra*, pp. 170–171).

" *the Employer may at any time sell* "

The provisions for revesting in the Contractor on completion in clause 53 (7), *supra*, p. 173, are expressly made subject to the present power of sale in the event of a re-entry under the present clause. The power is, of course, most valuable in cases where the Contractor is insolvent and will be effective to the same extent as the power of user commented on, *supra*.

" *due to him from the Contractor under the Contract* "

i.e. under sub-clause (4), *infra*, p. 255.

Assignment to Employer

(2) By the said notice or by further notice in writing within 14 days of the date thereof the Engineer may require the Contractor to assign to the Employer and if so required the Contractor shall forthwith assign to the Employer the benefit of any agreement for the supply of any goods or materials and/or for the execution of any work for the purposes of this Contract which the Contractor may have entered into.

This sub-clause is new. There seems no reason why, particularly if accompanied by an undertaking in damages, specific performance should not be ordered to enforce this obligation, nor why it should not be enforceable against the Contractor's trustee or liquidator. Since an assignee takes subject to all equities (see Hudson, 10th ed., pp. 725 and 731–734) the Employer will become liable to the Sub-contractor for unpaid moneys due, or even damages for previous breaches of the sub-contract by the main Contractor, which may well have occurred in typical re-entry circumstances. Assignment will therefore automatically carry a right to pay direct, any such sums being recoverable in turn from the main Contractor as part of the cost of completion under sub-clause (4), *infra*. But, as pointed out, *supra*, it is again symptomatic of the carelessness of the Employer's interest evident in clause 63 as a whole that a power to pay direct is not available, as in the RIBA forms, to cover determination cases —the Employer might well wish to negotiate with a Sub-contractor, had he such a power, without exposing himself to all equities by taking an assignment, and also might need to fall back on the power if a valid assignment could not be effected for any reason. The restriction of the period for requiring the assignment to 14 days is, it should be noted, somewhat short and will require a swift appraisal of the situation by the Employer's advisers. "The said notice," incidentally, appears to relate to *the Employer's* 7 day notice under clause 63 (1), so that the present reference to *the Engineer* appears to be, in part at least, *per incuriam*.

Valuation at Date of Forfeiture

(3) The Engineer shall as soon as may be practicable after any such entry and expulsion by the Employer fix and determine *ex parte* or by or after reference to the parties or after such investigation or enquiries as he may think fit to make or institute and shall certify what amount (if any) had at the time of such entry and expulsion been reasonably earned by or would reasonably accrue to the Contractor in respect of work then actually done by him under the Contract and what was the value of any unused or partially used goods and materials any Constructional Plant and any Temporary Works which have been deemed to become the property of the Employer under Clauses 53 and 54.

The valuation and certificate called for by this sub-clause (which is traditional) do not appear to have any practical consequence or any real bearing on the ultimate financial position of the parties, since the calculation required by sub-clause (4), *infra* (and indeed by ordinary legal principles; see Hudson, 10th ed., pp. 585 *et seq.*), is a comparison of the entire actual cost of completion by the Employer (*i.e.* payment made to the Contractor up to re-entry and to other contractors etc. thereafter) against the theoretical cost of the whole work under the terms of the original contract. The purpose of the present (partial) valuation and certificate therefore remains wholly obscure, unless it is ntended to protect the position in case a determination should be held to be unjustified, but this seems unlikely, and unnecessarily complimentary to the foresight and interest of the traditional draftsman or those instructing him. Ironically, the value of the work done at the time of the termination could only be relevant if the Employer was *not* intending to complete the work (for which the present clause makes no provision—see the commentary to sub-clause (1), *supra*, p. 246, and to sub-clause (4), *infra*). Nor is a really accurate valuation likely to be possible when the work is incomplete—in so far as the work is partially complete, it can in many cases be valued at contract rates only after a degree of physical measurement quite unnecessary if the whole works, or completed sections, are complete, when measurement will often, under the rules of a standard method, be a matter of calculation rather than measurement (see the commentary to clauses 56 and 57, *supra*). In addition, the extent or proportion of the allocation of " preliminary items " to partially completed work must invariably be a matter of judgment and opinion. This is not to say that an inventory of the current state of progress at the time of entry is not highly desirable in the Employer's interests, from the evidentiary point of view as showing slow progress since previous valuations, or relative to the contract as a whole, in cases where the re-entry is based on failure to proceed with the works with due diligence, or, of course, in a case where the Employer does not wish to complete the project at all (in which case, as pointed out, *supra*, he will have to rely on his common law right of rescission and not the right of re-entry under the present clause).

Payment after Forfeiture

(4) If the Employer shall enter and expel the Contractor under this Clause he shall not be liable to pay to the Contractor any money on account of the Contract until the expiration of the Period of Maintenance and thereafter until the costs of completion and maintenance damages for delay in completion (if any) and all other expenses incurred by the Employer have been ascertained and the amount thereof certified by the Engineer. The Contractor shall then be entitled to receive only such sum or sums (if any) as the Engineer may certify would have been due to him upon due completion by him after deducting the said amount. But if such amount shall exceed the sum which would have been payable to the Contractor on due completion by him then the Contractor shall upon demand pay to the Employer the amount of such excess and it shall be deemed a debt due by the Contractor to the Employer and shall be recoverable accordingly.

While this sub-clause does not in terms say that the Employer is himself barred from seeking to recover any of his losses from the Contractor until the final ascertainment and certification after the expiry of the maintenance period, it seems the only possible consequence and interpretation of the sub-clause as a whole, notwithstanding the valuation called for in sub-clause (3). Mention has already been made of the serious disadvantage under which this may place an Employer when the contract period is lengthy and the Contractor's solvency in doubt, particularly, for instance, if the Contractor has never started work at all, or the abandoned work is in its early stages, so that the " cost of completion " damages can be rapidly ascertained as soon as a completion contract is put out to tender and let. As stated in the commentary under sub-clause (3), *supra*, a valuation under that sub-clause would at once become relevant to the parties' requirements if the Employer was indeed free to proceed against the Contractor immediately without completing the work.

" *he shall not be liable to pay to the Contractor any money on account of the Contract* "

i.e. no money will be due, it is submitted, if there is an outstanding interim certificate in favour of the Contractor at the time of the re-entry, or if one were (wrongly) issued by the Engineer subsequently thereto.

" *cost of completion* "

These words are fairly wide, and might possibly be held to cover direct payments to Sub-contractors for pre-re-entry work if it could be shown that such payments were unavoidable and made under pressure in order to secure completion at reasonable cost or to mitigate delay—but on the facts this is likely to be difficult to establish. See further on this the commentary to sub-clause (2), *supra.*

" *damages for delay in completion* "

The better view in English law under most forms of contractual wording is that this would include any liquidated damages accrued due at the date of re-entry, but thereafter the Employer would have to establish his damage in the ordinary way. For the reasons for this, see Hudson, 10th ed., pp. 633–635. However, this is an uncertain subject without authority in the United Kingdom, and the express mention of damages for delay in the present clause, coupled with only one method for computing those damages in the contract (in clause 47), might lead to a contrary interpretation.

" *all other expenses incurred by the Employer* "

This expression needs to be construed, it is submitted, as meaning expenses which would be recoverable as damages for breach of contract under the ordinary rules of remoteness—see Hudson, 10th ed., Chapter 9.

FRUSTRATION

Payment in Event of Frustration

64. In the event of the Contract being frustrated whether by war or by any other supervening event which may occur independently of the will of the parties the sum payable by the Employer to the Contractor in respect of the work executed shall be the same as that which would have been payable under Clause 65 (5) if the Contract had been determined by the Employer under Clause 65.

This clause is not new, apart from the words " or by any other supervening event which may occur independently of the will of the parties," which probably adds nothing to the earlier provision. For the law of frustration generally, including the effect of the statutory provisions of the Law Reform (Frustrated Contracts) Act 1943, and the extreme rarity of the situations in which the doctrine can be invoked in the case of building or engineering contracts, see Hudson, 10th ed., at pp. 348–360 and also at pp. 267–273. See also the commentaries on clause 13 (1), *supra*, pp. 47–48, clause 20 (1), *supra*, p. 65, and clause 51, *supra*, pp. 155–156. See also pp. 36–37 and 40–41.

Alternative possible remedies, in a situation of practical difficulty in completing the work may be available under clause 40 (2), *supra*, p. 110 (where the work or a part of it is suspended for a period exceeding three months), or under clause 65, *infra*, where an outbreak of war has occurred.

" *the same as that . . . payable under Clause 65 (5)* "

i.e. a sensible mixture of payment at contract rates, where it is reasonable or fair to apply them, and in certain cases where it is not, on the basis of cost. This is, however, a careless or " loose " reference since, while clause 65 (5) (d) in fact incorporates clause 65 (6) (b) (c) and (d), it seems doubtful if these latter provisions can apply for the purpose of the present clause if the cause of the frustration is not war or the consequence of war, since these paragraphs of the later sub-clause are, by virtue of their language, expressly related to the consequences of war and not other possible causes of frustration—see the commentary, *infra*, pp. 253–259. There is, incidentally, concealed in what appears to be a fluctuations clause in clause 65 (clause 65 (6) (d)) a general indemnity of the widest possible scope which should be particularly borne in mind when considering the financial implications of clause 65.

WAR CLAUSE

Works to Continue for 28 Days on Outbreak of War

65. (1) If during the currency of the Contract there shall be an outbreak of war (whether war is declared or not) in which Great Britain shall be engaged on a scale involving general mobilisation of the armed forces of the Crown the Contractor shall for a period of 28 days reckoned from midnight on the date that the order for general mobilisation is given continue so far as is physically possible to execute the Works in accordance with the Contract.

This clause follows virtually without change the clause in the Fourth Edition, except for the purely consequential reference to the (post-1954) " Contract Price Fluctuations Clause " in sub-clause (6) (c). This latter optional clause was first published in March 1973 for use with the Fourth Edition, and republished in June 1973 for use with the present Edition, (and is commented on *infra*, p. 292). The policy of the present clause as a whole is clearly based on the assumption that there may be no variation of price clause in the contract, and that the main interest of the Contractor arising from an outbreak of war is to protect himself against a run-away wage and price inflation. On the other hand, the Employer may, for commercial or other reasons, not wish to complete the project, and accordingly is given a right to determine the contract on suitable terms under sub-clause (3). The clause differentiates between contracts where the works can and cannot be brought to the stage of being " usable by the Employer " within 28 days of the outbreak of war. If they can be, under sub-clause (2) the Contractor is bound to carry on until substantial completion, but then may elect to opt out of his maintenance obligations after that date, subject to deductions, at outbreak of war prices only, for any maintenance work which the Employer has to do and for which the Contractor would otherwise have been liable under the contract. If he opts to carry out the maintenance work, it is possible that he may not be held to his contract prices either, but this depends on the difficult question, arising on the wording, whether sub-clause (6) applies to a sub-clause (2) contract—as to this see the commentary to sub-clause (6), *infra.*

If the works are not at this " usable " stage, *the Employer* is by sub-clause (3) given the right, if he wishes, to determine the contract, and sub-clauses (4) and (5) are concerned with the financial and other arrangements in that event which are, broadly speaking, on a sensible part-contract and part-*quantum meruit* basis. If the Employer decides to continue, sub-clause (6) gives the Contractor protection by transferring war damage of every kind and consequential claims by third persons from the Contractor's area of risk to the Employer's (probably unnecessarily, at least in the case of the Works, because such damage is already so transferred under clause 20 (2)), and also by special " fluctuations " or variation of price clauses to cover price *or cost* increases of virtually every kind attributable to the outbreak of war (sub-clause (6) (c) and (d)).

In addition to the doubt whether the financial provisions of sub-clause (6) apply in a case where the contract is completed or the Works are usable within 28 days of the outbreak of war, and so cannot be terminated, there are two further oddities about this clause, namely, first, that the remedies in regard to damage to the Works in sub-clause (6) (a) apply to a group of situations such as civil war or insurrection, for example, which are considerably wider than the war as defined in sub-clause (1), upon which nevertheless the sub-clause (6) remedies are expressly made to depend. The matter makes even less sense because damage to the works in the identical list of situations mentioned in sub-clause (6) (a) are already Excepted Risks under clause 20 (3), and perhaps should be regarded as an example of the inconsistencies to which the piecemeal historical development of this contract can give rise. Secondly, and far more importantly, it should be appreciated that within what is apparently a minor tax-fluctuations clause provision in sub-clause (6) (d) there is in fact an indemnity against *any increase in* the *cost* of the Works to the Contractor (as also a right to a decrease) in any way attributable to or consequent on the outbreak of the war. The scope of this indemnity is so wide as to make unnecessary many of the more particular protections which are worked out for the Contractor in other parts of the clause.

In addition to all these remedies, clause 64, *supra*, ensures that the Contractor can, in appropriate circumstances, claim that the contract has been frustrated by war if the difficulties of completion become insurmountable. In that event, if his claim is upheld, he will be entitled to cease work on the contract, and his financial position will be regulated under the terms of the present clause—see the commentary, *supra*, p. 257. (That clause, however, also applies the valuation rules in the present clause to *non-war* frustrating events, and there must be a real doubt as to the applicability of some of the rules for compensation of the Contractor in the present clause which are expressly conditioned on war consequences—see the commentary to clause 64, *supra*.) The Contractor also has the substantial protection, if the Works have to be suspended for any length of time on the order of the Engineer, of the remedy available to him under clause 40 (2), *supra*, p. 110.

Effect of Completion Within 28 Days

(2) If at any time before the expiration of the said period of 28 days the Works shall have been completed or completed so far as to be usable all provisions of the Contract shall continue to have full force and effect save that:—

(a) the Contractor shall in lieu of fulfilling his obligations under Clauses 49 and 50 be entitled at his option to allow against the sum due to him under the provisions hereof the cost (calculated at the prices ruling at the beginning of the said period of 28 days) as certified by the Engineer at the expiration of the Period of Maintenance of repair rectification and making good any work for the repair rectification or making good of which the Contractor would have been liable under the said Clauses had they continued to be applicable;

(b) the Employer shall not be entitled at the expiration of the Period of Maintenance to withhold payment under Clause 60 (5) (c) of the second half of the retention money or any part thereof except such sum as may be allowable by the Contractor under the provisions of the last preceding paragraph which sum may (without prejudice to any other mode of recovery thereof) be deducted by the Employer from such second half.

" *completed . . . so far as to be usable* "

For the policy of this sub-clause see the commentary, *supra*. " Completed " means substantially completed under clause 48, it is submitted. " So far as to be usable " may, of course, be short of such substantial completion in many contracts—as *e.g.* where landscaping or finishing work remains to be done (though see the commentary to clause 48, *supra*, where it is suggested that the commercial effectiveness of the permanent work is probably the best test of substantial completion in a doubtful case).

(*a*) " *in lieu of fulfilling his obligations under Clauses 49 and 50* "

These words, coupled with the fact that the other provisions of the contract are to have full force and effect, mean that if substantial completion under clause 48 has not been achieved despite the " usability " of the Works, the Contractor must carry on and achieve it. Assuming, too, that a certificate under clause 48 was given while outstanding work remained to be done, the Contractor would be bound to complete that work in accordance with the written undertaking in that clause, unless he availed himself of the option in the present clause.

(*a*) " *against the sum due to him under the provisions hereof* "

i.e. against the overall contract sum, including the additional payments which may become due under sub-clause (6), *infra*. This paragraph indicates that the time for the allowance in (a) to be made will be at the end of the Maintenance Period when the Engineer should usually be in a position to estimate the cost of the necessary repairs.

(*a*) " (*calculated at the prices ruling at the beginning of the said period*) "

That is to say, inflation from the time of general mobilisation is, in regard to work of maintenance, at the risk of the Employer if the Contractor chooses to exercise his option. (It may also be so even if the Contractor opts to do the work, but this depends on whether sub-clause (6), *infra*, applies to a sub-clause (2) contract—see the commentary, *infra*, p. 262.)

Right of Employer to Determine Contract

(3) If the Works shall not have been completed as aforesaid the Employer shall be entitled to determine the Contract (with the exception of this Clause and Clauses 66 and 68) by giving notice in writing to the Contractor at any time after the aforesaid period of 28 days has expired and upon such notice being given the Contract shall (except as above mentioned) forthwith determine but without prejudice to the claims of either party in respect of any antecedent breach thereof.

Removal of Plant on Determination

(4) If the Contract shall be determined under the provisions of the last preceding sub-clause the Contractor shall with all reasonable despatch remove from the Site all his Constructional Plant and shall give facilities to his sub-contractors to remove similarly all Constructional Plant belonging to them and in the event of any failure so to do the Employer shall have the like powers as are contained in Clause 53 (8) in regard to failure to remove Constructional Plant on completion of the Works but subject to the same condition as is contained in Clause 53 (9).

Payment on Determination

(5) If the Contract shall be determined as aforesaid the Contractor shall be paid by the Employer (insofar as such amounts or items shall not have been already covered by payment on account made to the Contractor) for all work executed prior to the date of determination at the rates and prices provided in the Contract and in addition:—

(a) the amounts payable in respect of any preliminary items so far as the work or service comprised therein has been carried out or performed and a proper proportion as certified by the Engineer of any such items the work or service comprised in which has been partially carried out or performed;

(b) the cost of materials or goods reasonably ordered for the Works which shall have been delivered to the Contractor or of which the Contractor is legally liable to accept delivery (such materials or goods becoming the property of the Employer upon such payment being made by him);

(c) a sum to be certified by the Engineer being the amount of any expenditure reasonably incurred by the Contractor in the expectation of completing the whole of the Works in so far as such expenditure shall not have been covered by the payments in this sub-clause before mentioned;

(d) any additional sum payable under sub-clause (6) (b) (c) and (d) of this Clause;

(e) the reasonable cost of removal under sub-clause (4) of this Clause.

As stated, the Employer is given a discretionary power to determine the contract if the works are not " usable " within 28 days of the outbreak of war. It should be noted that the power appears to be exercisable at any time at the unfettered discretion of the Employer. The (traditional) words (" with the exception of this Clause and Clauses 66 and 68 ") in sub-clause (3) are strictly unnecessary (compare the far more tortuous and complicated wording of clause 63 (1), *supra*, p. 245) since the law gives effect to all appropriate provisions of a contract, even after rescission or determination, if they appear intended to cover the position at that time—see Hudson, 10th ed., pp. 346–347—though the reference is not without use in drawing attention to the clauses in question. The words " but subject to the same condition as is contained in Clause 53 (9) hereof " in sub-clause (4) are also strictly unnecessary for the same reason, and mean that accidental damage to the Contractor's plant not due to war or the other Excepted Risks under clause 20 is at the risk of the Contractor and not the Employer. The wording of these three clauses is on the whole well considered and calls for no comment. Sub-clause (5) in effect spells out in accurate detail a sensible mixture of contractual and reasonable remuneration which, where possible with fairness to the Contractor, ties him down to his contract prices, but in other cases awards him costs reasonably incurred by him. Here again, the very wide-ranging indemnity concealed within the apparent fluctuations-style provision in sub-clause (6) (d) should, however, be borne in mind. Paragraph (c) is also an obvious important potential residual category of claim from the Contractor's point of view.

Provisions to Apply as from Outbreak of War

(6) Whether the Contract shall be determined under the provisions of sub-clause (3) of this Clause or not the following provisions shall apply or be deemed to have applied as from the date of the said outbreak of war notwithstanding anything expressed in or implied by the other terms of the Contract *viz*:—

(a) The Contractor shall be under no liability whatsoever whether by way of indemnity or otherwise for or in respect of damage to the Works or to property (other than property of the Contractor or property hired by him for the purposes of executing the Works) whether of the Employer or of third parties or for or in respect of injury or loss of life to persons which is the consequence whether direct or indirect of war hostilities (whether war has been declared or not) invasion act of the Queen's enemies civil war rebellion revolution insurrection military or usurped power and the Employer shall indemnify the Contractor against all such liabilities and against all claims demands proceedings damages costs charges and expenses whatsoever arising thereout or in connection therewith.

(b) If the Works shall sustain destruction or any damage by reason of any of the causes mentioned in the last preceding paragraph the Contractor shall nevertheless be entitled to payment for any part of the Works so destroyed or damaged and the Contractor shall be entitled to be paid by the Employer the cost of making good any such destruction or damage so far as may be required by the Engineer or as may be necessary for the completion of the Works on a cost basis plus such profit as the Engineer may certify to be reasonable.

The opening words of this sub-clause raise a difficulty. Do they mean " whether the contract, being a contract subject to determination under sub-clause (3), is determined under that clause or not," or do they mean what they literally appear to say (*i.e.* that they apply as well in the case of a contract not qualifying for a determination under sub-clause (3) at all because of completion, or completion so as to be " usable," within 28 days of the outbreak of war, but where the Contractor has opted to carry out his maintenance obligations, perhaps more than a year after the outbreak of war)? If treated at their face value, the fluctuations clauses and wide indemnities contained in the later paragraphs (c) and (d), *infra*, appear to render unnecessary, at least from the point of view of price, the entitlement of and machinery for the Contractor to opt out of his maintenance obligations under sub-clause (2). Against this literal view, it seems illogical that a Contractor whose contract was nearly complete at the outbreak of war should be able to opt out of his maintenance obligations, while a Contractor whose contract still had some time to run could be held to them, unless in the one case the Contractor was not, and in the other was, entitled to the benefit of a comprehensive fluctuations clause. It is difficult to resist the conclusion that the draftsman only intended the present sub-clause to apply to sub-clause (3) contracts which had not yet been determined, but the language is not on its face so restricted.

Paragraphs (a) and (b) transfer the risks of third party claims and of damage to the Permanent Works and Temporary Works (see the definition of " the Works " in clause 1 (1) (l), *supra*, pp. 16, 21) but not (unlike the Fourth Edition), damage to unfixed materials. In the case of damage to the Permanent Works and Temporary Works, as opposed to third party claims, this is strictly unnecessary, since war etc. would appear to be adequately covered by the various " Excepted Risks " in clause 20 (3), *supra*, p. 66. It should also be noted that damage to Constructional Plant is not mentioned in the present paragraphs, any more than in clause 20, and accordingly it would appear to be at the Contractor's risk whatever the cause of damage (again in spite of clause 53 (9), *supra*, p. 175, which appears to assume the opposite when referring to the present clause). However, the Contractor will no doubt recoup his loss successfully by making use of the wide-ranging indemnity concealed within the fluctuations-style provisions of paragraph (d), *infra*.

Another most odd and indeed anomalous feature of this sub-clause is that a number of the risks referred to in paragraph (a) are obviously wider in extent and of lesser gravity than " war " as defined in sub-clause (1). What the wording appears to envisage is that if, for example, a war occurs as defined in sub-clause (1) during the currency of the contract, then a subsequent " revolution insurrection etc.", however unconnected with the war, is to confer the special rights and obligations of the present sub-clause, but not otherwise (*i.e.* if there is no " war " as defined). In other words, a Contractor seeking to rely on an event defined in paragraph (a) must *also* prove a war as defined in sub-clause (1) in order to be entitled to the remedies of the sub-clause. There seems to be no logic or sense to this and, as stated *supra*, the matter is compounded by the overlap of paragraph (a) with the provisions of clause 20 and the identical list of Excepted Risks there contained. It is difficult to believe that the wording represents any policy intention, and it would seem to be the result of some past mistakes of draftsmanship, no doubt due to fortuitous additions to earlier wording.

> (c) In the event that the Contract includes the Contract Price Fluctuations Clause the terms of that Clause shall continue to apply but if subsequent to the outbreak of war the index figures therein referred to shall cease to be published or in the event that the contract shall not include a Price Fluctuations Clause in that form the following paragraph shall have effect:—
>
> If under decision of the Civil Engineering Construction Conciliation Board or of any other body recognised as an appropriate body for regulating the rates of wages in any trade or industry other than the Civil Engineering Construction Industry to which Contractors undertaking works of civil engineering construction give effect by agreement or in practice or by reason of any Statute or Statutory Instrument there shall during the currency of the Contract be any increase or decrease in the wages or the rates of wages or in the allowances or rates of allowances (including allowances in respect of holidays) payable to or in respect of labour of any kind prevailing at the date of outbreak of war as then fixed by the said Board or such other body as aforesaid or by Statute or Statutory Instrument or any increase in the amount payable by the Contractor by virtue or in respect of any Scheme of State Insurance or if there shall be any increase or decrease in the cost prevailing at the date of the said outbreak of war of any materials consumable stores fuel or power (and whether for permanent or temporary works) which increase or increases decrease or decreases shall result in an increase or decrease of cost to the Contractor in carrying out the Works the net increase or decrease of cost shall form an addition or deduction as the case may be to or from the Contract Price and be paid to or allowed by the Contractor accordingly.

The reference in the opening words of this paragraph to " the Contract Price Fluctuations Clause " is not explained in the Conditions themselves, but the external cover of the Standard Form (almost certainly not strictly admissible) indicates that " available as a loose-leaf clause for use in appropriate cases is the Contract Price Fluctuations Clause (first issued on 29th March 1973 and revised June 1973) issued to replace the Variation of Price (Labour and Materials) Clause." This index-based clause is in fact included and commented on under clause 72, *infra*, p. 292. The proposed variation of price or fluctuations clause sketched out in the present sub-clause is, of course, extraordinarily wide. Commentary on it in such hypothetical circumstances cannot be of much value, but attention can be drawn to the fact that in this fluctuations clause it is " increase or decrease of *cost* to the Contractor in carrying out the Work " which is the basis of adjustment of the contract price, not specific increases in wage rates of labour or materials prices—so, for instance, an increase indirectly causing an increase in cost elsewhere—*e.g.* in a bonus scheme if it is contractually governed by changes in wage-rates—can be recoverable on the wording, it is submitted (see, however, in this context the recent House of Lords decision, on the very different wording of the RIBA fluctuations clause, in *William Sindall Ltd.* v. *N.W. Thames Regional Health Authority* [1977] I.C.R. 294, (1977) 4 B.L.R. 151, which held that additional bonus payments governed by increases in current wage rates were not recoverable).

(d) If the cost of the Works to the Contractor shall be increased or decreased by reason of the provisions of any Statute or Statutory Instrument or other Government or Local Government Order or Regulation becoming applicable to the Works after the date of the said outbreak of war or by reason of any trade or industrial agreement entered into after such date to which the Civil Engineering Construction Conciliation Board or any other body as aforesaid is party or gives effect or by reason of any amendment of whatsoever nature of the Working Rule Agreement of the said Board or of any other body as aforesaid or by reason of any other circumstance or thing attributable to or consequent on such outbreak of war such increase or decrease of cost as certified by the Engineer shall be reimbursed by the Employer to the Contractor or allowed by the Contractor as the case may be.

This paragraph has at first sight the appearance of a fluctuations clause similar to those now common in the U.K. as a response to increasing governmental interference on an ad hoc basis in matters directly affecting the economics of long-term contracts. The present sub-clause is, of course, traditional, and for that reason its probable almost total overlap (in so far as it is indeed a fluctuations clause of this kind) with clause 69, only recently added to the Standard Forms in the present Edition, has probably been overlooked. In this particular context it should be noted that the statute etc. must be " applicable to the Works "—not to the industry, it is submitted, or to Employers generally (contrast the key provision in clause 69, *infra*, " payable by the Contractor in respect of his work-people ").

However, concealed within the wording is an indemnity of the widest possible effect—" If the cost of the Works to the Contractor shall be increased . . . by reason of . . . any other circumstance or thing attributable to or consequent on such outbreak of war, such increase or decrease shall be reimbursed . . . or allowed . . . ." This would appear to be a perfectly general indemnity against *any* financial consequence of a war or its consequences upon the contract, and as already indicated, gives the appearance of an excess of caution to the various more detailed provisions in the present clause designed to protect the Contractor in the event of a war occurring during the contract. For the ambiguity as to whether this wide indemnity is available in the case of all contracts following on an outbreak of war, or only in the case of those contracts determinable under sub-clause (3), see the commentary to sub-clause (1), *supra*, p. 258, and to sub-clause (6) (a) *supra*, p. 262.

(e) Damage or injury caused by the explosion whenever occurring of any mine bomb shell grenade or other projectile missile or munition of war and whether occurring before or after the cessation of hostilities shall be deemed to be the consequence of any of the events mentioned in sub-clause (6) (a) of this Clause.

This extension is quite important, since it clearly includes " accidental " or " practice " damage caused by friendly forces as well as damage in the course of hostilities. There is no other reference, incidentally, to the effect of a cessation of hostilties.

SETTLEMENT OF DISPUTES

Settlement of Disputes—Arbitration

66. (1) If any dispute or difference of any kind whatsoever shall arise between the Employer and the Contractor in connection with or arising out of the Contract carrying out of the Works including any dispute as to any decision opinion instruction direction certificate or valuation of the Engineer (whether during the progress of the Works or after their completion and whether before or after the determination abandonment or breach of the Contract) it shall be referred to and settled by the Engineer who shall state his decision in writing and give notice of the same to the Employer and the Contractor. Unless the Contract shall have been already determined or abandoned the Contractor shall in every case continue to proceed with the Works with all due diligence and he shall give effect forthwith to every such decision of the Engineer unless and until the same shall be revised by an arbitrator as hereinafter provided. Such decisions shall be final and binding upon the Contractor and the Employer unless either of them shall require that the matter be referred to arbitration as hereinafter provided. If the Engineer shall fail to give such decision for a period of 3 calendar months after being requested to do so or if either the Employer or the Contractor be dissatisfied with any such decision of the Engineer then and in any such case either the Employer or the Contractor may within 3 calendar months after receiving notice of such decision or within 3 calendar months after the expiration of the said period of 3 months (as the case may be) require that the matter shall be referred to the arbitration of a person to be agreed upon between the parties or (if the parties fail to appoint an arbitrator within one calendar month of either party serving on the other party a written notice to concur in the appointment of an arbitrator) a person to be appointed on the application of either party by the President for the time being of the Institution of Civil Engineers. If an arbitrator declines the appointment or after appointment is removed by order of a competent court or is incapable of acting or dies and the parties do not within one calendar month of the vacancy arising fill the vacancy then the President for the time being of the Institution of Civil Engineers may on the application of either party appoint an arbitrator to fill the vacancy.

(For convenience, only a part of sub-clause (1) is set out above, and the remaining parts of set out in further stages, *infra*.)

One important change in the Fifth Edition version of this clause resolves a major ambiguity in the old clause in the Fourth Edition, namely whether the Engineer's preliminary decision is to be permanently final, if not " appealed " in time, or only until the end of the work—see B.C.F., p. 449, where the view was expressed that the bar only operated until completion, but see now the third sentence of the present clause, which expressly provides that the decision will be *permanently binding* if notice of arbitration is not given in the stipulated time. The present clause in addition contains slight but significant changes of wording which, allied to the change already mentioned, make it necessary to decide whether the clause is now in the form known to lawyers as a " *Scott* v. *Avery* " clause, under which an award of an arbitrator is an essential prerequisite to an action in the courts (or alternatively is of a kind where a time limit for making a claim or giving notice of arbitration is interpreted as precluding both an action in the courts as well as arbitration, subject to the court's statutory right to extend time under s. 27 of the Arbitration Act 1950).

The new clause (see *infra*, p. 275) also confers far wider powers upon the President of the Institution of Civil Engineers, one of which, which seems undesirable in principle, enables him at his discretion actually to compel the parties, possibly against the wishes of one or both of them, to adopt *whatever may be the current version at the date of the appointment* of a set of procedural rules to be published by the Institution from time to time—indeed though the wording is ambiguous, it suggests that the President could even modify or amend those rules at his discretion when giving such a direction. Whether this is so or not, it would be interesting to know on what principles the President proposes to exercise a discretion to compel an arbitrator and the parties to follow rules, in so far as they may depart from procedures which would otherwise be available on established legal principles in an ordinary arbitration, and of which the parties could have no knowledge at the time of contracting. No such objection, of course, can be taken to an agreement to abide by the rules *current at the date of the contract*).

In other respects there is no material departure from the earlier edition, and in particular the major ambiguities about the matters where early arbitration will be permitted still remain unresolved (see sub-clause (2), *infra*).

Apart from its unusual complication, the elaborate " two-tier " structure for settlement of disputes is in very many cases in practice, particularly where the dispute is primarily a financial claim by one side or the other, so unsuited to the parties' requirements that they are frequently constrained into circumventing it by agreement. As it stands, this structure is more often than not used tactically by one party or the other as a stalling device, and certainly does not appear, in the U.K. at least, to lead to resolution of disputes. Although, of course, a dispute can be referred to the Engineer by the Employer, this, when it occurs, will in practice often be after Final Certificate (*e.g.* for an indemnity on receipt of a third party claim)—prior to that the Employer will *usually* be in a position to deduct (see the commentary to clause 60 (1), *supra*, pp. 230–232 as to the right to do so), so that the Contractor will often be the party wishing to initiate the reference—*e.g.* of a disputed claim by the Contractor, or because of a disputed deduction by the Employer. It should be noted that *it is the Contractor only* who is required to give effect to the decision of the Engineer until review by an arbitrator, by virtue of the second sentence of the present sub-clause.

On the other hand, the wording of sub-clause (2) indicates that it will be the Contractor rather than the Employer who will be entitled to " early arbitration " under that sub-clause. The " two-tier " system's justification undoubtedly lies in the fact that many matters of dispute need rapid *temporary* resolution on Site—*e.g.* disputes as to the reasonableness of a nomination, as to removal of Contractor's plant from the Site, as to the adequacy of the Contractor's agent or employees, as to the justification for termination of a nominated sub-contract (see the further reference to these matters under sub-clause (2), *infra*, p. 277)—and the remedies available in arbitration or the courts may be too slow or unsuitable. In these sorts of situation there is much to be said for a system of day-to-day control by the Engineer, but the contract would do better to identify these points specifically rather than to provide for an Engineer's decision in every single case of dispute. In fact, no provision appears in practice to cause greater anxiety to Engineers, who not infrequently feel obliged to take independent counsel's opinion as to their duties under this part of the present clause, and who find the task of administering the contract impeded by the apparent necessity to analyse questions of liability and quantum in great detail before the end of the work in order to state (and often, quite unnecessarily as it happens, give reasons for) their decision, notwithstanding that nothing they decide will have any finality if either party is dissatisfied with it. In fact in the great majority of cases simply involving financial claims the reference to the Engineer is little more than an irritating and time-wasting formality, since his decision is likely to be a foregone conclusion, having previously been indicated to the Contractor or Employer when the claim was first advanced and the dispute arose (a " dispute " in this context means a rejection of a claim or contention put forward by the other party—see *Monmouth C.C.* v. *Costelloe and Kample* (1965) 63 L.G.R. 429, *per* Mocatta J. (overruled in the C.A. on other grounds)).

Furthermore, the clause as a whole appears to have been drafted without any recognition of the difficulties to which it may give rise when proceedings in the courts seem desirable rather than arbitration, or when there seems to be no dispute—this will be all the worse, of course, if the clause is held to be of the *Scott* v. *Avery* kind (as to which see *infra*, pp. 269–272). If it is, firstly, Order 14 proceedings in the High Court for summary judgment (placing the onus on the defendant to disclose a valid prima facie defence on affidavit if a stay for arbitration or leave to defend are to be obtained and speedy judgment is to be avoided) will not be available even where there seems to be no dispute; and, secondly, one of the powerful practical reasons for keeping a dispute in the High Court—namely the tripartite nature of the dispute and the involvement of a third party, which is, of course, a commonplace of building and civil engineering disputes—will be of no avail, so that the great advantages of High Court third-party procedure in keeping down costs, increasing the speed of proceedings, and avoiding the possibility of conflicting findings by different tribunals, cannot be obtained (since without the consent of all parties this procedure is not available in arbitration proceedings). There may be other excellent reasons for preferring High Court proceedings, incidentally, such as the need for an injunction to enforce a contractual provision—as *e.g.* clauses 15, 16 and 53 (6)—which is also not within the powers of an arbitrator.

It will be seen that the clause contemplates an initial reference of all disputes, whether before or after completion, to the Engineer, who apparently is not an arbitrator in the full sense, but whose decision is nevertheless now given permanent finality unless notice of arbitration is given within a certain period, which will then lead to an arbitration proper, and which is subject only to a restriction, the exact scope of which is very doubtful, upon "steps being taken in the reference" before completion (see the last part of sub-clause (1) and sub-clause (2)). Before dealing with the whole clause in detail, mention should be made of two problems common to all arbitration clauses in contracts which also provide for the decisions or certificates of the employer's architect or engineer to regulate the position between the parties in certain events. These are:—

(a) To what extent is an arbitrator appointed under the clause entitled to override certificates or decisions of the Engineer (or "certifier" as he usually is called in this context)? (The power to do this, if it exists, must of course include a power to disregard the *absence* of a certificate, where the certifier has decided on the merits to refuse a certificate which has been asked for.) In the case of *certificates* this problem, as already stated, no longer exists, since neither the provision for a Final Certificate under clause 60 (3), nor any other part of the contract, suggests that this certificate is to be binding; while the maintenance certificate is now expressly deprived of any final effect by clause 61 (2), *supra*. Moreover, the "open up review and revise" formula in the later sentences of the present sub-clause set out *infra* is also explicit that *all* certificates can be reviewed. (Certain provisions in the contract which do restrict the arbitrator's power to deal with a dispute on the merits, such as failure by the Contractor to comply with clause 52 (4) requirements (see clause 52 (4) (e) in regard to notice of claims), or with clause 56 (3) in regard to non-attendance at measurement meetings, and disputes as to the proper amount of VAT payable by the main contractor under clause 70 (5) (b), *infra*, p. 287, are referred to in the commentary to the later part of sub-clause (1), *infra*, p. 276.)

(b) To what extent, if the arbitrator is free to disregard certificates or decisions, are the courts also free to do so? This is a matter of immense practical importance, because in cases where it is thought no genuine dispute exists a valuable remedy under R.S.C. Ord. 14 (not available to a party in an arbitration) will enable a contractor, for instance, to obtain summary judgment without a certificate or in the face of an adverse certificate, in default of affidavit evidence that a genuine dispute on the merits exists, and on the other hand an employer will similarly be able to raise claims or counterclaims and obtain judgment, notwithstanding the issue of a certificate in favour of the contractor. This question has to be looked at against the legal background that, by virtue of section 1 of the Arbitration Act, all arbitration agreements are revocable with the leave of the courts, so that arbitration is in reality a discretionary remedy, however mandatory the arbitration clause itself may appear to be, and a party is, therefore, generally speaking, free to commence an action in the courts, subject to an application for a stay being granted. As stated, there are often very good reasons—*e.g.* a multiplicity of parties or the need for an injunction—which the courts have accepted as justifying the refusal of a stay—see Hudson, 10th ed., pp. 840–846. It is submitted that the only situations in which an arbitrator could be free to disregard a certificate or its refusal, but the courts prevented from doing so, would either be if the arbitration clause was couched in what is called " *Scott* v. *Avery* " form—strictly, a contract under which an award of an arbitrator is expressly made a condition precedent to bringing any action upon the contract; or else where provisions placing a time limit of some kind upon the right to go to arbitration are held, on their true construction, to be intended to ban all other forms of proceedings as well (see *Russell on Arbitration*, 18th ed., at pp. 58–61) thus having the same practical effect, where the time has elapsed, as a *Scott* v. *Avery* clause proper; or finally where a nowadays very rare type of clause provides that *either* a certificate of the certifier *or* an award of the arbitrator is to be conclusive as to some matter—as to this latter see Hudson, 10th ed., p. 320, and the case of *Lloyd Bros.* v. *Milward* there referred to. The present contract contains no provisions of this last kind, nor has any standard form in the U.K. for a number of years, so the question which remains is whether the present clause on its special wording is intended to achieve a "*Scott* v. *Avery*" result, so that an award of an arbitrator must be obtained before an action can be brought in the courts, and the time ban arising from failure to give notice of arbitration within the stipulated period will consequently deprive the complaining party of all rights permanently.

In considering this problem there is no question on the new wording but that, *if a dispute is referred to the Engineer for settlement and decision*, resort to the High Court becomes impossible, if the stipulated period has expired without notice of arbitration being given and equally no doubt that (subject to an application to the High Court to extend time to give notice of arbitration under the "undue hardship" section 27 of the Act of 1950) failure to give notice of arbitration in time will bar all further remedies. The question therefore may be expressed as follows:—

> Is the initial reference of all disputes for decision to the Engineer mandatory, in the sense that failure of the plaintiff or claimant to submit a dispute for decision is a bar to proceedings by arbitration or in the courts? For example, if an Engineer withholds a certificate to which the Contractor claims to be entitled, and the latter proceeds by writ, or by giving notice of arbitration, without any preliminary reference. Again, is the initial reference mandatory, in the sense that a defendant or respondent who has not yet himself disputed a claim can rely on the absence of the reference as a defence? For example, an Engineer grants the certificate upon which the Contractor claims, the Employer simply does not pay, and the Contractor issues a writ (note there is no time limit in the clause for referring a dispute to the Engineer, and once referred a three-month delay before an arbitrator can even be appointed becomes a possibility if not probability).

It is submitted that the true view of the first sentence of the present clause is that it is a simple contractual undertaking to refer disputes to the Engineer for decision. This may or may not amount to an arbitration agreement (quite possibly not, in view of the contrasting language in the clause expressly applying the Arbitration Acts to the later revision of the Engineer's decision; in view of the absence of any indication of a hearing or the taking of evidence (compare the case of *Pierce* v. *Dyke* [1959] 2 W.I.R. 30; and see Hudson, 10th ed., pp. 436 and 830, and see *per* Winn L.J. in the *Monmouth* case (1965) 63 L.G.R. 429); and the high probability that in most cases the Engineer himself will already be personally involved in the subject-matter of the dispute). Assuming, however, that it is, it is subject to revocation by leave of the courts under section 1 of the Arbitration Acts, and an action brought in breach of the agreement may or may not be stayed on the usual principles under section 4 of the Act, so that in appropriate cases a stay can be refused and the dispute proceed in the courts. If on the other hand, the initial reference to the Engineer is not an arbitration agreement, then while unilateral revocation by a party (as *e.g.* by proceeding in the courts) will be a breach of contract, the other party will be left with what would in most cases be a valueless right of action, since it will be impossible to prove damage (it was this factor in regard to arbitration agreements proper, and the refusal of the courts to support them by specific performance or injunction, which led to their being, for practical purposes, revocable at any time before award, and to the passage of the earlier statutory predecessors of section 1 of the Act of 1950, which prohibits revocation of arbitration agreements in writing without the leave of the court, and of section 4, which, in the form of the stay of proceedings, simply provided the statutory machinery whereby, by either granting or refusing a stay, the courts could decide whether or not the arbitration agreement should be revoked should one of the parties unilaterally seek to revoke it by proceeding in the courts).

Subject to the possibility, therefore, that a court might feel justified in enforcing the present provisions by injunction or otherwise in a case where palpable damage might be proved—as *e.g.* perhaps in some cases where proceedings were sought to be commenced before completion of the work—it is submitted that the present clause will *not* operate as a bar to such proceedings *where no reference to the Engineer has taken place*, or even perhaps where a reference has taken place but as yet no decision has been given—see however the decision of Mocatta J. on the Fourth Edition clause in *Monmouth C.C.* v. *Costelloe & Kemple Ltd.* (1964) 63 L.G.R. 131, Hudson, 10th ed., at p. 820, overruled on other grounds by the Court of Appeal in (1965) 63 L.G.R. 429. It seems, moreover, not impossible that if a defendant, on being sued in the courts, then took the dispute unilaterally to the Engineer (or if an Engineer seised of the matter beforehand gave his decision after proceedings started) and the decision was in the defendant's favour, the Engineer's decision *might* be held to operate retrospectively to bar the proceedings continuing any longer, by virtue of the third sentence of the present clause—see the very difficult House of Lords case of *Hosier and Dickinson Ltd.* v. *Kaye Ltd.* [1972] 1 W.L.R. 146, where an architect's final certificate issued *after* proceedings had commenced was held to be binding on the parties in those proceedings. That was, however, a decision on the very different wording of the RIBA forms, and seems open to doubt for a number of other reasons. Furthermore, the speeches in that case suggest that a plaintiff could defeat such a manoeuvre by giving a purely formal notice of arbitration following an adverse decision of the Engineer, which under the terms of the present arbitration clause would then deprive it of its finality. (Indeed, it seems correct, on this reasoning, for a party anxious to proceed in the courts who has himself sought the Engineer's decision, on seeing that it is adverse, to serve a formal notice of arbitration but nevertheless initiate proceedings in the courts and resist an application to stay on one of the usual grounds.)

On the other hand, it is submitted that, should a party desire arbitration under the present clause, it is not possible, without consent, to dispense with the initial reference to the Engineer, since on the wording of the fourth sentence of the present sub-clause it is clear that the arbitrator's jurisdiction under the clause is dependent upon, and cannot arise until, the Engineer's refusal to give a decision when requested, or upon dissatisfaction with his decision.

Whether or not there has been a reference of a dispute to the Engineer and a decision thereon within the terms of this clause may be a difficult question of fact—see the decision of the Court of Appeal in *Monmouth C.C.* v. *Costelloe & Kemple Ltd.* (1965) 63 L.G.R. 429, (1977) 5 B.L.R. 83, overruling Mocatta J. (illustrated in Hudson, 10th ed., p. 820), which is the only case in England to have considered this point in depth. It is important to notice that no time limit whatever is imposed by the clause on the initial reference—only on the later notice of arbitration. The reference to the Engineer could, therefore, be at any time which would permit any subsequent notice of arbitration to be given within the period allowed by the Limitation Acts.

" *in connection with . . . the carrying out of the Works* "

It is suggested that, contrary to a fairly widely held view, this particular form of words will permit an arbitrator to apply the legal remedy of rectification of a contract between the parties if the stringent requirements for that remedy have been satisfied—see Hudson, 10th ed., pp. 837–838, and the cases of *Printing Machinery Co.* v. *Linotype and Machinery Ltd.* [1912] 1 Ch. 566 and *Crane* v. *Hegeman-Harris Co.* [1939] 4 All E.R. 68 there referred to, where rectification was held not to be available to an arbitrator under the clauses in those contracts. The matter must be regarded as doubtful, however.

" *including any dispute as to any decision opinion instruction direction certificate or valuation* "

Compare these words, which are new at this point in the clause, with the identical words in the second part of the sub-clause, *infra*. Coupled with the new wording in clause 61 (2) in regard to the Maintenance Certificate and the absence of wording indicating finality in clause 60 (3) in regard to the Final Certificate, they highlight the obvious intention of the present Edition to leave all disputes open for decision on their merits. See, however, for some possible exceptions, the commentary to the second part of the clause, *infra*, p. 276.

" (*whether during the progress of the Works or after their completion . . .*"

These words indicate that all disputes (*e.g.* for an indemnity in respect of a third party claim received years after the Final Certificate, perhaps) and notwithstanding their possibly exclusively legal character, or their involvement of an area outside the Engineer's own expertise, will be within the present wording.

" *whether before or after the . . . breach of the Contract* "

The word " breach " in the present context seems to be *per incuriam* and to make no sense, unless it refers to some anticipated breach, which does not seem likely. The contract uses the word " determination " in the case of an Employer's re-entry under clause 65 (war) but " forfeiture " is the only word to be found in the case of an Employer's re-entry under clause 63 (and admittedly then only in the marginal heading, proscribed for interpretation purposes by clause 1 (3), *supra*, p. 24), and it is in any case doubtful if any of the present wording adds anything to " before or after completion." The language of sub-clause (2), *infra* (early arbitration), is similarly defective in regard to rescission situations, mentioning only clause 63 (1) re-entry, and making no allowance for a possible rescission at common law (as to the possibility of which see the commentary to clause 63 (1), *supra*, pp. 245–248).

" *decision in writing* "

See *supra*, pp. 267 and 272, as to what constitutes a " dispute."

" *the Contractor shall continue . . . with the Works and shall give effect to every such decision . . .*"

The obligation to continue work cannot be taken at face value in all cases—*e.g.* where the dispute arises after completion, or where it is fundamental—*e.g.* an assertion by the Contractor that there has been no contract finally concluded and that he is entitled to withdraw his tender, or that the Employer has repudiated the contract, or that he cannot be obliged to start work until full possession is afforded—and in any event if justified in not continuing, the damages for breach of the undertaking would only be nominal. Note it is *the contractor alone*, not the Employer, who is enjoined to give temporary effect to the decision. This suggests that this part of the clause is primarily concerned to secure (if applicable) the physical continuity of the work by the Contractor without slow-down or stoppage, whatever claims he may believe he may have, and lends support to the view that in law there is nothing to prevent the deduction and set-off of cross-claims by the Employer from amounts certified by the Engineer—first, because the contract does not at any point empower the Engineer to deal with or make deductions for cross-claims himself in the clause 60 certificates; secondly, because in a number of cases no separate certification or action is called for by the Engineer in order to establish the particular cross-claim; and even where this is so (*e.g.* in the case of liquidated damages under clause 47 (4) or direct payment of Nominated Sub-contractors under clause 59C), it is by no means certain that sufficiently clear " condition precedent " language has been used—see the commentary to clauses 60 (1) and (2), *supra*, pp. 230–232. Thus in general, it is submitted, if an Employer deducts from sums due under a certificate and the Contractor refers the matter for the Engineer's decision and the latter supports the Contractor, the Employer will simply give notice of arbitration, whereupon on the wording of the next (third) sentence of the present sub-clause, he will not be bound by that decision nor, it is submitted, required to implement it even temporarily. In the more usual case, of course, an Engineer will be more likely to support the Employer, who will probably have acted on the Engineer's advice in deducting, and where the Employer is not supported by his Engineer, no doubt the burden on the Employer in securing leave to stay an action brought by the Contractor, or to obtain leave to defend, will be correspondingly heavier, but there will be no absolute legal bar, it is submitted—see the commentary, *supra*, p. 231.

" *Such decision shall be final and binding* "

The omission in the present Edition of the vital words " until the completion of the Works " now means that a dispute, once referred and decided, will become permanently binding unless the appropriate notice of arbitration, as provided for in the next sentence of the clause, is given in time—see the commentary, *supra*, for the great importance of this in interpreting the clause as a whole. This highlights the need for Engineers to word their decisions with the greatest possible precision, and also to describe in the most careful terms the matter being decided—for example the precise grounds, should they differ, on which a Contractor makes a claim—since otherwise attempts may be made to argue that what may effectively be the same matter has not been decided when the claim is re-presented in another form.

" *within 3 calendar months* "

Subject, however, to the court's powers to extend time in cases of undue hardship under section 27 of the Arbitration Act 1950. This power is extremely conservatively exercised, however.

" *require that the matter shall be referred* "
" *written notice to concur in the appointment of an arbitrator* "

For purposes of the Limitation Acts, " proceedings commence " on the date of this written requirement, which for this purpose is the equivalent of an issue of a writ. There is in fact a suggested anomaly in the legislation on this subject, since an arbitration resulting from a stay of High Court proceedings does not obtain the benefit of the date of issue of the writ, and High Court proceedings which for one reason or another subsequently replace arbitration proceedings are conversely disadvantaged. In addition, while under the Limitation Acts defences and counterclaims enjoy the benefit of the date of issue of the original writ or notice requiring arbitration, as the case may be, a further suggested anomaly in the legislation does not accord the same advantage to third party proceedings or proceedings for contribution, which are often likely in building and civil engineering disputes. Indeed, it is not uncommon for a defendant contractor to be liable, for example, to a plaintiff employer in respect of sub-contracted work, for instance where the main contract is under seal and the writ has been issued just in time, but to be unable to recover from the sub-contractors in question because, as against them, the limitation period on the simple (*i.e.* unsealed) sub-contract may have already expired, or because it was either not possible, or not practicable in the very short time available, following receipt of the writ, to join the sub-contractor (for a striking example of this see *County & District Properties Ltd.* v. *Jenner* [1976] 2 Lloyd's Rep. 728). Great care needs, therefore to be exercised in the tactical conduct of disputes if the limitation period is near expiry, by way of service of protective or conditional notices or writs, notwithstanding that a different form of proceedings may be preferred and indeed intended.

> Any such reference to arbitration shall be deemed to be a submission to arbitration within the meaning of the Arbitration Act 1950 or the Arbitration (Scotland) Act 1894 as the case may be or any statutory re-enactment or amendment thereof for the time being in force. Any such reference to arbitration may be conducted in accordance with the Institution of Civil Engineers' Arbitration Procedure (1973) or any amendment or modification thereof being in force at the time of the appointment of the arbitrator and in cases where the President of the Institution of Civil Engineers is requested to appoint the arbitrator he may direct that the arbitration is conducted in accordance with the aforementioned Procedure or any amendment or modification thereof. Such arbitrator shall have full power to open up review and revise any decision opinion instruction direction certificate or valuation of the Engineer and neither party shall be limited in the proceedings before such arbitrator to the evidence or arguments put before the Engineer for the purpose of obtaining his decision above referred to. The award of the arbitrator shall be final and binding on the parties.

" *Institution of Civil Engineers' Arbitration Procedure* (*1973*) "

It has been suggested, *supra*, that the discretion conferred upon the arbitrator or President of the Institute to follow whatever may be in the Rules *at the time of the appointment* (not, it should be noted, at the time of the contract being signed and the arbitration obligation incurred by the parties) or possibly even ad hoc amendments made by the President, which the wording seems to indicate, may not be very wise. There appears to have been an expansion of interest and activity by the Institution in the field of arbitration in recent years, and without in any way criticising the present rules the history of U.K. domestic commercial or professional bodies (usually controlled by persons without legal experience and perhaps with administrative staff themselves experienced in litigation) governing the conduct of disputes has not in general been a very happy one, and the overall control by the courts over procedure in arbitrations, which in fact allows a considerably wider freedom to arbitrators than to judicial tribunals, seems preferable for domestic arbitrations unless the rules to be adopted are available for the fullest consideration and approval at the time of contracting.

" *the Arbitration* (*Scotland*) *Act 1894* "

See the commentary to clause 67, *infra*, p. 282.

" *power to open up review and revise any decision, opinion, direction, certificate or valuation* "

These words, which appear to have been considered by the courts for the first time in the case of *Robbins* v. *Goddard* [1905] 1 K.B. 294, only serve to emphasise what, it is submitted, an arbitration clause in general terms usually implies, namely that the arbitrator is not in general bound by the approval, satisfaction or certificate of a certifier unless there is some express term in the contract to that effect—see for this principle *Brodie* v. *Cardiff Corporation* [1919] A.C. 337. The same freedom enures for the benefit of the courts if they happen to be seised of a dispute instead of an arbitrator, it is submitted—see Hudson, 10th ed., pp. 447–448 and in particular the case of *Neale* v. *Richardson* [1938] 1 All E.R. 753, *per* Scott L.J. at p. 758. Thus, in the absence of an inhibition on early arbitration, a contractor can, for example, sue in the courts for monthly payment under clause 60 notwithstanding the absence of a certificate, it is submitted—see the criticism of the decision of the Court of Appeal in *Dunlop & Ranken Ltd.* v. *Hendall Steel Structures* [1957] 1 W.L.R. 1102, Hudson, 10th ed., p. 496, which at first sight might seem a decision to the contrary, and the many cases illustrated in Hudson, 10th ed., at pp. 438–442. The only provisions in the present contract which might possibly limit the arbitrator's powers to decide a dispute on the merits, and not caught by the present wording, might be clause 56 (3) (Contractor's absence from measurement meeting), clause 70 (5) (b) (VAT liability) and, just possibly, clause 63 (Employer's re-entry without Engineer's supporting certificate) though even in the latter case it is submitted that the words " opinion, decision," in the present sub-clause will include an opinion or decision as a result of which the Engineer refuses to grant *any* certificate for which he is asked under *any* of the terms of the contract —including the necessary supporting clause 63 certificate.

The Fifth Edition has now, self-evidently, adopted the policy that *all* the Engineer's certificates should be open to review without limit of time—see the new clause 61 (2), reversing the previous policy on the effect of the Maintenance Certificate, and the new clause 60 (3), which deliberately abstains from language seeking to give any special binding force to the new final certificate provided for in that sub-clause.

" *The award . . . shall be final and binding* "

—subject, of course, to the case stated procedure, which for practical purposes gives an effective right of appeal on a point of law under the English (but not Scottish) Arbitration Acts—see Hudson, 10th ed., pp. 864–866 and 868—and subject also to a power of review over unusual orders of costs—see Hudson, 10th ed., pp. 868–870, and the case of *Dineen* v. *Walpole* [1969] 1 Lloyd's Rep. 261 there referred to.

Save as provided for in sub-clause (2) of this Clause no steps shall be taken in the reference to the arbitrator until after the completion or alleged completion of the Works unless with the written consent of the Employer and the Contractor. Provided always:—

(a) that the giving of a Certificate of Completion under Clause 48 shall not be a condition precedent to the taking of any step in such reference;
(b) that no decision given by the Engineer in accordance with the foregoing provisions shall disqualify him from being called as a witness and giving evidence before the arbitrator on any matter whatsoever relevant to the dispute or difference so referred to the arbitrator as aforesaid.

Interim Arbitration

(2) In the case of any dispute or difference as to any matter arising under Clause 12 or the withholding by the Engineer of any certificate or the withholding of any portion of the retention money under Clause 60 to which the Contractor claims to be entitled or as to the exercise of the Engineer's power to give a certificate under Clause 63 (1) the reference to the arbitrator may proceed notwithstanding that the Works shall not then be or be alleged to be complete.

These provisions regulate the right to " early " arbitration—*i.e.* arbitration before completion or alleged completion (the latter, of course, being a case where the Engineer is refusing, despite being asked to do so, to issue a certificate under clause 48). The sense of the wording clearly refers to completion of the whole of the Works, but the lack of explicit reference negativing completion of Sections or parts is perhaps a little surprising. It should be appreciated at the outset that, even if an arbitration is commenced during the construction period, as a practical matter having regard to the length of time required for the preliminary stages of an arbitration, including pleadings, discovery, and so on, of the type of dispute likely to arise in building or civil engineering cases, the hearing itself would be unlikely to take place before the end of any but the longest contract period. Indeed the difficulties facing an arbitrator (as indeed the courts) in giving really rapid rulings, or interim orders, in a matter as complicated as an engineering contract are probably the principal justification of the " two-tier " system (see the commentary, *supra*), at least in regard to matters whose urgent though temporary resolution is needed for the effective administration of the contract.

Moreover, the meaning to be attached to the (new) expression " no steps shall be taken in the reference to the arbitrator " is not easy to decide, but the wording may have some reference to the expression " step in the action," with which lawyers will be familiar in the context of applications to stay proceedings under section 4 of the Arbitration Act—in other words, the intention may be that the earlier machinery in the clause for appointing the arbitrator may be implemented, and the necessary consents to act obtained from the arbitrator, but that thereafter no further action by way of obtaining directions or exchanging pleadings or particulars should take place.

Subject to the above, these provisions have the effect of enabling the three stipulated groups of *Contractor's* claims to be arbitrated before completion. The wording of the permitted claims, which is traditional and which does not give the appearance of being very carefully considered, is the same, apart from the addition of disputes under clause 12, as in the Fourth Edition. The wording will not, therefore, include simple claims for breach of contract by the Employer, but it should be appreciated that under the new provisions in clause 60 (1) and (2), the Contractor is now entitled to include in his application for interim certification *any* claim under *any* provision of the contract entitling him to claim. Since wrongful re-entry by the Employer under clause 63 is expressly included in the permitted claims, and since most of the more common breaches of contract by the Employer are now the subject of express contractual claims (see *e.g.* clause (7) (3) (late information) and clause 42 (1) (failure to give possession)) and, as stated, these are now certifiable on interim certificate, together with a formidable list of other possible claims under clause 60 (1) (d)—see the commentary thereto, *supra*, p. 233—it would seem that the " withholding of any certificate " wording in the present clause, depending on its true interpretation, may permit the Contractor to arbitrate *any* claim for which " provision is made under the Contract," as expressly contemplated by clause 60 (1) (d). Furthermore, many decisions of the Engineer under the Contract, such as the condemning of defective work, or refusal of extension of time (see clause 47 (4)) or on unpaid Sub-contractors under clause 59C, or refusing consent to termination of a sub-contract, which are adverse to the Contractor in the context of some counter-action by the Employer, will either themselves require some certificate of the Engineer, or else be reflected in later certificates for payment under clause 60, so that in either case the Contractor may be able to argue that there has been a " withholding " of a certificate to which he is entitled (for the meaning of " withholding " see *infra*). On the other hand, the Employer does not appear to be able to arbitrate *any* of his cross-claims during the currency of the contract, should the Engineer not support him in the manner required by the Contract, but this may be mitigated by the fact that (except in cases where Engineer support is a condition precedent, as probably in the case of liquidated damages, for example) he is in many cases not only expressly empowered to deduct from sums due under the contract but also because, as is submitted (see the commentary to clause 60 (1) and (2), *supra*, pp. 230–232), there is nothing in the contract to prevent him from using his ordinary right of set-off where no express right of deduction exists. However, there are many obvious situations where the Employer has no such sanction if he cannot prove damage—*e.g.* failure to provide a programme under clause 14 (1), a dispute over competence of Contractor's agent or employees under clauses 15 and 16, objection to removal of plant under clause 53 (6), a dispute as to the reasonableness of a nomination of a Sub-contractor under clause 59A (3), a dispute over the proposed termination of a nominated sub-contract under clause 59B (3), or as to its justification under clause 59B (4). It may be that the intention, which is not unreasonable, is that in some of these cases the Employer is bound to give effect to his own adviser's view if it is adverse to him, whereas the Contractor's express obligation to do so for the time being in the earlier part of sub-clause (1) is mitigated to the extent that early arbitration is permitted where the withholding of a certificate is involved.

" *except as to the withholding . . . of any certificate . . . to which the Contractor claims to be entitled* "

The terms of clause 60 (1) (d), commented on *supra*, p. 233, now make it clear that the Contractor's financial claims of every kind, if " provided for under the contract " (*i.e.* expressly conferred by the contract) are to be the subject of interim certification. At a time when the contract contained no such provision, and the time for paying such contractual claims was doubtful, Buckley J. held in *Farr* v. *Ministry of Transport* [1960] 1 W.L.R. 956, (1977) 5 B.L.R. 94, that the words above in the Fourth Edition applied to *any* certificate under the contract, since the words " under clause 60 " qualified " retention money " and not " any certificate " —see Hudson, 10th ed., p. 495. If this remains right on the new wording the Contractor could seek early arbitration of a claim by him for an extension of time, so disputing the deduction of liquidated damages under clause 47 (4), *supra*, p. 135 (actually there is a difficulty about this because, almost certainly *per incuriam*, clause 44 (3) does not provide for a *certificate* as clause 47 (4) assumes). However this may be, the important question is what precisely is meant by the word " withholding." Buckley J. in *Farr's* case expressed the view that it would include the *disallowance on principle* of a claim which would otherwise be included in an interim certificate (*i.e.* resulting in a reduced certified amount) but despite an *obiter dictum* by him to the contrary, it is submitted that the wording is perfectly general and will include disputes of valuation or amount as well as of principle (this, it is suggested, not only follows from the wording itself, but is essential in a contract which is potentially very lengthy, where consistent under-certification could mean financial ruin to a Contractor, where no other express remedy is open to the Contractor, and where it would be virtually impossible for him to allege a repudiation if all the Employer had done was to pay precisely what the Engineer had certified—see the discussion of *Farr's* case, Hudson, 10th ed., pp. 495–496, and see also the views expressed, in this context, on the RIBA " whether or not a certificate is in accordance with the contract " wording by Lords Reid, Dilhorne, Diplock and Salmon in *Gilbert-Ash* (*Northern*) *Ltd.* v. *Modern Engineering* (*Bristol*) *Ltd.* [1974] A.C. 689).

Whatever the answer may be to this last question, it is submitted that the change now effected by clause 60 (1) (d) means that the present wording will in practice enable the Contractor to arbitrate any disallowed claim under the Contract before the end of the construction period, that the Employer will be free to raise any defence or counter-claim by way of set-off, and that the only party likely to suffer any inhibition in bringing proceedings, or perhaps in counter-claiming a sum in excess of the Contractor's claim, will be the Employer. The whole machinery restricting early arbitration, having regard also to the length of time required in practice to bring arbitrations to the hearing stage, appears to serve little legal or practical purpose. Furthermore, as already stated, the present wording appears to have paid scant attention to some parts of the contract where it might have been thought that early arbitration would be highly desirable—as *e.g.* a dispute over consent to removal of plant under clause 53 (6), a dispute as to the reasonableness of an objection to a Nominated Subcontractor under clause 59A, or a dispute over the main Contractor's entitlement to determine, or whether it was justified, under clause 59B. Furthermore, depending upon the accidents of the wording of the various contractual provisions—see *e.g.* clause 30 (3) (Engineer's certification of amount due to Employer for damage to highways) there may not, as in the case of liquidated damages there is, be a " certificate to which *the Contractor* claims to be entitled " so that that matter might not be open to review till the end of the work. In all cases where a dispute cannot be fitted within the present wording, it would seem that the initial reference and settlement of that dispute by the Engineer is intended to prevail until the end of the work—see particularly the wording *supra* that it is *the Contractor* who is to give effect to the decision until completion.

The present provisions, which are largely traditional, are likely to be haphazard in operation, and could well be dispensed with altogether without serious damage to either party.

" *as to the exercise of the Engineer's power to give a certificate under clause 63 (1)* "

This appears to be inserted for the benefit of the Contractor rather than the Employer, so as to enable the former to dispute the validity of the

Employer's re-entry under clause 63. Consistently with that clause (see the commentary to clause 63 (1), *supra*, pp. 245–248) the present clause makes no reference to the possibility of a common law rescission by the Employer on the ground of the Contractor's abandonment or repudiation or fundamental breach of the contract.

" *Provided . . . that . . . a Certificate . . . under clause 48 . . . shall not be a condition precedent* "

This simply appears to restate the effect of the words " alleged completion " which occur earlier.

Vice-President to Act

(3) In any case where the President for the time being of the Institution of Civil Engineers is not able to exercise the functions conferred on him by this Clause the said functions may be exercised on his behalf by a Vice-President for the time being of the said Institution.

This sub-clause calls for no particular comment, but reference should perhaps be made to the commentary, *supra*, on the interest now being shown by the Institution in arbitration via the 1973 Arbitration Procedure Rules, and the President's apparent power to amend those rules on an ad hoc basis.

APPLICATION TO SCOTLAND

Application to Scotland

67. If the Works are situated in Scotland the Contract shall in all respects be construed and operate as a Scottish contract and shall be interpreted in accordance with Scots law.

The rather arbitrary test laid down by this provision is that the place of performance is to govern the law of the contract, if that place is Scotland. There is, however, no corresponding provision, as logically there should be, that English law should govern works carried out in England—desirable, perhaps, if the contract was concluded between Scottish parties for works in England.

This provision does not necessarily mean, however, that court proceedings on the contract would have to take place in Scotland. As between England and Scotland the choice of court will generally be governed by the presence within the jurisdiction of the defendant—see R.S.C. Ord. 11, r. 1 (f) and (g) under which the English courts at least cannot grant leave to serve writs outside the jurisdiction on persons ordinarily resident or domiciled in Scotland.

In the case of arbitrations, the mere residence of a respondent outside the jurisdiction may not prevent proceedings being commenced within the jurisdiction, since under R.S.C., Ord. 73, r. 7, leave may be given to serve a summons on a Scottish respondent for the appointment of an arbitrator and for certain other purposes connected with arbitration, but the rule applies only where the arbitration " is to be or has been held within the jurisdiction "—*i.e.* presumably where the terms of the submission to arbitration so provide. This latter is not completely clear from clause 66, *supra*, because the appointment of the arbitrator, failing agreement, is to be made by the President of the (English) Institution of Civil Engineers.

Where arbitration is concerned the general rule is that the validity and effect of the arbitration agreement are determined by the proper law of the (arbitration) agreement, but that the validity and effect of an award are determined by the law of the country where the arbitration is held (if that is different), but the whole matter appears to be very uncertain since there is a real doubt whether rules as to arbitration—*e.g.* under the Arbitration Act—are in this context rules of substantive or procedural law. In the present contract, however, clause 66, *supra*, p. 276, would seem to suggest that it is the Scottish Arbitration Act which will apply if the works are in Scotland, even if the arbitration is held in England. It still remains doubtful in such a case which country's courts would assume jurisdiction to control the arbitration under the provisions of the Scottish Act.

So far as the law of *procedure* is concerned, the bias will be towards holding that this will be governed by the *lex fori*—the place where the arbitration is held—though this may be different from the *proper law* of the contract (*i.e.* by which the contract will be interpreted and the parties obtain their remedies)—see the House of Lords case of *James Miller & Partners* v. *Whitworth Estates* [1970] A.C. 583, Hudson, 10th ed., pp. 824–825, which has done much to clarify the law on this subject. This distinction may be extremely important (for example an appeal on a point of law by way of case stated procedure does not exist without special agreement under Scottish law, and this has been held to be a procedural matter, whereas the right to an extension of time for a notice of arbitration under the hardship provisions of section 27 of the Arbitration Act 1950 has been held to be substantive and not procedural (see *International Tank and Pipe* v. *Kuwait Aviation Fuelling* [1975] 1 Lloyd's Rep. 8), (1977) 5 B.L.R. 147. So that express agreement is desirable, even if agreement exists on the proper law (as it will be if the present clause applies) as to the procedural law should the arbitration take place in a country other than that of the proper law. The reference in clause 66 to the two different Arbitration Acts (" as the case may be ") may not be sufficient—in the *Miller* case the original reference to the arbitrator was under the English Arbitration Acts, but the procedural law was nevertheless held to be Scottish—so that express agreement by the parties beforehand, communicated to the arbitrator, is essential as a matter of prudence to avoid dispute and the costs of an abortive hearing.

On the question of presence within the jurisdiction generally, it should be borne in mind that by section 437 (2) of the Companies Act 1948 a Scottish company carrying on business in England can be served at its principal place of business in England in accordance with the other requirements of that section, so that leave under Order 11 is unnecessary in such a case.

NOTICES

Service of Notice on Contractor

68. (1) Any notice to be given to the Contractor under the terms of the Contract shall be served by sending the same by post to or leaving the same at the Contractor's principal place of business (or in the event of the Contractor being a Company to or at its registered office).

The contract is somewhat haphazard in its requirements as to notice. There appears to be no formal requirement as to the Contractor's notices to the Engineer, or distinguishing between him and the Engineer's representative, despite their importance at many different points of the contract, *e.g.* under clauses 12 (1) and 52 (4) (a) and (b) and clause 69 (6), *infra.* Notice to the Contractor appears to be required under clauses 27 (2) (Street Works), 56 (measurement of work), 63 (1) (Employer's re-entry), 63 (1) (b) (Engineer's notice to proceed), 65 (3) (determination for war) and 66 (Engineer's decision and perhaps Employer's requirement of arbitration). A number of very important matters, however, are dealt with by Engineer's orders or directions to the Contractor, which by virtue of clause 15 (2), *supra*, p. 59 are sufficiently given to the Contractor's authorised agent on the site—*e.g.* under clause 40 (suspension of work), and clause 49 (2) (defects during or at the end of maintenance period).

The reference to " shall be served by sending the same by post " means, it is submitted, that a period or time limit for giving a notice is calculated by reference to the time of posting—*e.g.* under clause 63 (1).

Service of Notice on Employer

(2) Any notice to be given to the Employer under the terms of the Contract shall be served by sending the same by post to or leaving the same at the Employer's last known address (or in the event of the Employer being a Company to or at its registered office).

There are very few references in the contract to such a notice—see under clause 27 (4) (Street Works) and under clause 66 (Engineer's decision and, perhaps, Contractor's requirement of arbitration). See the commentary, *supra*, as to the effect on time limits and periods of the provision as to posting.

TAX MATTERS

Tax Fluctuations

69. (1) The rates and prices contained in the Bill of Quantities take account of the levels and incidence at the date for return of tenders (hereinafter called " the relevant date ") of the taxes levies and contributions (including national insurance contributions but excluding income tax and any levy payable under the Industrial Training Act 1964) which are by law payable by the Contractor in respect of his workpeople and the premiums and refunds (if any) which are by law payable to the Contractor in respect of his workpeople. Any such matter is hereinafter called " a labour-tax matter."

The rates and prices contained in the Bill of Quantities do not take account of any level or incidence of the aforesaid matters where at the relevant date such level or incidence does not then have effect but although then known is to take effect at some later date. The taking effect of any such level or incidence at the later date shall for the purposes of sub-clause (2) of this Clause be treated as the occurrence of an event.

(2) If after the relevant date there shall occur any of the events specified in sub-clause (3) of this Clause and as a consequence thereof the cost to the Contractor of performing his obligations under the Contract shall be increased or decreased then subject to the provisions of sub-clause (4) of this Clause the net amount of such increase or decrease shall constitute an addition to or deduction from the sums otherwise payable to the Contractor under the Contract as the case may require.

(3) The events referred to in the preceding sub-clause are as follows:—

(a) any change in the level of any labour-tax matter;

(b) any change in the incidence of any labour-tax matter including the imposition of any new such matter or the abolition of any previously existing such matter.

This clause was first published in January 1970 as a separate clause, then numbered 70, for use with the Fourth Edition, and was virtually forced on both the building and civil engineering industries by the increasing inability of governments to refrain from ad hoc fiscal legislation, changing virtually from year to year, and radically affecting the cost structure of reasonably long-term commercial transactions. The building and civil engineering industries in the U.K. found themselves, for example, the subject of industrial training legislation, special employment tax, and redundancy payments legislation, all materially affecting the return on capital employed, and any or all of which might be unforeseeable at the time of tender, yet imposed, with no saving or compensation for previously negotiated transactions, at some date during the construction period. The present clause, which has not altered from its original form (save for the omission of a no longer applicable saving clause relating it to the old Variation of Price clause where used) represents an attempt to safeguard the Contractor from contingencies which are, in reality, essentially unpredictable, and given the difficulty of the task the draftsmanship is of high standard, and the policy eminently understandable. Somewhat different but parallel provisions were evolved in the fluctuations clause 31 of the RIBA forms of contract at about the same time.

It will be seen that the crucial adjectival phrase in sub-clause (1) is that the " tax levy or contribution " must be " payable by the Contractor *in respect of his workpeople* "—as opposed to " in his capacity as an employer " in the RIBA forms. Industrial Training Act levies are expressly excluded from the operation of the clause. The express exclusion of " income-tax " presumably refers to PAYE deductions of workmen's income tax (otherwise why not corporation tax?) but, if so, seems unnecessary, as this could not in any event increase or decrease the Contractor's costs under sub-clause (2).

Clearly the phrasing of the clause is wide enough to include redundancy payments and SET, at which no doubt it was principally aimed. Its application to the recent spate of employment protection legislation can be expected, however, to produce difficulties.

The reference in the second paragraph of sub-clause (1) to the tax being effective at the date of tender takes an opposite stand to the RIBA forms (which include all rates foreseeable at that date provided they are fixed and certain); but there is no particular objection to either policy, the important factor being clarity and lack of possible confusion, which both forms successfully achieve in this respect. The express reference to National Insurance contributions will mean, incidentally, that whether or not the new "Contract Price Fluctuations Clause" (commented on *infra*, p. 292) applies, these particular payments will in any event be subject to fluctuation under the present clause—there is now no overlap with the new form of clause in regard to these particular items of cost.

(4) In this Clause workpeople means persons employed by the Contractor on manual labour whether skilled or unskilled but for the purpose of ascertaining what if any additions or deductions are to be paid or allowed under this Clause account shall not be taken of any labour-tax matter in relation to any workpeople of the Contractor unless at the relevant time their normal place of employment is the Site.

This is an important twofold restriction, namely that the clause is to apply only to manual labourers, and that they must be employed on the Site. This will exclude foremen (but not, presumably, gangers and charge-hands), as well as all clerical staff and watchmen, and also men working in the Contractor's depots or yards (rarer, of course, in engineering contracts than in building contracts, but see now the new clause 54 in regard to materials or goods off the Site, which might involve labour in the preparation, segregation and storage of those goods). For the definition of the Site, see the commentary to clause 1 (1) (n), *supra*, pp. 22–23.

(5) Subject to the provisions of the Contract as to the placing of sub-contracts with Nominated Sub-contractors the Contractor may incorporate in any sub-contract made for the purpose of performing his obligations under the Contract provisions which are *mutatis mutandis* the same as the provisions of this Clause and in such event additions or deductions to be made in accordance with any such sub-contract shall also be made under the Contract as if the increase or decrease of cost to the sub-contractor had been directly incurred by the Contractor.

Provisions for incorporation of similar clauses into sub-contracts are, for some reason, the rule rather than the exception in fluctuations clauses, but in the present case the incorporation is permissive and not mandatory, and in the case of Sub-contractors the restriction to men working on the Site is, of course, likely to be particularly important—see the comments *supra* in regard to the new clause 54 and materials or goods off the Site.

(6) As soon as practicable after the occurrence of any of the events specified in sub-clause (3) of this Clause the Contractor shall give the Engineer notice thereof. The Contractor shall keep such contemporary records as are necessary for the purpose of ascertaining the amount of any addition or deduction to be made in

accordance with this Clause and shall permit the Engineer to inspect such records. The Contractor shall submit to the Engineer with his monthly statements full details of every addition or deduction to be made in accordance with this Clause. All certificates for payment issued after submission of such details shall take due account of the additions or deductions to which such details relate. Provided that the Engineer may if the Contractor fails to submit full details of any deduction nevertheless take account of such deduction when issuing any certificate for payment.

This clause appears to have been included *per incuriam*, since it obviously overlaps with the provisions of the new clause 52 (4) (b), together with the sanctions in clause 52 (4) (e) and (f). Viewed in isolation, the clause does not say that the notice is a condition precedent. The proviso at the end in regard to details might suggest it very strongly at first sight; but it could be argued that the Proviso, as all the other provisions about details, is aimed at interim payment (or rather, of course, on the situation contemplated by the Proviso, deduction) and that it does not suggest that the ultimate right to payment is lost because of failure to give a *notice*. Such notices ought in fact to be conditions precedent, because the accuracy of wages sheets showing the number of men on site is difficult if not impossible to ascertain and check after a short passage of time, due to the high mobility of building labour and the virtual day-to-day fluctuations of the usual site labour force. Unless, of course, the giving of the notice is a condition precedent, the Employer has no effective sanction whatever to enforce compliance with the contract (being unable to prove damages). This argues that the requirement must, as a matter of business efficacy, be treated as a condition precedent, but the obviously unappreciated overlap with clause 52 (4) makes it impossible to express any concluded view.

Value Added Tax

70. (1) In this Clause " exempt supply " " invoice " " tax " " taxable person " and " taxable supply " have the same meanings as in Part I of the Finance Act 1972 (hereinafter referred to as " the Act ") including any amendment or re-enactment thereof and any reference to the Value Added Tax (General) Regulations 1972 (S.I. 1972/1147) (hereinafter referred to as the V.A.T. Regulations) shall be treated as a reference to any enactment corresponding to those regulations for the time being in force in consequence of any amendment or re-enactment of those regulations.

(2) The Contractor shall be deemed not to have allowed in his tender for the tax payable by him as a taxable person to the Commissioners of Customs and Excise being tax chargeable on any taxable supplies to the Employer which are to be made under the Contract.

(3) (a) The Contractor shall not in any statement submitted under Clause 60 include any element on account of tax in any item or claim contained in or submitted with the statement.

(b) The Contractor shall concurrently with the submission of the statement referred to in sub-clause (3) (a) of this Clause furnish the Employer with a written estimate showing those supplies of goods and services and the values thereof included in the said statement and on which tax will be chargeable under Regulation 21 of the V.A.T. Regulations at a rate other than zero.

(4) At the same time as payment (other than payment in accordance with this sub-clause) for goods, or services which were the subject of a taxable supply provided by the Contractor as a taxable person to the Employer is made in accordance with the Contract there shall also be paid by the Employer a sum (separately identified by the Employer and in this Clause referred to as " the tax payment ") equal to the amount of tax payable by the Contractor on that supply. Within seven days of each payment the Contractor shall:—

(a) if he agrees with that tax payment or any part thereof issue to the Employer an authenticated receipt of the kind referred to in Regulation 21 (2) of the V.A.T. Regulations in respect of that payment or that part; and

(b) if he disagrees with that tax payment or any part thereof notify the Employer in writing stating the grounds of his disagreement.

(5) (a) If any dispute difference or question arises between the Employer and the Contractor in relation to any of the matters specified in Section 40 (1) of the Act then:—

(i) if the Employer so requires the Contractor shall refer the matter to the said Commissioners for their decision on it

(ii) if the Contractor refers the matter to the said Commissioners (whether or not in pursuance of sub-paragraph (i) above) and the Employer is dissatisfied with their decision on the matter the Contractor shall at the Employer's request refer the matter to a Value Added Tax Tribunal by way of appeal under Section 40 of the Act whether the Contractor is so dissatisfied or not

(iii) a sum of money equal to the amount of tax which the Contractor in making a deposit with the said Commissioners under Section 40 (3) (a) of the Act is required so to deposit shall be paid to the Contractor; and

(iv) if the Employer requires the Contractor to refer such a matter to the Tribunal in accordance with sub-paragraph (ii) above then he shall reimburse the Contractor any costs and any expenses reasonably and properly incurred in making that reference less any costs awarded to the Contractor by the Tribunal and the decision of the Tribunal shall be binding on the Employer to the same extent as it binds the Contractor.

(b) Clause 66 shall not apply to any dispute difference or question arising under paragraph (a) of this sub-clause.

(6) (a) The Employer shall without prejudice to his rights under any other Clause hereof be entitled to recover from the Contractor:—

(i) any tax payment made to the Contractor of a sum which is in excess of the sum (if any) which in all the circumstances was due in accordance with sub-clause (4) of this Clause

(ii) in respect of any sum of money deposited by the Contractor pursuant to sub-clause (5) (a) (iii) of this Clause a sum equal to the amount repaid under section 40 (4) of the Act together with any interest thereon which may have been determined thereunder.

(b) If the Contractor shall establish that the Commissioners have charged him in respect of a taxable supply for which he has received payment under this Clause tax greater in amount than the sum paid to him by the Employer the Employer shall subject to the provisions of sub-clause (5) of this Clause pay to the Contractor a sum equal to the difference between the tax previously paid and the tax charged to the Contractor by the Commissioners.

(7) If after the date for return of tenders the descriptions of any supplies of goods or services which at the date of tender are taxable or exempt supplies are with effect after the date for return of tenders modified or extended by or under the Act and that modification or extension shall result in the Contractor having to pay either more or less tax or greater or smaller amounts attributable to tax and that

tax or those amounts as the case may be shall be a direct expense or direct saving to the Contractor in carrying out the Works and not recoverable or allowable under the Contract or otherwise then there shall be paid to or allowed by the Contractor as appropriate a sum equivalent to that tax or amounts as the case may be.

Provided always that before that tax is included in any payment by the Employer or those amounts are included in any certificate by the Engineer as the case may be the Contractor shall supply all the information the Engineer requires to satisfy himself as to the Contractor's entitlement under this sub-clause.

(8) The Contractor shall upon demand pay to the Employer the amount of any sum due in accordance with sub-clauses (6) and (7) of this Clause and it shall be deemed a debt due by the Contractor to the Employer and shall be recoverable accordingly.

This clause modifies and improves a VAT clause previously numbered 71 and issued in March 1973, only three months before publication of the present Fifth Edition, for use with the Fourth Edition (see that clause commented on in B.C.F., 2nd suppt., under pp. 295 and 455). The general policy of the clause is the same as that adopted in the building industry by the RIBA contracts. Broadly speaking, the effect is that the contract prices (*i.e.* the Bill prices) are exclusive of VAT (sub-clause (2)) and any VAT chargeable by the Contractor to the Employer under current VAT legislation must be paid separately and in addition by the Employer on interim certificate (sub-clause (4)). A distinction needs to be made between this basic VAT obligation (if any) of the Employer and the Contractor's own " input " VAT on his own suppliers' invoices with which (subject to any *post-contract changes* in the incidence of that VAT which might result, for example, from the possible application of exempt or zero-rating status to the Contractor's activities, and which will be recoverable under the new modified sub-clause (7), *infra*) the Employer will not be otherwise concerned. The clause now provides simple but necessary machinery to enable the Employer to have some knowledge of the relevant VAT prior to its payment on interim certificate (sub-clause (3) (b), which is new, and may be a response to this particular omission being noted in the Second Supplement to B.C.F. at p. 455), and for ensuring that the necessary appeals are pursued so that excessive VAT is not paid if the Employer disputes the amount (paragraphs (a) and (b) of sub-clause (4) and sub-clause (5)), and for repayment or adjustment once the true liability has been established (sub-clause (6)). Not surprisingly, perhaps, these disputes are withdrawn from the ambit of the arbitration clause 66—see sub-clause (5) (b)—which will no doubt be a source of relief to engineering arbitrators. As already mentioned, should subsequent changes in the recoverability, status or incidence of the Contractor's input VAT occur after the contract (which may, of course, increase or decrease his costs) what is in effect a small tax fluctuation clause will come into operation (the new sub-clause (7)).

Given the complexity of the subject-matter, the clause is well drafted and the principles of it seem clear, so that the final resolution of financial and other disputes should present no difficulty, though on an administrative day-to-day basis it may not always be possible to secure speedy or precise determination of the VAT amounts for monthly interim payment—this, however, is inherent in the subject-matter and can hardly be avoided.

METRICATION

Metrication

71. (1) If any materials described in the Contract or ordered by the Engineer are described by dimensions in the metric or imperial measure and having used his best endeavours the Contractor cannot without undue delay or additional expense or at all procure such materials in the measure specified in the Contract but can obtain such materials in the other measure to dimensions approximating to those described in the Contract or ordered by the Engineer then the Contractor shall forthwith give written notice to the Engineer of these facts stating the dimensions to which such materials are procurable in the other measure. Such notice shall where practicable be given in sufficient time to enable the Engineer to consider and if necessary give effect to any design change which may be required and to avoid delay in the performance of the Contractor's other obligations under the Contract. Any additional cost or expense incurred by the Contractor as a result of any delay arising out of the Contractor's default under this sub-clause shall be borne by the Contractor.

(2) As soon as practicable after the receipt of any such notice under the preceding sub-clause the Engineer shall if he is satisfied that the Contractor has used his best endeavours to obtain materials to the dimensions described in the Contract or ordered by the Engineer and that they are not obtainable without undue delay or without putting the Contractor to additional expense either:—

(a) instruct the Contractor pursuant to Clause 13 to supply such materials (despite such delay or expense) in the dimensions described in the Contract or originally ordered by the Engineer; or

(b) give an order to the Contractor pursuant to Clause 51:—

  (i) to supply such materials to the dimensions stated in his said notice to be procurable instead of to the dimensions described in the Contract or originally ordered by the Engineer; or

  (ii) to make some other variation whereby the need to supply such materials to the dimensions described in the Contract or originally ordered by the Engineer will be avoided.

(3) This Clause shall apply irrespective of whether the materials in question are to be supplied in accordance with the Contract directly by the Contractor or indirectly by a Nominated Sub-contractor.

A metrication clause was published for use with the Fourth Edition in January 1969, which contained a number of anomalies adverse to the Employer's interests (see B.C.F. 1st suppt. under p. 455). The present clause has dealt with some, but by no means all, of those anomalies.

Presumably the object of the metrication clause was to deal with the transition period when metric goods and materials might not yet be available in that measure on the market, or goods in the imperial measure might have ceased to be available, and a designer and tendering Contractor alike might not have been able to foresee this. The anomalies noted in B.C.F. arose because the clause as drafted in 1969 permitted claims in situations very different from this. The old clause gave a blanket protection to the Contractor, in the form of a number of alternative *obligations* to give instructions, all involving financial compensation to the Contractor, one of which was mandatory on the Engineer whenever a shortage occurred in either measure, and made no saving either

(a) for cases where the Contractor had not placed his order in time, or should otherwise have foreseen and avoided the difficulty, or
(b) where the shortage was caused by ordinary industrial shortages and not by metrication at all, or
(c) where the shortage occurred as a result of a breach of contract on the part of a supplier or sub-contractor (so that the main Contractor should have been able to pursue his remedy against the guilty party), or
(d) for cases where the Engineer might wish to adhere to his original design or Specification in the original measure and accept some delay, paying for the consequences.

The present clause follows closely the form of the old clause, but has made a number of changes in the wording. Anomaly (a) above has been dealt with in the new clause—see the new words " having used his best endeavours " in sub-clause (1) and, very importantly, the new words " if he is satisfied that the Contractor has used his best endeavours " in sub-clause (2), which are clearly a condition precedent to any obligation or entitlement arising under that sub-clause. Anomaly (d) has also been specifically dealt with—see sub-clause (2) (a).

Anomalies (b) and (c) almost certainly have not been dealt with, since the " best endeavour " wording is obviously insufficient to deal with (b) and probably insufficient to deal with (c), though in the latter case it is perhaps arguable that Sub-contractors and suppliers in contractual relations with the Contractor are, like his own employees, his agents and therefore their defaults are for this purpose his defaults. These two anomalies seem unacceptable—no doubt non-metrication industrial shortages might be said to justify an extension of time, though Sub-contractor's or suppliers' breaches of contract certainly should not, since this would break the chain of liability and excuse the guilty party. But a right to financial compensation in either situation seems impossible to justify.

Moreover, the scope of these two anomalies may well have been *increased* in the present clause by reason of the addition of the new words " *or* additional expense " after " without undue delay " in sub-clause (1), and " *or* . . . not obtainable . . . without putting the Contractor to additional expense " in sub-clause (2). These might well be said to mean that, *even though the goods are readily available without delay in the contract measure*, the Contractor can apparently claim a change to the other measure etc. *or an instruction to continue and purchase the goods as described in the*

Contract, if he can show he has suffered " additional expense." What does " additional expense " mean in this context, however? A higher price than the Contractor has estimated? Or a higher price than the other measure? In any event, there are clear signs that the new words may have been inserted either *per incuriam*, or as " legal verbiage " intended to be construed *ejusdem generis* with " undue delay." This is because it will be noted that under sub-clause (2) (a), where the Engineer simply confirms that the original contract measure is to be supplied, the Contractor's remedy is expressed to be under clause 13—but that clause, it should be noted, only applies (see *supra*, p. 51) to instructions " which involve delay or disrupt arrangements or methods of construction so as to cause him to incur costs beyond that reasonably to have been foreseen "—so that (whether or not the reference to clause 13 (1) is *per incuriam*) the Contractor will be unable to claim compensation under that clause in a case of simple additional expense not caused by delay or disruption as such. It seems possible, therefore, that the " additional expense " wording is intended to cover either slight delay (*i.e.* delay less than " undue delay ") or no delay in the strict sense at all, but cases where the Contractor has nevertheless suffered financial loss due to *disruption*—the non-availability of the appropriate materials in the contract measure might easily cause *loss of productivity* in the affected part of the Works, for example, or indeed elsewhere in the Works if the Contractor re-arranged his programme, but no overall delay to the Works as a whole. The probability is, however, that the use of the word " or " before " additional expense " is *per incuriam* for " and " in both the new parts of the clause.

Even where the Engineer decides to vary the work under sub-clause (2) (b) of the present clause, it may well be a difficult question under clause 52 whether a valuation of the variation should take account of the delay and disruption avoided thereby, but the Contractor's alternative entitlement to delay or disturbance costs under sub-clause (2) (a) suggests that this is not the intention, in the case of the present clause of the contract at least.

SPECIAL CONDITIONS

Special Conditions

72. The following special conditions form part of the Conditions of Contract.

(Note: Any special conditions which it is desired to incorporate in the conditions of contract should be numbered consecutively with the foregoing conditions of contract.)

One matter which should be considered under the heading of Special Conditions is the express stipulation, for the avoidance of doubt, of the *procedural* law to govern an arbitration wherever it might be held, or possibly regulating the country in which it should be held whenever any international element is involved in the contract—see the commentary to clause 67, *supra*.

Contract Price Fluctuations Clause

It is now proposed to comment on the "Contract Price Fluctuations Clause," referred to on the cover of the Fifth Edition and published in June 1973 for optional use with the Fifth Edition.

CONTRACT PRICE FLUCTUATIONS

(1) The amount payable by the Employer to the Contractor upon the issue by the Engineer of an interim certificate pursuant to Clause 60 (2) or of the final certificate pursuant to Clause 60 (3) (other than amounts due under this Clause) shall be increased or decreased in accordance with the provisions of this Clause if there shall be any changes in the following Index Figures compiled by the Department of the Environment and published by Her Majesty's Stationery Office (HMSO) in the Monthly Bulletin of Construction Indices (Civil Engineering Works):—

(a) the Index of the Cost of Labour in Civil Engineering Construction;
(b) the Index of the Cost of Providing and Maintaining Constructional Plant and Equipment;
(c) the Indices of Constructional Material Prices applicable to those materials listed in sub-clause (4) of this Clause.

The net total of such increases and decreases shall be given effect to in determining the Contract Price.

(2) For the purpose of this Clause:—

(a) "Final Index Figure" shall mean any Index Figure appropriate to sub-clause (1) of this Clause not qualified in the said Bulletin as provisional;
(b) "Base Index Figure" shall mean the appropriate Final Index Figure applicable to the date 42 days prior to the date for the return of tenders;
(c) "Current Index Figure" shall mean the appropriate Final Index Figure to be applied in respect of any certificate issued or due to be issued by the Engineer pursuant to Clause 60 and shall be the appropriate Final Index Figure applicable to the date 42 days prior to:—

(i) the due date (or extended date) for completion; or
(ii) the date certified pursuant to Clause 48 of completion of the whole of the Works; or
(iii) the last day of the period to which the certificate relates;

whichever is the earliest.

Provided that in respect of any work the value of which is included in any such certificate and which work forms part of a Section for which the due date (or extended date) for completion or the date certified pursuant to Clause 48 of completion of such Section precedes the last day of the period to which the certificate relates the Current Index Figure shall be the Final Index Figure applicable to the date 42 days prior to whichever of these dates is the earliest.

(d) The "Effective Value" in respect of the whole or any Section of the Works shall be the difference between:—

(i) the amount which in the opinion of the Engineer is due to the Contractor under Clause 60 (2) (before deducting retention) or the amount due to the Contractor under Clause 60 (3) (but in each case before deducting sums previously paid on account) less any amounts for Dayworks Nominated Sub-contractors or any other items based on actual cost or current prices and any sums for increases or decreases in the Contract Price under this Clause;

and:—

(ii) the amount calculated in accordance with (i) above and included in the last preceding interim certificate issued by the

Engineer in accordance with Clause 60.

Provided that in the case of the first certificate the Effective Value shall be the amount calculated in accordance with sub-paragraph (i) above.

(3) The increase or decrease in the amounts otherwise payable under Clause 60 pursuant to sub-clause (1) of this Clause shall be calculated by multiplying the Effective Value by a Price Fluctuation Factor which shall be the net sum of the products obtained by multiplying each of the proportions given in (a) (b) and (c) of sub-clause (4) of this Clause by a fraction the numerator of which is the relevant Current Index Figure minus the relevant Base Index Figure and the denominator of which is the relevant Base Index Figure.

(4) For the purpose of calculating the Price Fluctuation Factor the proportions referred to in sub-clause (3) of this Clause shall (irrespective of the actual constituents of the work) be as follows and the total of such proportions shall amount to unity:—

(a) 0.____* in respect of labour and supervision costs subject to adjustment by reference to the Index referred to in sub-clause (1) (a) of this Clause;

(b) 0.____* in respect of costs of provision and use of all civil engineering plant road vehicles etc. which shall be subject to adjustment by reference to the Index referred to in sub-clause (1) (b) of this Clause:—

(c) the following proportions in respect of the materials named which shall be subject to adjustment by reference to the relevant indices referred to in sub-clause (1) (c) of this Clause:—

0.____* in respect of Aggregates

0.____* in respect of Bricks and Clay Products generally

0.____* in respect of Cements

0.____* in respect of Cast Iron products

0.____* in respect of Coated Roadstone for road pavements and bituminous products generally

0.____* in respect of Fuel for plant to which the Gas Oil Index will be applied.

0.____* in respect of Timber generally

0.____* in respect of Reinforcing steel and other metal sections

0.____* in respect of Fabricated Structural Steel

(d) 0.10 in respect of all other costs which shall not be subject to any adjustment;

Total 1.00.

(5) Provisional Index Figures in the Bulletin referred to in sub-clause (1) of this Clause may be used for the provisional adjustment of interim valuations but such adjustments shall be subsequently recalculated on the basis of the corresponding Final Index Figures.

(6) Clause 69 — Tax Fluctuations — shall not apply except to the extent that any matter dealt with therein is not covered by the Index of the Cost of Labour in Civil Engineering Construction.

*To be filled in by the Employer prior to inviting tenders.

This carefully drafted clause was first published on March 29, 1973, and republished in June 1973, for possible use with both the Fourth and Fifth Editions. (A separate virtually identical clause appropriate to fabricated structural steel contracts was published at the same time, but is not commented on here, since the present commentary is equally applicable to it.) It has the effect of automatically increasing or reducing the contract price according to the performance of a number of identified official indices of labour, plant and materials. National Insurance Payments Fluctuations, and certain other labour tax fluctuations, are not dealt with in the clause and are recoverable in any event under clause 69, *supra*, p. 283. As one would expect, the adjustments to the Contract Sum are made on interim certificates throughout the currency of the contract (see sub-clause (1), which first provides for the increases or decreases arrived at in accordance with the rules contained in the clause as a whole to be added to or subtracted from interim payments, and then in the last sentence of the sub-clause provides for the Contractor's final entitlement under the contract to be similarly increased or decreased—this latter follows from the definition of " Contract Price " in clause 1 (1) (i), *supra*, p. 16). The points to note are:

(a) that the base date is six weeks prior to the date for return of tenders—see sub-clause (2) (b); but the Current Index Figure against which the Base Figure is compared, will also be calculated on a date six weeks " in arrears " at the time of the last payment due under the clause—see sub-clause (2) (c). Accordingly the overall difference between the two dates will be the same as the overall construction period, and therefore fairly, if not exactly, representative of the inflation likely to have occurred, but the time-lag will be advantageous in order to enable the index information to be received and applied.

(b) that the clause continues to operate after the extended date for completion has passed, (*i.e.* when the Contractor will be liable to pay liquidated damages) but only at the index levels ruling (six weeks before) the extended date and not at subsequent index levels—see sub-clause (2) (c). It follows that the clause will not be allowed to operate downwards in favour of the Employer after that date, which is at the very least a theoretical possibility, even in present inflationary times; but on the other hand, the true view no doubt is that the liquidated damages will have been fixed, notionally at least, with this particular consequence of delay in mind (for this latter principle see B.C.F., pp. 176–177, discussing the old R.I.B.A. fluctuations, clause 31).

(c) that the rather formidable language of sub-clauses (2) (d) and (3) only means that on each certificate the Engineer will assess the full value *since the last certificate* of the additional work carried out by the Contractor himself (*i.e.* excluding Nominated Sub-contractors, and also, of course, excluding work where the Contractor has already been compensated for the fluctuations element by having been paid actual cost at current prices—as *e.g.* under clause 12 of the Conditions and many other provisions in the contract). Obviously other fluctuations payements, *e.g.* under clause 69 for labour taxes, or clause 70 (7) (VAT incidence changes) should also be excluded.

(d) that this " Effective Value " is then itself split into the sub-headings stipulated in sub-clause (4) by applying the stipulated fractions to it, and the necessary increases or decreases to be paid to the Contractor are then calculated upon the " Effective Value " of each sub-heading according to its own appropriate index increase or decrease. One minor difficulty which can arise on the wording of clause (2) (d) is that, while it provides for adjustment of calculations based on Provisional Index figures which are subsequently replaced by Final figures, it does not deal in terms with the common situation where the Engineer decides to allow additional sums in a later interim certificate in respect of work done in an earlier certificate—taken literally the present wording would require the application of an obviously inappropriate later index to these additional sums for the purpose of calculating the necessary fluctuations. In this case, however, the obviously correct adjustment can be made by the Engineer using his wide correcting powers in clause 60 (7), *supra*, p. 239, so as to correct the sums which should have been certified in the earlier certificate together with the appropriate fluctuations calculations relating to those sums.

(e) that 15 per cent. of the contract price (representing a generous allowance for overheads and profits) has been excluded from the operation of the clause—see sub-clause (4) (d)—which is a sensible protection for the Employer and which, if it does not accord with a tendering Contractor's own assessment of his pricing methods, can be compensated for by him when pricing the contract as a whole.

(f) that the percentages in sub-clause (4) (b), which will be inserted by the Employer's advisers, will inevitably be somewhat arbitrary —but Contractors who take a view on the percentages which differs from the Employer's can take this into account when tendering—and the Employer's advisers should appreciate that the modification of these percentages by agreement with or at the request of the successful tendering Contractor may possibly have an important price consequence, so that other tenderers should be given the opportunity to re-tender on the new percentage basis if the lowest tender price is considered to be of importance in the selection of the Contractor.

The clause is to be unreservedly welcomed as an ingenious and imaginative provision enormously simplifying the administrative procedures and expense of operating fluctuations clauses, and obviating the many disputes and serious abuses to which traditional fluctuations clauses can so easily give rise, especially in the light of the virtual impossibility of ascertaining accurate market prices at the base dates for materials in basic price lists (this latter particularly in the case of engineering as opposed to building contracts) or of restricting or controlling extravagant payments to labour in the form of bonuses negotiated by the Contractor after the contract is signed, but tied to the current rates of wages for labour and hence often recoverable under the terms of the old Variation of Price Clause. For the difficulties and abuses of fluctuations clauses (happily no longer possible if the present clause is used), see Hudson, 10th ed., pp. 566–568.

CHAPTER 3

FORMS ISSUED WITH THE CONDITIONS

IN this chapter it is proposed to give a very short commentary on the three Forms issued together with the Conditions, namely the Form of Tender (which in association with a subsequent written acceptance may itself constitute the full contract between the parties), the Form of Agreement (which normally but not necessarily will subsequently be concluded between the parties) and the Form of Bond (which, it is contemplated by clause 10 of the Conditions, may be an optional further document if required by the Tender).

PART I
FORM OF TENDER

SHORT DESCRIPTION
OF WORKS:—

All Permanent and Temporary Works in connection with*................
....

Form of Tender

(NOTE: The Appendix forms part of the Tender)

To ....
....
....

GENTLEMEN,

Having examined the Drawings, Conditions of Contract, Specification and Bill of Quantities for the construction of the above-mentioned Works (and the matters set out in the Appendix hereto), we offer to construct and complete the whole of the said Works and maintain the Permanent Works in conformity with the said Drawings, Conditions of Contract, Specification and Bill of Quantities for such sum as may be ascertained in accordance with the said Conditions of Contract.

We undertake to complete and deliver the whole of the Permanent Works comprised in the Contract within the time stated in the Appendix hereto.

If our tender is accepted we will, when required, provide two good and sufficient sureties or obtain the guarantee of a Bank or Insurance Company (to be approved in either case by you) to be jointly and severally bound with us in a sum equal to the percentage of the Tender Total as defined in the said Conditions of Contract for the due performance of the Contract under the terms of a Bond in the form annexed to the Conditions of Contract.

Unless and until a formal Agreement is prepared and executed this Tender, together with your written acceptance thereof, shall constitute a binding Contract between us.

We understand that you are not bound to accept the lowest or any tender you may receive.

†To the best of our knowledge and belief we have complied with the general

conditions required by the Fair Wages Resolution for the three months immediately preceding the date of this tender.

We are, Gentlemen,

Yours faithfully,

Signature ....

Address........................

....

Date...............................

* Complete as appropriate

† Delete if not required

See clause 1 (1) (g), 1 (1) (f) and 1 (1) (e) of the Conditions for definitions of the " Drawings " (which will be " referred to in the Specification "), " Specification " (" referred to in the Tender ") and " Contract " (this is rather a circular reference in the second paragraph of the Tender, since according to the definition in clause 1 (1) (e) the word includes all the other documents, including the priced Bills of Quantities and the written acceptance of the Tender). Eventually all these definitions interrelate—but it is highly desirable that, in addition to being referred to by name in the Tender, the Specification and Bills should on their faces be identified as the definitive tender documents and bear at least the initials or signature or stamp of the Contractor's authorised agents, or some other specific marking to avoid any possibility of confusion with other versions of the same document. Drawings will no doubt be identified by number in the Specification, but, even so, these again should be stamped or initialled as the Tender Drawings, with the date if possible, so as to avoid any possible confusion, which not infrequently occurs in practice, when the contract documents are ultimately drawn up for a formal contract, or when a simple written acceptance brings a contract into being.

It will be noted that the Tender contemplates a binding contract coming into existence on written acceptance notwithstanding the further obligation to execute a sealed contract (as to which, see clause 9 of the Conditions and the commentary thereto, *ante*, p. 38, and also to the Form of Agreement, Part II, *infra*, p. 301). Furthermore, this binding contract will arise *before* the provision of sureties in accordance with the provisions of the third paragraph of the Tender—see, for the interpretation of the (optional) surety obligation, clause 10 of the Conditions (where the use of the word " if " shows that it is an optional undertaking), which uses identical wording to that of the present document, and the commentary thereto, *ante*, pp. 38–39. However, if sureties are not forthcoming when required, the Employer will be able to rescind—see the South African case of *Swartz & Son (Pty) Ltd.* v. *Wolmaransstadt Town Council* [1960] 2 S.A.L.R. 1, but he may, of course, elect whether or not to do so and may instead affirm the contract. Note that clause 10 refers to " sureties " or a " guarantee "—this will mean a *secondary* liability of the bondsman assumed only on proof that the Contractor has failed duly to perform the contract, and that sums are in consequence properly due to the Employer as damages for breach of contract or under the terms of the Contract—not, as in some expressly worded bank guarantees which are becoming increasingly common in international commerce, a liability to pay on demand without need for proof of any default—see *Edward Owen* v. *Barclay's International Ltd.* [1977] 3 W.L.R. 764, (1977) 6 B.L.R. 1 (C.A. per Lord Denning M.R.), and see *General Surety and Guarantee Co.* v. *Francis Parker Ltd.* (1977) 6 B.L.R. 16, *per* Donaldson J., for the presumption against such an absolute obligation, in the absence of sufficiently explicit wording. See also the Form of Bond, Part III, *infra*, p. 302. Incidentally, the present document should strictly contain the " Delete if not required " symbol in the third paragraph, in the light of the optional nature of the obligation contemplated by clause 10 of the Conditions.

" *such sum as may be ascertained* . . ."

This tender document avoids any mention of price—see the definitions of " Tender Total " and " Contract Price " in clause 1 (1) (h) and 1 (1) (i) respectively, *ante*, p. 16, and the use of the " Contract Price " expression in the Form of Agreement and the commentary thereto, *infra*, pp. 301–302.

" *complete and deliver* "

The time obligation will be regulated by clause 41 of the Conditions (notification of Date of Commencement by Engineer within a reasonable time of written acceptance) and by clause 43 of the Conditions and the Appendix to the present document.

". . . *Permanent works comprised in the Contract* "

See the very wide definition of " Contract " as including virtually all the documents including the written acceptance.

FORM OF TENDER (APPENDIX)

APPENDIX

NOTE: Relevant Clause numbers are shown in brackets following the description

Amount of Bond (if any)	(10)		..........% of Tender Total	
Minimum Amount of Insurance	(23 (2))		£..........................	
Time for Completion	(43)		Liquidated Damages for Delay (47)	
			Column 1 (see Clause 47 (1))	
For the Whole of the Works——(a)	Weeks		£.........(b)	per Day/Week (c)
			Column 2	Column 3
For the following Sections			(see Clause 47 (2))	
Section (d)			£.........	£.........
......................——	Weeks		Per Day/Week (c)	per Day/Week (c)
Section (d)			£.........	£.........
......................——	Weeks		per Day/Week (c)	per Day/Week (c)
Section (d)			£.........	£.........
......................——	Weeks		per Day/Week (c)	per Day/Week (c)

Section (d)	£..........	£..........
......................—— Weeks	per Day/Week (c)	per Day/Week (c)
Period of Maintenance	(49 (1))	................Weeks
Vesting of Materials not on Site	(54 (1) and 60 (1)) (e)	
1............................	4................................	
2............................	5................................	
3............................	6................................	

Standard Method of Measurement adopted in preparation of Bills of Quantities (57) (f) ....
....

Percentage for adjustment of P.C. Sums	(59A (2) (b) and (5) (c))	..........%
Percentage of the Value of Goods and Materials to be included in Interim Certificates	(60 (2) (b))	..........%
Minimum Amount of Interim Certificates	(60 (2))	£...........

(a) To be completed in every case (by Contractor if not already stipulated).
(b) To be completed by Engineer in every case.
(c) Delete which not required.
(d) To be completed if required, with brief description.
(e) (If used) materials to which clauses apply are to be filled in by Engineer prior to inviting tenders.
(f) Insert here any amendment or modification adopted if different from that stated in Clause 57.

For the " Tender Total " in the " Amount of Bond " reference, see the definition and commentary under clause 1 (1) (h). For the great difficulty of ascertaining the contract intention in regard to the figures to be inserted in Column 2, and why and in what circumstances these should differ from those set out in Column 3 in respect of the same Section, see the commentary to clause 47 (2), *ante*, pp. 132–134. The alternative offered in the Appendix for days or weeks for liquidated damages will mean that, in the event of weeks being adopted, a full week must elapse before the damages will be recoverable, no apportionment or fractional calculation being possible, it is submitted. The footnote (e) in regard to clause 54 (1) is important as showing (which the clause in the Contract Conditions does not specifically say) that this provision is intended to be a discretionary and policy matter for the Engineer/Employer to decide at the pre-tender stage before the documents go out to contract.

PART II
FORM OF AGREEMENT

Form of Agreement

THIS AGREEMENT made the ....day of .... 19.......... BETWEEN .... of .... in the County of .... (hereinafter called " the Employer ") of the one part and............................ of .... in the County of ....(hereinafter called " the Contractor ") of the other part WHEREAS the Employer is desirous that certain Works should be constructed viz. the Permanent and Temporary Works in connection with.................. ....and has accepted a Tender by the Contractor for the Construction and completion of such Works and maintenance of the Permanent Works.

NOW THIS AGREEMENT WITNESSETH as follows:—

1. In this Agreement words and expressions shall have the same meanings as are respectively assigned to them in the Conditions of Contract hereinafter referred to.

2. The following documents shall be deemed to form and be read and construed as part of this Agreement, viz:—

(a) The said Tender.
(b) The Drawings.
(c) The Conditions of Contract.
(d) The Specification.
(e) The Priced Bill of Quantities.

3. In consideration of the payments to be made by the Employer to the Contractor as hereinafter mentioned the Contractor hereby covenants with the Employer to construct and complete the Works and maintain the Permanent Works in conformity in all respects with the provisions of the Contract.

4. The Employer hereby covenants to pay to the Contractor in consideration of the construction and completion of the Works and maintenance of the Permanent Works the Contract Price at the times and in the manner prescribed by the Contract.

IN WITNESS whereof the parties hereto have caused their respective Common Seals to be hereunto affixed (or have hereunto set their respective hands and seals) the day and year first above written

The Common Seal of...............
.... Limited
was hereunto affixed in the presence of:—
or
SIGNED SEALED AND DELIVERED
by the said ....
....
in the presence of:—
....
....

For the documentation in paragraph 2 see the commentary, *supra*, on the Form of Tender. The Agreement adds nothing in legal terms to a simple written acceptance of the Form of Tender, save for the very important fact that it will be under seal, the practical consequence of which will be the doubling of the effective period of limitation during which proceedings can be brought if defective work is discovered after completion. There seems no reason to suppose that the courts would not specifically enforce the execution of the present Agreement under seal, which will be a contractual obligation of the Contractor by virtue of his Tender, the incorporation in the Tender of the obligation set out in clause 9 of the Conditions, *ante*, p. 38, and the Employer's written acceptance of the Tender. For the limitations on the Engineer's authority to contract on behalf of the Employer (and hence, in the present context, to accept or negotiate changes in the Tender) see the commentary under clause 51, *supra*, p. 151.

" *Contract Price* "

All the Tender Documents in the present Fifth Edition avoid stating in numerical terms any overall contract price, though the " Tender Total " (relevant only for calculating the amount of the Bond under clause 10 and of the retention money instalments under clause 60 (4)) will either be stated in or capable of being calculated from the Priced Bills—see clause 1 (1) (h). " Contract Price " is defined in clause 1 (1) (i). Most surprisingly, the expression " Contract Price " is not used anywhere in clause 60, either in relation to interim certificates or the Final Certificate, and it might at first sight perhaps be thought that the inference was that clauses in the contract making, as from time to time they somewhat haphazardly do, provision for additions to or subtractions from the " Contract Price " should be given effect to only at the end of the project. It seems, however, from evidence elsewhere that the expression is intended to include sums payable on interim certificate as well as to refer to the sums finally due under the contract—see in particular clause 59B (4), which uses the expression " shall be included in the Contract Price " in a context which indicates that it will be paid on interim certificate, though later recovered back on final certificate.

PART III
FORM OF BOND

Form of Bond

BY THIS BOND [1] We .... of.. in the County of .... [2] We .... Limited whose registered office is at ....in the County of.................. [3] We................................. and ....carrying on business in partnership under the name or style of.. at .... in the County of.....................(hereinafter called " the Contractor ") [4] and .... of .... in the County of .... and .... of...in the County of......... .... [5] and .... Limited whose registered office is at...................................... in the County of .... (hereinafter called " the [4] Sureties/Surety ") are held and firmly bound unto .... (hereinafter called " the Employer ") in the sum of........................... pounds (£..................) for the payment of which sum the Contractor and the [4] Sureties/Surety bind themselves their successors and assigns jointly and severally by these presents.

Sealed with our respective seals and dated this.......... day of .... 19.......

WHEREAS the Contractor by an Agreement made between the Employer of the one part and the Contractor of the other part has entered into a Contract (hereinafter called " the said Contract ") for the construction and completion of the Works and maintenance of the Permanent Works as therein mentioned in conformity with the provisions of the said Contract.

NOW THE CONDITION of the above-written Bond is such that if the Contractor shall duly perform and observe all the terms provisions conditions and stipulations of the said Contract on the Contractor's part to be performed and observed according to the true purport intent and meaning thereof or if on default by the Contractor the Sureties/Surety shall satisfy and discharge the damages sustained by the Employer thereby up to the amount of the above-written Bond then this obligation shall be null and void but otherwise shall be and remain in full force and effect but no alteration in terms of the said Contract made by agreement between the Employer and the Contractor or in the extent or nature of the Works to be constructed completed and maintained thereunder and no allowance of time by the Employer or the Engineer under the said Contract nor any forbearance or forgiveness in or in respect of any matter or thing concerning the said Contract on the part of the Employer or the said Engineer shall in any way release the Sureties/Surety from any liability under the above-written Bond.

Signed Sealed and Delivered by the said
in the presence of:—

The Common Seal of
LIMITED
was hereunto affixed in the presence of:—

(*Similar forms of Attestation Clause for the Sureties or Surety*)

[1] *Is appropriate to an individual,* [2] *to a Limited Company and* [3] *to a Firm. Strike out whichever two are inappropriate.*

[4] *Is appropriate where there are two individual Sureties,* [5] *where the Surety is a Bank or Insurance Company. Strike out whichever is inappropriate.*

This is a common-form and effective bond, and calls for little comment —for the law on this subject see Hudson, 10th ed., Chapter 17. For the obligation to provide bondsmen and for the position in the event of failure to do so, see the commentary to clause 10, *ante*, pp. 38–39, and the Form of Tender, *supra*, p. 298.

This is self-evidently and expressly a bond enforceable only on proof of damage—not on demand, as is now not uncommon in some international contracting (see the commentary under Part I *supra*, pp. 298–299). The saving for alterations or waivers or other concessions made by the Employer in regard to contract obligations is a necessary feature of the bond, since under rather archaic legal rules bonds can be invalidated and the bondsman released in such events.

APPENDIX A

(At the date of this Article the new (1977) F.I.D.I.C. contract, closely modelled on the present Fifth I.C.E. Conditions had not been published. Nor had the new (1976) standard method " C.E.S.M.M.," commented on under clause 57, *ante*, pp. 193–195.)

THE USE OF BILLS OF QUANTITIES IN CIVIL ENGINEERING AND BUILDING CONTRACTS*

1. The Associated General Contractors of America and the Federacion Americana de la Industria de la Construccion have recently added the *imprimatur* of the approval of their organisations to the contract known as the " Conditions of Contract (International) for Works of Civil Engineering Construction " which has been widely used since 1957 for international projects (principally of a civil engineering character, though building projects can also theoretically be governed by the contract). These latter Conditions are published jointly by the two Federations in Europe known as the Federation Internationale des Ingenieurs-Conseils (F.I.D.I.C.) based at the Hague, and the Federation Internationale, des Entrepreneurs Europeens de Batiment et des Travaux Publics (F.I.E.E.B.T.P.), based in Paris. These " FIDIC " International Conditions were, however, modelled so closely on the then English I.C.E. Conditions (Fourth pre-1973 Edition) that, over by far the greater part of the contract (including particularly the parts relating to the subject-matter of the present article), they are virtually indistinguishable from the pre-1973 English domestic form. It is not the purpose of this article to comment in any detail on the " FIDIC " contract but to note that both in Europe and America its use will bring employers and contractors alike into contact with a possibly unfamiliar and, till now, almost exclusively English concept—namely the type of contract which has been variously described in England as a " Bill of Quantities " form of contract, or a contract " with Bills of Quantities " or " of which Bills of Quantities form part." A further factor tending in the same direction is the considerable effort being made by interested bodies in the United Kingdom (in particular the professional institutions associated with Quantity Surveying in the building industry) to promote the use of Bills of Quantities in the contracts (usually of course building contracts) used by property developers in the rest of Europe.

2. It may, therefore, be of interest to explain in the course of the present article exactly what English Bills of Quantities are; the precise practical and legal effects of incorporating Bills of Quantities into a contract in the manner which has developed in England; and, rather shortly, the arguments for and against this type of contract.

3. As a general observation, it may perhaps be said that, even in the United Kingdom, the various parties in the relevant industries who for years have been most concerned with the promotion and day-to-day use of Bills of Quantities appear to show little understanding of the legal and commercial consequences of doing so, so that a lawyer confronted with the technical documents themselves, and the archaic and often cryptic language used in the contract to effect their

* Article by the author reproduced from *Journal of Maritime Law and Commerce*, Washington D.C., U.S.A. (1975), Vol. 6, No. 3.

incorporation and define their function, can expect to derive little assistance from his own clients', or their so-called " experts'," instructions when endeavouring to assess the exact contractual implications of Bills in relation to a specific problem (for all practical purposes this will almost invariably arise in the form of a claim by the contractor for additional payment over the original contract price).

(a) *The function of Bills of Quantities*

4. Ignoring " cost-plus " and " labour-only " types of contract, there are broadly speaking three main categories of possible building or civil engineering contracts where prices are tendered in competition.[1] Firstly, where the work is not sufficiently pre-planned or capable of estimation at the time of tender, a contract may be used incorporating what is usually called a " Schedule of Rates " or " Schedule of Prices," in which the contractor undertakes to do any or all of a number of described construction-processes, involving both work and the supply of materials, at quoted prices per unit of construction. In such contracts there is, in principle, neither a stated total contract price, nor any possible variation of the contract work as such (unless some quite different construction-process from those quoted is ultimately called for), since the instructions given by the Engineer or Architect from time to time, or any drawings or specifications supplied by them, merely constitute the identification of the precise extent of the contract work, and so ultimately of the contract price. These contracts are usually known in English parlance as " Schedule " contracts. Secondly, where the work is capable of more precise pre-estimation, there may be a contract in which the Contractor, after carefully analysing the specification and drawings so as to ascertain all the various construction processes and expenditure required, tenders a total contract price. This price will not be altered, apart from some express special provision like a fluctuations clause, unless the contract work has been varied or changed in some way on the orders of the Employer or Engineer. Such contracts are often known in England as " Lump Sum " contracts, and any document incorporated into them showing units of construction and prices (sometimes also confusingly called a " Schedule of Rates ") *exists only for the purpose of valuing such variations.* (These contracts appear to be the commonest type of contract, incidentally, used in the United States for the generality of relatively sophisticated and pre-planned building projects, though the use of " Schedule "-type contracts in civil engineering is not, I believe, uncommon.) Any Bills of Quantities found in association with contracts of this second type have no legal effect beyond their use in the valuation of variations and, in some cases, as a basis for interim payment. Indeed, such Bills may not even perform these functions, and may simply be used as a guide issued to contractors at the tender stage by the Employer's advisers so as to reduce the time and expense of the estimating process required to arrive at the " Lump Sum." In the English jargon of 50 years ago, such Bills " do not form part of the contract," and the contract remains essentially a " Lump Sum " contract. Thirdly and finally, there is the modern English contract " of which Quantities form part " or " with Quantities " which is now used in by far the greater proportion of projects in the United Kingdom in both the building and civil engineering industries. In these contracts, the employer's advisers have themselves analysed the drawings and specification and have broken down the entire project into its constituent trades and processes, and have then stated, directly by calculation from the drawings where possible,

[1] See for a summary of these types of contract, *Hudson on Building and Engineering Contracts*, (10th ed., 1970), pp. 200–212.

or by estimation where not, precise quantities for each construction-process. The tendering contractors are required when tendering to price the individual items in these Bills of Quantities, which are then grossed up to produce a total contract sum, and this priced document usually fulfils three quite separate contractual functions, namely (a) as a basis for valuing variations, (b) as a basis for assessing interim payments and (c) *as a basis for producing a final re-measurement or re-calculation of the ultimate contract sum, whether or not the work has been varied.* This last function, with which the present article is primarily concerned, is frequently confused, even by the most ardent and experienced protagonists of Bills of Quantities, with the variation valuation function, and it is of cardinal importance to understand the distinction. How the ultimate quantities can differ from the original contract quantities independently of any variation of the work being called for may at first sight seem puzzling, but, broadly speaking, this can happen in two ways. Firstly, while wherever possible the rules for measuring quantities enable them to be calculated with precision from the drawings and specification without any need for physical measurement on site, the precise quantities of some work items cannot be the subject of exact calculation beforehand and often will need physical measurement—*e.g.* the removal of soft or unsatisfactory material from excavations and the substitution of imported fill, which will depend upon the ascertainment of the suitability of the sub-soil after excavation has taken place, and on physical measurement or estimation of the quantities of unsuitable material ultimately replaced. Again, separate prices may be included for excavation in rock where found, which obviously cannot be determined precisely beforehand. This type of difference in quantities is particularly to be expected in civil engineering contracts, or in the " engineering " parts (*i.e.* excavation, for example) of building contracts, and can at times be relatively substantial. Secondly, there may simply have been errors in " taking-off " or estimating the quantities from the Contract drawings or other documents when preparing the Bills. In a large and complicated project this can easily happen.

(b) *What Bills of Quantities are*

5. The Bills of Quantities themselves consist of fairly bulky paged documents, usually sub-divided into individual numbered Bills. In the building industry, the sub-division usually, though not necessarily, is into trades commencing, for example, with Site Clearance, Earthworks and Excavation, and continuing with Concrete, Brickwork, Asphalting, Roofing, Carpentry, Joinery, Structural Steel, Metalwork, Plumbing and Engineering, Plastering, Painting and Decorating, Electrical, Drainage, Fencing, and so on. Each Bill is in the form of a series of vertical columns, commencing on the left with an item number for identification purposes in combination with the page and Bill number, followed by successive columns for a technical verbal description of the unit of construction requiring to be priced, a specified numbered quantity of the unit in question, the price or rate per unit (this will have to be inserted by the contractor), and finally, in the right hand column, the grossed-up price, resulting from multiplication of the billed quantities by the contractor's quoted rates, also inserted by the contractor. These last prices are then totalled by the contractor at the bottom of each page, and carried forward by him to a summary total at the end of each Bill. The totals for each Bill are themselves usually carried forward to an overall grand summary of the individual Bill totals, which will then show the total tendered contract price. In the civil engineering industry, the Bills are, however, more usually sub-divided into the different constituent parts of the project rather than into trades—in a sewerage contract, for example, various Bills might

cover different lengths of pipe or tunnel, possibly identified by manhole numbers or chainages, and other Bills might deal separately with structures, such as water-treatment plant, sedimentation tanks, pumping station, manholes themselves, and so on. In both industries, there is invariably an initial Bill called the " Preliminary Bill " or " Preliminaries." * This Bill, which as will be seen is of fundamental commercial importance, contains what are called " Preliminary Items " of generalised expenditure relating to the project as a whole—*e.g.* insurance, initial mobilisation of plant and labour force, provision of site huts or other accommodation, site electricity and water supply, superintendence, and possibly some special items of plant not directly affected by work quantities (such as tower cranes, concrete batching plants or some types of " temporary works "). While one might have thought that the Preliminaries Bills should contain only items of once-for-all expenditure which are quite independent of the amount of work done, the Standard Methods of Measurement (as to which, see below) in fact appear to have no policy in the matter, and recommend variously that some matters governed by the length of the contract period, or by the physical quantity of work (*e.g.* supervision) should be included as well.** Rather oddly, these Preliminary Bills often also contain references to each numbered condition of the contract, against which the Contractor may be invited to price. The precise purpose or consequence of this last practice seems to be unexplained. Contractors in the United Kingdom in fact frequently ignore and do not price a large proportion of the individual items in the Preliminary Bill, and also themselves often " write-in " large and vaguely worded items into the total for the Preliminaries Bill, (or indeed in the General Summary at the end of the Bills) with the objects firstly, of obtaining a relatively large initial payment at the beginning of the contract for financing purposes under the provisions for interim payment, and, secondly, to justify the calculation of a larger claim than might otherwise be the case should any delay or disturbance to the contractor's programme arise as a result of some matter for which the employer is responsible (on the basis that delay to the whole contract will increase " Preliminary " expenditure).***

(c) *Standard Methods of Measurement*

6. It is obvious that detailed documents which are designed to effect an ultimate remeasurement of the whole work will fail in their intention unless there is agreement as to the exact technical manner of measuring the quantities of work—thus, to take a simple example, measurement of the cubic content of excavations could theoretically be based on (a) physical measurement of the excavated material with or without an allowance for " bulking " or (b) physical measurement of the void left by the excavation or (c) by a theoretical calculation from the volume shown on the drawings of the structure to be accommodated by the excavation without any allowance for any necessary excavation for working-space outside its area and depth or (d) by a calculation as in (c), but with physical measurement of, or an arbitrary price or allowance for, " overbreak " outside the net volume of the structure. Bills of Quantities will, therefore, need to contain provisions indicating the methods of measurement to be used for all the very varied work-processes in the Bills. To avoid the complication, expense

* In C.E.S.M.M. (1976) now, however, called " General Items "—see the commentary under clause 57, *ante*, pp. 193–194.

** See now, however, the new system of " Method Related Charges " in C.E.S.M.M. (1976), referred to *ante*, pp. 193–194.

*** Compare the " Adjustment Item " now suggested under Section 5.26 of C.E.S.M.M. (1976).

and misunderstanding that this might involve, contracts in both industries in the United Kingdom incorporate by reference what are called " Standard Methods of Measurement " which are published by the appropriate professional bodies. These documents do not, however, confine themselves to their principal function of prescribing the precise methods of measuring work, but, with the no doubt originally laudable additional object of attempting to secure uniformity of all tendering procedures and practices, advise, enjoin, or recommend, with varying degrees of urgency, the selection of particular units of construction into which the work should be sub-divided for pricing purposes. These recommendations take the form of suggesting or requiring that certain items of described work should, on the one hand, be deemed to include particular ancillary or subsidiary processes inevitably or contingently necessary to complete that work, or, on the other hand, that they should not (*i.e.* that the ancillary or subsidiary or contingent process in question should be separately described and priced in the Bills). To take a simple example, the Standard Methods state that where concrete is described and priced, the necessary form-work or shuttering should be separately described and priced; again, excavation in rock (with appropriate definitions of rock) is to be separately described and priced from excavation in ordinary material. On the other hand, the rates for excavation may be required to include for any necessary pumping, or abnormal dewatering methods, or timbering and sheet-piling for the support of sides of excavations, and so on. Making all allowances for the relatively simpler work-processes in civil engineering, it must be commented that the Standard Method of Measurement for building work published by the Royal Institute of Chartered Surveyors and the National Federation of Building Trade Employers in the United Kingdom is a document of remarkable complexity and length, running to 110 closely printed pages, and requiring considerable time and the most high degree of professional skill both in preparing Bills which comply with it in all respects, and in giving effect to the Bills on remeasurement of the work. The object appears to have been to break down building work to the last possible minutiae of its composite elements, and this task appears to have been pursued with a zeal which may have blinded those concerned to the overwhelming practical convenience and relative cheapness of administration if larger and more general composite items or units are used. A significant, if perhaps unexpected, consequence has been that this growing complication of Bills of Quantities, far from encountering opposition from the contracting side of the building industry (which has discovered that, for reasons which will be explained, it can be a fertile source of escalation of the contract price with little or no " downside " potential) has actually led to pressure by the contractors themselves on their own members to refuse to tender for contracts without Bills of Quantities, with the result that an agreement between members of the English N.F.B.T.E. not to tender for any contract over £8,000 in value which did not use Bills of Quantities came up for review by the courts under the provisions of the English Restrictive Trade Practices Act of 1956, and was ultimately held to be contrary to the public interest.[2] Furthermore, great pressures are exerted on employers in the building industry in the U.K., both by architects and quantity surveyors (the latter being, of course, the profession employed in the U.K. both to draw up the Bills of Quantities at the tender stage and thereafter to administer, in association with the architect, the contractual provisions relating to interim and final payment) to use Bills of Quantities, although a " Lump Sum " version of the standard form of building contract (*i.e.* not using Bills) is available. Those in a position

[2] *Re Birmingham Association of Building Trade Employers' Agreement* [1963] 1 W.L.R. 484.

to follow and understand the growth of the " Bills of Quantity industry " in the U.K., and indeed the growth of the power and influence of quantity surveyors as against that of the architects, may view this trend with some concern.

7. In the civil engineering industry in the U.K. there is no separate profession concerned with, or having a vested interest in, the preparation or administration of Bills of Quantities and this, coupled perhaps with the greater simplicity of engineering processes, has produced a shorter and somewhat more elastic Standard Method of Measurement in that industry.* It can also be said that the nature of civil engineering work itself makes for possibly considerable disparities in the ultimate quantities (without any change in the permanent work itself) and for this reason the existence of a contract using Bills, which in essence introduces a " Schedule " element into the contract price, has more commercial justification than in building contracts, and may possibly obtain a somewhat keener price than a " Lump Sum " type of contract would do in the same circumstances, since any contingent element in the price to cover unforeseen differences in the ultimate quantities is removed. Indeed, it is not uncommon in engineering Bills of Quantities to find what are described expressly as " provisional quantity items "—these have no special legal consequences, but would seem merely to amount to a warning that the item in question is likely to be particularly unpredictable as to quantity.

8. In both industries, however, it remains a serious criticism of Bills prepared in accordance with either of the U.K. Standard Methods that, for all their complication, the Standard Methods do not in fact provide a clear-cut basis for remeasuring any ultimate disparities in quantities. One basic reason for this is, as already stated, that neither Standard Method lays down any really clear scheme or set of principles defining the exact items of expenditure which are to be included in the Preliminaries Bills and not in the later unit rates of construction.** Another is that it appears to be widely accepted by quantity surveyors and engineers that the contractor should be allowed to allocate overheads and other general or particular allowances or items of expenditure in any way he wishes, as between the Preliminaries Bill on the one hand and the later Bills containing the unit construction rates on the other, without giving any overt indication in the documents of what he has done. As a result, whenever differences of any substance occur in the ultimate quantities, claims for additional payment over and above the quoted unit rates of construction are frequently advanced by contractors, and in the ensuing argument they will make assertions (which it is accordingly not possible to refute conclusively from any available documents) as to their original internal pricing of the contract, with a view to showing that the unit construction-rates are inadequate and inappropriate—and this whether the ultimate quantities have moved in an upward or downward direction.[3] Even if it was considered justifiable or desirable, the absence of a really clear scheme regulating adjustments to be made to the Bill rates or prices to take account of increases or decreases in the ultimate quantities (which would in any case not be necessary but for the lack of precision permitted in the pricing of the Preliminaries Bills) is a fertile source of dispute and, from the employer's point of view, of uncertainty as to the ultimate contract price, and a major cause of

* See now, however, C.E.S.M.M. (1976), which appears to have moved noticeably in the direction of greater complication and sub-division of items and descriptions.

** C.E.S.M.M., *via* its system of " Method Related Charges," does now seem to be moving in this direction—see the commentary under clause 57, *ante*, pp. 193–194.

[3] See further for this, paragraph 10, *infra*.

the popularity of contracts using Bills with the contracting side of the industry in the U.K.

(d) *The legal and practical effects of Bills of Quantities*

9. Originally, Bills of Quantities were used in building contracts only, and with little or no express incorporation or precise indication of their intended function. Indeed, their first use was as a corporate service to the tendering contractors, and it was the successful tenderer, and not the employer, who was to be liable for the quantity surveyor's fees. Ultimately, in the face of very imprecise incorporating provisions in the building contract (often consisting of a simple undertaking to do the work " in accordance with the Drawings and the Bills ") the courts in England recognised the parties' intention that Bills so incorporated should have a full contractual remeasurement function.[4] At the present day it remains, however, of fundamental importance to consider the exact terms in which the Bills are incorporated into the contract. Until the latest Fifth (post-1973) ICE Conditions, completely different wording was used in the two industries in the U.K. In the building industry, the standard form, after requiring the Contractor to carry out and complete the work " described in the Contract Bills *and* shown on the Drawings," provides nevertheless that " the work included in the Contract Sum is deemed to be that which is set out in the Contract Bills," and that any " error in quantity " is " deemed to be a variation required by the Architect." [5] In the civil engineering industry, the Fourth (pre-1973) Edition of the standard form (as also the present FIDIC International Contract) stated that " the quantities . . . in the Bill of Quantities are the estimated quantities but they are not to be taken as the actual and correct quantities . . . the Engineer shall . . . ascertain and determine by admeasurement the value in accordance with the Contract of work done in accordance with the Contract." [6] Before 1973 these were the only contractual provisions regulating the function of the Bills of Quantities. The latest Fifth Edition (1973) of the English domestic ICE forms has now, however, adopted two further sets of wording in addition to the old " admeasurement " requirement, which are of considerable significance in encouraging (and indeed in the second case expressly permitting) claims for payment at rates and prices different from those in the Bills of Quantities—these are: (a) " Any error in description in the Bill . . . or omission therefrom . . . shall be corrected by the Engineer and the value of the work carried out shall be ascertained in accordance with . . . (the provisions of the variation clause) " [7] and (b) " Should the actual quantities executed . . . be greater or less than those stated . . . the Engineer shall . . . determine on appropriate increase or decrease of any rates or prices rendered unreasonable or inapplicable in consequence thereof. . . ." [8] These are the sum total at the present day of the provisions of the relevant contracts which bring about and regulate the remeasurement function of the Bills. In addition, of course, all the English contracts have quite separate and fairly elaborate provisions for the valuation of any variations which may have been ordered on behalf of the Employer. While relying initially on the prices in the Bills for the valuation of variations, these separate provisions all

---

4 For the case law and history of the emergence of Bills of Quantities to their present status see *Hudson on Building and Engineering Contracts* (10th ed., 1970), pp. 509–515, and the unreported cases of *Patman & Fotheringham Ltd.* v. *Pilditch* (1904) and *Meigh & Green* v. *Stockingford Colliery Co. Ltd.* (1922) there referred to.

5 See Clauses 12 (1) and (2), RIBA Conditions of Contract.

6 See Clauses 56 and 57, Fourth Edition ICE and FIDIC International Conditions.

7 See Clause 55 (2), Fifth Edition ICE Conditions.

8 See Clause 56 (2), Fifth Edition ICE Conditions.

expressly permit the contract (*i.e.* Bill) prices to be departed from, and a " fair valuation " or " reasonable price " basis substituted, wherever the Engineer or Architect considers this to be reasonable. Under the building standard forms and the Fifth (post-1973) Edition of the civil engineering standard form, therefore, it is clear from the above wording invoking the variation-valuation clauses of the contracts in question that differences in quantities may result in departures from the bill prices, at the discretion of the Architect or Engineer or an arbitrator, notwithstanding that no variation has been ordered on the employer's behalf. The " admeasurement " provision in the Fourth Edition of the ICE and the current " FIDIC " form of contract is, however, silent about the principles to be used on remeasurement, and while certain rather obscure references to discrepancies in the ultimate quantities which are to be found in the ICE variation clause have enabled contractors to claim for many years that in the event of such discrepancies it is the intention of the clause that they should be paid at " reasonable prices " differing from those in the Bills, as permitted by the terms of the clause in the case of variations proper, the better view has been that this is not so.[9] Even on this latter view, however, the lack of precision in the Standard Methods which has already been mentioned as to the exact elements of expenditure to be priced in the Preliminary Bills has enabled civil engineering contractors to claim additional payment under the preliminary items themselves as part of the process of " admeasurement " under the remeasurement clause, on the argument that increases will have taken place in the quantity or amount of expenditure allegedly priced in those items as a consequence of any substantial alteration in the construction quantities, even though different prices for the actual construction processes in the later part of the bills may not be allowed.

10. The first practical consequence of Bills of Quantities as they have come to be used in the U.K. is, therefore, that in addition to their permitting the work to be measured in the event of differences in the ultimate quantities, the employer cannot, even where there have been no variations ordered by him, rely on that remeasurement being carried out at the unit prices in the Bills, nor are there any clear criteria (as *e.g.* some agreed contractual percentage addition or reduction in the prices in the event of the differences in quantities taking place in either direction reaching stipulated proportions) laid down for the adjustment of the unit prices on remeasurement. This uncertainty of price in practice invariably operates in an upward direction, though theoretically it can operate downwards, since the uncertainty of the contractor's distribution of his expenses between the preliminary Bills and the later Bills, and the fact that he is not required to disclose the make-up of his prices at any pre-contract stage, makes it extremely difficult for the employer's advisers to advance or justify lower prices, if the quantities differ, while on the other hand contractors, with their special internal knowledge of their pricing and construction methods and intentions, can easily advance arguments based on an alleged allocation of expenditure when pricing the contract to justify a higher price, in whichever direction the quantities may have moved (other things being equal, of course, unit prices should usually be *reduced*, if the ultimate quantities are greater, but it is virtually unheard-of in the U.K. for engineers to attempt to reduce the Bill rates when valuing such work under the remeasurement provisions).

11. The second practical consequence of the use of Bills derives from the

[9] See Clause 51 (2), first proviso, of both the Fourth Edition ICE and the FIDIC International Conditions, commented on in detail by the author in his *Building and Civil Engineering Standard Forms* (1969), pp. 382–384 and in his *The International Civil Engineering Contract* (1974), pp. 98–99.

wording of the associated provisions incorporating a Standard Method of Measurement. Thus the RIBA standard building forms provide that " unless otherwise expressly stated in respect of any specified item or items " the Bills " shall be deemed to have been prepared in accordance with the principles of the Standard Method . . . ," [10] and the full and very obscure wording of the previously quoted remeasurement provision itself is " Any error *in description* or in quantity in *or omission of items from* the . . . Bills . . . *shall be corrected* and deemed to be a variation." This wording has been fastened upon by contractors to produce a new and ingenious type of claim, wherever it can be shown that the extraordinarily complicated recommendations of the Standard Method as to the sub-division of work for pricing purposes have not been followed. Thus if, for example, the quantities of concrete (which, from an examination of the drawings or the specification or Bills themselves, is obviously to be fair-faced) are set out in the Bills without any separate items for form-work or shuttering, the contractor will claim additional payment on the ground that there has been an " omission of an item " from the Bills. Again, if a single price for excavation is quoted, but rock is encountered in the excavations, a claim will be advanced on the basis that the contract price was for " soft " and that a separate item of rock should have been included in the Bills. The legal basis of this type of " Standard Method " claim rests upon one unsatisfactory case many years ago in England where the point was in fact conceded.[11] Even though the view has been expressed that these claims are without foundation,[12] quantity surveyors and architects in England regularly advise their employers that such claims should be allowed. (The great difficulty of proving damage in any claim for professional negligence against the quantity surveyor in such a case, as he will argue that a higher price would have been tendered on properly prepared Bills, no doubt reinforces this tendency.) It should be appreciated that this type of claim only needs to be advanced where there is, by definition, no variation—in other words, where the contract as a whole indicates clearly that the particular process or expenditure is part of the described work which the Contractor has to carry out. (In other cases, of course, the variation-valuation provisions will be sufficient to protect the contractor). Such claims are essentially without merit, because either (a) the contractor has noticed the " error " in the Bills when pricing, and if he intended to claim was stealing a march on both the employer and his competitors in tendering an apparently lower price or (b) he has not noticed the " error," in which case his prices will in any event have included for the process or contingent expenditure involved.

12. In the civil engineering industry, the incorporating words are " Except where any general or detailed description of the work in the Bill of Quantities expressly shows to the contrary, Bills of Quantities shall be deemed to have been prepared and measurements shall be made according to the procedure set forth in the Standard Method . . ." and in the Fourth (pre-1973) Edition there was no " correction of errors or omissions " provision as in the RIBA standard forms, or such as now exists in Clause 55 (2) of the Fifth Edition.[13] Nevertheless, contractors in this industry have been, if anything, even more prone to advance this type of claim, partly because the Bills in this industry are usually prepared by ordinary practical engineers without the meticulous professional training in the preparation of Bills enjoyed by quantity surveyors in the building industry;

---

10 See Clause 12 (1).

11 *Bryant & Sons Limited* v. *Birmingham Saturday Fund* [1938] 1 All E.R. 503.

12 See *Hudson on Building and Engineering Contracts*, 10th ed., pp. 513–520 and the author's *Building and Civil Engineering Standard Forms*, pp. 21–23 where the matter is fully discussed.

13 Quoted *supra*, paragraph 9.

partly because engineering projects and processes are far more variable than building contracts and considerable flexibility may be needed in describing the work and in adapting the Standard Method to a particular project; partly because the Standard Method is, as a consequence, itself a more flexible document and so open to differing interpretations; and partly because one " omitted " item may produce very large sums of money by reason of the very large quantities to be found in such contracts. Here, too, the " Standard Method " basis of claim seems even more doubtful [14] (except in the case of the latest English Fifth Edition of the ICE Conditions, which has undoubtedly sought deliberately to permit this type of claim by its new wording in Clause 55 (2) [15]), and is equally devoid of merit.

13. It should be appreciated that what is primarily at stake in this " Standard Method " type of claim is the fundamental " inclusive price principle," as it has been called in the English courts,[16] which obtains in all legal systems in the interpretation of nearly all service contracts—namely that where prices are quoted for described work they are, in the absence of some contrary indication, the *whole* price, inclusive of all contingent or necessary work needed in order to do and complete the described work. The " Standard Method " claim is based on the argument that the incorporation of a complicated external document for a very obvious purpose (indicating, as already explained, the technical methods of measuring the quantities) will, once that external document is read in detail, mean that, by virtue of what are essentially only recommendations as to the sub-division of work for pricing purposes, the contract prices are no longer to be inclusive of all the necessary work processes if the document is not meticulously followed, and no matter how obviously this is the case. It is interesting to note that in a civil engineering case,[16] where no actual question of Standard Method incorporation was involved but where the wording of a recommendation in the Standard Method had itself been repeated *verbatim* in the Bills (the wording referred to an additional item being provided for working space outside the plan area of structures, but no such item was in fact to be found in one part of the Bills), six judges (though not the final majority of three in the House of Lords) out of the total of nine involved in the case during its various stages were in favour of the " inclusive price principle," and would have rejected the claim.

(e) *Advantages and Disadvantages of Bills*

14. The two arguments advanced in favour of Bills of Quantities are, first, that they greatly reduce the cost of tendering, and, second, that they provide a more meticulous and accurate basis for comparing tenders and valuing variations and interim payments. The first of these arguments may seem theoretically correct but requires very careful examination. All substantial contractors in the United Kingdom now employ highly skilled estimating staff, with full quantity surveying qualifications. Quite often, and this is particularly the case in the civil engineering industry, there may even be separate teams, one making an overall " prime-cost " estimate of the cost of the entire project on the one hand, and the other meticulously analysing and notionally pricing the Bill items, partly as a cross-check on the prime-cost estimate of the other team, and partly to detect any errors in quantities in the Bills or to identify items where a likelihood of

[14] See the author's *Building and Civil Engineering Standard Forms*, pp. 402–405,, and his *The International Form of Civil Engineering Contract* (1974), pp. 116–120.

[15] Quoted *supra*, paragraph 9.

[16] *A. F. Farr Limited* v. *Ministry of Transport* (1965) unreported, illustrated in *Hudson on Building and Engineering Contracts*, 10th ed., p. 520.

relatively substantial variations or differences in ultimate quantities exists. If such items can be successfully identified, low unit-prices where the quantities overstate the likely ultimate quantities, and high unit-prices where they understate them, will produce an apparently attractive total tender price which will secure the contract as against other competing contractors, or possibly induce the employer to undertake the project without savings, but which on remeasurement will produce a very substantial increase in both the contract price and the contractor's level of profitability. It seems very doubtful, therefore, if the existence of Bills does indeed reduce the amount of the contractors estimating staff devoted to a project at the tender stage, and many might consider that the uses to which Bills are now put in the United Kingdom may have actually increased it. Indeed, the premium for survival as an engineering contractor in the U.K. today must rest as much upon skill in exploiting the profit opportunities afforded by the contract documents (generally known as " loop-hole engineering ") as in the efficiency of the control and management of the project itself. The argument of the lower tender price also proceeds upon the assumption that contractors do in fact price individual work processes within a project in the way in which they are set out in the Bills, rather like a list of goods in a shop, and add up the total to reach the tender price. This is nearly always a fiction—in the two teams referred to above it will be the " prime-cost " team's valuation which will prevail in the contractor's mind for tendering purposes in the event of any difference between the two, and any such difference will then be distributed by him across the individual items in the Bills prior to tender.* Objective prices for a detailed individual work process simply do not exist in all but the most straightforward cases—availability of labour and prevailing rates of wages in the district of the project; questions of physical access or congestion or other difficulties of the site; the type of plant and organisation; the availability or otherwise of previously written-down plant or of cheap sources of materials; seasonal considerations; and many other factors all combine to make an individual item-pricing exercise highly academic, even if clear-cut allocations of expenditure as between preliminary and direct construction costs were available, as they are not, in the Bills. When the prospect of rates higher than the Bill rates being used on remeasurement, either because of simple difference in quantities or because of the " Standard Method " type of claim, and the " tailored " element in the contract price resulting from the contractor's analysis at the tender stage of likely variations or errors in the quantities, are compared against the possibly illusory savings of professional estimating man-power on the contractor's side and the very substantial professional fees payable by the employer for quantity surveying services in addition to those of architects, engineers and other consultants, it seems highly unlikely that the ultimate cost of most projects will be reduced by the use of Bills of Quantities.

15. The second variation-valuation argument has even less validity. This occurs partly because, in the case of variations, the U.K. standard forms enable the Bill rates to be escaped from without difficulty—understandably, since it will often not be right to value variations, by reason of their timing or extent or character, on the same basis as properly co-ordinated and pre-planned work. In the case of comparing tenders and for purposes of interim payment, too, the Bills are not precise documents by reason of the absence of any clear principle in distinguishing between preliminary and other expenditure—furthermore the heavy weighting of the Preliminary Bills in order to obtain substantial early

---

* This view is corroborated by the general " Adjustment Item " now expressly contemplated by Section 5.26 of C.E.S.M.M. (1976).

payments, and in consequence a financing element in the price, is, as already stated, yet another use to which the Bills can be put by the tendering contractor. Indeed, excessive weighting of the prices of the earlier work-processes in a project, such as bulk excavation and foundation work (the practice is sometimes described among contractors as " front-loading ") is a further not uncommon device used by contractors to obtain an early financing element in the contract price, which not surprisingly is often accompanied by increasing pressures as the contract proceeds to escape, on one pretext or another, from the correspondingly leaner prices quoted by the contractor for the later work-processes. Bills of Quantities could only perform the function of permitting an accurate comparison of tenders, or precise measurement or valuation of variations or interim payment, if the successful Contractor was contractually obliged to give a detailed make-up of his tender prices before the contract was signed. Contractors in the U.K. have always resisted any such proposal violently, though they are usually ready and indeed anxious to assert an internal make-up of their prices once the time for making a claim has arrived.

16. For the several reasons which I have endeavoured to make plain in this Article, employers and their professional advisers in countries other than the U.K. would do well to ponder carefully before yielding to the blandishments of those putting forward contracts for construction projects which use Bills of Quantities, certainly if their incorporation is effected in the terms which are now nearly universal in the U.K. The principal criticism is not that remeasurement is permitted (*i.e.* the " Schedule " principle), but that it is permitted in a way which positively encourages apparently binding " Schedule " prices to be departed from to an unpredictable extent governed by no clear criteria. The effect is to present employers and their advisers with an apparently attractive original contract price based on individual rates and prices which will almost invariably be exceeded, even in the absence of any variation called for by the employer, should the ultimate quantities change markedly in either direction, and which quite possibly, with the " Standard Method " type of claim, may do so even in cases where no change in the quantities has occurred. Many of these disadvantages could, of course, be cured by altering and improving the policies and draftsmanship of the incorporating provisions.

Appendix B

This Appendix is concerned with what in England became known from 1977 onwards as " the Rule in *Dawnays' Case* "—namely that Employers were liable to pay contractors in full on interim certificate without any right of defence or set-off where breach of contract by the contractor was alleged. Part I consists of an article in the L.Q.R. in January 1973 criticising in depth the legal basis of the rule and suggesting that reconsideration of the matter by the House of Lords was urgently necessary. Part II is an article written one year later recording the over-ruling of the *Dawnays* cases and the restoration of the preceding *status quo* effected by the House of Lords in July 1973 in the *Gilbert-Ash* case, and Part III is a Note in L.Q.R. in 1975 analysing the precise extent of the later House of Lords decision in *Mottram Consultants* v. *Bernard Sunley Ltd.*

Part I

SET BACK TO SET-OFF*

1. In April 1971 the Court of Appeal reached a conclusion in the case of *Dawnays Limited* v. *F. G. Minter Ltd.*[1] which surprised, if it did not astonish, most practitioners in the somewhat specialist field of building and civil engineering contracts. It is perhaps a mark of its novel character, as well of its everyday practical importance, that between April 1971 and July 3, 1972 no less than five unsuccessful attempts have subsequently been made in the Court of Appeal to avoid or distinguish its consequences,[2] and in November 1972 H.H. Judge Fay Q.C. felt able to distinguish these decisions in the somewhat differently worded contract which was before him, though it is understood this latter case is also under appeal.[3] To date leave to appeal to the House of Lords has been consistently refused by the Court of Appeal, and that House itself refused leave to appeal in the original *Dawnays* case. Since the judgments in both *Dawnays* and the subsequent cases are relatively brief and by no means clear as to their exact *ratio decidendi*, and since the principle, on the basis of some dicta in those judgments, can be expected to be invoked throughout the whole field of commerce wherever progress payments are due to contractors for work and materials, it may be useful, at the present stage of what has been a meteoric career, to examine this new doctrine of the Court of Appeal with some care. Unfortunately, in view of the complexity of the contracts under review this can only be done at some length.

---

* Article by the author reproduced from (1973) 89 L.Q.R. pp. 36–63.

1 [1971] 1 W.L.R. 1205; [1971] 2 All E.R. 1389 (Lord Denning M.R., Edmund Davies and Stamp L.JJ.).

2 *Frederick Mark Ltd.* v. *Schield* [1972] 1 Lloyd's Rep. 9 (Davies, Karminski and Roskill L.JJ.); *G.K.N. Foundations Ltd.* v *Wandsworth London Borough Council* (1972) 70 L.G.R. 276 (Lord Denning M.R , Roskill L.J. and Sir Gordon Willmer); *John Thompson Horseley Bridge Ltd.* v. *Wellingborough Steel & Construction Co. Ltd.*, Bar Library No. 41a, February 18, 1972 (Lord Denning M.R., Phillimore and Roskill L.JJ.); *Token Construction Co. Ltd.* v. *Naviewland Properties Ltd.*, Bar Library No. 170, May 11, 1972 (Davies, Karminski and Orr L.JJ.); *Carter Horseley (Engineers) Ltd.* and *John Thompson Horseley Bridge Ltd. and another* v. *Dawnays Ltd.*, Bar Library 208a, July 3, 1972 (Lord Denning M.R., Phillimore and Cairns L.JJ.).

3 *Modern Engineering (Bristol) Ltd.* v. *Gilbert Ash (Southern) Ltd.*, November 3, 1972, H.H. Judge Fay Q.C., unreported.

2. Briefly, the principle appears to be that in contracts of a certain kind a defendant sued for the price of work done, whether for an interim or progress payment on account on the one hand or for a final payment on the other, will not *as a matter of construction of the contract* be permitted to set-off in the same proceedings a claim for damages for breach of the contract, unless the damages are " *liquidated and ascertained sums which are established or admitted as being due* " [4] (in this context " established " means, the judgments make clear, established in arbitration or legal proceedings). The practical effect is that in these contracts a plaintiff suing for the price of his work is entitled to judgment, with no stay of execution however weighty and grave the nature of the defendant's counterclaim, and notwithstanding the long delay before litigation or arbitration can finally dispose of the issue. As yet no claim has reached the Court of Appeal where the plaintiff is a contractor's liquidator, though a division of the Court presided over by Edmund Davies L.J. has applied the principle, with some obvious misgivings, in a case where the court clearly considered that the defendant's counterclaim was not only almost certainly well-founded, but that to allow judgment to be entered might well drive the defendant himself into liquidation.[5]

3. While the cases so far have with one exception [6] been cases where the plaintiff's right to payment arose upon a certificate of a building owner's architect relating to the work of the plaintiff, either as a main or sub- or sub-sub-contractor, there are dicta, particularly of the Master of the Rolls, which suggest this may not necessarily be the vital factor, and that the commercial urgency of financing the contractor through the project,[7] or (in cases where the plaintiff is a subcontractor) the fact that the moneys claimed by the plaintiff have been actually received by the defendant from the building owner or from a superior contractor,[8] may be in some way relevant to the *ratio decidendi*. It is submitted, however, that these are, on analysis—particularly since the principle has now been applied to final payments where no financing element any longer exists,[9] and also to main contracts where no question of money in the hands of the defendant can arise [10] —only arguments *ad hominem* to justify the decision on the instant facts. But the principle could certainly apply, if the Court of Appeal's present enthusiasm for it continues undiminished, to cases of automatic progress or stage payments, which are common in commerce, as opposed to the more sophisticated certified payments based on professional advisers' opinions and valuations which are usually found in building and civil engineering contracts. In cases where certificates are involved, the principle may be said to accord a status of " temporary finality " to the certificate in question.

4. Before considering the cases in detail, it may be useful to examine the relevant parts of the main RIBA contract and its related " FASS " sub-contract, and then to consider the pre-*Dawnays* position, as it was then thought to be, in regard to the three commonest matters giving rise to a set-off or counterclaim,

---

[4] *Per* Lord Denning M.R. [1971] 1 W.L.R. at p. 1209. See also his comments in the *G.K.N.* case, *infra*, paragraph 11.

[5] *Token Construction Ltd.* v. *Naviewland Properties Ltd.*, C. of A., May 11, 1972.

[6] *G.K.N. (Foundations) Ltd.* v. *Wandsworth B.C.*, where the contract substituted the employer for the architect in the formal payment provisions.

[7] *Dawnays*' Case at p. 1209G.

[8] *Ibid.*, at p. 1210, and see the Master of the Rolls' dicta in the *John Thompson* case *infra*, para. 12.

[9] *G.K.N. Foundations Ltd.* v. *Wandsworth B.C.*, *infra*, para. 11; *Token Construction Ltd.* v. *Naviewland Properties Ltd.*, *infra*, para. 13; the second *John Thompson* case, *infra*, para.14; and see the original *Dawnay* case itself.

[10] *Mark* v. *Schield* [1972] 1 Lloyd's Rep. 9, *infra*, para 10.

namely disputes as to valuation, defective work, and delay in completion. As a preliminary comment, although attempts have obviously been made to co-ordinate the FASS and RIBA forms, the draftsmanship shows a different provenance. There is often considerable difficulty in relating the two, even though the FASS form is expressed to be supplemental to the main contract and expressly provides that the sub-contractor is deemed to have notice of the provisions of the main contract.

5. Dealing first with the questions of defective work and valuation, the scheme of all modern contracts is that these are initially resolved by the architect when certifying interim payment, since not only is he expressly enjoined by clause 30 (2) of the RIBA main contract forms only to value work " properly executed," but the concept of " value " in any event clearly involves a deduction or no allowance at all, depending on the facts, if work is known to be defective. So far as damages for delay are concerned, these are in all modern contracts dealt with under machinery separate from the payments machinery and are not to be dealt with in the certificate for payment. It is in fact crucial to an understanding of the issue in the *Dawnays* case to examine with the greatest care the actual provisions and scheme in both contracts for payment on the one hand, and for liquidated or other damages for delay on the other, and it must be said that the reports available give little indication of this having been done. The main points to notice are:

(a) In both the RIBA and FASS forms, each interim valuation is a retrospective valuation of *all* the work done to date, *not of the work done since the previous certificate*—see clauses 30 (2) and 11 (a) of the RIBA and FASS forms. This is of fundamental importance.

(b) The sum to be certified, whether on interim payment or final payment, is expressed to be the difference between the latest total valuation and *the total previously paid, not the total previously certified.* (The actual words are " less any instalments previously paid under this condition " in clause 30 (2) of the RIBA contract, and " less the amounts previously paid " in clause 11 (b) (iii) of the FASS form. See also clause 30 (6) of the RIBA forms in regard to the final certificate.) This is one indication in the contracts that the draftsman at least did not consider that earlier certificates would be invariably and automatically honoured as the court now says that they must be. Thus, it is difficult to see how an architect can now, in the light of the *Dawnays* decision, issue a later interim certificate which complies strictly with the contract if an earlier certificate has not been paid, since his later certificate, if it gives credit only for prior payments as required by the contract, will enable the contractor, on the *Dawnays* principle, to summary judgment twice over on the two certificates, each of which will overlap the other in certifying monetary payment for the same work.

(c) It follows from this scheme of payment that initial valuation or other decisions reflected in earlier interim certificates are constantly liable to be revised upwards or downwards in later certificates, and earlier approval of work passed for payment may subsequently be withdrawn on defects becoming apparent to the architect. A moment's consideration, and a few examples, will show why this approach is in fact vitally necessary in a building project. Thus in February the architect may allow the value of concrete poured during January which appears to be satisfactory. In March it begins to fail in a way which shows that in breach of contract it was poured during a period of heavy frost, or perhaps that the form-work was struck after inadequate curing time, so it must now be condemned and removed. He therefore deducts and disallows its value in his March certificate. Similarly if a structural failure due to bad workmanship occurs after an earlier payment. Again, in January he values a large consignment of bricks brought to the site on the basis of the vouchers supplied by the contractor. In ensuing months, the number of unused bricks diminishes, but completed brickwork, valued on the quite different basis of the prices for brickwork in the Bills of Quantities, takes its place. The later certificates will reduce and finally extinguish the delivered brick allowance, while substituting the brickwork valuation. Again, for many different reasons valuations or measurements which can only be approximate in an earlier month can be made much more precisely in a later month, or a special financial claim of the contractor (*e.g.* for fluctuations in wage rates) provisionally allowed on interim certificate may turn out to be unjustified and so be withdrawn in a later certificate. All this means that, both in regard to defective work and to questions of valuation, or the allowance of special permitted claims on interim certificate, even the *Dawnays* " temporary finality " of an interim certificate must yield to a later revising interim or final certificate, quite possibly issued after proceedings for summary judgment may have been commenced on the earlier certificate.

(d) Both contracts, however, specify certain matters to be dealt with by deduction from the amount certified on interim or even the final certificate—it should be noted that the architect himself makes no deduction in his certificates, but it is the employer who has to make the deduction from the amount which has been certified. In the RIBA form, this can occur under clause 2 (1), (employment of other contractors on contractor's refusal to obey an instruction), clauses 19 (3) and 20A (payment of insurance premiums by the employer on contractor's default) and clause 27 (c) (direct payments from the employer to unpaid sub-contractors) as well as, very importantly in the context of the *Dawnays* case, under clause 22 (liquidated damages for delay). Each of these provisions in the main RIBA contract deals specifically with the particular right of deduction involved, and very similar if not identical wording is used in each case—

> " shall be recoverable from the Contractor by the Employer as a debt or may be deducted by him from any monies due or to become due to the Contractor under this Contract " (clause 2 (1)); " may deduct . . . the amount paid from any monies due or to become due to the Contractor " (clauses 19 (3) and 20A); " and deduct the same from any sum due or to become due to the Contractor " (clause 27 (c)); and " the Contractor shall pay or allow to the Employer a sum . . . as liquidated and ascertained damages . . . and the Employer may deduct such sum from any monies due or to become due to the Contractor under this Contract " (clause 22).

The FASS form approaches such matters of counterclaim somewhat differently. This contract also contains, as one would expect, a number of specific provisions imposing a liability on the sub-contractor to pay or allow sums to the main contractor (*e.g.* clause 9 (b), where the main contractor has himself carried out remedial work necessitated by the sub-contractor's defective work; a more general provision—clause 3 (b)—indemnifying the Contractor against liabilities incurred by the latter whether under the main contract or otherwise as the result of sub-contractor's work; and in particular clause 8 (a)), in regard to damages for delay, under which the sub-contractor is to " pay *or allow* to the Contractor a sum equivalent to any loss or damage suffered or incurred by the Contractor "). The matter of deduction is then dealt with in regard to all such possible counterclaims under the terms of the sub-contract by one general provision. This is Clause 13, which under the heading " Contractor's Right to Deduction or Set-Off " provides:

> " The Contractor shall notwithstanding anything in this Sub-Contract be entitled to deduct from or set-off against any money due from him to the Sub-Contractor . . . any sum or sums which the Sub-Contractor is liable to pay to the Contractor under this Sub-Contract."

(This particular clause was the principal provision of the sub-contract considered by the Court of Appeal in *Dawnays'* case and was there, it is submitted wrongly, held to be ineffective to assist the defendant.)

(e) Clauses 8 (a) and 13 of the FASS form are, in the special context of delay, complemented by clause 27 (b) of the RIBA form, which enjoins the main contractor, on receipt of an acrhitect's certificate which includes the value of a nominated sub-contractor's work, to pay the sums in question to the sub-contractor within a stipulated period less only (*inter alia*) " any sum to which the Contractor may be entitled in respect of delay in the completion of the sub-contract works."

(f) In both contracts there is a stipulated completion date, and machinery for extending the time for completion, which in the RIBA form depends solely upon the Architect's opinion, and in the FASS form upon the Architect and Contractor acting together in a rather complicated collaboration. Both contracts, however, provide for a special architect's certificate that the work should reasonably have been completed by a certain date, and this certificate is in each case made a condition precedent to the right to deduct damages for delay. In the case of the RIBA form the damages are liquidated damages, but as has been seen, in the FASS form they are general damages. There is in fact a good reason for this, because in the case of sub-contracts it is virtually impossible to make any pre-estimate of the damage likely to be suffered by the main contractor should the sub-contractor's work be delayed—whether any damage is suffered at all depends on whether the sub-contractor's work in the event turns out to be on the " critical path " of the main contractor's own actual progress. Furthermore, the quantum of the damage will vary enormously according to the state of progress elsewhere.

(g) Both contracts confer important express rights on the Contractor or Sub-Contractor in the event of the non-payment of a certificate—a right of determination under clause 26 (i) (a) of the RIBA form, and a right to suspend work under clause 11 (e) of the FASS form. These provisions have in fact been criticised as being unnecessary in view of the ordinary common-law protection of a contractor on non-payment, but they seem doubly so if the Contractor is entitled to summary judgment on a certificate with no set-off or stay of execution permissible. In addition, clause 11 (d) of the FASS form very importantly assumes that interim certificates are not binding on the Contractor, since it requires the main Contractor to assist the Sub-Contractor in arbitration if the latter is aggrieved by the amount certified in respect of the sub-contract work on interim certificate.

(h) The main RIBA contract contains three further most important provisions in this context. Firstly, clause 30 (8) provides expressly that no certificate other than the final certificate " shall of itself be conclusive evidence that any works or materials to which it relates are in accordance with the contract." Secondly, clause 35 (3) enables an arbitrator to " ascertain and award any sum which ought to have been the subject of or included in any certificate and to open up, review and revise *any* certificate, opinion, decision, requirement or notice and to determine all matters in dispute . . . in the same manner as if no such certificate, opinion, decision, requirement, or notice had been given." Thirdly, clause 35 (2), while providing that references to arbitration " shall not be opened " until after practical completion of the main contract work, makes a specific exception (*inter alia*) for disputes, " whether or not a certificate has been improperly withheld or is not in accordance with these Conditions." An identical provision to this last is to be found in the arbitration clause of the FASS form (first proviso to clause 24). That form certainly assumes (see clause 11 (d) summarised in (h), *supra*) that disputes as to the amount certified on interim certificate can be arbitrated during the currency of the main contract work.

6. It is now possible to state the position in regard to interim certificates as it was understood before *Dawnays*' case.[11] This can perhaps be best indicated by a series of propositions, *viz.*—

(a) If there was no arbitration clause, a contractor would usually be unable to sue unless he obtained a certificate—it was a condition precedent to the contractor's right to claim payment.

(b) An interim certificate, though it created a " debt due " in the above sense, was never, however, conclusive as to the quality of work—compare clause 30 (8) of the RIBA form—so that an employer could, even in the absence of an arbitration clause, obtain leave to defend in the usual way on sufficiently cogent prima facie evidence despite the fact that his own architect might have taken a different view from himself in allowing work to be passed.

(c) An interim certificate was even more vulnerable to a counterclaim or set-off for delay since, under the scheme of virtually all contracts in this field since the nineteenth century, questions of damages for delay, liquidated or otherwise, could not be dealt with in the payment certificates themselves. Indeed a body of law grew up to the effect that, where the right conferred by the contract was to deduct liquidated damages, failure to deduct either on interim or final certificates might deprive the employer of a right to damages accrued up to the time of the payment.[12] Furthermore, it is perhaps not insignificant that one of the earliest leading cases on assignees taking subject to equities [13] was in fact a building case where an employer was held entitled to set-off both a claim for damages in the form of loss of rents resulting from the builder's delays and also for defective work—obviously unliquidated claims.

(d) Where, however, there was an applicable arbitration clause in general terms, *a fortiori* a clause expressly permitting an early arbitration of the dispute in question, the builder might recover more than had been certified, or notwithstanding the absence of any interim certificate. This was the view expressed tentatively in Hudson, Tenth Edition; though in the case of the RIBA forms the view depended on the exact meaning to be attached to the words " whether or not a certificate has been improperly withheld or is not in accordance with these conditions " in clause 30 (2) of the RIBA conditions, which expressly prevented early arbitration of other disputes. As already stated, clause 11 (d) of the FASS forms clearly assumes that such claims can be arbitrated in both contracts.

7. Before considering the recent cases, it may be useful to point out what the cases applying the *Dawnays* principle do not, or have not so far, decided.

(a) They are all cases where, on the facts, the plaintiff relies on a certificate, and the defendant has either taken a different view from the architect, or has failed to secure the necessary counter-certification (*e.g.* with regard to damages for delay) by the architect. As already explained, whenever an architect agrees with the employer's contention with regard to defective work or as to valuation, the appropriate adjustment can be made good in the next payment certificate,

---

11 See *e.g. Hudson's Building and Engineering Contracts* (10th ed., 1970), pp. 492–497.

12 See the cases collected in *Hudson, supra*, at pp. 635–636.

13 *Young* v. *Kitchin* (1878) 3 Ex.D. 127.

and that later certificate must, it is submitted, afford a good defence to an action brought on the earlier certificate.

(b) The right to deduct liquidated damages for delay, in the case of the main RIBA form of contract (provided the architect has duly certified as required by clause 22 of the Conditions) is so explicit that it may be regarded as unaffected by any decision or judgment handed down so far.

(c) The cases are concerned only with a concept of " temporary finality." They do not preclude any of the matters raised by the employer or superior contractor by way of set-off from being litigated or arbitrated in other proceedings.

8. Finally, it should perhaps be pointed out that there is nothing objectionable in itself in a concept of " temporary finality." This already existed before *Dawnays* wherever a contractor was unable to recover payment without an appropriate interim certificate, in the absence of an applicable arbitration clause. In such a case he would be bound, at least until the end of the work, assuming an arbitration or litigation was then permitted. Nor is it unreasonable that an architect's decision on disputed matters should be stipulated to be binding on both parties until the end of the work, particularly where he is free to revise that decision in any subsequent certificate. But the potential injustice, in times when even solvent companies can and do put subsidiary companies into liquidation with impunity, is so great that it is submitted that only clear wording should bring this about. The criticism of the *Dawnays* line of cases is that they appear to ride rough-shod over the express wording of the contracts with which they deal, and in some cases even over the architect's opinion, on the basis of some sort of overriding commercial principle which is to apply not only in the absence of clear wording but it seems in the face of apparently conflicting wording. Furthermore, there seems no justification, on any possible view, for applying the principle, whatever it may be, to the final payments under the contract, as it will be seen has now been done in at least two cases.

9. It is now proposed to summarise and discuss the cases in chronological order. The *fons et origo* is *Dawnays Limited* v. *F. G. Minter Ltd.*[14] This was a case of a steel-work sub-contractor inder the FASS form suing a main contractor upon an architect's certificate. That certificate had been accompanied by a notice to the sub-contractor from the architect warning him that the certificate did not take account of damages for delay in completion caused by the sub-contractor's delays. It is not clear from the report whether the architect had certified on the subject of delay in accordance with the proviso to clause 8 (a) of the FASS form —the Master of the Rolls appears to have treated this as irrelevant, though stating that, since the architect had apparently decided to revise an earlier decision about the period of delay, " in any case no sums were payable for delay." The main contractor (who had been paid for the sub-contractor's work on the certificate in question) had in Order 14 proceedings obtained a stay under section 4 of the Arbitration Act on the basis of his cross-claim for damages for delay. The Court of Appeal lifted the stay, indicating that the question of damages could be arbitrated in due course at the end of the work in the main contract. Lord Denning M.R., after stating the facts and referring to the provisions for interim payments said:

> " That is the ordinary understanding in these matters. The interim certificate is regarded as the equivalent of cash. The sub-contractor needs the money so as to get on with the rest of his work. On principle, and in practice, once a certificate is issued, it must be paid, save only for permitted deductions." [15]

[14] [1971] 1 W.L.R. 1205.
[15] *Ibid.* at p. 1208.

(It may be pointed out that no element of financing was in fact present in the *Dawnays* case, since the payment (subject only to retention, presumably) seems to have been either the only or the last payment due to the plaintiffs, though it would certainly only be an early interim certificate of the defendant contractors.) In dealing with clause 13 of the FASS form (and the related clause 27 (b) of the RIBA form) the Master of the Rolls said:

> ". . . I hold that both clauses . . . refer to liquidated and ascertained sums which are established or admitted as being due. The reason is because, taking the various words, it is only such a sum which is capable of being 'deducted'; it is only such a sum as to which it can be said that the sub-contractor is 'liable to pay': it is only such a sum of which it can be said that the main contractor is 'entitled.' . . . It is not permissible to deduct claims which are unliquidated and are still matters of dispute." [16]

The Master of the Rolls, after referring to the lapse of time before arbitration proceedings might be commenced and concluded, continued:

> " Every businessman knows the reason why interim certificates are issued and why they have to be honoured. It is so that the sub-contractor can have the money in hand to get on with his work and the further work he has to do . . . an interim certificate is to be regarded virtually as cash, like a bill of exchange. It must be honoured. Payment must not be withheld on account of cross-claims, whether good or bad—except so far as the contract specifically provides. Otherwise any main contractor could always get out of payment by making all sorts of unfounded cross-claims. All the more so in a case like the present where the main contractors have actually received the money." [17]

Edmund Davies L.J., similarly dismissed clause 13:

> " Can Mr. Knight utilise clause 13 in that way in the present case? In my judgment clearly not. Its concluding words refer to 'any sum or sums which the sub-contractor *is* liable to pay'—not '*may* be liable to pay,' nor 'which is asserted by the main contractor to be due.' . . . The simple fact is that the defendants can assert no definite and liquidated sum as being unquestionably due to them from the plaintiffs. Unless and until they can do this they cannot invoke clause 13 in the manner sought by the defendants. Any other view would involve that the sub-contractor could be kept out of his money . . . for an unconscionable period with possibly disastrous results. I should require the clearest possible provision in the sub-contract before I would conclude that this is what the parties understood and intended. . . ." [18]

Edmund Davies L.J. then went on to hold (contrary to the Master of the Rolls and the headnote) that clause 27 (b) of the main contract (which did use the word " may ") would have enabled the main contractor to deduct had it been included in the sub-contract. Finally, Stamp L.J. gave a very short judgment expressing his agreement with the Master of the Rolls' interpretation of clause 27 (b) of the main contract, and that it applied only to ascertained sums in the same way as clause 13 of the sub-contract.

The above passages contain all the statements of principle made in the case. It may be commented:

---

[16] *Ibid.*, at p. 1209.
[17] *Ibid.*, at pp. 1209, 1210
[18] *Ibid.*, at pp. 1210, 1211.

(1) The judgments are short, and appear to treat the whole matter as one of first impression and as admitting of little difficulty or doubt.

(2) There is no recognition of the fact that the FASS contract is formally expressed to be " supplemental " to the main contract, and in addition by clause 1 that the Sub-Contractor is deemed to have notice of all the provisions of the main contract, and by clause 3 that he gives indemnities to the main contractor against failure to observe and comply with all its provisions. That main contract undoubtedly permits the deduction of liquidated damages for delay (this may or may not explain the express reservations made in the judgments as to liquidated and ascertained sums).

(3) The interpretation placed by the court on clause 13 of the FASS contract and by two of its members on clause 27 (b) of the main RIBA contract robs both provisions of any force at all and renders them wholly otiose. The FASS form makes no provision at any point for payment of liquidated and ascertained sums by the sub-contractor to the main contractor. On what, therefore, is the right of deduction in clauses 13 and 27 (b) supposed to operate? In addition, there is no possible need for an express right to deduct sums " established or admitted as being due "—these would be recoverable either in the action which " established " them, or on Order 14 if admitted. Furthermore, " established," on the meaning given to it by the court, could never give rise to a right to deduct since, as all the judges point out, the process of " establishing " will take a long time and must inevitably succeed and not precede the issue of interim certificates, if not the final certificate. Indeed, no arbitration of any of the counter-rights of the main contractor against the sub-contractor conferred by the sub-contract can even be " entered on " until completion of the main contract work—1st proviso, clause 24, FASS. In practice, of course, the whole concept of " established or admitted to be due " makes no commercial sense—in real life contractors in serious default do not usually make admissions however obvious their responsibility.

(4) The reasoning behind the interpretation fastens on the words " is liable " in clause 13 and " may be entitled " in clause 27 (b). The court ignores altogether the words " under this Sub-Contract " in clause 13. These indicate, it is respectfully submitted, the general intention already mentioned to permit deduction wherever the sub-contract stipulates for counter-payments or allowances by the sub-contractor—" any sum or sums which the Sub-Contractor is liable to pay to the Contractor under this Sub-Contract " might as well have been expressed " any sum or sums which the Sub-Contractor is required to pay to the Contractor under this Sub-Contract." The provision is also particularly necessary to safeguard the main contractor against the special right to suspend work conferred on the Sub-Contractor for non-payment of an interim certificate in clause 11 (e). Hence the words " notwithstanding anything in this sub-contract " in clause 13.

(5) The interpretation ignores the fact, already mentioned, that while the architect is not to deal with damages for delay in his payments certificate, a special certificate of the architect (under clause 8 (a)) is expressly required before the contractor is entitled to damages from the sub-contractor. The words are " Provided that the Contractor shall not be entitled to claim any loss or damage under this clause unless the Architect shall have issued to the Contractor a certificate in writing. . . ." Surely this is a certificate " establishing " " liability " and " entitling " the Contractor to damages, even for the purposes of the Court of Appeal's interpretation? This certificate, as it happens, is required to be in identical terms with the certificate provided for under clause 22 of the main

contract, which, as already stated, does permit liquidated damages to be deducted in the clearest possible terms. Furthermore, the use of the word " allow " in the expression " The Contractor shall pay or *allow* " in clause 8 (a) of the FASS form is significantly identical with the expression used in clause 22 of the main contract, and in each case contemplates deduction from a sum claimed. The only difference between the two sets of machinery is that, whereas in the main contract the employer's deduction is a precise one (which, incidentally, he calculates for himself without any architect's certificate) it is inevitably less precise in the sub-contract. Thus the court's interpretation seems to mean that the Architect's certification is accepted as binding in regard to the sums due on the interim certificate, but rejected as to the certificate establishing liability to pay damages for delay—on this view, the latter certificate might as well never be given at all, since it clearly will not bind an arbitrator and consequently appears to have no practical function whatever.

(6) The concept of what " every businessman knows " propounded by the Master of the Rolls is, with the greatest respect, not in accordance with commercial realities. Business men would be utterly astonished, it is submitted, if there were told that progress payments in a sub-contract for services must be made by the main contractor to the sub-contractor regardless of how badly or belatedly the latter was doing his work, in the absence of a " liquidated and ascertained claim established or admitted to be due." Furthermore, in the special context of sub-contracts, arguments *ad hominem* can lead to the oddest results. For example, main contractors can be, and often are, small local firms, and a defaulting nominated specialist sub-contractor may be a national household name. Insolvency is far more common among main contractors than among specialist sub-contractors. Who should be financing whom?

(7) The fact that the main contractor has himself been paid a sum representing the value of the sub-contractor's work, also commented on by the judges, is also, it is submitted, wholly irrelevant. A moment's consideration of the payment provisions in both contracts will show that, under the machinery there set up, if the sub-contractor is in a position to sue on an architect's certificate at all, that certificate must already have been paid to the main contractor, in most cases a few days earlier. This fact is an inevitable consequence of the main contractor/sub-contractor payments machinery, is therefore equally inevitably contemplated by clause 13 of the FASS form, and carries no implication of unreasonableness by the main contractor in seeking to set-off or deduct, nor does it assist in the interpretation of the clause. It is no answer to a main contractor who has in fact and in reality suffered heavy financial damage and has a claim to the extent of £x, and who seeks to set it off against the sub-contractor's claim for £y, to be told that he has already been paid £y by a third person. The sub-contractor would not have had his cause of action without the certificate and consequential payment being made in favour of the main contractor.

(8) Even the reference in the judgments to the excessive time before an arbitration can be started does not bear very close examination on the facts of the *Dawnays* case. Presumably on Order XIV a Defendant applying for a stay would be put on terms to agree to an early arbitration, particularly since the FASS arbitration clause expressly states that, with the parties' consent, an immediate arbitration can be held in any dispute of any kind. So it was the Plaintiffs in *Dawnays* who had it in their power, by consenting, to bring about an immediate arbitration if they objected to the delay which would otherwise occur in dealing with the Defendant's counterclaim.

10. The second case which develops the doctrine is *Frederick Mark Ltd.* v.

Schield.[19] This was a main RIBA contract, where the building owner sought to set-off against a claim by a contractor on interim certificate counterclaims in respect of defective work and also of valuation. It may be inferred from the report that the building owner was taking a different view from his architect (who otherwise, as already pointed out, could remedy such matters in a later certificate). The Court of Appeal, following *Dawnays*, confirmed the Master's and Judges' orders giving leave to sign final judgment. Roskill L.J. gave the single judgment of the court. After referring to the existence of the provisions for interim and final payment (without identifying or quoting any of them) he stated:

> " It seems, therefore, reasonably plain that the pattern of this contract is to ensure that the building owner does pay and that the builder does receive from time to time the payments due under the interim certificates. The architect is, of course, the agent of the building owner and he is there both to safeguard his principal's interest and equally to act fairly to the builder. The contract charges him and him alone with determining what are the amounts which he thinks should be paid in all the circumstances under any interim certificate or certificates which from time to time he thinks it right to issue during the currency of the work." [20]

After referring to the length of time which might elapse before arbitration and counsel's arguments that the action should be stayed Roskill L.J. continued:

> " It is plain that, were that to be so, the receipt of any money by the builder from the building owner could be indefinitely delayed and that would be so whether the claims ought to be set-off or the counterclaim were in the end proved to be well-founded or totally ill-founded. It seems to me that the purpose of these provisions in this contract in this context and the purpose of the structure of the contract in relation to interim certificates is to safeguard the builder during the currency of the contract against the non-receipt by him of any money broadly covering the work done and material supplied down to the date or dates when the interim certificates are issued." [21]

Then, after referring to counsel's attempts to distinguish *Dawnays*,

> " but what matters is not perhaps the precise resemblance of the (FASS) contract . . . to the present contract or the precise differences between the (FASS) form and the present contract. What matters is what all the members of the court said was the result, as a matter of construction that contract . . . the Court of Appeal . . . said that, having regard to the terms of that contract and the nature of an interim certificate . . . the whole purpose of the structure of that contract was to see that payment was properly made under interim certificates as the work progressed without there being any correlative right on the part of building owners to set-off and counterclaim and thus avoid paying the sums claimed to be due under interim certificates." [22]

Roskill L.J. then quoted extensively from the part of the Master of the Rolls' judgment in *Dawnays* relating to the long delay involved in arbitration and, referring to a criticism by counsel of the Master of the Rolls' reference to a bill of exchange, said:

---

[19] [1972] 1 Lloyd's Rep. 9.
[20] *Ibid.*, at p. 10.
[21] *Ibid.*, at p. 10.
[22] *Ibid.*, at p. 11.

> " It is plain that his Lordship was only using a bill of exchange as a convenient analogy, as a type of instrument, a debt arising under which cannot . . . in general be made the subject of set-offs and counterclaims so as to avoid immediate payment of the sum due. Of course an interim certificate is in many respects not analogous to a bill of exchange . . . what the Master of the Rolls was saying was that the debt due under an interim certificate is a debt of a class which, by reason of the contractual provisions of the contract, ought not to be allowed to be made the subject of a set-off or counterclaim as a reason for not paying the sum which the architect had duly certified as due from the building owner to the builder." [23]

It may be commented:

(1) The decision itself is, as already pointed out, far less potentially anomalous than the *Dawnays* decision, since unless the architect and building owner differ, matters of over-valuation and undetected defective work can usually be put right in subsequent certificates.

(2) Nevertheless, there is no examination of any contractual provision in the judgment, which at least occurred on a very limited scale in the *Dawnays* case, and it is not hard to see that the *Dawnays* " financing " principle, already criticised in the sub-contractor/contractor context, was thought to make a detailed consideration of the main RIBA contract unnecessary. It seems extraordinary that judgment could have been given on this quite different contract, and in a case where the nature of the set-off was entirely different, without at least considering and explaining why clause 30 (8) of the RIBA form did not apply —clause 30 (7) of that form provides that in certain circumstances the final certificate shall be " conclusive evidence *in any proceedings under this contract* (*whether by arbitration . . . or otherwise*) that the works have been properly carried out and completed . . . ," and, is immediately followed by clause 30 (8) which, as already stated, provides expressly " Save as aforesaid no certificate of the Architect shall of itself be conclusive evidence that any works or materials to which it relates are in accordance with the contract." This last sub-clause, of course, is referring directly not only to interim certificates, but also to questions of defective work, and by implication to the " proceedings . . . (whether by arbitration . . . or otherwise) " referred to in clause 30 (7).

(3) While the judgment, as in the *Dawnays* case, stresses the delays involved in arbitrating a counterclaim, it is remarkable that there is no discussion of clause 35 (2), which is the clause permitting immediate arbitration of disputes as to " whether or not a certificate has been improperly withheld or is not in accordance with these Conditions." Very arguably this clause means that an immediate arbitration *can* be held in regard to questions of defective work or valuation covered by an interim certificate. Perhaps without being aware of having done so, therefore, this judgment seems to have disposed summarily of the difficult question already referred to, namely whether a contractor can sue for payment without an interim certificate in his favour,[24] since it would seem altogether bizarre if an interim certificate was to be temporarily conclusive against the employer as to value and/or defects, but not also temporarily conclusive against the contractor as well. Furthermore, in regard to most claims for defects, there is a possibility of the special immediate arbitration permitted under clause 2 (2) of the RIBA form wherever the employer or contractor disputes the basis of an architect's instruction—*e.g.* an order to remove defective work. (If it is of any

[23] *Ibid.*, at p. 11.

[24] See *Hudson*, *supra*, at pp. 494–496, and see, *supra*, paragraph 6 (d).

interest, the present writer has indicated both in *Hudson* and in his commentaries on the Standard Form that it seems likely that the contractor is not bound by the architect's interim certificates under the RIBA or FASS forms, and this view is clearly shared by the draftsman of the FASS form—see clause 11 (d) of that form. It appears to have been rejected by the *Mark* decision, however).

(4) While referring extensively to the " financing " principle of *Dawnays*, the judgment does, however, introduce a welcome note of unexceptionable principle in the two passages quoted above which suggest that the true ratio of both decisions is based on the parties' agreement to accepting the architect as arbiter, albeit a temporary one, on questions of interim payment. It is clear that this principle, if enunciated as clearly as it was by Roskill L.J., might have been a serious embarrassment to the Court of Appeal in the *Dawnays* case, since it seems plain that the architect in that case was on the builder's side against the sub-contractor, and the principle so enunciated would obviously have called for a careful investigation as to whether the architect had certified as required by clause 8 (a) of the FASS form in regard to damages for delay. As already pointed out, the Court of Appeal chose in the earlier case to disregard this factor.

(5) It is submitted that in the context of main contracts the " financing " principle is in fact as ill-founded and misleading as in the case of sub-contracts. Such arguments, like those based on the delays of arbitration, may obviously be highly relevant when considering the cogency of evidence required, or terms to be imposed, when granting leave to defend. But they are, it is submitted, of no real relevance on issues of construction. Provisions for interim payment in building contracts have existed largely unchanged in England since the nineteenth century—yet no court has ever enunciated the *Dawnays* principle before. It seems inconceivable that in a matter of such practical and everyday importance that this has been entirely accidental. As a matter of commercial reality, no employer would expect to pay for bad work without deduction—save only if his architect is made the arbiter as to the quality of the work. The Court of Appeal appears at the moment to take the view that employers have bottomless purses *vis-à-vis* main contractors, and main contractors *vis-à-vis* sub-contractors. Such arguments are wholly unrealistic—the building owner using a standard form may be a young married couple, with their savings and future mortgaged in purchasing a plot of land and in building on it. The Contractor may be a great national contractor building thousands of houses a year on the one hand, or an incompetent local builder obviously heading for bankruptcy on the other. If provided with really cogent evidence that the builder was grossly in delay, causing heavy unexpected expenditure for rented furnished accommodation for the owners, or that there were serious structural defects caused by bad workmanship, requiring perhaps an expensive outside technical investigation to decide on cause and remedy, what court would say in either case that, as a matter of business efficacy, the financing element must prevail, that no deduction was permissible, and that the employers must wait to pursue their remedy in lengthy and expensive litigation, or in a liquidation? The " financing " principle, it is respectfully submitted, has no validity whatever unless one first takes a view on the merits in favour of the plaintiff.

(6) It is submitted that the only respectable principle which can be applied in considering this question is the " architect/arbiter " principle as enunciated by Roskill L.J. The question of construction involving that principle can only be decided, however, after looking at a number of provisions in either contract in considerable detail—in the case of defects or valuation disputes under the

RIBA forms at clauses 2 (2), 30 (2), 30 (6), 30 (7), 30 (8), 35 (2), and 35 (3), and in the case of the FASS forms at a number of equally relevant comparable provisions (including particularly clauses 11 (d) and 13). In addition, Buckley J.'s judgment in *A. E. Farr Ltd.* v. *Ministry of Transport*,[25] which examined a comparable provision in the ICE standard form, also needs to be carefully considered in the context of the provisions for early arbitration in both forms. The answer if this had been done might possibly have been the same in the *Mark* case, but it would have been one which would have inspired considerably more confidence, and would incidentally have clarified a number of other difficult problems.

11. The third case is that of *GKN Foundations Ltd.* v. *Wandsworth L.B.C.*[26] This appears to have been a contract using a modified FASS form. The Borough Council treated themselves as main contractors (they were using their own direct labour force) and the Plaintiffs were employed as specialist " sub-contractors " to do the foundations for " the Employer " under what was in reality a direct contract. In addition, the FASS form was modified so as to eliminate all references to " the Architect " and to substitute references to " the Employer." The provision for payment, instead of providing that the Contractor should from time to time apply to the architect for certificates (compare clause 11 (a) of the FASS form), was modified to " (a) the Employer shall ascertain or cause to be ascertained the total value of the Contract works and of any variations, (b) within 14 days of the ascertainment of any interim payments the Employer shall notify and pay to the contractor the total value . . ." (etc. as in clause 11 (b) of the FASS form). Clause 13 of the FASS form (permitting set-offs [27]) was renumbered clause 14 but otherwise unaltered. The Council in fact used its own quantity surveyors to ascertain the value of work done. The sub-contractor was paid some £8,000 on two interim certificates, but against later inertim certificates and a final certificate totalling in all some £14,000 the Borough Council sought to deduct a similar sum as unliquidated damages for delay. In the first of two judgments the Master of the Rolls held that while the valuer could no doubt have reduced the figures to take account of defects (this confirms what has already been stated in this article) he could not do so in the case of delays. The fact that there was no architect made no difference. Nor was the final payment in any different position to the interim payments.

> " It should be paid without any deduction for unlimited damages. Clause 14 . . . only enables the employer to deduct and set-off sums which the contractor ' is liable to pay to the employer under this contract.' That means only liquidated and ascertained sums, because these are the only sums you can ' deduct ' or ' set-off .' You cannot deduct unliquidated damages for delay. The truth is that the contractors have done work to the value of £23,212. They are entitled to be paid it. There was some slight delay in completing the whole work. Yet the council seek to deduct over £14,000 on account of it. I do not think they are entitled to do this. They have had the value of the work and ought to pay for it. If they have suffered any damage for delay, let them bring a cross-action. After all, GKN Foundations Ltd. are good for the damages, if any have been suffered." [27a]

Roskill L.J. said, quoting his own judgment in *Mark's* case, that the sole question was whether the debt was of a class which by reason of the contractual

[25] [1960] 1 W.L.R. 956.
[26] *Supra*, n. 2.
[27] See para. 5 (d), *supra*.
[27a] See (1972) 70 L.G.R. at pp. 279, 280.

provisions of the contract ought not to be allowed to be made the subject of a set-off or counterclaim.

> " It seems to me plain that, although there is no provision in the clause for either interim or final certificate as such, nonetheless the purpose of this clause was to provide that the building owners should in each case notify or ascertain the sums due, then, having so ascertained and notified them, pay each such sum as a sum specifically ascertained and notified . . . the debt claimed is a debt in the special class which I have mentioned. But even if I were wrong in that respect, it seems to me that clause 14 would in any event exclude the right [to deduct]. A clause indistinguishable from clause 14 appeared in the contract as clause 13 in *Dawnays*' case and was construed by this court as excluding any right to set-off such as was then claimed." [27b]

It may be commented:

(a) The extension of the principle to include a final payment seems little short of astonishing, since here no financing element is involved—according to the Master of the Rolls in such a case, apparently, the ratio is (i) that the employer has had the benefit of the work, and (ii) that the damages in question are unliquidated, so that as a matter of construction, and however incontrovertibly in delay, the contractor is entitled to payment in full without deduction.

(b) Roskill L.J. clearly saw a possible difficulty in the absence of any provision for architect's certificates in the contract, but his reliance in the alternative on clause 14 seems, with respect, *per incuriam*. If the debt was not itself of the special class to which he referred, how could an express right to deduct conferred by clause 14 have the effect of eliminating the ordinary right of set-off? Clause 13 in *Dawnays* had been held not to assist the sub-contractor—not to put him out of court. On the other hand, it may be conceded that no particular ground for criticising or distinguishing this decision arises from the absence of the usual architect's certification machinery—provisions in building contracts for the owners' satisfaction used to exist quite commonly and for the present purpose the payment provisions can be treated as of similar effect to an architect's certification.

(c) The basic criticism is the same as that of the *Dawnay* case, and must be that the Master of the Rolls' references to the difficulties of deducting unliquidated sums are inconsistent, first, with the general law of set-off, which is not limited to liquidated claims, and secondly with the facts (i) that the main RIBA contract (to which the FASS form is usually expressed to be supplemental) expressly permits the deduction of a number of unliquidated sums (*e.g.* the cost of employing another contractor under cluase 2 (1)) as well as of the liquidated damages under clause 22—and indeed deliberately qualifies its provision for the payment in the final certificate with the words " *Subject to any deduction authorised by these conditions*, the said balance . . . shall be a debt payable . . . etc."—and (ii) that, as already pointed out, there are no liquidated and ascertained sums in the FASS form on which clause 13 can operate—only unliquidated sums such as the cost of remedial work carried out by the main contractor under clause 9 (b), or the unliquidated damages for delay in clause 8 (a). A further and separate example of an express right to deduct unliquidated damages is to be found in clause 20 (c) of the FASS form (the determination clause).

(d) The Master of the Rolls' judgment contains statements *ad hominem* which are, with the greatest respect, not helpful if the issue is one of construction. Thus " the employer has had the benefit of the work " is not really a useful concept when construing any form of sub-contract. The main contractors who will

[27b] *Ibid.*, at p. 281.

usually use that contract are not likely to regard themselves as having the benefit of a sub-contractor's work in any sense, the more so if it has been badly done so that they have had to spend money rectifying it, or if they have seen their own contract dislocated and turned from profit to loss by a sub-contractor's delays. Nor is a statement that a particular defendant is good for the money very reassuring in an industry notorious for its insolvencies, and when household names like Rolls Royce can become insolvent over-night.

12. The fourth case is *John Thompson Horseley Bridge Limited* v. *Wellingborough Steel & Construction Company Limited.*[28] Little needs to be said about this case. Plaintiff steel-work erectors, who were in fact sub-sub-contractors, but on terms having the effect of incorporating the FASS form, were alleged to have erected the steel inaccurately, causing delay and necessitating remedial work before other work could continue. (This is in fact an increasingly common complaint in the present day in this particular part of the industry.) The defendant sub-contractors put forward what the Master of the Rolls described as " the astonishing proposition " that though they had been paid themselves for the plaintiffs' work they could retain these sums by way of set-off in respect of their own damage. The Master of the Rolls said:

> " The sub-contractors have been paid the very sums which are due to the sub-sub-contractors. In these circumstances the case is quite indistinguishable from other cases previously heard in this Court. *In any case, I am of opinion that, when the sub-contractor has received the sums payable to the sub-sub-contractors, the law would imply that he must pay this over to the sub-sub-contractors. He cannot hold them up pending a cross-claim.*" (Italics supplied.)

It may be commented:

(a) As already pointed out, the machinery of certification and payment is such that all sub-contractors' claims must inevitably involve prior payment of the main or superior contractor. Without such payment there would, in fact, be no cause of action by the sub-contractor in the first place. Furthermore, the scheme of all sub-contracting in building contracts is one of " no privity " between sub-contractor and building owner or superior contractor. In consequence the sum due under the superior contract is paid in full, whatever the position may be between the payee and his own sub-contractor. The practical reasons for this are obvious, and formal recognition of it occurs, for example, in the proviso to clause 30 (5) (c) of the RIBA contract (which deals with the settlement of accounts between employer and main contractor in respect of nominated sub-contractors' work) which reads: " Provided that no deduction shall be made in respect of any damages paid or allowed to the contractor by any sub-contractor or supplier."

(b) The italicised words of the Master of the Rolls quoted above, which are the concluding words of this judgment, must, with the greatest respect, be treated with reserve. It cannot be a cause of action, if A does work for B, that C may have paid B a sum which includes the value in a different contract of A's work. Apart from price differences, A's entitlement must rest on his own contract with B, express or implied. If what is meant is that a term such as is mentioned should be implied in A's contract with B, common-sense would recoil, it is submitted, if, for example, work was very badly done by A, B then did considerable work himself to get it right so as to get paid by C, and was then told that A, by virtue of C's payment alone, was in law entitled to payment in full from B

[28] *Supra*, n. 2.

without any set-off. So too, if by wholly unjustifiable delay A had greatly increased B's costs in doing his own work or in completing it to time.

13. The fifth case is *Token Construction Limited* v. *Naviewland Properties Limited.*[29] This was not an RIBA main contract, but the interim payments clause seems to have been in very similar terms. There was no arbitration clause at all. The work was completed, and there was cogent evidence before the Court that the building was structurally unsafe and would have to be largely demolished and re-erected, which the defendant employers were proceeding to do. A final certificate had not been given, but there were outstanding interim certificates totalling some £222,000 against some £184,000 paid. Davies, Karminski, and Orr L.JJ. held that although the work was complete so that the "financing" element did not apply, and though the evidence of defective work was cogent and the result of summary judgment might well be to drive the defendants into liquidation, the principle of the *Dawnays, Mark* and *GKN* cases must be applied and no deduction could be permitted. So Davies L.J. said . . .

> "The building owner, by putting forward his counterclaim in 1970, has held up the monies which otherwise would be due to the plaintiffs on the certificate; and . . . if the certificates are not to be honoured it may well be a matter of years before the matter is finally adjudicated upon."

In regard to counsel's argument that no financing element was involved, Davies L.J. said . . .

> "But that is to ignore the fact that the plaintiffs here have had to spend money on materials and labour with what result remains to be seen when this action comes to be tried; but they have had to spend the money, and either they are out of pocket themselves of for ought we know they have a loan at a bank or on which they have had to pay interest."

It may be commented:

(a) Though the judgment is not clear on the point, it seems likely that the defects in this building were discovered after the last interim certificate had been given, so that an opportunity to redress the matter in a later interim certificate did not arise (interim certificates, unlike the final certificate, cannot be "negative" so as to create a reverse debt from contractor to employer, so further work is necessary to enable an adjustment to be made). The absence of an arbitration clause, however, meant that no inhibition on an immediate investigation by the Court of the merits of the counterclaim existed, so that the delay before starting an arbitration, relied on so heavily in preceding judgments, could not be a relevant factor on the question of construction of this contract.

(b) If there was no arbitration clause it is in fact difficult to see how, on general principles relating to the binding effect of certificates, the final certificate, which would presumably have to be given once the work had been completed satisfactorily by the Defendants, could fail to bind the parties conclusively. Yet it seems unlikely, depending on the terms of the contractual provision for final certification, that the architect would have been able to make deductions in that certificate in respect of the earlier cost of making good defective work. If this were indeed so, the building owners in this case may have been deprived of all remedy, though this cannot be stated for certain without seeing the exact wording of the provision in question.

(c) The judgment appears to be at least partly based on the real or fancied financial difficulties of plaintiff builders, while ignoring altogether the financing difficulties of defendant building owners required to finance the demolition and

---

[29] *Supra*, n. 2.

reconstruction of the building at their own expense and also to pay for work which had the true position been known, would probably never have been certified in the first place.

14. The sixth case in the Court of Appeal brings the wheel full circle in at least one sense and, even in such an arid topic, must provoke a wry smile. In *Carter Horseley (Engineers) Ltd. and John Thompson Horseley Bridge Ltd.* v. *Dawnays Limited*,[30] Court of Appeal, July 3, 1972, the same steel-work erectors as those who, in spite of serious complaints as to their work, had on another project obtained judgment in full as sub-sub-contractors against Wellingborough Steel & Construction Ltd. (see paragraph 12 above) now obtained final judgment in the face of precisely similar complaints as sub-sub-contractors of Dawnays Limited on the very project and in regard to the same subject matter as Dawnays had earlier obtained judgment in full against the main contractors Frederick Minter Ltd. in the original *Dawnays* case. Carter Horseley were again sub-sub-contractors, this time to Dawnays, under an incorporated FASS sub-contract. Dawnays at least had shown themselves as unaware of " what every businessman knows " as Frederick Minter Ltd. originally had been since, having obtained judgment and payment from Minters on that very ground, they had proceeded to fight to the Court of Appeal their own liability to pass on the moneys to John Thompson (Horseley Bridge) Ltd. (By this time, however, the work on the main contract was complete and the final certificate issued.) Against £27,000 included, though not expressly in the architect's certificates in respect of John Thompson's work, Dawnays sought to set off some £15,000 for remedial work carried out by Dawnays (presumably this was expressed as a payment due to Dawnays under clause 9 (b) of the FASS form as well as ordinary damages for breach in the alternative). No arguments on behalf of Dawnays for distinguishing or avoiding the earlier *Dawnays* case are referred to in the judgments of the Master of the Rolls and Cairns L.J., but it seems possible that repudiation of the sub-sub-contract by John Thompson in abandoning work in a defective and incomplete state may have been the basis of the argument, or just possibly the absence of any express mention of the work in the architect's payments certificates. However, Lord Denning M.R. held that what was sauce for the goose was sauce for the gander, and no set-off was permitted. It may be commented that, as already stated, the architect has no power in his certificates to disallow sums for remedial work carried out by the main or any superior contractor—the only right, under both contracts, would be for the employer or superior contractor to deduct. This may explain why the architect did not identify the sub-contractor's work in his certificate. The decision means, therefore, that even if the architect has himself condemned work which the main or superior contractor has then rectified to obtain final payment, the guilty sub-contractor is then entitled to final payment without deduction. Further comment seems superfluous. It may perhaps be further commented that a petition for leave to appeal to the House of Lords in this case was dismissed in November, 1972, but the appellants in their petition accepted that the original *Dawnays* decision (in which of course they had both participated and won) had been rightly decided, and limited their argument before the House to the contention that the Respondents had on the facts abandoned their sub-sub-contract, and that if so the *Dawnays* principle should not apply.

15. The seventh case is *Modern Engineering (Bristol) Ltd.* v. *Gilbert Ash (Southern) Ltd.*[31] Yet again, the plaintiffs were specialist steelwork erectors, and

---

[30] *Supra*, n. 2.
[31] *Supra*, 3.

sub-contractors of defendant main contractors. The relevant part of the claim was for money due on certificates of the architect, against which the defendants cross-claimed for delay (the extent of which had been certified by the architect) and defective work. The sub-contract provided that payments, both interim and final, would be made " as and when the value of such works under the terms of the Principal Contract is included in a certificate to the Contractor and the Contractor receives the monies due thereunder." After providing that interim payments should not signify approval of the work done or prejudice any claim of the Contractor against the sub-contractor for making good defects or otherwise, the contract provided:

> " If the Sub-Contractor fails to comply with any of the conditions of this sub-contract, the Contractor reserves the right to suspend or withhold payment of any monies due or becoming due to the Sub-Contractor. The Contractor also reserves the right to deduct from any payments certified as due to the Sub-Contractor and/or otherwise to recover the amount of any bona fide contra accounts and/or other claims which he, the Contractor, may have against the Sub-Contractor in connection with this or any other contract."

The plaintiffs asked for summary judgment, but H.H. Judge Fay Q.C. considered that O. 14 proceedings were inappropriate and ordered the trial of a preliminary issue on this point. Perhaps as a result of this, the judgment, of all those reviewed in this article, is one of quite exceptional lucidity and thoroughness. The learned judge first examined the basic principles of the ordinary law of set-off, pointing out that this practice had been constantly applied in Official Referee's business, and indicating the considerable weight of both judicial and statutory authority emphasising the justice and desirability of set-off in avoiding wasteful litigation of cross-actions, so that the original rule preventing set-off of unliquidated damages had long since been abandoned. Prior to *Dawnays*, the learned judge pointed out, the widely held view in the legal profession was that set-off applied notwithstanding the presence of certificates, and many trials had been held in the Official Referees' Courts on this basis. The *Dawnays* cases must now be treated, however, as laying down that contracts with provisions for payment on certificate not only negatived the ordinary right of set-off but, in so far as they might purport to afford an express right of contractual set-off, any such provisions must be strictly and narrowly construed. Applying these principles the learned judge considered, however, that the express right " to suspend or withhold payment," followed by the express right to deduct " any . . . claims which the [Contractor] may have . . . in connection with this . . . contract " did effectively entitle the Contractor to set-off the sums in question, notwithstanding that they were unliquidated. While it may be somewhat unusual to cite an unreported judgment from the Official Referees' division of the High Court, and notwithstanding that an appeal may be pending from this particular decision, it must be said that this judgment makes the first really careful analysis of the principle of the *Dawnays* cases, and is the first attempt to relate that principle to the law of set-off as a whole, as well as to examine it both in its earlier and more recent historical context. It is submitted that it will be indispensable to any Court concerned to review or interpret the *Dawnays* cases.

16. It is not necessary to do more than state a series of opinions or conclusions, namely:

(a) In building and civil engineering contracts and probably many other contracts for services which stipulate for part payment on a certified basis, or quite possibly also on a stipulated automatic or reasonable or stage payment basis, the Court of Appeal now appears to take the view that the financing difficulties of contractors in general are so great that they must always be paid in full, even on the final payment or instalment, without any right of set-off of a counterclaim, however cogent the evidence in its support may be and even in defiance of the architect's opinion, in the absence of the clearest and most express provision to the contrary. Moreover, any sums which can be set-off may require to be liquidated and ascertained.

(b) The *fons et origo*, the original *Dawnays* case shows signs of a serious confusion between considerations which might be extremely relevant to the discretion exercisable in giving leave to defend, but which with respect are almost wholly irrelevant to the issue of construction.

(c) The construction placed by the Court of Appeal on clause 13 of the FASS form in the *Dawnays* case is not supported by a really careful and detailed examination of the remainder of the FASS form itself or of the main contract to which it is expressed to be supplemental.

(d) The only decision which can be supported at all is that in *Mark* v. *Schield*, but even in that case it is clear that the Court's reasoning was clouded if not dominated by the erroneous aspects of the earlier case and there appears to have been no sufficiently detailed consideration of the relevant RIBA contractual provisions which justifies any real confidence in the decision itself.

(e) The principle, which in its operation is little more than a charter for contractors and sub-contractors in breach of contract throughout the whole field of commerce, urgently requires consideration by the House of Lords.

PART II

SET FAIR FOR SET-OFF*

The *quietus* to the *Dawnays Ltd.* v. *F. G. Minter Ltd.* line of cases has come more quickly and decisively than many may have expected. The House of Lords in *Gilbert-Ash* (*Northern*) *Ltd.* v. *Modern Engineering* (*Bristol*) *Ltd.* [1973] 3 W.L.R. 421, in allowing the appeal on the instant sub-contract before them, regarded themselves (with the exception of Lord Morris of Borth-y-Gest) as bound or entitled to review the entire line of recent cases in the Court of Appeal starting with *Dawnays Ltd.* v. *F. G. Minter Ltd.* [1971] 1 W.L.R. 1205, which were the subject of an article twelve months ago in 89 L.Q.R. 36. As will be seen, even Lord Morris made one vital observation which certainly did nothing to reduce the scale of the demolition effected by the remainder of the House, since he agreed with all his other brethren that there was no principle of law or construction in building contracts or sub-contracts such as had been enunciated or evolved in the course of the earlier cases.

The *Gilbert-Ash* case was, in fact, the last case reviewed in the article in 89 L.Q.R. 36; see at pp. 61, 62. It may be remembered that in that case H.H. Judge Fay Q.C., in the course of his exceptionally careful and thorough judgment in first instance, distilled the essence of the *Dawnays* cases, in words which cannot be improved upon, as " laying down that contracts with provision for payment on certificate not only negatived the ordinary right of set-off, but in so far as they might purport to afford an express right of contractual set-off, any such provision must be narrowly and strictly construed." Applying that principle loyally, though with obvious and carefully researched misgiving,

* Note by the author reproduced from (1974) 90 L.Q.R. pp. 21–27.

Judge Fay nevertheless found it impossible to construe the terms of the sub-contract before him (which expressly permitted the deduction of " any bona fide contra-accounts and/or other claims which . . . Contractor may have against the Sub-Contractor in connection with this or any other contract ") as doing other than permit the usual rights of set-off, or as being restricted to the special " admitted or established " limited category of claims which the *Dawnays* cases had prescribed. In the case before him, the claim was to set off unliquidated damages for both delay and defective work, and it was not denied, and indeed admitted, that the claim was " bona fide." The Court of Appeal, applying what Cairns L.J. described as " the rule in *Dawnays*' case," reversed Judge Fay. Readers new to this subject will perhaps not be surprised that the House of Lords unanimously held that the words in the sub-contract before them quoted above could only mean what they said. Lord Morris could " see no escape from this conclusion." Lord Reid did not " see how it can be limited to sums which have either been found to be due or agreed." Lord Diplock described the contention that the words in the sub-contract should be limited in the *Dawnays* sense as seeming " at first sight virtually unarguable," and the words as " too clear to permit any other interpretation," and the Court of Appeal's construction as " strained and erroneous." There was in his view " no possible ambiguity whatever in the sub-contract." Lord Salmon said: " if words mean what they say, I am incapable of understanding how paragraph 4 can be read as taking away the contractor's right of set-off."

As already indicated, four members of the House felt constrained to express their views on the *Dawnays* cases notwithstanding, of course, that decisions on one contract do not usually govern those on other contracts with different wording. Thus Lord Reid said: " the Court of Appeal have come near to laying down a general rule " and Lord Diplock said: " this strained and, as I think, clearly erroneous construction of the plain words . . . was the result of the application by the Court of Appeal of what Cairns L.J. described as ' the rule in *Dawnays*' case ' " (pp. 441, 442) and again: " from the judgments in these cases . . . it would appear that *Dawnays*' case has come to be regarded not as a mere decision on the construction of a particular clause in a particular contract but as authority for a general principle of law applicable to all building contracts and sub-contracts which contain provision for payment of the price of the works by instalments " (p. 442) and again: " a presumption of law as to the intention of the parties to a building contract or sub-contract which is strong enough to compel the court to place so strained a construction . . . as was adopted by the Court of Appeal in the instant case, is, in my view, more candidly classified as a principle of law rather than as a mere canon of construction " (p. 443). Lord Salmon said: " My Lords, it is because in construing the present contract . . . the Court of Appeal has relied so heavily on its previous decisions and the rule or principle enunciated in them that the validity of those decisions may, and indeed, in my view, should be reviewed in the present case " (pp. 450, 451) and (of *Dawnays*) " That case and five subsequent decisions of the Court of Appeal seem to have laid down what Cairns L.J. referred to in the instant case as ' the rule in *Dawnays*' case ': namely a rule that the general principle [*sc.* of set-off] has no application to any known form of building contract or sub-contract " (p. 448).

There was in fact a further factor which necessarily involved at least a partial review of the *Dawnays* case itself. This was that the relevant sub-contract, as in the *Dawnays* case, incorporated or referred to a principal (and indeed identical) form of main contract in terms similar to those which had led the Court of Appeal in the *Dawnays* case to base a part at least of their reasoning on the terms of the identical (RIBA) principal contract. Viscount Dilhorne therefore had no doubt that the appeal required a full consideration of the main RIBA contract, and even Lord Morris appears to have shared this view.

On the question of the *Dawnays* principle, Lord Morris, while explicitly rejecting the need to review or consider other decisions on different contracts, said:

> " When parties enter into a detailed building contract there are, however, no overriding rules or principles covering their contractual relationship beyond those which generally apply to the construction of contracts: . . . Nor, if a contract provides for the issuing of interim certificates, should it be supposed that debts of a special class will come into existence, *i.e.* debts in relation to which there cannot under any circumstances be any defence or set-off. Provisions governing such interim certificates will probably be found in the contract " (p. 427).

This passage, most observers would suppose, implicitly condemns the *Dawnays* line of cases, but in another part of his opinion Lord Morris, after referring to the *Dawnays* case itself and Edmund Davies L.J.'s discussion of the vital clause 13 of the sub-contract in that case, said:

> " The decision of the Court of Appeal in that case turned upon the meaning of the particular words in question: it cannot guide decision in the present case. . . . Had the case come up for review I consider, as at present advised, that an appeal ought to have failed " (p. 430).

Since Lord Morris had carefully reviewed the terms of the instant and identical main RIBA contract before him and found no support in it for the *Dawnays* principle, it may be possible to reconcile these two passages on the basis that, while he regarded the main RIBA contract cases in the Court of Appeal (including in particular *Frederick Mark Ltd.* v. *Schield* [1972] 1 Lloyd's Rep. 9) as wrongly decided, he regarded the particular wording of clause 13 of the FASS sub-contract as justifying the actual decision in *Dawnays.* If this is correct, Lord Reid's opinion shows Lord Morris to have been in a minority of four to one on this point.

Lord Reid, dealing with the main RIBA contract, said that he found no need to decide the question under that contract (since the *Gilbert-Ash* sub-contract was so clear), and while he found the question " far from easy " he was on the whole inclined to think that the Court of Appeal had reached the right conclusion in *Dawnays* and the subsequent cases in regard to that main contract. He then, however, made the vitally important qualification " But it may be that, if [the contractor] attacks the certificate as not being in accordance with the conditions of the contract, he can have an arbitration on the matter under clause 35 and withhold payment pending a decision of that question " (p. 425). Turning, however, to sub-contracts, Lord Reid said of the Court of Appeal's " general rule that . . . sums due under an architect's certificate must be paid at once . . .": " That may be right under the RIBA form of contract in cases between employer and contractor—we cannot decide that in this case. But it is certainly not right in cases between contractor and sub-contractor " (p. 426). Lord Reid, therefore, was inclined to think that the employer cases (*i.e.* predominantly *Mark* v. *Schield*) might be right, but his crucial qualification shows that he considered that, even if so, while the courts would be bound, an arbitrator would not. This latter qualification in fact raises a question (whether a court, in the absence of a *Scott* v. *Avery* clause, will enjoy the same powers of review as an arbitrator if seised of a matter) on which there are two Court of Appeal decisions in England contrary to Lord Reid's implied view (*Robins* v. *Goddard* [1905] 1 K.B. 294 (see p. 302, *per* Stirling L.J.) and *Neale* v. *Richardson* [1938] 1 All E.R. 753 (*per* Scott L.J.)); but in any event Lord Reid's qualification would rob the *Dawnays* doctrine in the main RIBA contract cases of most if not all its practical sting.

The remaining three opinions (of Viscount Dilhorne and Lords Diplock and Salmon) are, however, quite unqualified. Viscount Dilhorne, in a closely reasoned opinion, reviewed with the greatest care and thoroughness all the relevant provisions both of the main RIBA contract and of the sub-contract. In each contract he held that there was nothing to exclude the ordinary right to claim a set-off or counterclaim at common law or in equity. Of the sub-contract before him he said: " Even if the sub-contract does not give, as it does, an express right to make such deduction, I can see nothing in the contract to exclude the contractor's common law and equitable rights to set-off and counterclaim " (p. 438). (Lord Reid had in fact thought that the express right of set-off in the sub-contract which he held to be effective, was intended to supersede the common law right of set-off, but he seems to have been alone in this.) Turning to the preceding cases, Viscount Dilhorne considered that in *Dawnays*' case no consideration appeared to have been given to the question whether the common law or equitable rights of set-off had been excluded by the sub-contract, and he came to the conclusion that that case had been wrongly decided and that the other five cases in the Court of Appeal had also been wrongly decided.

Lord Diplock, after reviewing the common law and equitable doctrines of set-off, and after commenting that " It is not to be supposed that so elementary an economic proposition as the need for cash flow in business enterprises escaped the attention of judges throughout the 130 years which had elapsed between *Mondel* v. *Steel* and *Dawnays*' case in 1971, or of the legislature itself when it passed the Sale of Goods Act in 1893 " (p. 444), said of *Dawnays*' case and the vital clause 13 of the sub-contract (see for this 89 L.Q.R. at p. 41) there considered:

> " This clause, so far from negativing the contractor's entitlement to the remedy available to him at common law of setting up breaches of warranty in diminution or extinction of the price, states expressly (albeit unnecessarily) that he is entitled to that remedy. In reaching the contrary and, as I think astonishing conclusion that the use of the words ' deduct ' and ' liable ' excluded the deduction of bona fide claims for breaches of warranty which, though quantified by the contractor, were still matters of dispute, the Court of Appeal relied strongly on the terms of the main contract in the RIBA standard form, which were subsequently held in *Frederick Mark Ltd.* v. *Schield* to have a similar effect as respects amounts certified in interim certificates as due from the employer to the contractor " (p. 445).

Lord Diplock concluded that there was no provision in the RIBA Standard Form of main contract which excluded the common law remedy and that accordingly the *Mark* case was wrongly decided. His opinion concluded with the words " there was in my view no plausible ambiguity in the relevant sub-contract in *Dawnays*' case, which I would hold to be wrongly decided. I would hold the same as respects all the cases in the Court of Appeal which followed on it " (p. 448).

Lord Salmon, after pointing out the dangers of the " cash flow " principle as so dramatically exemplified in the case of *Token Construction Ltd.* v. *Naviewland Properties* (May 11, 1972, Court of Appeal, unreported, 89 L.Q.R. at p. 58), said of the crucial clause 13 in *Dawnays*' case: " I find it difficult to think of any words more apt to make it crystal clear that the contractor's rights of set-off are preserved lest it might be argued that they had been taken away " by the certificate payments clause (p. 451). He ended his opinion by saying that he found nothing in any of the standard forms which supported the view that the defendants were deprived of their ordinary rights of set-off. He felt driven to the conclusion that *Dawnays*' case and those which followed it were wrongly decided.

Summarising the effect of the *Gilbert-Ash* case, the House were unanimous (a) that the sub-contract before them permitted set-off, and (b) that no general principle of the kind enunciated in the *Dawnays* cases existed. The House appears to have decided (a) by four to one (Lord Morris dissenting) that the *Dawnays* case itself was wrongly decided, (b) by four to one (Lord Reid *dubitante*) that *Mark* v. *Schield* was wrongly decided, and by at least three and possibly four of their Lordships that all the remaining cases were wrongly decided.

There are a number of other interesting conclusions to be drawn from the opinions in this case. Firstly, the House was unanimous that a particular provision in the instant sub-contract—" If the sub-contractor fails to comply with any of the conditions of this sub-contract, the Contractor reserves the right to suspend or withhold payment of any moneys due or becoming due to the Sub-Contractor "—was void and unenforceable as a penalty. Secondly, and of very considerable importance in regard to the RIBA forms, Lord Reid, Viscount Dilhorne, Lord Diplock and Lord Salmon were all ready to hold that the words " whether or not a certificate is in accordance with the conditions of the contract " in clause 35 (2) permitted a dispute whether the work certified was in fact defective to be arbitrated during the currency of the contract. This also lends considerable support to the view that disputes as to the *amount* of interim certificates could be similarly arbitrated. Hitherto there has been no authority as to the meaning of these very important words.

The decision is also of considerable interest in the context of the practice of both the Court of Appeal and of the House of Lords in giving leave to appeal. Lord Reid said: " I doubt whether leave to appeal would have been given in this case were it not for the fact that in a series of cases beginning with *Dawnays*' case, the Court of Appeal have come near to laying down a general rule. . . ." Again, Lord Diplock said:

> " On the face of them the judgments of the Court of Appeal in *Dawnays*' case do not purport to lay down any principle of law or construction of general application. The decision appeared to turn upon the particular words used in a particular clause of a sub-contract entered into between a main contractor and a sub-contractor nominated under an RIBA contract. It was in this belief that the Appeal Committee of this House refused leave to appeal from the judgment of the Court of Appeal, as seemingly it did not raise any point of law of such general importance as to make it appropriate for consideration by your Lordship's House. Refusal of leave to appeal does not imply approval by this House of the judgment sought to be appealed against. That judgment carries the same authority as any other unappealed judgment of the Court of Appeal—neither more nor less."

These passages seem to imply that, even though the House of Lords consider that a question of pure construction of a contract may well have been wrongly decided, leave will not be granted unless the error in construing the contract arises from the application of some incorrect general principle. This may be unexceptionable in the case of a contract unique to its own particular parties, but can it be right where a decision not only admittedly over-turns the settled practice in the Official Referees' Division for many years in regard to that or similar contracts, but is reached on a clause (cl. 13) in the most widely-used standard form of building sub-contract in the United Kingdom? Many practitioners must be aware how extraordinarily difficult it has become in recent years to obtain leave to appeal to the House of Lords, either in the Court of Appeal or in the House of Lords itself. The House may be forgiven, in view of the extraordinary brevity of the judgments in the *Dawnays* case, for not appreciating that a point of law of such importance was involved. But surely the Court of Appeal, either then or later, must have appreciated the importance, novelty, and practical consequences of their own decisions, particularly with the advantage, not enjoyed by the House of Lords, of having had full argument before them? It is surely desirable that leave should, wherever possible, be given by the Court of Appeal rather than the House of Lords, with the attendant saving in costs and professional and judicial time of the preparation and hearing of the petition for leave to appeal (where, as it happens, the permitted costs allowed to a successful petitioner under the House of Lords rules are derisory).

PART III

NOTE*

The decision of the Court of Appeal in *Dawnays Ltd.* v. *F. G. Minter Ltd.* [1971] 1 W.L.R. 1205 provoked a spate of five further cases in the Court of Appeal between 1971 and 1972 (commented on in an article at (1973) 89 L.Q.R. 36), all of which held that interim certificates for payment for building work under various types of main and sub-contract must be paid in full without any deduction for set-off or counterclaim, and that in proceedings under Order XIV neither leave to defend, nor a stay of execution of judgment, nor a stay for arbitration would be permitted, however bona fide the defence or counterclaim, which must be pursued in separate proceedings. In July 1973, however, the House of Lords in the last of these cases (*Gilbert-Ash* (*Northern*) *Ltd.* v. *Modern Engineering* (*Bristol*) *Ltd.* [1974] A.C. 689) unanimously overruled the Court of Appeal in the case before them, unanimously decided that no general rule such as that enunciated in the *Dawnays* case existed, and by a majority of at least 3 to 1 overruled all the five preceding decisions. This House of Lords decision was the subject of a further note at (1974) 90 L.Q.R. 21.

In *Mottram Consultants Ltd.* v. *Bernard Sunley Ltd.* [1975] 2 Lloyd's Rep. 197, however, the House of Lords by a majority of 3 to 2 (Lord Cross of Chelsea, Lord Wilberforce and Lord Hodson, Lord Salmon and Lord Morris of Borth-y-Gest dissenting) held that in the particular contract before them leave to defend should be refused. As there has been some disposition, in the building industry at least, to regard the decision as in some way resurrecting the *Dawnays* doctrine, this latest decision merits examination. It should be said at once that the Court of Appeal heard this case at a time when the *Gilbert-Ash* case was known to be coming before the House of Lords at any moment, and before the Court of Appeal the only argument advanced on behalf of the successful Sunleys' was that the case was indistinguishable from and governed by the *Dawnays* principle. Leave to appeal was granted by the Court of Appeal following the *Gilbert-Ash* decision in the House of Lords, and in consequence Sunleys' were compelled to abandon their previous principal argument in seeking to support the Court of Appeal's decision.

The facts were a little complex. Mottrams' were developer/agents for the

* Note by the author reproduced from (1975) 91 L.Q.R. pp. 471–475.

Government of Zaire, and in this capacity were employers of Sunleys' under a cost-plus contract for the construction of a supermarket in Zaire. The contract provided for certification by the architect on a monthly basis in respect of sterling expenditure (*i.e.* outside Zaire) and on a weekly basis for local expenditure in Zaire. Clause 28 (d) of an original printed form of contract used by Mottrams' provided for payment against certificate " less only: (i) retention money . . . (ii) any sum previously paid (iii) any amount which the employer shall be entitled to deduct from or set-off against any money due from him to the contractor . . . in virtue of any provisions of the contract or any breach thereof," but before contracting the parties expressly deleted the permitted deduction (iii).

After the contract had got under way, it was found that there were difficulties in arranging for architect's certification at such short intervals as a week, and from April 1972, a " new arrangement " was operated, whereby in substitution for the architect-certified weekly payments for local expenditure, Sunleys' own " imprest accounts," showing their actual local payments, were used for purposes of interim weekly payment, any adjustments being made on the monthly certificates. Subsequently, in August 1972, following some complaints by Sunleys' about delays in honouring cheques paid by Mottrams' under the new arrangement, the arrangement was formally recognised by exchange of letters, which provided that Sunleys' weekly imprest accounts should be " for all purposes of the contract deemed to be architect's weekly certificates being subject to adjustment if necessary in the [architect's] monthly certificates." Almost as soon as this agreement had been formalised, however, it became clear, as a result of a special enquiry by a quantity surveyor despatched from England in August 1972, that widespread frauds had been perpetrated on Sunleys' by local sub-contractors, with the result that very large sums had been paid to and by Sunleys' since April 1972, against Sunleys' imprest accounts in respect of work and materials which had never in fact been provided at all. Sunleys' agreed to forego a fairly substantial sum which had been certified, and carried on work for a few more weeks after this discovery, continuing to submit their imprest accounts in accordance with the " new arrangement," but terminated the contract on September 12th, 1972, when Mottrams' made it clear that no further payment could take place until, in effect, the whole of the alleged arrears of over-payments had been worked off. Though the report does not make this clear, it would seem that Sunleys' terminated the contract before the architect was in a position to regularise the overpayments position in the next monthly certificate. Sunleys' then proceeded under Order XIV for a balance due, consisting partly of architect's certifications and partly of their post-April imprest accounts, after giving credit for the sum already mentioned and certain other special credits, and also for the total sums paid to date; and Mottrams' sought to defend against a fairly large part of the claim alleging work never carried out, negligence in preparing the imprest accounts, and substantial sums overpaid in addition to the sum for which credit had been given.

In a characteristically forthright and thorough opinion Lord Salmon held that Mottrams' should have leave to defend, on the basis that even if clause 28 (d) of the contract should be interpreted as excluding set-off, it did not exclude either a direct defence other than set-off, or a counterclaim; that there was a strong prima facie case that it was an implied term of the " new arrangement " that Sunleys' should exercise reasonable care in making payments out of their imprest accounts and not debit Mottrams' with sums of money not in fact spent on work and materials at all; and that there was also a strong prima facie case that Mottrams' could deduct the monies previously overpaid from the latest imprest accounts which they had refused to pay by virtue of the express wording of clause 28 (d) (ii) as monies " previously paid." Lord Morris of Borth-y-Gest gave an equally strong dissenting opinion, but the interest of the case inevitably must lie in the single contrary opinion of Lord Cross of Chelsea, and the reasons given in it for the majority view of the House. While acknowledging the demise of the *Dawnays* doctrine effected by the *Gilbert-Ash* case, Lord Cross considered first the position under the main agreement between the parties, and pointed out that clause 28 (d) in terms stipulated the " only " sums which could be deducted on payment of a certificate and continued: " when the parties use a printed form and delete parts of it one can, in my opinion, pay regard to what has been deleted as part of the surrounding circumstances in the light of which one must construe what they have chosen to leave in. The fact that they deleted (iii) shows that the parties directed their minds (*inter alia*) to the question of deduction under the principle of *Mondel* v. *Steel* and decided that no such deductions should be allowed. *A fortiori* no deduction could have been allowed for an alleged mistake by an architect in issuing a certificate. The claim to re-open the certificate would have had to be dealt with in an arbitration under clause 33." Turning to the " new arrangement " Lord Cross said: " The fact that the variation embodied in the letters expressly provided that any necessary adjustment should be made by the architect in the monthly certificates shows clearly that Mottrams' were not to be entitled to withhold payment of any part of the sum appearing in a weekly imprest account because they thought that some of the expenditure included in a former account or that account itself had not been properly incurred. It was for the architect to put that right, if need be, in a monthly certificate."

It will be seen, therefore, that the majority view turned upon special circumstances and special wording both in the instant contract before the court and in the " new arrangement " made subsequently. Incidentally, the decision appears to resolve, in one short sentence, what has been a doubtful point with a considerable body of conflicting authority on the admissibility and relevance of deletions from a printed contract in order to interpret the remainder—see *Glynn* v. *Margetson* [1893] A.C. 337, 357. and (contra) *Ambatielos* v. *Jurgens* [1923] A.C. 175, 185, and the many other cases on both sides collected in *Chitty on Contracts* (23rd ed.), para. 625.

What the judgment of Lord Cross of Chelsea unfortunately does not make entirely clear is whether a provision for payment against a certificate in the " less only . . . (expressed exceptions) " form is to be construed as excluding defences or set-offs other than the expressed exceptions. In the passage preceding the passage previously quoted he said: " I cannot see how it could have been argued that such a deduction could be made. Condition 28 (d) states that the only sums which can be deducted from the amount stated to be due in an interim certificate are (i) retention money and (ii) any sum previously paid. *It is, moreover, to be noted that* the printed form which the parties used provided for a third permissible deduction which the parties deleted. . . ." Unhappily, these words seem equally consistent with the deletion of the provision in question being on one view an additional factor, or on another view the deciding factor, in the reasoning underlying the majority's interpretation of the principal contract before them. This is by no means an academic question, since wording in the " less only " form is not unknown in building contracts—see clause 27 (b) of the main RIBA forms on contract, which enjoins payment of sub-contractors by the main contractor with a rather similar " less only " formula.

APPENDIX B—PART III

It is submitted that the right of set-off is so fundamental, and the potential injustices and anomalies of departing from it so great, that the mere use of the words " less only " when referring to certain inevitable deductions required by the scheme of the contract (prior payment, retention money, and so on) should not be construed as intending to apply to and exclude other contingent situations which might justify a deduction under the general principles of law relating to defence, set-off, or counterclaim. But this must await elucidation in the courts, which in present financial conditions it may be predicted will not be long in forthcoming.

APPENDIX C

THIS Appendix contains three articles which appeared in the *New Civil Engineer* in 1973 and 1974, the first of these (Part I) being an initial appraisal of the newly published Fifth Edition by the author, Part II being an article by way of reply on behalf of the Committee responsible for the Fifth Edition, and Part III being a short rejoinder by the author.

PART I

ICE CONDITIONS OF CONTRACT*

THE MODEST REVISION WHICH BECAME A TORRENT OF CHANGE

IT is an open secret that at least a part of the long period of nearly 20 years which has elapsed, since the publication of the Fourth Edition of this contract, was taken up in arriving at a virtually finalised version of a new and radically revised contract, but that at the last moment a section of one of the approving bodies withheld agreement to the final version, with the result that it had to be scrapped. Perhaps as a result, the new Fifth Edition of the ICE Conditions has been described by those responsible for its production as a " a modest revision," aimed primarily at improving the clarity of the contract and at removing drafting or other anomalies.

It should be made clear at once, however, that the new contract, though maintaining much of the framework and original wording of the old, makes most radical changes at a number of points. In addition, any policy in regard to improving its clarity and the removal of anomalies appears to have been, to say the least, uneven. There is also a certain uneveness of draftsmanship, already noted by Mr. Abrahamson.

At a number of points there appear to have been pointless re-arrangements or stylistic changes—*e.g.* in clauses 34 and 50. Again, express references are frequently made to other clauses in a particular provision which, on close analysis, appear to add nothing to the meaning or effect of the provision in question—*e.g.* the reference to clause 51 at the end of clause 7 (3) (claim for late information), and the similar reference to a variation order at the end of clause 13 (3) (claim for unforeseeable expense in obeying instructions). So too, in clause 12 (2), what appears to be a wholly unnecessary series of powers is conferred upon the engineer—these powers already exist in other provisions of the contract and could clearly be used in a clause 12 situation in any event—and this is followed in clause 12 (3) by an apparently unnecessary reference to the exercise or non-exercise of these powers.

Again, is some significance supposed to attach to the words " a cause due to . . . fault, defect, error or omission in design of the Works " in clause 20 (3), as opposed to the words " a cause . . . due to the Engineer's design of the Works " in the earlier contract? And what is the intention underlying the addition, after the words " (so far as is practicable) " in clause 11 (1), of the words " and having taken into account any information in connection therewith which may have been provided by or on behalf of the Employer " (in the context of the contractor

* Article by the author reproduced from *New Civil Engineer*, November 1, 1973.

being " deemed to have . . . satisfied himself . . . as to the nature of the ground and sub-soil ")?

I entirely agree with Mr. Abrahamson that changes from an earlier accepted wording should only be made if they appear to have some positive intention either to clarify or alter an earlier meaning. Changes which appear to do neither can only distract both a commentator and any person familiar with the terms of the earlier contract.

But these are relatively minor criticisms and civil engineers will be more concerned with questions of policy and change from the old contract.

Those familiar with the evolution of the standard forms in the building and civil engineering industries in the United Kingdom have come to expect a steady tide of revision against the commercial interest of the employer and in favour of the contractor in particular in permitting more and more financial claims to be made by the latter—with the result that the original quoted contract price becomes less and less realistic, and little more than a lure for unwary employers to enter into projects which they would not undertake if the ultimate true cost was known to them.

But in the case of the present " revision," that tide has now become a torrent. This is particularly odd since one sees that members of the Department of the Environment, the GLC, and British Rail were present, both on the main committee and on the working party. It is difficult to see why anyone with a full understanding of the practical consequences of the changes should have approved of the terms of the new contract on behalf of employers.

Indeed it is possible to argue that hardly an important substantive provision in the contract has not, to a greater or lesser extent, been altered so as to strengthen the financial position of the contractor and weaken that of the employer. What certainly reflects a welcome, if perhaps unwitting, sense of realism is that the new form of tender will no longer contain any stated contract price.

The only respects in which the employer appears to have received any consideration at the hands of those responsible for the contract are, with one exception, of a relatively minor character. Thus the power of the contractor to treat the contract as abandoned etc. under clause 40 (2) (suspension ordered by the engineer) now has a saving in those cases where the suspension has been ordered as a result of a default of the contractor, as recommended in my *Building and Civil Engineering Forms* at p. 364 (there is a corresponding saving, also recommended by me in B.C.F., in clause 40 (1) to protect the contractor in the case of acts or omissions of the engineer or employer).

Again, a small saving has been made to the Metrication clause to cover cases where the contractor has himself been the cause of the deficiency of materials in the measure in question, but no effort has been made to cure the far more serious anomaly in this clause, noted in the first supplement to B.C.F., namely that the clause enables the contractor to advance a financial claim where the shortage in question is due, not to the measure in question not yet being available in the market, at which the clause on a sensible view should obviously be aimed, but merely to the usual type of temporary industrial shortage.

Again, there are a number of references, though largely of a " window-dressing " character in view of the provisions of the old clause 24 of the previous conditions, recognising more specifically what the law would in any event imply, namely the responsibility of the contractor for the safety of operations on the site—see clause 8 (2), clause 15 (2), clause 16, and clause 19.

The one really important respect in which the employer does derive an advantage from the new contract, not noticed by either of your previous contributors, arises from clause 61 (2). That clause makes it plain that the maintenance certificate will now *not* bind either party and, together with new provisions for a Final Certificate, has the effect that the employer can complain before an arbitrator (and possibly also before the courts, though as to this, see *infra*) if defects emerge at any time during the usual period of limitation.

This advantage to the employer is, of course, balanced by the fact that the contractor as well is free to advance financial claims (subject to any inroads as to giving notice which, as will be seen, are very small under the new clause 52 (4) of the conditions) at any time during the period of limitation. But in any case there is no evidence of contractors having suffered from any inhibition in practice under the old contract. So far as one can see, these appear to be the only respects in which the employer can derive comfort from the new conditions.

Before turning to the host of improvements in the contractor's position, I should perhaps point out that, by comparison with the assiduity with which the contractor's position has been constantly modified and improved, little or no interest appears to have been taken in the process of clarifying some really important ambiguities or anomalies in the contract, which have been known for many years.

For example, while the opportunity has been taken to clarify the arbitration clause and its prior special reference to the engineer in one respect in that it is now made quite plain that the engineer's decision will have permanent binding force in the absence of a notice of arbitration within the prescribed time, no attempt has been made to clarify another and perhaps even more important doubt, namely whether, in the absence of any reference at all to the engineer, proceedings can be commenced in the courts by either party. In other words, using an expression well known to lawyers, is the arbitration clause, or is it not, of a " *Scott* v. *Avery* " character?

Again, the very important ambiguity arising from the words " withholding by the engineer of any certificate . . . to which the contractor claims to be entitled," in the context of an early arbitration under clause 66 (2) before completion of the work, remains wholly unresolved, since the wording is identical with the earlier condition, and advisers will be left to derive what assistance they can from the *obiter dicta* of Buckley J. in *Farr* v. *Ministry of Transport* [1960] 1 W.L.R. 956, discussed in *Hudson*, 10th ed. at pp. 495–496.

Again, no attempt has been made to tackle, in the interests of both parties, the quite illogical requirements for insurance of the works in clause 21 of the conditions, and the definition of " the site " in clause 1, important in so many other provisions of the contract, remains as unsatisfactory as ever.

The conclusion seems irresistible that any initial impetus for " a modest revision," or for a genuine clarification of important ambiguities, which may have existed when the revision of this contract commenced, rapidly gave way to the pressures for improvement at all possible points of the contractor's financial position under the contract.

This financial improvement is most clearly evidenced by a group of vitally important expressly permitted new financial claims, considered together with clauses 51 (1) and 52 (4). Clause 52 (4) lays down a new code for notice of claims, applying to all claims under the contract. It requires notification within 28 days wherever there has been a " notified " different rate or price fixed by the engineer under clauses 51 or 56, and " as soon as reasonably possible after the happening of the event " in all other cases.

These requirements have little if any practical sanction, however, since by paragraph (e) the only effect of a failure to give notice within the required time will be to limit the claim financially " to the extent that the engineer has not been prevented from or substantially prejudiced by such failure in investigating the said claim."

Those familiar with the methods of putting forward and calculating claims in a form which will be acceptable to engineering arbitrators, will realise that the requirements of this clause will seldom prove of any serious practical embarrassment to a contractor.

Newly permitted financial claims are as follows:

Under clause 7 (3): this clause contemplates delay in receipt of information or instructions, and requires the engineer, in much the same way as the RIBA clause 24, to certify the additional cost on interim payment. Incidentally, in this, as in all other claims, the word " cost " includes expressly *all* off-site overheads of every kind—see clause 1 (5).

Under clause 12: this is not, of course, a new type of claim, but the strict notice requirement (which most impartial observers would think justifiable in view of the otherwise absolute nature of a contractor's obligation to complete, and his probably far greater experience of unfavourable conditions and their effect on his owh method of working), have now, however, been eliminated in favour of the already described and much watered-down clause 52 (4). Very significantly too, the contractor is now to be paid *profit* on his additional " cost," together with *all* consequential costs of every kind.

Under clause 13: this remarkable new provision appears to entitle the contractor to claim, under the " beyond that reasonably to have been foreseen by an experienced contractor " formula, *any* unexpectedly heavy expenditure arising from compliance with *any* engineer's instruction. Sub-clause (1) of clause 13 appears to make it quite clear that, as indicated by Mr. Abrahamson in his commentary, even an instruction by the engineer requiring the contractor to discharge properly one or other of his contractual obligations—*e.g.* to provide sufficient timbering or pumps or watching or lighting, or temporary shoring and so on—will instantly attract the possibility of a claim by the contractor.

In other words, this provision appears to mean that, if the contractor wishes to argue that any of his contractual obligations have turned out to be more onerous than he expected, and if he can show an associated instruction of the engineer (as will be easy, since as soon as he sees the possibility of a claim he will indicate to the engineer that he does not, for example, intend to provide more than the amount of protective plant or work which he will assert that he had foreseen and allowed for in his prices) the contract price for the work in question can be jettisoned and a new price substituted. This provision alone is sufficient to rob the contract price for almost any part of the work of any claim to certainty.

Under clause 14: clause 14 (3) to (6) now lays down a new and rather unusual code whereby the engineer may initiate an enquiry as to the contractor's methods of construction and, if he does so, is then *compelled*, on receipt of the necessary response from the contractor, either to approve the proposed methods or to require changes in them, if necessary supplying both design criteria and calculations to the contractor.

Some engineers may be flattered by the appearance of power and control afforded by these new provisions, but if so they will be well advised not to be caught in such a trap. In the first place such intervention will come near to undermining the new contractual provisions—at least in regard to claims by third parties—placing the responsibility for the safety of the work upon the contractor; and in the second place, needless to say, sub-clause (6) at once makes provision for a new financial claim by the contractor on the usual " reasonable foreseeability " basis.

The only consolation for the trapped engineer, when faced with the dilemma of approval or rejection, is that approval (which, as already explained, may have exposed his clients to claims in tort by third parties based upon any subsequent failures of the contractor's method of work) will at least not expose his clients to a financial claim from the contractor (always assuming of course, that the approval has been promptly given since, again, a special claim is permitted on this ground). This clause will clearly be used to support the argument that the engineer is under a *duty* to give instructions when difficulties arise—as to which see further *infra*. Engineers should be careful to abstain from the initial enquiry which will activate the provisions of this clause and so place the contractor in position to move over to the attack, unless there are really compelling reasons.

Under clause 31: this claim arises from activities of other contractors employed by the employer, and is, of course, unexceptionable in principle.

Under clause 55: sub-clause (2) of this clause now adopts the " error in description in the Bill of Quantities or omission therefrom " formula and wording of the RIBA forms, and requires the " correction " of any " errors in description or omissions " in the Bills of Quantities. This provision, together with the incorporation of the Standard Method in clause 57, is, of course, an invitation to claims of the " loophole-engineering " kind, now so widespread in the United Kingdom, which are based on the well-known single (and doubtful) decision some 30 years ago in *Bryant* v. *Birmingham Saturday Fund* [1938] 1 All E.R. 503, commented on and criticised at pages 517–520 in the tenth edition of Hudson. As there pointed out (see page 518), the wording of the RIBA forms lends considerably more support to this type of claim than the old ICE wording, and the assiduity of the contractor's representatives negotiating the present contract, it is flattering to suppose as a result of noticing this, has resulted in clause 52 (2) now being reworded so as to comply exactly with the RIBA wording.

The amendment, therefore, is clearly intended as a further encouragement for this type of claim which, on any impartial view, is of an essentially disreputable kind if a contractor has noticed the error or omission (as contractors specialising in this claim endeavour to do) during the tender stage, and has then proceeded to tender without warning or qualification; and equally where he has not noticed the error (when his original prices will have covered the contingency or work in any event). For a fuller explanation and criticism of the policy of permitting such claims readers may refer to my recent article on the RIBA contract in *The Quantity Surveyor*, Vol. 29, No. 6, pp. 134–5, May/June 1973.

Under clause 56: sub-clause (2) of this clause is now explicit that increases or decreases in the actual quantities executed may render the rates or prices in the bills " unreasonable or inapplicable," and a financial claim therefore becomes possible under the terms of this clause. (It should be appreciated that this clause, of course, operates where there has been no variation of the work.)

This must surely be the most damaging provision in the contract, apart from clause 13 (3) commented on above. It is particularly hard to justify in the case of engineering contracts, where all parties know that differences between the final and tendered quantities are likely to be more substantial than in the case of the essentially more predictable work of building construction.

Indeed, one of the secrets of successful (and legitimate) tendering in the civil engineering field is to " take a view " where substantial increases or decreases in the original billed quantities can be foreseen or guessed at. It is, moreover, remarkable if a claim of the present kind is to be contemplated, in addition to the departure from the rates or prices in the bills permitted in the case of variations under clause 52, that the contractor should not at the very least be compelled to supply the fullest internal make-up of his rates and prices at the time of tender, so that the manipulation of preliminary items in the bills, or unfounded assertions as to the overhead or other costs included in items for individual work-processes on the one hand, or elsewhere in the bills on the other, can be effectively refuted when claims of the present kind are made.

Yet the contract is entirely silent on this point, thereby enabling a contractor to advance ingeniously argued claims for extra payment, tailoring his assertions and arguments to fit the facts according to whether or not the change in the quantities actually carried out is in an upward or downward direction.

A discussion of this group of major claims cannot end without reference to two slight, but nevertheless extremely significant, changes of wording in the contract, which may presage an entirely new type of financial claim by the contractor, and which is really subversive of the basic concept of contracting itself—namely the undertaking of the contractor to bring the project to completion, whatever difficulties or accidents may be encountered (subject in the present contract, of course, to the " impossibility " qualification in clause 13 and to the important but nevertheless carefully limited cases of damage due to the " excepted risks " under clause 20 (3)).

The new clause 7, replacing the old clause 8 headed " Further Drawings and Instructions " (which was always regarded as the special power to supply working drawings giving full effect to the original (unvaried) contract intention, and which in the earlier conditions was expressed only to be a *power* and not a *duty*), now contains importantly different wording—" shall have full power and authority to supply *and shall supply* to the contractor from time to time . . . such *modified or* further drawings and instructions as shall . . . be necessary for . . . proper and adequate construction, completion and maintenance of the Works." (New words in italics.)

It is not difficult to see that this new wording can lend support to the argument that the clause is no longer concerned with a power to supply further working drawings giving effect to the original contract intention, but now imposes a *duty* to supply *modified* drawings etc. (*i.e.* to vary the works) if this is *as a fact* necessary for the proper completion of the works.

This subtle change of emphasis is paralleled in the new wording in clause 51. The old clause 51 read " The Engineer shall make any variation of the form . . . of the Works . . . that may in his opinion be necessary and for that purpose . . . shall have power to order. . . ." The wording now reads " The Engineer *shall order* any variation . . . that may in his opinion be *necessary for the completion of the Works* and *shall have power to order* any variation that . . . shall in his opinion be *desirable* for the *satisfactory* completion . . . of the Works."

Here again, the first part of the new wording lends itself to this same interpretation—namely that it is now the *duty* of the engineer to *vary* the work should difficulties or factors arise rendering completion to the original design in varying degrees difficult or too expensive. Yet another ground for financial claims (equivalent perhaps to a reversion to cost plus) has therefore been handed to the contractor, at least very arguably, even if he were not already sufficiently equipped under clauses 12, 13, 55, and 56, and by the excepted risks in clause 20 (3).

Before considering the other policy changes, special mention should perhaps be made of the important, but complicated and in places anomalous, new code for Provisional and Prime Cost Sums and nominated sub-contracting now contained in clauses 58, 59A, 59B, 59C and also, very importantly, the Proviso to clause 60 (7).

Clause 58 is to be welcomed, and lays down at last, for the first time in a United Kingdom standard form of contract, a coherent set of provisions conferring an effective power to nominate, and giving logical and sensible meaning by way of definition to the terms in question. Clause 59A, notwithstanding the seemingly inevitable express claims permitted to the contractor under clause 59A (3) (b), contains a sensible and logical series of provisions in relation to the right of the contractor to object to unsatisfactory nominations (subject only to the almost insuperable difficulty of giving meaning to the words " equivalent to those contained in clause 63 " in sub-clause (1) (d)).

The welcome applies to the first three sub-clauses. Then the anomalies begin. By sub-clause (5) (a) the contractor is now entitled to retain (in direct contradiction, of course, to the policy of the old conditions) *any* discount he may succeed in obtaining for prompt payment. This discount seems to be wholly without limit.

The contract has therefore gone from the sublime to the ridiculous—no other standard form in the United Kingdom permits a cash discount of unlimited extent. This must inevitably open the way to collusive quoting by sub-contractors or suppliers of excessive rates of discount and other serious abuses, ultimately at the expense of the employer, and it is noteworthy that it does not seem to have been appreciated that, in view of the valuable plum now offered to the contractor by this clause, some sort of specific ground of objection against entering into sub-contracts not permitting an adequate or any discount might have been expected under sub-clause (1).

As it is, it may be expected that contractors will rely upon the generalised " reasonable objection " ground in sub-clause (1) as entitling them to refuse nominations on the ground that the sub-contractor in question is unwilling to allow any, or any sufficient, discount.

Secondly, in a remarkable sub-clause (6), while the employer is apparently enabled to obtain judgment or an award in an arbitration, *in full* for damages for breach of the main contract where a nominated sub-contractor is in default, the employer in this sub-clause promises the (main) contractor that he will not *enforce* that judgment (presumably by way of execution) against the contractor " except to the extent that the Contractor may have been able to recover the amount thereof from the Sub-Contractor."

Nothing is said in this part of the clause as to what is to happen if the contractor recovers a sum sufficient, for example, to meet *his own* damages but insufficient to meet the employer's. Who has the priority? Nor is it quite clear how this provision is to be enforced—presumably if the employer levies execution upon the main contractor under a judgment the latter is then entitled to bring an action for an injunction or damages for breach of contract against the employer—an extraordinarily roundabout and complicated remedy.

Disregarding these procedural difficulties, however, the short point about this provision is, of course, that in effect the employer *is now guaranteeing the solvency* of all nominated sub-contractors to the main contractor, notwithstanding that the contractor may have failed to exercise any of his rights of objection at the time of nomination, at least to the extent of any claim by the employer against the contractor arising out of a default of the sub-contractor.

Clause 59B carries the matter a stage further, because this deals with situations where the default of the sub-contractor has reached proportions justifying the determination of his sub-contract. While this clause *appears* to lay down a code enabling the employer to refuse to consent to, or alternatively to insist upon, determination of the sub-contract, careful examination of its wording shows that the contractor can determine the sub-contract without the consent of the employer, and further that the employer cannot himself direct a forfeiture unless the contractor has first enabled him to do so by giving the employer a particular formal notice in writing.

The clause then goes on to provide, remarkably, for the contractor to be paid on interim certificate the whole of his own loss, the whole of the money due to the first guilty sub-contractor, and the whole of any money due to any later alternative sub-contractor; however, but only on final certificate, the employer is then entitled to recover back from the contractor the difference between what he has paid in this way and what he would have paid had the original sub-contract gone through to completion in the normal way—but this recovery-back is again limited, in accordance with the new " irrecoverability " principle, to protect the main contractor if he himself is unable to recover the sums in question from the guilty sub-contractor.

The matter does not stop there because, in what must surely be an ill-considered provision, the Proviso to clause 60 (7) expressly forbids the engineer to delete or reduce any sum previously certified in respect of the work or materials of nominated sub-contractors (as would, of course, happen in the normal way if defects subsequently appeared in their work after it had been certified and paid for) " if the Contractor shall have already paid . . . that sum to the Nominated Sub-Contractor."

This amounts to an immunity for sub-contractors doing defective work once they are paid, at least until final certificate, and on the wording will even apply in a case where the nominated sub-contractor is still working on the site and earning further interim payments when the defects are discovered, so that the latter payments cannot be reduced to take account of defective work which has now emerged in respect of work previously certified and paid for. Nor does the matter end there because, by the Proviso (b) to the same sub-clause, the employer is obliged to reimburse the contractor on final certificate for the amount of any over-payment made by the main contractor to the defaulting sub-contractor which the main contractor has been unable to recover from the latter. Here again, the new " irrecoverability " principle reigns supreme.

To summarise this complicated code, not only has the main contractor been given (very properly) wide-ranging rights to object to the employment of nominated sub-contractors but, even if he does not exercise those rights, the employer now guarantees that there will be no financial claim whatever made against the main contractor arising out of the default of sub-contractors unless the main contractor is financially able to recoup what he owes to the employer from the sub-contractor in question.

In addition, in all cases where determination (or rescission at common law) of the sub-contract takes place (which is virtually at the option of the contractor should he and not the employer wish to effect it), then all the consequential loss and expense of that determination will be payable by the employer to the main contractor, in the event that the latter is unable to recover the same from the sub-contractor.

This is a subversion indeed of the system of nomination as it has been understood in the United Kingdom, and is in stark contrast with, for example, the provisions of CCC/Wks/1 where neither these results, nor indeed the results which arose on an insolvency of the sub-contractor under the RIBA forms of contract in the *Bickerton* case in the House of Lords, can arise (by virtue of the unqualified provision in CCC/Wks/1 that the main contractor should be responsible in all respects for the acts or omissions of nominated sub-contractors as if they were his own sub-contractors).

It can, however, be said, as a very limited defence of some of the present provisions, that they do at least avoid " breaking the chain " of liability and so enabling guilty *but solvent* sub-contractors to escape from the full consequences of their own breaches of contract.

A practical guide to other detailed changes

This next section indicates very briefly, in numbered order of clauses, such substantive changes effected by the new conditions as are likely to be of some practical importance and which have not as yet been commented upon.

Clause 22 (Main Indemnity Clause)

This clause has been " tidied up " in one or two minor respects—the indemnity given by the contractor previously in respect of damage to crops on the site is now given by the employer to the contractor, and not vice versa. So, too, in the case of damage which is " the unavoidable result of the construction of the Works in accordance with the Contract." The important change, however, is that both the contractor's indemnity and the employer's counter-indemnity under sub-clause (2) are in each case to be reduced proportionately, to the extent that the act or neglect of the other party or his servants may have contributed to the loss or damage giving rise to the claim. This may well have the effect of saving the indemnity clause, in such a situation, from being invalidated under the line of cases stemming from charter-party law and applied by Mocatta J. in *A.M.F. International Ltd.* v. *Magnet Bowling and G. P. Trentham Ltd.* [1968] 1 W.L.R. 1028—(see Hudson, 10th ed., at pp. 309–310).

Clause 31 (Other Contractors of Employer)

Here, too, an express financial claim by the contractor is permitted where he has suffered disturbance.

Clause 44 (Extension of Time)

The clause itself now expressly includes increased quantities over and above the bill quantities as a ground for an extension, and it is now, of course, the case that in virtually all the places in the contract where new financial claims are now permitted an express right to an extension of time is also prescribed in the provision in question. The ever-present solicitude for the interests of the contractor now, however, takes the form of requiring the engineer to consider the question of extension of time on no less than *three* separate occasions (indeed more than that if more than one ground of extension exists).

Under sub-clause (2), the engineer is to consider and grant an extension on receipt of a notice from the contractor within 28 days of the cause of the delay (and is expressly permitted to do so even in the absence of any claim for an extension from the contractor). Under sub-clause (3), the engineer is required to reconsider the matter (this time the reconsideration is mandatory even if no claim has been made) on the due date for completion or extended completion.

Finally, under sub-clause (4), the engineer is required to reconsider the whole question afresh when the works are actually completed in what is called a " final review " of the circumstances. For some reason, this final review is only to benefit the contractor, since the engineer is not permitted to *decrease* any extensions previously given by him on this final review.

Clause 47 (Liquidated Damages)

The new clause contains a most sophisticated machinery to cover separate liquidated damages for different " Sections " of the Works (*i.e.* phased completion dates), as well as the old machinery for reducing liquidated damages when a substantial part of the works (now also a substantial part of a particular section) has been completed and occupied by the employer.

Clause 49 (Maintenance)

There has been a perhaps significant modification of the wording in regard to the required state of the works at the expiration of the period of maintenance. Under the old conditions it was " in as good and perfect a condition (fair wear and tear excepted) . . . as that in which they were at the commencement of the Period of Maintenance." Now it is " in the condition required by the Contract (fair wear and tear excepted)." The words " the condition required by the Contract " would appear to refer, though it is not by any means clear, to compliance with the written lists or schedules of defects supplied by the engineer during the period of maintenance or within 14 days thereafter.

Clause 52 (Valuation of Variations)

Clause 52 (1) now adopts, more or less verbatim, the RIBA " similar character " formula for valuing variations (compare clause 11 (4) of the RIBA Forms). This would seem to leave little scope for clause 52 (2), which nevertheless stands and remains as before. The notice under clause 52 (2) is no longer, however, described in terms which could suggest that it was a condition precedent.

Clause 53 (Constructional Plant)

The new clause follows the old very closely, though the reference to " Essential Hired Plant " has now been abolished. A major ambiguity occurs under sub-clauses 53 (1) (b) and 53 (3). These may either mean that all attempts to control the ownership in, or rights over, hire purchase plant have now been given up, and the clause only purports to refer to plant which is either the property of the contractor or hired by him on non-hire-purchase terms; or else they may actually amount to a prohibition of the use by the contractor of any hire-purchase plant on the site. The latter appears to be the more likely result on the wording, but this may be an oversight.

Clause 54 (Goods and Materials Off Site)

This is a wholly new clause and is designed to enable the contractor to obtain payment for goods and materials manufactured or prepared for the project and ready for incorporation in the works but not yet brought to the site. It follows the general RIBA policies, and although the clause does not say so, the appendix seems to be clear that it is the employer and not the contractor who will prescribe and identify any such goods at the tender stage.

Clause 60 (Payment)

This clause does much to remedy the inadequacies of the old clause 60, which were remarkable and notorious. There is now provision for the submission of a final account by the contractor, and for the issuing of a final certificate. The times for release of retention are now precisely identified, and the clause is in general logical and clear, with the exception of the Proviso to sub-clause (7) already commented upon, and with the perhaps rather surprising provision in sub-clause (6) for a high contractual rate of interest, not only in cases where the employer fails to make payment against a certificate (as to which there can be little objection) but also in cases where the engineer has failed to certify sums which are due. The draftsmanship therefore seems to suggest, though it is not clear, that the right to interest will accrue if the engineer has honestly but mistakenly under-valued the work of the contractor.

Clause 63 (Determination)

In general, this clause is the same as its predecessor, but there is an additional sub-clause (2) purporting to confer upon the employer the right to require the contractor to assign to him the benefit of any agreement for the supply of goods or materials or execution of work for the purpose of the contract. This sort of provision is, of course, not likely to be easy to enforce, though perhaps specific performance might be granted by the Court against a contractor or his liquidator in such a situation. One other change in the wording, whether accidental or not it is impossible to say, may have unexpected results. This is the substitution of the word " fundamentally " for the word " flagrantly " in the sentence " is otherwise persistently or fundamentally in breach of his obligations under the Contract " which is, of course, one of the grounds for determination under this clause. The reason why this might be so important is because with the usual carelessness of the employer's interest, this clause has never contained any express words indicating that the rights under the clause are additional to, and not in substitution for, the employer's common law right to rescind upon a repudiation by the contractor. An express determination clause is particularly needed where breaches which are of considerable commercial importance to the employer may not necessarily be regarded by lawyers as " fundamental " for the purpose of the common law doctrine of rescission. Hence it was fully understandable that the old ground should use the word " flagrantly," with its connotation of deliberate defiance, and for obvious commercial reasons it was perfectly justifiable that in a case of deliberate defiance the employer should have the determination remedy under the clause, even if the breach might be relatively minor. Now deliberate defiance is no longer a ground of determination, but the breach must be " fundamental." Hence the right of the employer to determine has been marginally but nevertheless very sensibly diminished. But this is not all, since the use of the word " fundamentally " may now support the argument that the remedies in the determination clause are indeed intended in substitution for, and not in addition to, the common law remedy, since one of the express grounds is now a fundamental breach of contract by the contractor (the basis of the common-law remedy). This is a perfect example of what Mr. Abrahamson indicated in his own commentary, namely the unwisdom of changing particular words unless a clear-cut policy or intention is being followed. The reason why it may be of great importance to an employer to have the alternative common-law remedy available is that in some cases of fundamental breach the employer may prefer to abandon the project (as *e.g.* where excessive delay on the part of the contractor has ultimately resulted in the project " missing its market ") in which case the common law remedy of rescission, accompanied by an immediate right to damages on the basis that the project will never be completed, is essential to him.

Why the client will not like the fifth edition

The practical advice to contractors must be to use the contract whenever they can. The practical advice to consulting engineers must be that, although they will be certain to receive unexpected bonuses in the shape of considerably higher fees than their original contract expectation based on the ultimate cost of the project, they are likely to find themselves immersed in constant litigation.

If the criticisms I have made have had a ring of asperity, it must be because there appears to be a fundamental inability on the part of the professional advisers of employers generally, both in the building and civil engineering industries, to understand that an employer is *not* served by a form of contract which may produce a lower tendered price than would otherwise be the case, if the result is to expose the employer, in the middle of the project, when he is fully committed financially and " over the barrel," to unexpected claims for additional payment, the extent of which is more likely to depend upon the aggressiveness of the particular contractor he has engaged in exploiting the loopholes and opportunities afforded by the Contract Conditions, rather than by any sound engineering or technical or financial reason.

The tendency is also extraordinarily unfair to the more reputable type of contractor who believes that there is merit in sticking to his price and leaving behind a satisfied customer. That type of contractor is rapidly being driven out of business in the United Kingdom, since his less scrupulous competitors are enabled to win the auction at the tender stage, and then recoup their profit by pressing claims.

This contract will unfortunately give rise to constant and often unmerited litigation. It was possible to say, as I have done in my own commentaries on the Standard Forms, that the old ICE Conditions preserved a roughly fair balance between employer and contractor, and that the major criticism which could be made against them was their deplorable obscurity. The present Contract Conditions are, with a few exceptions, as obscure as ever.

But it is no longer possible for any informed commentator to suggest that they preserve any sort of balance between the reasonable commercial interests of the two parties involved. There are many signs in the wording of the contract that this is not accidental.

Consulting engineers will be aware of the type of contractor who constantly demands meetings, and who by sheer persistence can ultimately wear down the resistance of engineers—in particular in regard to the fixing of reasonable rates under the old clause 52 of the conditions. The present contract at a number of points positively *enjoins* the engineer to make his decisions only " after consultation with the Contractor," so that the contractor will be in a position constantly to *demand*, as a matter of contractual right, meetings throughout the contract with a view to pressing his claims. In the past, a point of time could be reached where an engineer could indicate that he had heard enough and saw no point in further meetings. If he does so now, he risks being said to be in breach of contract.

The overriding commercial interest of an employer is to know, as accurately as possible, barring variations ordered by his advisers, fluctuations clauses, and any quite exceptional risk which he is prepared himself to shoulder, the full extent of his financial commitment before the start of a project. If the contract enables him to know this, he can either avoid committing himself at all, or can effect any necessary savings beforehand.

This commercial need is far outweighed by any consideration of a keener tender price, let alone a price which is only a price in name. It is as much in the interests of the contracting side of the industry as of employers that this basic reality should be understood.

It is impossible to believe that, once experience of working the new conditions begins to accumulate, a really radical reappraisal of the policies underlying many of the standard forms in the United Kingdom will not need to be called for.

Mr. Abrahamson in his article said that it was not for lawyers to concern themselves with matters of policy. In the sense in which he was writing he was perfectly correct. But where documents of such complexity, length, and often obscurity, are put before professional men and advisers for execution and signature in the often hurried atmosphere of the commercial transactions which they are designed to govern, the underlying commercial policies and anomalies are not likely to be understood until it is too late.

Moreover, where the documents are intended for public consumption and to govern a multitude of important commercial transactions throughout the country, not excluding government contracts, the interest of the consumer requires protection, and it is the lawyer who may be best able to analyse and expose the policies and anomalies concealed behind the screen of length, obscurity and complication.

PART II

NEW ICE CONDITIONS OF CONTRACT *

BY SIR WILLIAM HARRIS, CHAIRMAN OF THE JOINT CONTRACTS COMMITTEE, AND DAVID GARDAM Q.C. LEGAL ADVISER FOR THE FIFTH EDITION

The policy of the contract

IT is important to state the principles which the JCC adopted, because it appears to be a fundamental disagreement with these which lies at the root of much of the criticism. These principles may be stated as follows:

It is a function of a contract to define upon whom the various risks of an enterprise shall fall, and it was decided that the Contractor should only price for those risks which an experienced contractor could reasonably be expected to foresee at the time of tender. This is the principle that lay behind clause 12 (2) in the Fourth Edition and it is maintained in the Fifth Edition. We agree with the commentator who said, " It is cheaper in the long run for the Employer to pay for what does happen rather than what the Contractor thought might happen in those areas of doubt which the Contractor cannot influence." (*NCE*, 28 June 1973, page 51.)

It is the right and the duty of the Employer to decide and by his Engineer, to design and specify that which is to be done and it is the Employer's duty to allow the Contractor to do that which is to be done without hindrance.

It is the duty of the Contractor to do what the contract requires to be done, as designed and specified by the Engineer, but, subject to any specific requirement in the contract, it is his right and duty to decide the manner in which he will do it.

If there are to be exceptional cases where the Contractor is to decide what to do, or to design what is to be done, or where the Employer or the Engineer is to decide how the work is to be done, the contract must expressly provide for this and for the necessary financial consequences for the protection of the Contractor.

Mr. Wallace on the other hand believes that the overriding commercial interest of an employer is to know, as accurately as possible, barring variations and fluctuations and any quite exceptional risk which he is prepared himself

* Reproduced from *New Civil Engineer*, December 20, 1973.

to shoulder, the full extent of his financial commitment before the start of a project, and, apparently, that that interest overrides the commercial interests of contractors. Mr. Wallace presumably considers, therefore, that all risks (except the very exceptional), even those over which the Contractor has no control, and which emanate from the instructions of the Engineer on any matter, whether mentioned in the contract or not, shall be borne by the Contractor.

The Committee did not accept that approach which they considered was not best suited to the public interest or to the efficiency of the industry. One obvious difficulty of Mr. Wallace's approach is to know the dividing line between quite exceptional risks which the Employer is prepared to shoulder, which may be as variable as Employers themselves, and other risks which an experienced contractor cannot reasonably be expected to foresee.

In civil engineering, where engineers' and contractors' skills are pitted against " the great forces of nature " there never can be any certainty of the final cost at the time of tendering and the Committee agreed, unanimously, that the overall commercial interests of employers are best served by a clear definition of where responsibilities lie. It is the duty of the Engineer in reporting on the tenders, to advise the Employer, to the best of his ability, on the contingencies for which provision should be made over and above the " Tender Total " and during the progress of the work to avoid variations to the maximum extent possible. But it is quite, inequitable and *uneconomic* for the Employer to expect the Contractor or the Engineer to accept on his behalf risks which neither can reaonably be expected to foresee: nor should he be able to interfere at will with the orderly progress of the contract without consequential payment.

Mr. Wallace's attitude is one which was widely adopted in England in the nineteenth century and no doubt it could be argued that a policy along the lines which he suggests should be adopted today. Unfortunately, however, he obscures any merit in his viewpoint by regarding contracts for civil engineering works as a battle between the Contractor—in dishonest collusion with suppliers and sub-contractors—and the Employer—aided by incompetent allies in the shape of engineers and unknowledgeable legal advisers—in which battle the Contractor is for ever " going over to the attack," preparing " traps " for the Employer and the Engineer or wearing down the resistance of the Engineer by constant meetings and argument, the objective of the battle being to have the Employer " over the barrel "—presumably incapable of resisting any longer the Contractor's demands. In our experience such a view of the civil engineering industry as a whole in this country is completely unreal.

One of the most important " policy " changes is that the Fifth Edition has been made, clearly and unequivocably, a " measure and value " contract. This receives scant attention from the commentators: indeed in some of their detailed criticisms they appear to have ignored it. Although for many years the Fourth Edition has been used basically as a " measure and value " rather than a " lump sum " contract, legal advise from a number of eminent counsel has indicated that for a variety of reasons this concept was open to doubt.

The Committee has quite deliberately removed this doubt and to do so has had to make a series of alterations of which the removal of any reference to a " tender sum " in the Form of Tender is the ultimate conclusion. Mr. Wallace's jibe about " a welcome, if perhaps unwitting, sense of realism " in respect of this change is unworthy.

Clarity and removal of ambiguities

It will be seen that there are many cases where we have deliberately not changed words used in the Fourth Edition. For example words like " instructions," " directions," " requirements " and " orders " used in different places throughout the Conditions, were retained because, although in an entirely new Contract the use of a single word throughout might well have been adopted, to have made such a change throughout the existing text would (in the terms of Mr. Abrahamson's " cardinal principle ") have implied a change of meaning where none was intended. But we do not agree with Mr. Abrahamson when he makes a distinction between the issue of instructions and nomination. By clause 58 (4) the Contractor requires an *order* to employ a sub-contractor nominated by the Engineer. In ordinary English parlance an order is an instruction and it is pure semantics to pretend otherwise.

Mr. Abrahamson is quite right in his criticism of the use of " drawings and instructions " in clause 7 (1) and 7 (3) and " drawing or specification " in clause 7 (2). The phrase " drawing(s), specification(s) and (or) instructions " should have been used in all three sub-clauses. This is a case of not going far enough in changing the wording of the Fourth Edition. Clause 7 should be amended at a suitable opportunity; but, in any case, if the Contractor foresees that further drawings, specification or instructions are necessary for the orderly progress of his work he will be wise to give adequate notice in writing.

Mr. Abrahamson criticises the use of the phrases " such sum in respect of the cost incurred as the Engineer considers fair in all the circumstances " in clause 14 (6), " the amount of such loss expense or damage as the Contractor could not reasonably avoid " in 59A (3) and " appropriate increase or decrease of any rates or prices " in 56 (2) as compared with " such cost as may be reasonable " in several other clauses. He says, " Never change your language unless you wish to change your meaning." That principle was in fact applied. In clause 14 (6) the different wording was chosen deliberately to indicate that the Engineer might award a lesser sum if in all the circumstances he thought it fair to do so.

In clause 59A (3) the phrase " such cost as may be reasonable " would have been obviously too narrow to give effect to the Committee's intention: in clause 56 (2) it is not cost which is being talked about and the phrase would have been quite inappropriate.

In clauses 51 and 52 when " valuing variation " it is always the work not the change which is valued. If the variation consists only of a " change in the specified sequence or timing of construction " the work remains work of a similar character to work priced in the Bill, but it may not be executed under similar conditions and in that case has to be valued on the basis of the rates and prices in the Bill so far as may be reasonable, failing which a fair valuation shall be made. The drafting is quite correct.

Regarding clause 60, it would seem, with respect to Mr. Abrahamson, that he has misread sub-clause (2). It says ". . . the engineer shall certify . . . the amount . . . due to the contractor (say £100) . . . less a retention (say £3)." The sum received by the contractor is thus not the same as the " amount due " as there defined. Sub-clause (5) (a) then provides that there ". . . shall be paid . . . 1½ per cent. of the *amount due* " (£100)—*i.e.* £1·50 which is the result intended.

The lawyers have some drafting criticisms of clause 13, but as they also have other criticisms of this clause we shall deal with it as a whole in the next section.

As regards drafting generally, JCC believes that whilst, for the reasons already given, the style and language of the Fourth Edition has been retained and may not be ideal by modern standards, nevertheless the meaning of the text should be clear to anyone—" including Mr. Coleman's chaps with mud on their boots " (*NCE* 6 December, 1973)—who takes time to study it with reasonable care. But many of the situations for which provision has to be made in the contract are difficult and complex and accordingly whatever language is used careful study of the text is essential. The Committee does not claim perfection (could any lawyer drafting an entirely new contract?), but it does believe that the more serious and important ambiguities have been removed. Any remaining can be dealt with as time and circumstances may require—if they are considered to be of sufficient importance.

The tide that has become a torrent

Mr. Wallace's irresistible conclusion that " any initial impetus for a modest revision . . . rapidly gave way to the pressures for improvement at all possible points of the contractor's financial position " is quite unjustifiable. It is simply not true to say that there has been a torrent of revision against the commercial interest of the Employer and in favour of the Contractor in permitting more and more financial claims to be made. Look a little more closely at this tide which he says has now beome a torrent.

Clause 7 (3)—Is Mr. Wallace suggesting that in contracts under the Fourth Edition delay in the receipt of information or instructions which put the contractor to extra cost could not be the subject of a valid claim? Certainly contractors have not taken this view and have, not surprisingly, entered many claims for what amounts to damages for breach of contract in such cases. The clause does not give rise to any new claim, it is only an attempt to express a term which has for a long time been implied. See for instance *Neodox Ltd.* v. *Swinton and Pendlebury* 3 C (*Hudson*, 10th ed., p. 137). As Mr. Abrahamson correctly points out, the remedy provided by the contract is in fact less than that which is available as damages for breach of contract in that a possible head of claim for " loss of profit due to delay " is not included. This was accepted by all members of the Committee.

Mr. Abrahamson's reference to clause 12, however, does bring out the fact that in the Fifth Edition care has been taken to state specifically, in each-case where entitlement to extra payment arises, whether overheads and profit are included. The term " cost," which is defined in clause 1 (5), is used throughout the Conditions where overheads are payable and only in the case of clause 12 (3) is provision made for " a reasonable percentage addition thereto in respect of profit " on work done and plant used. Lack of such definition in the Fourth Edition has been a cause of much dispute. Rates and prices determined in accordance with clause 52 clearly include the profit element.

Clause 12—Although it is under his heading of " newly permitted financial claims," Mr. Wallace concedes that this is not, of course, new. Moreover, his further comments are somewhat at variance with those in his book where he admits that " considerable expense may be incurred before the cause has been diagnosed." In clause 12 (2) the " wholly unnecessary series of powers " conferred upon the Engineer were already set out in clause 12 (3) and 12 (4) of the Fourth Edition. Their omission might have lead parties to believe the Engineer was intended no longer to have them. The words in parenthesis were put into clause 12 (3) to avoid a doubt which the Committee considered might exist without them.

Clause 13—This clause troubles both Mr. Abrahamson and Mr. Wallace, and Mr. Akroyd thinks that any claims consultant worthy of his salt ought to be able to drive a horse and cart through it.

It is first necessary to be aware of the evil which clause 13 (3) is designed to correct. Under the Fourth Edition the Contractor was obliged to comply with and adhere strictly to the Engineer's instructions and directions on any matter whether mentioned in the Contract or not, and there was no specific provision for payment. If one applies the sort of *reductio ad absurdum* argument adopted by Mr. Abrahamson, the Engineer could direct the Contractor to move his head office nearer to the site to facilitate communication between it and the site, and the Contractor might get no payment! More seriously, and more practically, the Engineer could issue instructions for the work to be done in a quite unprecedented manner, which would put the Contractor to great and often unnecessary, uncontemplated and unrecoverable expense. As it stood clause 13 was a thoroughly unjust clause.

Mr. Abrahamson complains that " to give a contractor a right to compensation, the instruction or direction need not be in writing or confirmed by a contractor in writing "; but then this never has been the policy of the contract, except in regard to orders for variation. Mr. Abrahamson misrepresents the position when he says " although notice of any claim *may* be required *eventually* under clause 52 (4)." Let him read clause 52 (4) again. The contractor is *obliged* to give notice *in writing* of his intention to claim to the Engineer *as soon as reasonably possible* after the happening of the events gives rise to the claim.

The word " arrangements " was chosen for its width. It expresses the Committee's intention. Then Mr. Abrahamson and Mr. Wallace suggest that an instruction by the Engineer to the Contractor to remedy a breach of contract or properly to perform his contractual obligation may give rise to a claim. Their argument is quite untenable. Any experienced contractor knows that if he does not perform his obligations at the proper time the Engineer may instruct him to do so and that he may find that he is then delayed and disrupted and incurs costs as a result. Such costs are the natural consequence of breaking the contract and obviously cannot be recovered from the innocent party by the party in breach.

It is absurd to suggest that the clause can reasonably be interpreted to mean that " an instruction to discharge properly one or other of his contractual obligations will instantly attract the possibility of a claim by a contractor." The clause does not state, as Mr. Akroyd says it does, " The engineer now has to certify extra payment if he issues instructions which involve the contractor in delay or disrupt the contractor." Let him read the clause again before starting to drive his horse and cart.

Under clause 13 (3) before there can be a claim there must be, as a consequence of the instruction, either delay, or disruption, and cost incurred beyond, not what the Contractor foresaw, but beyond that " reasonably to be foreseen by an experienced contractor ": whether cost is in that category is, in any particular case, a matter of opinion for decision by the Engineer.

Nor does the clause provide as Mr. Wallace suggests that if the Contractor wishes to argue that any of his contractual obligations has turned out to be more onerous than he expected and if he can show an associated instruction of the Engineer the contract price for the work in question can be jettisoned and a new price submitted. Such an interpretation is a grotesque misrepresentation of the words used in the contract.

Clause 14—Mr. Wallace criticises particularly 14 (3)–14 (6). In so doing he ignores the obligation upon the Contractor, in clause 14 of the Fourth Edition, to furnish for his (the Engineer's) information particulars in writing of the Contractor's arrangements for the carrying out of the Works and of the Constructional Plant and Temporary Works which the Contractor intends to supply, use or construct as the case may be " whenever required by the Engineer. The " trap " for engineers as he calls it has always existed and this Fourth Edition clause has for many years given rise to doubt as to the Engineer's responsibility for the safety of Temporary Works, such as falsework, if he calls for the particulars of it—as in practice he frequently does. The Committee took the view that the contractor should be entirely responsible for the " adequacy, stability and safety of all site operations and methods of construction " (clause 8 (2)), but that the Engineer has a responsibility to satisfy himself that if the methods proposed by the Contractor are used " the Works can be executed in accordance with the Drawings and Specification and without detriment to the Permanent Works when completed " (clause 14 (3)). It is only if he considers that the Contractor's proposed methods fail to meet that test that the Engineer should withhold his consent and require the Contractor to make such changes as will enable the Engineer to give it. The Engineer would be failing in his duty to the Employer if for example he permitted the Contractor to apply loads to permanent members of a structure during erection which would overstress or otherwise damage them, or if he permitted the use of falsework for a cast *in situ* beam which would in his opinion allow deflection during casting to an extent which would cause him to reject the finished product.

The Engineer is not responsible under the contract for " safety," but, if he exercises his powers under this clause with due regard to his professional responsibilities, he will provide an added safeguard—and the grounds on which he may exercise them are now, for the first time, clearly defined.

But there are two sides to this. Clause 14 (3) recognises that the Contractor may need to know design criteria of the Permanent Works to enable him to devise safe temporary works and methods of construction. But clause 14 (6) recognises that these may not have been provided in the tender documents and that if they or any other requirements of the Engineer " could not reasonably be foreseen by an experienced contractor at the time of tender " the methods on which the Contractor has based his tender could be entirely misconceived. The purpose of making specific provision for compensation for this and for unreasonable delay is to enable the parties to settle without recourse to arbitration or litigation.

Mr. Rowley (*NCE* 22 November) has been misled by Mr. Wallace's earlier comment in construing clauses 14 and 22. It cannot of course be seriously suggested that a request for information, of itself, could possibly he held to be an act causing or contributing to loss, injury or damage to a third party. The Engineer has no duty towards the Contractor which *requires* him to request details of method or temporary works—omission to do so would be a matter solely between an engineer and his employer under the terms of his employment.

If, however, having called for and obtained information in accordance with 14 (3), the Engineer ignores 14 (7) and proceeds to *instruct* the Contractor as to how he is to do the work or that he is to make a specific change in the design or construction of temporary works, then the Employer might be at risk under 22 (1) (a) if something were to go wrong in consequence of the Engineer's instruction.

All that the Engineer is called upon to do is to give his consent to the Contractor's proposed methods or to inform him " in what respects in the opinion of the Engineer they fail to meet the requirements of the Drawings and Specification or will be detrimental to the Permanent Works " (14 (4) (b)). It is the Contractor who is *compelled* to find methods which will " meet the Engineer's requirements and obtain his consent "—it is not for the Engineer to tell him how to do it.

The Contractor's redress (if any) lies in 14 (6).

Clause 14 (7) makes it quite clear that the Contractor is not relieved of any of his duties or responsibilities by the *consent* of the Engineer to the Contractor's proposed methods—but engineers must remember that it is the Contractor's responsibility to devise methods of construction and to design temporary works—not theirs. If they wish to do this they must provide for it in the tender documents.

If clause 14 is followed properly then the giving of the Engineer's consent would be qualified by sub-clause (7) (which might well be referred to in the letter). Alternatively, if the Engineer is not satisfied and he so signifies in the terms of sub-clause (4) (b), this again cannot be an act causing damage. If the Contractor's response to this is satisfactory then (4) (a) would be applied or if not then (4) (b) would be repeated. In none of these cases is there any act by or on behalf of the Employer which could he held to have caused or contributed to damage to third parties such as would put the Employer at risk under clause 22.

Having said all this however, it must be remembered that, irrespective of the Contract the Engineer has always owed a duty of care to anyone he could reasonably foresee might be injured as a result of inadequate or unsafe measures adopted by the Contractor of which the Engineer was—or ought to have been —aware,

Clause 55 is seen by Mr. Wallace as an invitation to claims of the " loophole engineering " kind and he imputes a deliberate intention on the part of the Committee to encourage disreputable claims. In his book (B.C.F. at pp. 403 and 404) he rightly refutes the proposition that general directions or recommendations of a standard method can or should override what would otherwise be the clear meaning of the contract documents as a whole and the bills in particular. It was to further these principles, yet recognising the practical problems associated with their application, that clause 55 (2) was added.

Again in his book Mr. Wallace draws attention to the importance of the words in clause 57 ". . . except where any general or detailed description of the work in the Bill of Quantities expressly *shows* to the contrary . . ." (as distinct from the word " states " which is used in the RIBA form). This phrase has been retained.

It follows, if doubt arises, that unless it is expressly shown to the contrary, either in some preamble or in a particular item, the mandatory or precatory terms of a standard method must be presumed to have been followed. This surely means that whilst the legal axiom that the particular overrides the general should always apply, it can only do so if the particular is expressed in clear and unambiguous terms.

If the particular is not so expressed, it might possibly be held that in the case of a lump-sum contract, work shown on drawings for which there was no item in the bill but which was nevertheless contingently and indispensibly necessary to the construction of the whole of the works must therefore be deemed to be included in the lump-sum price quoted by the contractor. This cannot be applied in the case of a measure and value contract.

In that case the contingently and indispensably necessary criterion could only be applied to particular items of the Bill, as the Contractor, although undertaking to construct the whole of the works, has only agreed to do so at the rates and prices quoted against the description of each item in the Bill. If the description is deficient on that basis, then there is an error to be corrected.

For example, in a contract for the construction of a bridge, suppose the drawings clearly show supporting piers, but the Bill includes no items for them. The piers are indeed indispensably necessary for the completion of the bridge, but could it possibly be contended that their cost had to be included in the items for the deck or abutments? In the case of a lump-sum contract it might just be possible so to contend, though to do so would put in question the purpose and status of the Bill. In the case of a measure and value contract there is no doubt that the supporting piers as constructed would have to be measured pursuant to clause 56.

It remains to consider how the contingently and indispensably necessary criterion could be applied to particular items in the Bill. As clause 57 says that (subject to the " expressly shown " exception) Bills shall be deemed to have been prepared according to the procedure in the SMM, it is considered that where the SMM specifically provides for particular work (*e.g.* formwork) to be billed separately, and this is not done nor is it expressly shown that this work is included in the Bill items, then the " contingently and indispensably necessary " criterion could not be held to override the failure to comply with clause 57.

Where, however, no specific provision is made in the standard method and the work in question can on any reasonable construction be held to be contingently and indispensably necessary then the cost of such work can be held to be included in the price for that item. Take a simple example: nails in formwork without which formwork could not be constructed.

Mr. Wallace says that clause 55 (2) is one of the newly permitted financial claims, but at the same time states that such claims are " now widespread in the U.K." which, if correct, presumably refers to contracts under the Fourth Edition. The difference is that the new clause 55 (2) expressly provides for the correction of errors, thereby removing doubt and emphasising to engineers the importance of avoiding errors and ensuring that item descriptions are clear, unambiguous and comprehensive, particularly where any departure from the standard method is involved.

Clause 56 (*2*), which Mr. Wallace condemns as " surely the most damaging provision in the contract," does not in fact introduce any innovation. Under clause 52 (2) the Engineer has always had power to fix a new and fair rate where the nature or amount of any omission or addition, relative to the nature or amount of the whole contract work or any part of it, was such that the rate or price of any item or work was rendered unreasonable or inapplicable. Some commentators, Mr. Wallace among them, contend that " any addition or omission " meant only additions or omissions ordered by the Engineer and did not include those arising as a result of quantities of work executed being greater or less than those stated in the Bill of Quantities. Such a contention ignores clause 51 (2) of the Fourth Edition.

Clause 56 (2) of the Fifth Edition now makes clear what a consensus of legal opinion always thought was the correct interpretation of the Fourth Edition. It should be realised that the Engineer, as well as the Contractor, may initiate a revision of rate under 56 (2) and that the revision may be up or down. Thus a balance is preserved between the Employer and the Contractor.

As to the criticism that a contractor is not compelled to reveal the make-up of his prices, Mr. Wallace should know that a contractor who is unwilling to produce such data to the Engineer would have little chance of convincing him that he was entitled to any increase of rate, or of changing the Engineer's opinion that there should be a decrease.

Mr. Wallace says that such provision is particularly hard to justify in the case of engineering contracts . . . and that " one of the secrets of successful (and legitimate) tendering . . . is to ' take a view ' where substantial increases or decreases in the original billed quantities can be foreseen or guessed at." His attitude is Victorian. Does he seriously suggest that multi-million pound contracts should be matters of guesswork or deliberate gambles? Of course if the contractor has underpriced or alleges he has distributed his costs elsewhere he is not entitled to take advantage of this in connection with 56 (2) which is precisely why the clause is worded ". . . if . . . such increase or decrease *of itself* shall so warrant."

Mr. Wallace has noticed and criticised that, in clause 14 (3)–(6) as in clause 7 and clause 51, the Engineer has on occasions a duty to provide necessary instructions. He is wrong, however, to suggest that such a duty is new. It has always been there, *e.g.* the implied term to provide necessary instructions and details written in reasonable time in all the circumstances previously referred to (*Neodox* v. *Swinton and Pendelbury*, *supra*) and clause 51 (1) in the Fourth Edition, of which Mr. Wallace quotes only a part. It is necessary to set out the opening sentence of that clause in full:

> " The Engineer *shall* make any variation of the form quality or quantity of the Works or any part thereof that may in his opinion be *necessary and* for that purpose or *if for any other purpose it shall in his opinion be desirable* shall have the power to order the Contractor to do and the Contractor shall do any of the following . . ."

The italics here indicate that the purpose of giving the Engineer the power which is given him in the clause is to enable him to fulfil his obligation to make variations which in his opinion are necessary and to exercise his discretion to make variations which he thinks are desirable. Perhaps the fact that so learned a commentator as Mr. Wallace had not appreciated the point before indicates that the change of wording adopted by the Committee in the Fifth Edition was desirable.

It is, however, a serious misinterpretation of the new clause to say that it is now the duty of the engineer to vary the work should difficulties or factors arise rendering completion to the original design in varying degrees difficult or too expensive. The Engineer's obligation remains precisely as it was, *viz.* to order those variations which in his opinion are necessary. The words " for the completion of the Works " are added. These emphasise that that which is necessary to rescue a particular contractor is *not* included; and that the Contractor has a right to complete the works and, if a variation is necessary to enable it to be physically possible to do so, the engineer must make the variation. The Engineer remains as before the judge of necessity, subject only to the review of his opinion by the arbitrator.

Turning to the other side of this question, Mr. Wallace says that " the only respects in which the employer appears to have received any consideration . . . are, with one exception, of a relatively minor character." Mr. Wallace can take full credit for drawing attention in his book to the defects in clause 40 (1) and 40 (2). But as to clause 61, it is carping to say that contractors have not suffered from any inhibition. Does it not suffice that the matter has now been made clear and so is of advantage to both parties? Perhaps it would be helpful to point out a few examples of where any fair-minded person might consider that amendments have been made to the benefit of the employer.

Clause 44. Not only may an employer's rights to liquidated damages be endangered if the extension of time provisions are not operated properly, but also he may find himself exposed to a claim for acceleration costs if the Contractor is pressed to complete by the original contract date and eventually proves his entitlement to an extension. Moreover in the Fourth Edition there is no provision for extension of time if delay is caused by the Employer or Engineer or for the Engineer to extend the time (and thereby safeguard the Employer's position) without application by the Contractor. The changes made in clause 44 (and in clauses 7, 13, 14 and 31) are therefore very much in the commercial interest of the Employer. They are, of course, also in the interest of the orderly progression of the work and therefore in the interest of the Contractor. The Contractor is under obligation to complete within the time for completion prescribed in the Contract (or the extended time for completion) and to programme—and re-programme—his work accordingly. How can he possibly do this, if, when required to produce a new programme, he does not know whether the contract time has been extended? Again when the due (or extended) date for completion is reached must not both parties know the position? And on the issue of the Certificate of Completion it is surely right to provide for a final review so that the correct amount of liquidated damages, if any, can be determined. This must be a one-way adjustment because any re-programming by the Contractor must always be based upon the time available contractually. Moreover a decision on Extension of Time will help to accelerate settlement of the Final Account.

Clause 46 has been amended to remove the anomaly of giving a contractor an extension of time in circumstances where he has been responsible for delay. Surely this is to the advantage of the Employer rather than the Contractor.

Clause 49. The " as good and perfect condition as that in which they were at the commencement of the Period of Maintenance " of the Fourth Edition might, as a result of latent bad work or materials, be less than the state of perfection called for by the contract, yet a defect due to that latent breach of contract might not appear within the Period of Maintenance—hence the change of wording. The clause means what it says and has nothing to do with lists of defects as suggested by Mr. Wallace. Again the change is in the Employer's interest.

Clause 52 (4), which Mr. Wallace dismisses as having little or no practical sanction, again is intended to operate fairly to both parties, but is considered to be of more practical value to the Employer than the equivalent provisions of the Fourth Edition. As interpreted by the Courts (see *Terson* v. *Stevenage Development Corporation*) clauses 52 (2) and 52 (4) of the Fourth Edition did not always prevent a contractor from successfully presenting, at the end of the contract, a detailed claim of which only the most oblique or general notice had been given years before. At this time the Engineer's site staff might be dispersed and the Contractor himself be without records appropriate to the claim. Such a situation should not be able to arise under the new provisions.

So, what has become of Mr. Wallace's tide that has become a torrent? Of all the examples which he puts forward to support his view only one—clause 13 (3)—can be said to be new and that was clearly necessary and justifiable. The remainder set out expressly what was previously claimable in common law or otherwise under the contract. He ignores the fact that the tide flows both ways. There was no thought on the part of the JCC or Working Party to draw up a balance sheet of advantages to " us and them." Their whole objective was to achieve a rational and equitable definition of responsibilities.

Other points of criticism

Nominated sub-contracts—Clauses 59 (*A*), (*B*) *and* (*C*).

These were undoubtedly the most difficult clauses to deal with, because the whole concept of nominated sub-contractors raises many complex difficulties, as recent decisions in the courts show. One of the most serious of these difficulties is the problem of the defaulting or insolvent sub-contractor who is a source of great potential loss and increased expense. The Committee had to decide upon whom that risk should rest: upon the Employer who chose the sub-contractor, and ordered the Contractor to employ him, or the Contractor who was obliged to employ him. The Committee decided that, despite the power of objection given to the Contractor, he who called the tune should pay the piper and the clauses are designed so that if loss should ultimately be suffered as a result of his chosen specialist's fault or bankruptcy, that loss should be upon the Employer. The Contractor, however, is under an obligation to do all he can to avoid such loss and to recover it from the sub-contractor. Where one has, as a basic premise, an artificial situation, it must follow that clauses designed to give it legal enforceability will themselves appear to be somewhat tortuous and complicated.

The Committee took the view that, as far as possible, as Mr. Wallace has it, the chain of liability should not be broken and that the responsibilities and liabilities should be spelt out clearly: also that employers and engineers should face up to this situation and consider carefully, in each case, whether " nomination " is in fact necessary.

Mr. Wallace gives insufficient emphasis to the various risks which the Contractor takes if he decides to forfeit the sub-contract without the Employer's consent. In that event the whole of the increased costs incurred as a result of the forfeiture fall upon him unless he succeeds in establishing that the forfeiture was in fact justified, which might be difficult in face of the Engineer's opinion to the contrary. He makes it difficult for anyone to take his commentary seriously when he says that " the contract has therefore gone from the sublime to the ridiculous " on the sole ground that the contractor is now allowed to retain such discounts as sub-contractors may offer for cash. Cash discount has in the past presented considerable difficulties in practice concerning which there has been no consistency either of application or of proof of receipt. Further, the discount allowed not infrequently depends upon the commercial reputation of individual (main) contractors and the Committee decided that this would be better left between the main and sub-contractors. Main contractors who are efficient and pay promptly would reflect in their tenders the cash effect of the recovery in cash discounts.

Mr. Wallace has a good point, however, when he asks who is to have priority if the Contractor does not recover enough to cover both the Employer's loss and his own. When the clause was drafted it was assumed that a sub-contractor would be pressed to the point of liquidation or bankruptcy so that there would eventually be a dividend to apply pro rata to both heads of claim. Admittedly this does not deal with the case where the Contractor might first recover the amount of the Employer's loss (by, say, garnishee proceedings) before proceeding to wind up the sub-contractor. It might be assumed that the Employer should have priority because that amount which the Contractor may have suffered is to some extent within his own control and the Employer cannot be expected to be responsible, but it is a point which ought to be considered and dealt with by an amendment.

Pointless Re-arrangements etc. (clauses 7, 11, 20, 34 and 50)

The Committee considered that the cross-referencing of clause 7 (3) to clause 51 makes clear that the issue of a drawing may be an order in writing under clause 51. Likewise if the Engineer gives an instruction expressly under clause 13 (1) which involves a variation, he cannot escape the consequences of clause 52; that is why clause 51 is referred to there.

The intention underlying the addition in Clause 11 (1) of the words " having taken into account any information . . . provided by . . . the Employer " (*e.g.* soil survey data) is to clarify the standing of such information. It means that the

Contractor is both entitled and obliged to take note of it as a matter of fact, but he is nevertheless " deemed to have satisfied himself " (*i.e.* used his own endeavours) to supplement such information by inspection, inquiry and so on as he may consider necessary.

In clause 20 (3) significance *is* intended to be attached to the words " a cause due to . . . fault defect error or omission in the design of the Works." It was decided that the previous shorter form of words did not adequately cover the case where damage occurs because a design which is competent and capable of being built is very difficult to build, *e.g.* the erection of a complex girder. Contractors have been known to argue that when damage occurs in those circumstances it is solely due to the design, because had it been a different kind of design the problem would not have arisen. But that argument is inconsistent with the principle that it is for the Contractor to decide how to do the work: the difficulty of erection is a risk he has to take, so clause 20 (2) has been altered to make clear that is is only when there is something *wrong* with the design that there is an excepted risk.

The old version of clause 34 was a near but not exact reproduction of the Fair Wages Resolution. It was not however a quotation and this would now need to be construed according to the current meaning of the terms used. For example—" trade union " would take the meaning given it in the Industrial Relations Act—which may not be the same as that intended by the Resolution. Hence the decision to quote it verbatim.

The only changes made in clause 50—the search for defects clause—are the correction of two typographical errors and the widening of the term " search " to " the carrying out of such searches, tests or trials." Not only is this a change of some substance and in no sense pointless or stylistic, but it is a change in the Employer's interest.

Safety (clauses 8 (2), 15 (2), 16 and 19)

We find extremely mischievous Mr. Wallace's description of the references to the Contractor's responsibility for safety in clauses 8 (2), 15 (2), 16 and 19 as being " largely of a window dressing character." Safety on sites is a matter of grave concern in the industry. Despite a contractor's legal responsibilities for the safety of operations on the site, too many accidents still occur, and the Committee thought it right to take the opportunity to emphasise these obligations in the contract. Mr. Wallace, by belittling them, shows a lack of concern for the day-to-day affairs of the industry.

Claims (clause 52 (4))

Although Mr. Abrahamson welcomes the demise of the " unrealistic " notice requirement of clause 12 (2) in the Fourth Edition, Mr. Wallace bemoans it passing and criticises the procedure for making claims in clause 52 (4). In the Committee's view and in the experience of its members the notice provisions of the old clause 12 (2) were impractical and operated to the prejudice of a good contractor, who, when faced with an emergency, got on with the work and made his claim afterwards.

The old clauses favoured a contractor who was more intent on presenting claims than getting on with the work. In our view clause 52 (4) provides all that is necessary in the way of protection for the Employer and Engineer without injustice to the Contractor. It is a simpler procedure which avoids pitfalls which were present in the previous edition.

Hired Plant (clause 53)

The Committee considered that with the present structure of the industry it would in many cases be virtually impossible to determine the ownership of plant, in the context of subsidiary or associated companies: or to require plant-hirers or suppliers of hire-purchase plant to accept a " vesting " clause in their contracts. It was therefore unrealistic to apply the vesting requirements other than to " Plant, goods and materials owned by the Contractor or by any firm in which the Contractor has a controlling interest." In the case of hired plant the Employer should in most cases be able to arrange to pay the hire charges if he wishes to retain the plant on the site. They saw no difficulty in a plant-hirer accepting the requirement of sub-clause (3).

Such an arrangement, however, is not practical in the case of hire-purchase plant and the Committee decided to eliminate hire-purchase plant from the ambit of the clause. In this connection there is a choice either to allow the unfettered use of hire-purchase plant, in which case the Employer is at risk of finding that only hire-purchase plant is being used and there is thus a restraint on his exercise of the Forfeiture Clause, or alternatively the clause can be drawn so that the use of hire-purchase plant is prohibited, leaving it to the discretion of the Employer to waive this provision in any particular case. Clause 53, as drawn, adopts the latter course, but if in practice it is found that a waiver is sought or has to be granted in the majority of cases, it will be a simple matter to revise the clause so as to adopt the first alternative. This can be done by adding at the end of 53 (1) (b) the words " and the expression ' hired Plant ' shall not include Plant hired under an agreement for hire-purchase."

The proviso to clause 60 (7) which expressly forbids the engineer to delete or reduce any sum previously certified in respect of work or materials of nominated sub-contractors, if the Contractor shall have already paid that sum to the nominated sub-contractor, has been criticised as conferring an immunity upon the sub-contractor who does defective work. It does nothing of the sort.

The execution of defective work is a breach of contract, and an employer whose contractor does defective work (or a contractor whose sub-contractor does defective work) has two possible remedies: (i) he may refuse to pay for the work, or refuse to pay the full value of it, until the defect is put right, or (ii) he may pay for it and sue the contractor/sub-contractor (as the case may be) for damages. Once the work has been paid for, only the last remedy is available. The proviso to clause 60 (7) in no way affects either the sub-contractor's or the contractor's liability for defective work. The contractor remains liable in damages to the employer and the sub-contractor to the contractor.

On the other hand, the proviso does something to prevent an unjust situation from arising in circumstances where a nominated sub-contractor's work has been completed before the main contract work is complete. In such a case, suppose the completed sub-contract work has been certified in the sum of (say) £5,000, and the Contractor, as he is bound to do, has paid it to the sub-contractor. Later the Engineer finds cause to be dissatisfied with the sub-contract work and deducts the £5,000 from the next certificate due to the Contractor. The Contractor then has no chance to exercise the just remedy noticed above, nor can he compel the sub-contractor to return to the site. All he can do is to incur expenses in remedying the defects in order to obtain payment of the £5,000, and then hope to recover from the sub-contract in an arbitration or action. The Committee considered that in such circumstances, it was fairer that both the employer and the contractor should be in the same position. In fact, now that the House of Lords has re-established an employer's right to set off claims for damages against certified sums (*Modern Engineering* v. *Gilbert Ash* (*Northern*) *Ltd.* [1973] 3 W.L.R. 421), the proviso gives less protection to the contractor than the Committee thought that it would when it was decided to add it to Clause 60 (7).

Forfeiture (clause 63)

The word " flagrantly " was changed because it has not got a clear and precise meaning. It is emotionally charged and should not be used in a contract. The concept of deliberate defiance is adequately covered by the word " persistently " which Mr. Wallace ignores. The word " fundamentally " has a meaning known to lawyers and is, we believe, what was meant to be added by " flagrantly " in the old clause. The clause can certainly be exercised in circumstances when the common law right of rescission could not be, *e.g.* mere lack of diligence or persistent non-fundamental breach of contract. It remains to consider whether the words " without prejudice to any other rights and remedies " should be added after " then the employer may . . ." We do not think this necessary. A common law right as for instance, the right to damages, can only be excluded by clearly expressed words, and there are none such in this clause.

Arbitration (clause 66)

We are convinced that the arbitration clause bears no resemblance to a *Scott* v. *Avery* clause which is one which provides that the award of an arbitration is a condition precedent to the bringing of an action in the courts, because there are no words in clause 66 which can reasonably be interpreted as having that result.

Metrication (clause 71)

Mr. Wallace criticises this clause and notes only a small saving to cover cases where the Contractor has been the cause of the deficiency. The clause as amended clearly refers to shortages of materials in the measure specified, in a period of change-over where neither party can be sure of what in the event will be available. The old clause has not presented difficulty in practice, so far as is known, so, as its usefulness is likely to be of short duration, it was decided that a major revision was not justified.

NEW ICE CONDITIONS OF CONTRACT*

I have read with interest the correspondence resulting from my earlier article, and the full reply of the committee itself (*NCE* 20/27 December 1973). Very little has been said which has led me to modify my views.

Mr. Mott (*NCE* 29 November 1973) and others say that I " assume a disposition and love of legal proceedings which does not exist." Mr. Mott should realise that litigation in this field usually takes the form of arbitration and is therefore private and without publicity, and that in any event proceedings which go the full course are only the tip of the iceberg, that thousands of man-hours are absorbed in advancing, considering and compromising claims which, if there was a clearer and better balanced contract, would not happen. In my view there is infinitely more litigation in building and civil engineering than in other comparable industries.

Turning to the more detailed reply of the committee. I fear that here too some time has been spent accusing me of, and refuting, opinions I do not hold. It is said that I consider that " even those (risks) over which the contractor has no control

* Article by the author reproduced from *New Civil Engineer*, May 23, 1974.

and which emanate from the instructions of the engineer on any matter, whether mentioned in the contract or not, shall be borne by the contractor." It is suggested that I have advocated that the engineer should " be able to interfere at will with the orderly progress of the contract without consequential payment." I am also accused of " regarding contracts for civil engineering works as a battle between contractors *in dishonest collusion with suppliers and sub-contractors* and the employer *aided by incompetent allies in the shape of engineers and unknowledgeable legal advisers*." Apart from my stating at one point that a new provision about discounts is open to collusive quoting by sub-contractors, I find no possible support for any of the italicised wording which, if I may say so without discourtesy, seems to me exaggerated and unhelpful.

I find the statement that " one of the most important policy changes is that the Fifth Edition has been made, clearly and unequivocally, a " measure and value " contract," and the surprise expressed that all commentators have paid scant attention to this, puzzling. In over 50 years no one has ever suggested, so far as I am aware, either in a standard work or in legal proceedings, that clause 55 of the Conditions does not mean what it says, and that changes in the contract quantities will not produce a comparable change in the contract price.

Nor does anything the committee says indicate any important change of policy in this particular sense, let alone one which justifies what are said to be a consequential " series of alterations " to the contract.

The committee says that clause 13 (3) is necessary because of the admittedly rather odd wording " shall comply with . . . the engineer's instructions and directions on any matter connected [with the works] (whether mentioned in the contract or not)." I have never heard of a contractor who is armed with an engineer's instruction involving a change from the contract expectation failing to obtain additional remuneration as a result of this wording. Even if the traditional wording could defeat a contractor in such a situation, it does not justify the wording of the new sub-clause (3), which is expressly wide enough to permit a claim for matters which are " mentioned in the contract " and therefore either expressly or by inference a part of the contractual obligation of the contractor. This aspect of the wording is, in the view both of Mr. Abrahamson and myself, dangerous and damaging.

I do not think that the committee's reply to Mr. Abrahamson's point that no writing is required derives any assistance from the notice requirement in clause 52 (4).

I do not understand the statement that the " trap " for engineers existed previously under clause 14 in the Fourth Edition. I would never advocate that an engineer who exercised a power to control a contractor's method of working should not render his employer liable to make additional payment if the requirement exceeded a reasonable contract expectation—under nearly all contracts this would in any event be a variation. What I object to is a provision which is so worded that it " puts the engineer on the spot " the moment he makes a mere request for information.

The committee contends that the wording of the old clause 51 of the Fourth Edition always imported a contractual obligation on the engineer to vary the work where this was " necessary," so that the new wording does no more than clarify the position. I can only say that in the 50 years or more that the old wording has obtained in the U.K. there has not been a single decision or ruling to this effect, whereas there has been a long line of cases emphasising the absolute character of the contractor's obligation to complete notwithstanding any difficulties which may be encountered—for example the decision (itself on the

1955 ICE Conditions) in *Pearce* v. *Hereford Corporation* (1968) 66 L.G.R. 647, where the contractor was held disentitled to additional remuneration notwithstanding compliance with agreed instructions from the engineer.

I reiterate my view that the new wording may involve a most fundamental change in the previous position, depending upon what the courts will make of the words " necessary for the completion of the works."

With regard to my criticism of the new clause 55 (2) the committee's reply states that " it was to further these principles [that the standard method should not override what would otherwise be the clear meaning of the contract] yet recognising the practical problems associated with their application that clause 55 (2) was added."

I can see no possible result from the wholesale adoption of the RIBA wording in this new provision but to encourage and strengthen contractors' " Standard Method " claims. The practical example cited in support of the committee's argument would usually, depending upon the sum total of the contract descriptions, constitute a variation. The basis of my criticism of this type of claim, which I do not think has been met, is that if a sensible construction of the contract as a whole indicates that work is included in the contract price, it is wrong that recommendations in a Standard Method should enable that sensible construction to be overruled.

The reply to my criticism under clause 56 (2) is that this contains nothing new, and merely clarifies " what a consensus of legal opinion always thought was the correct interpretation of the Fourth Edition." I have never been aware of any such legal consensus, my own published works indicate an opposite opinion, and there has never been either dictum or decision to that effect in the courts, which would be remarkable in a matter of such fundamental financial importance (namely a contention that remeasurement under clause 56 should be carried out in accordance with the valuation rules in clause 52).

Nor is my criticism that the make-up of prices is not required to be disclosed at the beginning of the work met by the statement that a contractor refusing to produce a make-up of his prices would not be able to obtain an increase of rate. I made it clear that I was not talking of cases of refusal to give a make-up but of the ability to tailor an alleged make-up of a rate in support of a claim after the event, which would be impossible if the make-up was known at the beginning of the job.

The criticism I made in regard to the new clause 44 related to the considerable number of occasions on which the engineer (whether or not the contractor makes any claim) is called upon to make decisions as to extension of time. The committee's reply that this in some way safeguards the employer seems to hint at yet another new contractor's claim—namely for acceleration costs if the engineer's decision refusing an extension of time is subsequently held to be incorrect. Even if this were right, I do not see how the complicated requirements for repeated extensions of time decisions can help the employer—on the contrary, the possibility of mounting such claims on the facts is surely increased by the express requirements for a series of decisions on extension of time at a number of stages during the construction period.

I am glad to note the explanation of the new wording in clause 49 and am happy to concede that the committee may well be right in its construction of it.

My criticism of clause 60 (7)—in regard to defective work by nominated sub-contractors—appears to have been misunderstood. I was not suggesting that this provision confers a permanent immunity on such sub-contractors, but a temporary immunity " at least until Final Certificate." I cannot understand why the committee feels that, if a sub-contractor has been paid before his defective work is discovered, " equality between contractor and employer " demands that *neither* of them should be able to impose any sanction against the guilty sub-contractor until the Final Certificate.

Another serious anomaly in the new nomination provisions, on which I have not commented before, is that it would seem that *wrongful* terminations of the sub-contract by the main contractor, provided they are carried out with the employer's consent, will attract full financial protection and reimbursement for the main contractor under the provisions of clause 59B. This could only be justified in the case of a determination without the contractor's consent, and represents serious dangers for the employer and quite anomalous results.

I note the committee agrees that the wording of clause 53 does mean that the use of hire-purchase plant on the site is prohibited, and that the contract requires amendment if such plant is to be used.

With regard to clause 63, my criticism was that the new wording of the determination clause introduces a risk that this remedy may now be held to be exclusive of the common-law remedy. The committee's reply agrees that the criticism can be met by a single " without prejudice " phrase but does " not think this necessary." I find this odd when the committee's reply to the comment that new wording elsewhere in the contract will support a new financial claim by the contractor is so often that the new wording is only intended to restate more clearly the previously existing position.

With regard to clause 66, a similar confidence is shown in the pre-existing legal position which many would regard as extremely doubtful, while no reply is given to the vitally important ambiguity relating to the arbitration of disputes on interim certificate.

It seems to have been assumed that I have been in favour of " root-and-branch " reform of the Fourth Edition. This is not so. The policies of the Fourth Edition have attracted little, if any, criticism from me and I am on record that I consider that it struck a fair balance between the parties. What it required was clarification and the remedying of a number of omissions. The new edition has achieved this admirably at two very important points—the payment provisions under clause 60 and the nomination procedures and powers under clause 58 and the earlier part of clause 59A. The new indexed-based fluctuations clause is excellent. But the new edition has made a series of radical policy changes which have completely altered the commercial balance of the contract, the combined effect of which is that it has now become more of a service contract than a price contract, with nearly all the important commercial risks transferred from the contractor to the employer. It is the Fifth Edition which in my opinion should call for radical reconsideration on grounds of policy once its implications are understood.

APPENDIX D

IN January 1977 the author in the Note set out in Part I hereunder explained the enormous potential significance in the law of tort of the appeal then pending in the House of Lords in the *Anns* case. The article, reproduced in Part II, which followed in January 1978 seeks to analyse and explain the effect of the speeches in that case. Bearing in mind that the present contract under discussion in this commentary is a civil engineering contract, and that the *Anns* case was primarily concerned with dwelling-houses, readers should appreciate that the new liability in tort, as will be seen, is closely associated with the concept of danger to person or property (other than the Works themselves), nevertheless its rapid extension into the civil engineering field can be confidently predicted—see already the Court of Appeal decision in *Batty* v. *Metropolitan Property Realisations Ltd.* [1978] 2 W.L.R. 500, the subject of the author's note in Part III, *infra*.

PART I

FROM BABYLON TO BABEL, OR A NEW PATH FOR NEGLIGENCE?*

IN a vigorous dissenting opinion in *Donoghue* v. *Stevenson*, Lord Buckmaster said (1932) A.C. 562, 577, 578

> " There can be no special duty attaching to the manufacture of food apart from that implied by contract or imposed by statute. If such a duty exists, it seems to me it must cover the construction of every article, and I cannot see any reason why it should not apply to the construction of a house. If one step, why not fifty? Yet if a house be, as it sometimes is, negligently built, and in consequence of that negligence the ceiling falls and injures the occupier or anyone else, no action against the builder exists according to English law, although I believe such a right did exist according to the laws of Babylon."

That statement is now, of course, very much past history. Both inside and outside England the tort of negligence has been extended without difficulty far beyond manufacturers of food to include all other goods, as well as repairers, assemblers and distrubutors of goods; repairers of electric wiring in houses (*Hartley* v. *Mayoh & Co.* [1954] 1 Q.B. 383); builders' control of their current building operations (*A. C. Billings & Sons Ltd.* v. *Riden* [1958] A.C. 240); builders' permanent work (*Gallagher* v. *McDowell Ltd.* [1961] N.I. 26 (Northern Ireland)); architects' design of permanent work (*Voli* v. *Inglewood Shire Council* (1963) 110 C.L.R. 74 (Australia)); architects' decisions as to current building operations (*Clay* v. *A. J. Crump & Sons Ltd.* [1964] 1 Q.B. 533); and indeed almost any human or commercial activity in which physical damage to person or property can be foreseen as a sufficiently proximate or direct result of the negligent act or omission complained of. However, since the decision of the House of Lords in *Hedley Byrne & Co. Ltd.* v. *Heller & Partners Ltd.* [1964] A.C. 465 a number of decisions in the Court of Appeal have given the tort of negligence, in terms of principle and rationale, a distinctly ragged appearance. An opportunity for a radical and authoritative re-appraisal of the law is about to arise in the House of Lords.

---

* Reproduced from (1977) 93 L.Q.R. 16–21.

The story may be said to start in January 1970, when in *Ministry of Housing and Local Government* v. *Sharp* [1970] 2 Q.B. 223 Salmon L.J. said (at p. 278D, E)

> " So far, however, as the law of negligence relating to civil actions is concerned, the existence of a duty to take reasonable care no longer depends upon whether it is physical injury or financial loss which can reasonably be foreseen as a result of a failure to take such care ";

and Lord Denning M.R. in the same case, said (at p. 268H)

> ". . . the duty to use due care in a statement arises . . . from the fact that the person making it knows, or ought to know, that others, being his neighbours in this regard, would act on the faith of the statement being accurate. . . . It is owed, of course, to the person to whom the certificate is issued . . . it also is owed to any person whom he knows, or ought to know, will be injuriously affected by a mistake. . . ."

Sharp's case was one of purely financial damage suffered by a third person who was neither vendor nor purchaser following a negligent search of a register of local land charges and the consequential issue of an inaccurate " clear " certificate.

Six months later, in July 1970, the Court of Appeal (of which Lord Denning M.R. was again a member) in *S.C.M.* (*United Kingdom*) *Ltd.* v. *W. J. Whittall and Son Ltd.* [1971] 1 Q.B. 337 re-asserted, in a negligent act case, the classical view that financial damage to be recoverable must be consequential upon damage to person or property—see *e.g. per* Lord Denning M.R. at pages 345H 346B, who explained the *Hedley Byrne* case as creating an exception where the economic loss was " the immediate—almost, I might say, the intended—consequence " of a negligent statement, and *per* Winn L.J. (at p. 350A) who found himself " unable to concur in the full breadth of " Salmon L.J.'s dictum in *Sharp's* case.

In June 1972, in another very similar negligent act case (*Spartan Steel & Alloys Ltd.* v. *Martin & Co.* (*Contractors*) *Ltd.* [1973] Q.B. 27) the Court of Appeal allowed one category of financial damage (loss of profit on a batch of spoilt steel due to a negligently caused loss of electric power in a factory) but not another (loss of profit on the production of steel which could not be started until the current was restored) where the loss on production foregone was admittedly as foreseeable as the loss on spoilt production. Lord Denning M.R. justified this restriction on grounds of public policy but, perhaps not surprisingly, Edmund Davies L.J. dissented on the ground of the foreseeability of the damage.

Already however, the Court of Appeal in December 1971 in *Dutton* v. *Bognor Regis U.D.C.* [1972] 1 Q.B. 373 had arrived at perhaps the most remarkable and far-ranging decision extending liability in the law of tort for many years. A local authority had failed to appreciate that a private developer's building was being constructed on " made ground " and their building inspector passed trenches and foundations which a careful inspection would have shown to be insufficient to deal with this condition. The house then passed through two sets of hands, the second purchaser not employing a surveyor, though her mortgagees had done so. The house subsequently settled and developed cracks which required repair. The Court of Appeal (Lord Denning M.R., Sachs and Stamp L.JJ.) held that the council's servants owed a duty of care to subsequent purchasers, and that the duty extended to economic loss. In the course of his judgment Sachs L.J. (at p. 403F) expressly adopted Salmon L.J.'s broad dictum in *Sharp's* case, which had been expressly disapproved by Winn L.J. the year before in the *S.C.M.* case.

It is important to appreciate that all the above cases expressly invoke the *Donoghue* v. *Stevenson* principle as their *ratio decidendi*. Moreover, while in *Sharp's* case there was undoubtedly a statement (in the form of a " clear certificate ") which was the more proximate cause of the economic loss, it was preceded by a negligent act (the search) and in *Dutton's* case, there seems to have been only a negligent act (inspection). Again, while in *Dutton's* case there may appear to be the element of physical damage (the cracks), this is misleading The *Donoghue* v. *Stevenson* principle is concerned with liability for a chattel causing (physical) damage to the person or to other property (not damage to the chattel itself). The *Dutton* principle, if it is right, means that in *Donoghue* v. *Stevenson* the plaintiff could have sued for replacement of the ginger-beer bottle—looked at in reverse, the *Donoghue* v. *Stevenson* principle when applied to real property such as a house will mean that the defendant will be liable for physical damage to other property (*e.g.* the chattels of the occupier or the buildings of adjoining occupiers) but not for repair to the house itself. Though at one point Lord Denning M.R. does state that there was damage to property (at p. 396E) it is fair to say that the court as a whole did realise that they were concerned with an " economic loss only " claim. This serves to emphasise how near in character to a contractual warranty of suitability this new tortious liability is, and indeed how the *Dutton* case anticipated and, it if was right, rendered almost wholly unnecessary (in the case of dwelling-houses at least) the Defective Premises Act 1972, which did impose precisely such a " tortious warranty " on all concerned with the provision of dwelling-houses (though not, perhaps, local authorities who may arguably not be included in the persons defined as owing the new duty under the Act).

It is no part of this Note to discuss the correctness or otherwise, on legal or policy grounds, of the *Dutton* case, but only to emphasise its novelty and overwhelming commercial and practical importance. It may well mean, for example, that apart from builders and developers, advisers in many fields will owe a duty in tort in regard to purely financial damage suffered by third persons, though Lord Denning M.R. (at p. 395C–E) suggested that there might be a distinction between professional men giving advice on financial or property matters (who would owe a duty only to their clients) and those giving advice in regard to the safety of buildings or machines where " the duty is to all those who may suffer [financial] injury in case his advice is bad." (There has always, of course, been liability for *physical* damage resulting from negligent statements—see *e.g. The Rhosina* (1885) 10 P.D. 131, where a ship went aground following negligent advice. See also the recent decision of the House of Lords confirming the liability in tort of a valuer to third persons in *Arenson* v. *Casson, Beckman Rutley & Co.* [1975] 3 W.L.R. 815.)

This topic has already been the subject of a penetrating and valuable article by P. P. Craig at (1976) 92 L.Q.R. 213. The essence of that study was to suggest that the " telescoping " of the *Donoghue* v. *Stevenson* " neighbour " principle of reasonable foreseeability with the *Hedley-Byrne* " economic loss only " recoverability for negligent statements must in both cases give rise to an unacceptable expansion of liability, and that some new test other than simple reasonable foresight will be required in economic loss cases. The House of Lords now, should it wish to do so, will have a direct opportunity to grapple with this problem as a result of a rather odd accident of the post-*Dutton* litigation.

In the *Dutton* case one of the arguments of counsel for the defendant local authority was that the suggested liability was unacceptable on policy grounds, since the authority might find itself liable to subsequent owners of houses many years later should cracks or damage then develop. Lord Denning M.R. disagreed and sought to follow a view expressed in a dictum of Diplock L.J. in *Bagot* v. *Stevens Scanlon & Co. Ltd.* [1966] 1 Q.B. 197, 203. In that case, on a preliminary issue as to limitation, it was conceded by counsel that if the liability of architects to their clients was in tort and not in contract then they would not be protected by limitation, since the damage there had been suffered, and hence the cause of action had arisen, when the defects manifested themselves and not at the much earlier date when the negligent acts took place. Diplock L.J. held that the liability was in contract, which disposed of the matter, but then expressed the view *obiter* that counsel's concession had in any case been wrong, and that the damage was suffered on receipt of the badly constructed property, and not later when the consequential failures occurred. So Lord Denning M.R.'s dictum, itself *obiter*, relied upon another *obiter dictum* given without the benefit of argument—the latter fact expressly recognised by Sachs L.J., who declined to decide the question in the *Dutton* case. However, the spate of cases against local authorities and others which has now succeeded the *Dutton* case has rapidly raised the limitation point again, and in *Higgins* v. *Arfon B.C.* [1975] 1 W.L.R. 524, *Riley* v. *Baker* (unreported) and *Anns* v. *Walcroft Property Co. Ltd.* (unreported), Mars-Jones J., Plowman V.-C. and Judge Fay respectively followed Lord Denning M.R.'s view and held that time began to run when the house with the incipient defects was conveyed to the plaintiff (there is some doubt as to the exact date in the *Riley* case, which may have been earlier still at the time of the negligent act).

Eventually in *Sparham-Souter* v. *Town and Country Developments* (*Essex*) *Ltd.* [1976] Q.B. 858 (a local authority case despite its name) the limitation point reached the Court of Appeal once more. The difficulty of the point should be appreciated. If an inadequate beam is specified or constructed, and 10 years later the beam fails, with the result that the occupier is injured or a valuable antique smashed or a neighbour's property damaged, there is no doubt that those causès of action arise then. What, however, if the inadequacy of the beam is, for any reason, discovered or appreciated before it fails, so that remedial work will avert any damage, and the action is the new action in tort for economic loss? (This was the situation in the important Canadian case of *Rivtow Marine* v. *Washington Iron Works* [1973] 6 W.W.R. 692, discussed in (1976) 92 L.W.R. at pp. 235, 236.) The Court of Appeal (Lord Denning M.R., Roskill and Geoffrey Lane L.JJ.) held that the cause of action arose when the damage manifested itself *and the person with the then current interest in the house should with reasonable diligence have discovered it*. Lord Denning M.R. with characteristic frankness acknowledged a change of view. Roskill L.J. regarded himself as presented with " an unenviable choice between unattractive alternatives, a position which was never envisaged when *Dutton's* case was decided but which we must face in this court unless and until that decision is overruled by the House of Lords or the position . . . remedied by legislation."

Within three weeks of this decision, the unsuccessful plaintiff in the *Anns* case was granted leave to appeal to the Court of Appeal out of time and by agreement his appeal was formally allowed and leave to appeal to the House of Lords granted to the defendant authority (Merton London Borough Council)—see [1976] Q.B. 882. Bearing in mind that these latter cases all reached the Court of Appeal on a preliminary point as to limitation, however, this by itself would not have allowed the substance of the *Dutton* decision to be questioned, but on a Petition for Leave the House of Lords has now, with the consent of the plaintiff agreed in the *Anns* case that the validity of the *Dutton* case itself may be the subject of the appeal as well as the limitation point, on the argument that no effective view can be expressed on that point unless the precise nature or extent of the *Dutton* liability is established: see [1976] 1 W.L.R. 1108.

Should the House decide so to treat it, therefore, *Anns* v. *Walcroft Property Co. Ltd.*, which it is understood may reach the House of Lords in February 1977, may live to rank as perhaps the most important decision in the law of tortious negligence since *Donoghue* v. *Stevenson.*

PART II

TORT DEMOLISHES CONTRACT IN NEW CONSTRUCTION*

THE Court of Appeal in the case of *Dutton* v. *Bognor Regis U.D.C.*[1] broke new ground in the field of negligence in two principal directions. The first novel element was the extension of liability into a further area of " financial damage only " negligence, following on the decision in *Ministry of Housing and Local Government* v. *Sharp*,[2] itself partly based on the well-known case of *Hedley Byrne & Co. Ltd.* v. *Heller & Partners Ltd.*[3] In the *Dutton* case the Court of Appeal imposed what many regarded as a new duty of care on those concerned with the construction of a new building, and in particular on the responsible by-law authority, extending to cases where the only damage involved was the cost of repairing the building on discovery of defects in it. Hitherto, contract alone was thought to impose such a duty. As will be seen, there is an element of controversy about whether physical damage was present on the facts or formed part of the *Dutton ratio decidendi*.[4] But on any possible view, however, the physical damage (if any) was *to the house itself* and the damage related to the financial cost of *repairing the house*. By analogy with cases of dangerous chattels or manufactured products, the damage recoverable was for the *cost of repair of the chattel/product itself*, not of other property damaged by the failure or dangerous condition of the chattel/product. Thus, launching a new house into circulation can be seen, on the authority of *Dutton*, to impose a quite different and wider duty than in the case of the English law of chattel/products hitherto, not dissimilar from a tortious warranty of quality and closely analogous for all practical purposes with the duty of care imposed on those concerned with the construction of new dwelling-houses by the Defective Premises Act 1972.

For the purposes of this article the expression " financial damage only " is used in this special sense even though there may be present (only incidentally, as will be submitted) an element of physical damage to the house/chattel/product itself. Again, so as to avoid confusion, this article is not concerned with true physical damage to *other* property (*e.g.* to the goods of occupiers, or to adjoining properties) or with personal injuries, both of which present no special problem and have already been absorbed into the general law of negligence in England without difficulty [5] once the doctrine of " caveat emptor," as applied in *Bottomley* v. *Bannister* [6] and *Otto* v. *Bolton* [7] had been successfully circumvented. Both

* [Re-printed from (1978) 94 L.Q.R. 60.]
1 [1972] 1 Q.B. 373.
2 [1970] 2 Q.B. 223.
3 [1964] A.C. 465.
4 See (1977) 93 L.Q.R. 16, 18, 19, and see also *infra*.
5 *Ibid.* at pp. 16, 17.
6 [1932] 1 K.B. 458.
7 [1936] 2 K.B. 46.

these cases appeared to confer immunity on the vendors and lessors of property but now, as will be seen, they have been finally given their death blow for most practical purposes.

The second more restricted, though socially most important element of novelty in the *Dutton* decision, was the extension of the liability beyond developer, builder, professional designer or supervisor, or contractor or sub-contractor concerned with the new building, to the local authority responsible for making inspections to ensure by-law compliance. As will be seen, the present article is not primarily concerned with this last aspect of the matter, but with the wider implications for the tort of negligence.

The *Dutton* case has now itself been reviewed in the House of Lords [8] in *Anns* v. *Merton L.B.C.*[9] The headnote to the case concerns itself, perhaps understandably in view of the proportionate part of the speeches directed to it, almost exclusively with the relationship between the alleged duty of care owed to future occupiers and owners of houses at common law by the defendants (who were the by-law authority under the Public Health Act 1936) on the one hand, and the statutory power or duty under which they were acting under the Act on the other, which was said to preclude the common law liability. While this part of the decision was a necessary and important hurdle which had to be cleared by the plaintiffs if they were to succeed, a proper understanding of the substantive decision will nevertheless be of crucial importance in the development of the law of negligence in the United Kingdom, and also of considerable importance in the field of limitation of actions (at least while the English Limitation Acts remain in their present not very satisfactory form in cases other than personal injuries claims). It must be said, too, that the *Anns* speeches verge on the perfunctory in their discussion of the wider substantive question involved, so that the great importance of the case arises as much from necessary implication as from explicit statements of principle in the speeches.

In the *Anns* case the building in question, which was constructed in 1962, had not in the event had its foundations constructed down to the depths shown on the deposited plans. Movement started to occur in 1970, resulting in some cracking of the main walls and the usual other symptoms, such as sticking of doors and sloping of floors. The plaintiffs were all occupiers of flats or maisonettes on long leases obtained directly from the developer/builder in 1962 or subsequently by assignment in 1967 and 1968. Since it was the limitation question which was the preliminary point at issue before the House (though by agreement the House had consented to deal with the substantive issues of law as well) the House was dealing for the latter purpose with assumed facts as pleaded or agreed in advance of the trial of the action, and in the absence of any then available evidence or agreement were asked by the parties to rule on two different factual hypotheses—either that there had been no inspection at all by the Council, or that there had been a negligent inspection, and that in either case a competent inspection would have avoided the damage by ensuring that the foundations were taken down to a sufficient depth.

Dealing first, and so as to remove it from the present discussion, with the question of the statutory basis of the Council's function as by-law authority, the House held that the distinction between statutory duties and powers, previously thought to be of major significance in this context, was irrelevant to the existence of a duty of care, which might exist in either case. In the case of a mere power there would be a duty to give proper consideration on policy grounds to the question whether or not to inspect (*i.e.* to exercise the power), so

[8] As forecast (1977) 93 L.Q.R. 16–21.

[9] [1977] 2 W.L.R. 1024. Noted by Keith Stanton (1977) 93 L.Q.R. 488.

that the degree of immunity from liability in the event of failure to inspect, though great, was not absolute. When, however, an inspection was made in such a case, while again there might be an element of discretion as to the extent or type of inspection to be made, the duty was to take reasonable care if and in so far as an inspection did take place.[10]

All the House were unanimous in either disapproving of or holding that the well-known case of *East Suffolk Rivers Catchment Board* v. *Kent* [11] was not authority to the contrary. This part of the case can perhaps be left with the observation that, where performance of a statutory duty or power does not necessarily involve damage to third persons, a duty of care to avoid unnecessary damage may exist, subject, in the case of statutory powers, to a possible policy discretion in the statute which might justify an omission to exercise the power in whole or in part, in a case where reasonable grounds for doing so (*e.g.* of economy or administrative practicality) could be shown to exist. The decision and reasoning is, with respect, both logical and to be welcomed in the field of statutory duties generally.

Turning to the duty of care itself, the House was unanimous in holding " that it must be within the contemplation of the Council that if the foundations were covered in without adequate depth or strength injury to safety or health might be suffered by owners or occupiers of the house." [12] The element of danger to physical safety or health is constantly emphasised in Lord Wilberforce's speech, and it is submitted is of the greatest importance in assessing the precise ambit of the decision—at three points the speech points out that the whole function of the Council under the Public Health Act 1936 was to protect the *health and safety* of owners and occupiers of dwelling-house and houses [13]:

> " It must be in the reasonable contemplation not only of the builder but also of the local authority that failure to comply with the by-laws' requirement as to foundations may give rise to a hidden defect which in the future may cause damage to the building affecting the safety and health of owners and occupiers " . . . " what is recoverable is the amount of expenditure necessary to restore the dwelling to a condition in which it is no longer a danger to the health or safety of persons occupying. . . ." [14]

The speech of Lord Wilberforce also stresses the lack of opportunity for subsequent inspection:

> " It [the duty] must be related to the fact that once the inspector has passed the foundations they will be covered up, with no subsequent opportunity for inspection." [15]

These facts, therefore, were sufficient to establish the necessary proximity to found a common law duty of care, and called for application of the principle that, prima facie, such proximity should create a duty unless some other consideration was present which should negative or reduce the scope of the duty.[16]

---

10 This paragraph is a somewhat free and expanded rendering of Lord Wilberforce's speech which was adopted by Lord Diplock, Lord Simon of Glaisdale and Lord Russell of Killowen. Lord Salmon differed in taking the view that failure to hold an inspection at all could not create a liability in negligence: see at p. 1042A.

11 [1941] A.C. 74.

12 [1977] 2 W.L.R. at p. 1038C.

13 *Ibid.* pp. 1032F, G. 1033F.

14 *Ibid.* p. 1033H, 1039F.

15 *Ibid.* p. 1035E.

16 See *ibid.* at p. 1032D, *per* Lord Wilberforce, adopting Lord Reid's remarks in *Dorset Yacht Co. Ltd.* v. *Home Office* [1970] A.C. 1004, 1027. This, incidentally, is now clearly the established doctrine in English jurisdictions for the approach to be adopted when considering a possible new area of duty.

No such negative consideration existed—" As the building is intended to last, the class of owners and occupiers likely to be affected cannot be limited to those who go in immediately after construction," [17] but " A right of action can only be conferred on an owner or occupier who is such when the damage occurs. This disposes of the possible objection that an endless, indeterminate class of potential plaintiffs may be called into existence." [18]

The phrase " when the damage occurs " in the above passage poses, of course, the very difficult question of limitation which was before the House. Lord Wilberforce stated that, apart from personal injury or damage to (other) property, the damages recoverable would include damage to the dwelling-house itself.[19] In his view, the damage in the instant case was, on the facts, physical damage, and what was recoverable was the cost of restoring the dwelling to a condition where it was no longer a danger to health or safety.[20] In his view, the cause of action did not arise immediately upon delivery or conveyance of the house with its inadequate foundations, but " *only . . . when the state of the building is such that there is present or imminent danger to the health or safety of persons occupying it.*" [21] This wording, it will be noted, differs very importantly from the Court of Appeal's decision in *Sparham-Souter* v. *Town and Country Developments* (*Essex*) *Ltd.*,[22] on near identical facts, which indirectly gave rise to the *Anns*' appeal—namely that the cause of action did not accrue " before a person capable of suing discovered, or ought to have discovered, the damage." It was from this ruling that the appellants in the *Anns*' case were effectively appealing.

It is at this point that the speech of Lord Wilberforce, with the greatest respect, may give rise to perhaps unforeseen difficulties, not only in the *Anns*' case itself (if it is fought through to a conclusion) but in the future. Lord Wilberforce undoubtedly, of course, was influenced by the appearance in 1970 of cracks indicating movement—" If the fact is that defects to the maisonettes first appeared in 1970 then, since the writs were issued in 1972, the consequence must be that none of the present actions are barred by the Act." [23]

It was previously suggested that, while attention might be diverted by the presence of the cracking, etc. into assuming that the claim in this type of case was for physical damage, in reality and as a matter of principle it was not—the cracks were only the *symptoms* of past, perhaps trivial, movement, but for practical purposes the repair costs claimed would be for remedying the underlying cause of further future movement or failure.[24] The claim is, it is suggested, a " financial damage only " claim of a certain kind since it is the cost, not of repairing present damage which, if it exists at all, is only incidental, but of removing the " present or imminent danger to the health or safety of occupiers " which is expressly said to be the occasion of the liability arising.[25] Whether this is right or wrong in the instant case, in many cases in practice there will unquestionably be no physical damage at all—only a real apprehension of danger. For example, in the last few years alone, millions of pounds have had to be spent in the U.K. strengthening frameless buildings, box-girder bridges, and buildings containing high-alumina cement, to name but three examples of technical failure, before any physical damage had occurred at all. In real life

---

17 [1977] 2 W.L.R. at p. 1034A.
18 *Ibid.* at p. 1038D.
19 *Ibid.* at p. 1039E.
20 *Ibid.* at p. 1039F.
21 *Ibid.* at p. 1039H.
22 [1976] Q.B. 858.
23 [1977] 2 W.L.R. at p. 1040A.
24 See (1977) 93 L.Q.R. at p. 19.
25 See [1977] 2 W.L.R. at p. 1039F, H.

it can and does happen—*e.g.* it may be found that a structural design error has been made, such as beams of inadequate strength being used, or that breaches of contract have taken place—*e.g.* materials of the wrong kind being used—and once the knowledge is available it becomes urgently necessary to take remedial action, though as yet no damage whatever has occurred.

A further closely associated difficulty on the facts was clearly present to Lord Salmon (who when at the Bar had considerable experience in the building contract field)—

> " It seems to me, however, that since in fact no damage manifested itself until February 1970 it may be very difficult to prove that damage had in fact occurred four years previously. In the unlikely event of the defendants overcoming this difficulty, the fact that the damage went undetected for four years would not prevent the statute running." . . .
>
> " I do not think that if and when this action comes to be tried the defendants should be prevented from attempting to prove that the claim . . . is statute-barred. A building may be able to stand undamaged on defective foundations for years and then perhaps eight years or so later damage may occur. Whether it is possible to prove that damage to the building had occurred four years before it manifested itself is another matter, but can only be decided by evidence." [26]

This part of the case can be passed over with the observation that it may well have left important questions of principle unanswered, and that in cases of expense reasonably incurred to avoid *anticipated* danger due to a known breach of the by-laws or good building practice or design a new theory may need to be evolved if one is to circumvent the arguments on limitation which succeeded, as indicated by Lord Salmon, in the personal injuries case of *Cartledge* v. *Jopling* [27] and led, in the case of personal injuries only, to the Law Reform (Limitation of Actions, etc.) Act 1954. Possibly the new theory may be that this type of damage is not suffered until the responsible property owner himself becomes liable to others for the safety of the premises—*i.e.* once he becomes aware of the defect—so that his cause of action only arises at that time. But on any view a test based on the existence of physical damage will frequently be inappropriate.

The *Anns* case is of far wider importance in other respects, however. The speeches explicitly support the view of Lord Denning M.R. in *Dutton* v. *Bognor Regis U.D.C.*[28] that *the builder* of the house will owe the same duty of care to subsequent owners and occupiers and (*per* Lord Wilberforce) that in addition he may be liable for breach of statutory duty if the building does not comply with the by-laws.[29] Indeed, a very recent decision of the New Zealand Court of Appeal, in which that Court, following the *Dutton* case, held a builder liable in tort for cost of repair only to a subsequent purchaser, is cited with express approval by Lord Wilberforce.[30] While no doubt the rule in *Bottomley* v. *Bannister* and in *Otto* v. *Bolton* may still have some application in cases where a vendor has not himself or by his agent constructed the house, it is clear that, if he is the builder he will enjoy no such immunity.[31] A question remains,

26 *Ibid.* at p. 1049, 1050.
27 [1963] A.C. 758.
28 [1972] 1 Q.B. 373, 393.
29 [1977] 2 W.L.R. at p. 1039C.
30 *Bowen* v. *Paramount Builders* (*Hamilton*) *Ltd. and Mackay* [1977] 1 N.Z.L.R. 394 (discussed in detail *infra*, p. 384).
31 See [1977] 2 W.L.R. at pp. 1039F to C, *per* Lord Wilberforce and 1047A to H, *per* Lord Salmon.

however, whether any duty will be imposed on private owners who build, using independent contractors, but not with a view to sale or leasing, and who after building, possibly many years later, subsequently dispose of their houses.

Another consequence of the case will be its impact on the liability in tort, in this type of " financial damage only " case, of professional men, such as architects, surveyors or engineers associated with the design or with supervision of construction of buildings, to persons other than their immediate clients. Lord Denning M.R. suggested in *Dutton's* case [32] that a distinction needed to be made between professional men concerned with a subject-matter involving possible danger to persons or property, and other professional men, such as lawyers, accountants and so on, where liability might be limited, in " financial damage only " cases, to the client (or, it may perhaps be suggested, to restricted classes of persons almost certain to rely on or be affected by their advice, as in *Hedley Byrne* v. *Heller*.[33] Professional men as such are not mentioned in Lord Wilberforce's opinion, but the repeated emphasis on the health and safety basis of the liability in the *Anns* case suggests some support for the distinction made by Lord Denning.

It is submitted that the following tentative conclusions can be drawn as to the present state of English law to be deduced from the *Anns* opinions:

(a) A duty of care in tort of a " financial damage only " kind (*i.e.* for the cost of remedying the dangerous state of a new building) will exist where the act or omission complained of can be related to the possible safety or health of its future owners and occupiers, and possibly of their property. The liability in tort will *not*, it is submitted, extend, on present authority, to questions of quality or amenity or commercial value—and a body of case-law can be expected to develop deciding on which side of the line a particular defect will fall.

(b) The duty of care will be imposed on all concerned with the initial production of a new building—local authority, contractor, subcontractor, professionals, owner/developer. No doubt it will be applied equally in cases of repair, conversion or alteration of existing as opposed to new buildings, and will not necessarily be limited to dwelling-houses.

(c) An owner/developer will not enjoy any immunity by virtue of his status as a vendor/lessor—except to the extent that his contract or conveyance may expressly protect him as against his immediate vendee/lessee.[34] Whether he can escape liability if he relies on independent contractor designers or builders remains undecided.

(d) While in the *Anns* case the position is unfortunately somewhat confused by the presence of some physical damage (*i.e.* the cracks and other symptoms or early warning of a possible major failure), there seems no reason to suppose that in a " pure financial loss " situation of reasonably anticipated danger without present damage Lord Wilberforce would not have held that the liability existed—witness his approving reference to *Bowen* v. *Paramount Builders* (*Hamilton*) *Ltd.* and *Mackay* [35] and the dissenting judgment of Laskin J.[35a] in the Canadian Supreme Court case of *Rivtow Marine Ltd.* v. *Washington Ironworks* [36] which explicitly adopted this line of reasoning.

(e) The last word may not have been said as to the time when the cause of

---

32 [1972] 1 Q.B. at 395C, E.
33 [1964] A.C. 465. See *per* Lord Salmon at [1977] 2 W.L.R. at p. 1048A to C.
34 See [1977] 2 W.L.R. at pp. 1038H to 1039A, *per* Lord Wilberforce.
35 Discussed *infra*.
35a As he then was: now Chief Justice of Canada.
36 (1973) 6 W.W.R. 692, 715, cited P. P. Craig (1976) 92 L.Q.R. at pp. 236, 237.

action arises in cases where there is as yet no physical damage to the house. When, to adopt Lord Wilberforce's exact formulation, can it be said that " the state of the building is such that there is present or imminent danger to the health or safety of persons occupying it " in such a case? Surely, on this wording, from the day the building is constructed, if the structural or design deficiency is a serious one, though no one may be able to predict with certainty when, or even if, it will fail (the performance of most materials used in building and civil engineering is not predictable within fine limits, and all design must involve a relatively substantial safety factor). Lord Salmon, as the passages already quoted from his speech show, treated this aspect of the case as being entirely dependent on the timing of the first physical damage to the building. It is respectfully suggested that an inquiry to determine precisely when the first, perhaps literally microscopic, damage occurs to the fabric of a building or of its component materials may not only be difficult if not impossible, as Lord Salmon clearly appreciated, but in the legal sense it may also be an irrelevant exercise. Not all failures are conveniently slow and progressive. It may be that Lord Denning's formulation in *Sparham-Souter* v. *Town and Country Developments* (*Essex*) *Ltd.*—the date when " a person capable of suing discovered, or ought to have discovered, the damage "—will need to be adopted, but with " damage " treated as synonymous with " danger." Alternatively, and far more satisfactorily to all concerned, section 2 of the Limitation Act 1939 should be amended in the same sense as Lord Denning's formulation.

(f) There seems logically no reason why the new " financial damage only " duty should be limited to buildings. Presumably it will apply to any chattel or product, such as an aircraft or motorcar or plant or machinery, which is in a state where damage to safety or health of the public may be apprehended—*e.g.* a new car supplied with defective brakes. The law of tort has long ago, of course, as already indicated, accommodated this liability where damage to other persons or property actually results.[37] But if the *Anns* view is logically applied to chattels, an owner will be able to recover the cost of repair before any such damage has occurred—at most, if the view expressed above as to " pure financial damage " cases like the *Rivtow* case is not correct, and some physical damage is needed to found the liability, the owner need only prove some minor internal defect manifesting itself in his car or other product as a symptom of the underlying dangerous condition, which often will not be difficult. It is obvious that an expanding body of case-law can now be expected to develop in England in this wider field, as prospective plaintiff's advisers flex their legal muscles.

A discussion of the *Anns* case cannot properly end without reference to the important judgments in the New Zealand Court of Appeal in December 1976, two months before the *Anns* hearing, in *Bowen* v. *Paramount Builders* (*Hamilton*) *Ltd. and Mackay*.[38] There, a small two-flat property investment was constructed by builders for their client, they supplying details, plans and specification against a rough sketch provided by him. The building was in known peat country, about which little building experience was then available, but the vendor of the land to the client had provided what was said to be an adequate " sand-pad "

---

[37] In the U.S. as long ago as 1915—see *Quackenbush* v. *Ford Motor Co.* 153 N.Y.S. 131.
[38] [1977] 1 N.Z.L.R. 394.

over the site on to which normal foundations were intended to be placed. The building inspector queried the adequacy of the builders' normal foundations. After stopping work temporarily, the builders made an ineffective change in the design, notified the local authority, and continued. The client then noticed brickwork showing signs of misalignment and, becoming nervous about the site, agreed with the builders on certain works which would mask this, and then sold the whole property shortly before its completion to a purchaser without saying anything about the trouble. Almost immediately thereafter a major subsidence took place. The purchaser sued the builders in negligence for the cost of certain remedial work, not as yet carried out, which would contain but not completely cure the problem, and for the ultimate residual loss of value of the building. The court held by a majority that on the facts the builders were negligent in not warning their client of the danger and obtaining qualified advice before proceeding with their modified design, and that the damages claimed by the purchaser were recoverable. In so doing, the court [39] all recognised and discussed in the most explicit terms the distinction between damage to the house itself and damage caused to other property (on the basis of which distinction Speight J. had held that the builders owed no duty in law to the purchaser). Furthermore, while all agreed that physical damage had in fact occurred, the court was faced with the fact that the first (misalignment) damage had occurred before the purchaser acquired the property, so that an analysis and the exact timing of the purchaser's cause of action had more than usual importance. Richmond P.[40] distinguished, for purposes of determining the cause of action, between the earlier (misalignment) " minimal " damage, and the later " structural " damage, while Cooke J.[41] considered that there might be successive causes of action for successive stages of damage. But the entire court also expressed the view [42] that in appropriate cases the remedy in tort would also be available for repairs designed to prevent damage where none had as yet occurred. The court were well aware that the *Anns* case was due for early hearing in the House of Lords—see particularly *per* Cooke J.[43] who indicated his desire to avoid any unnecessary or unintended divergence on a point of common-law principle. It is pleasant to be able to record that there seems to be a close harmony between the reasoning in the *Bowen* and *Anns* cases. The discussion of the economic and other consequences of the new duty is more wide-ranging in the *Bowen* case, and practitioners in particular will find it invaluable since it envisages at a number of points many of the problems and difficulties likely to arise in this field as it is applied and developed (*e.g.* problems of successive damage, and whether warning to a purchaser or client or contractee will avoid the duty to others).

By way of postscript, it may be of interest to indicate some recent trends in this part of the law in the United States. So far as the rule in *Otto* v. *Bolton* is concerned, its formal demise, advocated by almost all textbook writers [44] had by 1970 been formally approved by the Supreme Courts of no less than seven States.[45] In these cases builder/vendors had been variously held liable to purchasers for financial damage (*i.e.* cost of repair) based on an implied warranty of care or suitability, but plaintiffs had also been successfully basing their claims

---

39 (Richmond P., Woodhouse and Cooke JJ.).
40 *Ibid.* at p. 414.
41 *Ibid.* at p. 424.
42 (*Per* Richmond P. at p. 414, finding " highly persuasive " Laskin and Hall JJ.s' judgments in the *Rivtow* case, *per* Woodhouse J. at p. 417 and *per* Cooke J. at p. 423).
43 *Ibid.* at pp. 423–424.
44 See *e.g.* Williston on Contracts (3rd ed. 1963), para. 926A.
45 See the full review of the history of this doctrine in the U.S.A. up to that date by the Supreme Court of Arkansas in *Wawak* v. *Stewart*, 449 S.W. 2d 922 (1970).

in tort notwithstanding a contract of sale or lease with the defendant. Thus in an early decision in 1961 the Supreme Court of Wisconsin held a builder/vendor liable in negligence to a purchaser for the cost of repairs after settlement of a house due to failure to backfill properly round the walls,[46] and in 1963 in California the Supreme Court similarly held that builder/vendors owed a duty in tort to all their prospective house-buyers in a case where, as in *Dutton*, the house had settled necessitating repair work.[47] In that case the argument that there should be no liability since, on the analogy of liability for manufactured goods, the damage was to the house itself, not to other property, was expressly advanced and rejected. In 1974, indeed, the Supreme Court of California, while constrained for limitation reasons to decide the case in contract on an implied warranty basis, indicated that a vendor of a new apartment building was equally liable in negligence to investment purchasers of the building for loss of rent resulting from a series of minor defects in the building, such as ceilings buckling, sliding doors sticking, and water on patio decks ponding, and caused by the flexing of undersized beams installed by the vendor's contractors.[48] The court stated that the liability in tort of builders and first owners now extended to diminution in the value of the construction, and further that the strict liability doctrine of dangerous chattels was properly applicable to new buildings[49] (the practical effect of this would be to make the developer vicariously responsible for an independent contractor). In contract the implied term was to the effect that the completed structure had been designed and constructed in a reasonably workmanlike manner.[50]

While a case involving liability to *subsequent* purchasers or occupiers does not appear to have reached a Supreme Court (and indeed in *Oliver* v. *City Builders Inc.*[51] the Supreme Court of Missouri held in 1974 by a majority of 6 to 3 that no duty existed to a second later purchaser) there seems no reason to doubt that in the great majority of states in the United States the builder will be under the same duty to later purchasers as that now confirmed *obiter* in the *Anns* case in the United Kingdom. The possible liability of municipal or state and other regulatory agencies overseeing building construction in the United States and elsewhere to later purchasers and occupiers must, of course, be a peculiarly domestic matter depending on their exact statutory function,[52] and the rather sweeping ambit of the duty in the case of builder/developers as expressed by the Supreme Court of California, which seems wider than that in the *Anns* case, with the latter's emphasis on safety, might well not be followed in other states.

In this particular context, there seems to be no sign in the United States of any resistance by the courts to a simultaneous liability of the defendant in both contract and tort.[53] It may be that the considerable extension of the tortious responsibility now owed by builders and professional men, may soon lead, where limitation difficulties arise between contracting parties, to a full reconsideration of this particular point by the courts in England.

---

[46] *Fisher* v. *Simon*, 112 N.W. 2d 705.
[47] *Sabella* v. *Wisler*, 377 P. 2d 899.
[48] *Pollard* v. *Saxe*, 525 P. 2d 88.
[49] *Ibid.* p. 90.
[50] *Ibid.* p. 91.
[51] 303 So. 2d 446 (1974).
[52] See *e.g. Neabel* v. *Town of Ingersoll* [1967] O.R. 343 (Ontario) where the pre-*Dutton* view prevailed.
[53] Contrast the position in England: *Steljes* v. *Ingram* (1903) 19 T.L.R. 534; *Groom* v. *Crocker* [1939] 1 K.B. 194; *Bagot* v. *Stevens Scanlon & Co. Ltd.* [1966] 1 Q.B. 197. But see now *Esso* v. *Mardon* [1976] 1 Q.B. 801.

Part III

NEGLIGENCE AND ECONOMIC LOSS*

The courts have been rapidly and, in view of its importance, inevitably faced with the need to apply to particular facts the principles governing the developing area of tortious liability confirmed and explained by the House of Lords in *Anns* v. *Merton L.B.C.* [1977] 2 W.L.R. 1024, noted by Keith Stanton at (1977) 93 L.Q.R. 488 and commented on at length by the present writer *ante*, p. 60. A number of the forecasts and views expressed in that article find confirmation in *Batty* v. *Metropolitan Property Realisations Ltd.* [1978] 2 W.L.R. 500.

The facts in *Batty* were that a developer and builder walked over an area subject to landslip, and as a result of their inspection decided to go ahead, the builder purchasing the land and selling it to the developer, who then financed the construction of the houses upon it by the builder. Nothing on the land itself indicated that anything might be wrong, but suspicious signs did exist on land nearby and on adjoining land. A serious slip occurred on land below one of the houses after it had been sold, which damaged the house's garden but not the house itself or its foundations. However, the evidence was that the house was now eventually doomed, since within 10 years further movement was inevitable which would ultimately destroy the foundations. The plaintiff purchaser sued the developer in contract and tort and the builder in tort only.

In finding both defendants liable, the Court of Appeal, as against the developer, was faced (as forecast *ante*, p. 72) with the contention that a duty in tort could not be established if liability in contract (which had also been established against the developer in the instant case) existed as well. The court held that it was bound by *Esso Petroleum Co. Ltd.* v. *Mardon* [1976] Q.B. 801, which had already decided against this argument, and that there was no need to limit the *Esso Petroleum* case, as had been contended, to cases of a common calling or of professional skill (as in the *Esso* case).

In the case of the builders, the court had no difficulty in holding that the principle of the *Anns* case applied equally to builders as it did to local authorities exercising their powers under the Housing Acts: see at p. 512H (and compare *ante*, p. 67) *per* Megaw L.J. (who delivered the leading judgment of the court) and the short concurring judgment of Bridge L.J. at p. 514G. The argument that the duty should not extend to other land but only to the building or site upon which the builder himself was to carry out work was fairly summarily rejected (see *per* Megaw L.J. at p. 510F).

The most interesting question concerned the need for physical damage. Doubts about this had been expressed at pp. 64–66 *ante* where it was pointed out that the evidence of any damage, if it existed at all, was fortuitous and logically irrelevant, and that on a true analysis it must follow that the *Anns*' principle would impose liability even in cases where no physical damage to the plaintiff's property had yet occurred but where future damage could be foreseen. Indeed, for this reason, the ruling as to the time when the cause of action arose as defined in the *Anns* case *ante*, pp. 65, 66, 68 might need re-definition. While holding that in *Batty's* case the damage caused by the slip to the garden itself (though not to the house or its foundations) might be a sufficient (albeit " possibly accidental ") damage to establish liability, Megaw L.J. obviously preferred to deal with the

* Reproduced from (1978) 94 L.Q.R. 331.

matter on a wider basis. After quoting from Lord Wilberforce's speech in *Anns*, where he had said that the cause of action " can only arise when the state of the building is such that there is present or imminent danger to the health or safety of persons occupying it," Megaw L.J. proceeded: " Was there not here imminent danger to the health or safety of persons occupying this house, at the time when action was brought? . . . Why should this not be treated as being a case of imminent danger to the safety and health of people occupying the house? No one knows, or can say with certainty—not even the greatest expert—whether the foundations of the house will move and the house perhaps suddenly tumble tomorrow, or in a year's time, or in three years' time, or in 10 years' time. The law, in my judgment, is not so foolish as to say that a cause of action against the builder does not arise in those circumstances because there is no *imminent* danger. I would reject that submission ": (p. 513C, D).

It was submitted at p. 67 *ante* that while, for purposes of liability, all the cases commencing with *Dutton* v. *Bognor Regis U.D.C.* [1972] 1 Q.B. 373 and including *Anns*, mentioned physical damage as a possible necessary ingredient of liability, this was, on analysis, incorrect in principle, and that many cases could arise where, before any physical damage occurred, the likelihood of damage could be foreseen. This had, indeed, been the expressed basis of the dissenting judgment of the present Chief Justice of Canada in *Rivtow Marine Ltd.* v. *Washington Ironworks* (1973) 6 W.W.R. 692, 715 (surely destined to be a " locus classicus " in this field) and expressly stated by all three judges in the Court of Appeal in New Zealand in *Bowen* v. *Paramount Builders* (*Hamilton*) *Ltd.* [1977] 1 N.Z.L.R. 394 (see *ante*, p. 70) and since Lord Wilberforce mentioned all these judgments with approval, the *Anns* case at least suggested approval in principle of liability being established in such a case. If so, it was suggested that the test as to when the period of limitation should begin formulated by Lord Wilberforce would not be entirely satisfactory, and that a test (reasonable foreseeability of future damage) such as that formulated by the Court of Appeal in *Sparham-Souter* v. *Town and Country Developments* (*Essex*) *Ltd.* [1976] Q.B. 858, would require to be formulated to determine when the cause of action arose and time began to run. It was also suggested that the actual physical damage in all these cases was logically irrelevant both to cause of action and to quantum of damage. *Batty's* case goes very far to support this, and to reinforce the view that the new liability in tort is of the wider *Bowen* and *Rivtow* kind, with actual physical damage irrelevant.

Batty's case, too, is important in that loss of value, on the particular facts (the house was unsaleable and for all practical purposes, therefore, now valueless save in regard to the remaining years in which it might be inhabited) supplanted cost of repair as the measure of damage. The second plaintiff, wife of the first plaintiff, was also awarded a small sum as damages for physical and mental distress.

INDEX

[**Author's Note:** *In this Index I have endeavoured to keep to a minimum references to the various articles of the author in the Appendices to this book. Any reference to a page number higher than* 303 *will be such a reference, but in addition I have placed the page numbers of these references in brackets for ease of identification.*]

Index

INDEX

Index

INDEX